Mechanistic Organic Photochemistry

Reinhold Chemistry Textbook Series

CONSULTING EDITORS

Harry H. Sisler   Calvin A. VanderWerf
University of Florida   *Hope College*
Gainesville, Florida   *Holland, Michigan*

SELECTED TOPICS IN MODERN CHEMISTRY

Harry H. Sisler and Calvin A. VanderWerf, Editors

ii

Consulting Editors' Statement

Mechanistic Organic Photochemistry is a logical outgrowth of the marked research emphasis photochemistry is receiving today—an emphasis which, in retrospect, most chemists would agree is overdue. Written primarily for the organic chemist and biochemist, this text introduces the nonspecialist to the language, principles, and qualitative theory of organic photochemistry in logical, concise, and thoroughly comprehensible and readable fashion.

The lucid systematic discussion of photochemical reactions and mechanics makes *Mechanistic Organic Photochemistry the* textbook for senior level and first-year graduate courses in which photochemistry is an integral topic. An engrossing chapter on natural photochemical processes should serve to stimulate the imagination of all creative organic chemists.

Dr. Neckers writes with the authority and confidence of a master teacher and a productive research worker in the exciting and rapidly expanding field of photochemistry. *Mechanistic Organic Photochemistry* is an indispensable addition to the library of every organic chemist and biochemist. The nearly 1000 references make it an invaluable aid for literature searchers in any area of photochemistry.

We are pleased to add *Mechanistic Organic Photochemistry* to our growing list of distinguished and useful advanced textbooks in chemistry.

Calvin A. VanderWerf
Harry H. Sisler

Mechanistic Organic Photochemistry

DOUGLAS C. NECKERS

Department of Chemistry
Hope College
Holland, Michigan

REINHOLD PUBLISHING CORPORATION, *New York*
A Subsidiary of Chapman-Reinhold, Inc.

Preface

Organic photochemistry is one of the most rapidly expanding areas of chemical knowledge. Perhaps because they provide an important synthetic method for preparing exotic and unusual chemical compounds or because they simply provide a unique and rewarding intellectual experience, photochemical reactions are appearing very frequently in the current literature.

Sparked by the pioneering synthetic and mechanistic contributions from the laboratories of Professors Barton, Hammond, Zimmerman, Yang, and others, organic chemists have, the world over, tried to unveil the mysteries of those processes initiated by electromagnetic radiation. Only a cursory examination of the current chemical journals will convince any nonbeliever of the importance of photochemical reactions. Indeed, for an author attempting to gather the existing knowledge of photochemical reaction processes, the rapid growth of the discipline precludes any exclusively up-to-date coverage.

The behavior of the first excited state has opened an entire new gamut of chemical reactions. Fortunately, we may think of some of these reaction processes in a similar fashion to already known and sometimes understood reactions in solution. An understanding of the behavior of free radicals in solution, for example, provides an excellent, but not all-inclusive background for the photochemist.

This book has a twofold purpose. Essentially it presents, in simple terms, background information and an introduction to photochemical reactions. In addition, however, it attempts to gather some of the more important photochemical reaction processes into certain arbitrary but hopefully systematic groups.

The treatise is intended, primarily for organic chemists and biochemists whose major interest is something other than photochemistry. Students at the senior or first year graduate level should find it useful.

A complete listing of all of those friends and colleagues who have provided stimulating discussions and inspirations is not possible in the space allotted. However, in particular the author thanks Professors Earl S. Huyser, Larry A. Singer, Nicholas J. Turro, and Paul de Mayo as well as President Calvin A. Vander Werf of Hope College for their reading of all or part of the manuscript and their excellent and penetrating criticism. Furthermore, the author thanks the personnel of Reinhold Publishing Corporation for their patient guidance to an unexperienced writer. Mrs. Wilma Baumann contributed her typing skills to portions of each draft. However, the major portion of the typing, much of the proofreading, and a large dose of inspiration was provided by the author's wife, Suzanne. Without her, the scratches and unintelligible scribbles would still be undecifered.

September, 1966   **Douglas C. Neckers**

Contents

ix

Mechanistic   Organic   Photochemistry

CHAPTER
1

Introduction

Historical Introduction

Photochemical reactions of organic materials have been known since ancient times. The early Greeks and Romans recognized that dyestuffs fade when left in the sunlight and that sunshine is necessary and essential for the growth of plant and plant-like materials. Little investigation into the effect of solar energy on the everyday life of man was made, however, until Stephen Hales, the noted Englishman, first described the nature of the photosynthetic process. Since his brilliant researches around the turn of the 18th century, chemists and physicists alike have come to look upon photochemistry as an important and most interesting aspect of the nature of man and his environment.

That photochemistry has been important to the scientific world can be demonstrated most aptly by the men who have been attracted to its intricacies. Stark, Planck, and the ingenious Albert Einstein have all contributed to the theoretical understanding of light waves and their effects on molecular species. Each has attempted, in his own way, to understand the processes involved when a chemical compound reacts because of photo-irradiation.

To two Europeans, however, belongs the distinction of important preliminary investigations in the experimental science of organic photochem-

1

istry. About 1900, Ciamician, an Italian, and Silber, a German, collaborated in a series of scientific publications, which showed that the organic chemist can expect many and various modes of behavior from organic compounds upon irradiation. From their researches has developed the entire present day field of organic photochemistry.

Historically, photochemistry has grown sporadically. At times, researches in the discipline of photochemistry were abundant, and intellectual development of the science, rapid and sophisticated. During other periods, few new reports appeared. Lulls sometimes lasted for years and even decades. Currently, studies of photochemical systems are very fashionable, and investigations of photochemical reactions are numerous.

A period of photochemical growth lasted for the four decades, from 1900 to 1940. Although the volume of reported research was not as large, the results obtained were theoretically and empirically important. During this period, Einstein postulated that in order for a compound to react photochemically, a light absorption process must occur. The concept of the quantum yield was proposed, and the Franck-Condon principle was developed. The evaluation of the energies involved in photochemical reactions, the kinetics of photochemical chain processes, and the derivation of the Einstein law of photochemical equivalence all arose during this period. Reviews and reference books by such authors as W. A. Noyes, Jr. and P. Leighton, G. B. Kistiakowsky, R. K. Rollefson and M. Burton served to collect and evaluate the then existing information.

The period from 1940 to 1958 saw primarily a development of gas phase photochemistry. Due principally to the efforts of W. A. Noyes, Jr. and his students and F. Blacet and his students, gas phase photochemistry became a sophisticated science. Schönberg and Mustafa, working in Egypt, provided most important discoveries in solution phase photochemistry. Many pioneering investigations of photochemical dimerization reactions, photochemical addition reactions, and photochemical abstraction reactions laid the groundwork for modern mechanistic approaches.

Recently, photochemistry has attained a new popularity. Just as organic chemists are generally no longer satisfied with only identifying products and improving yields of ground state chemical reactions, so also have photochemists become interested in mechanisms of photochemical reactions. Photochemists now desire to describe and to trace the exact reaction pathway of a molecule from the initial light absorption to the final product formation. Ideally, photochemists desire to follow the step by step molecular progression from absorption of light by the reactants to the production of products several steps later.

In practice, of course, this ideal is a difficult one to attain, and only for a few very simple reactions is any understanding possible on such an electronic basis. Photochemists have been partially successful, however, in understanding very specific parts of very specific solution phase and gas phase photochemical reactions. Thus, the spectroscopist has helped the photochemist to define and to describe those processes that result in light absorption and degradation of excited electronic states, while the free radical chemist has helped the photochemist to describe what happens to organic molecules after they have absorbed electromagnetic radiation. Physical and spectroscopic principles have been tentatively applied to organic molecules.

The mechanistic organic photochemist must answer the following principal questions. First, why do molecules absorb light at all? Second, what happens to these particular molecules after they have absorbed light to prepare them for chemical reaction? Third, what reaction intermediates are involved? Finally, how does production of reaction products cause the degradation of this initially absorbed energy, and how are the reaction intermediates removed from the system? Unfortunately, the photochemist has, to this time, only been able to answer one or two of these questions as they apply to specific systems. Continued effort among organic chemists everywhere will help to unravel the mysteries of photochemical reaction systems.

Theoretical Background

The development of mechanistic photochemistry followed, of necessity, the development of quantum theory. Only after some knowledge of the electronic transitions occurring in the absorption of light waves by molecules had been obtained, could organic photochemists hope to describe reactions of excited molecules. Only after molecular spectra had been somewhat successfully interpreted, could electronic theories be invoked to explain molecular photochemical behavior.

Theoretically, ultraviolet spectroscopy had its beginnings in the mid-19th century when Lambert found that absorption of light of a single wavelength, *monochromatic light*, is exponentially related to the thickness of absorbing material, eq. (1):

(1) $I_x = I_0 e^{-ax}$

where I_0 = incident light intensity, I_x = excident light intensity, a = a constant, characteristic of the material doing the absorbing and wavelength of light being absorbed, x = thickness of the layer of absorbing material. Shortly afterward Beer found that with solutions, the constant a is directly related to the concentration of the material absorbing the light. Thus, the Beer-Lambert law of light absorption was proposed; eq. (2).

(2) $\text{Log } I_0/I = abc$

a = a constant characteristic of the absorbing material and the wavelength, b = the path length of the solution, and c = the concentration of the solution in grams/liter.

The general Beer-Lambert law, written above in the accustomed logarithmic fashion, describes the quantitative aspects of light absorption. It states that the amount of light absorption at a single wavelength is directly proportional to the absolute concentration of the absorbing material. If the concentration is given in moles per liter, then Beer's law becomes eq. (3):

(3) $\mathrm{Log}\, I_0/I = A = \epsilon bc$

where ϵ is the molar extinction coefficient of the molecule at one particular wavelength and A the absorptivity. Generally, ultraviolet and visible spectra are reported with the molar extinction coefficient, ϵ, measured at the wavelength of light of maximum absorption, λ_{max}.

The energetics of light absorption were first described by Einstein and by Max Planck. In 1901 Max Planck postulated, in order to explain certain experimental observations of black body radiation, that light is emitted and absorbed in specific energy units called *quanta*. The Einstein law of photochemical equivalence, a direct result of Planck's quantum postulate, states that ideally each absorbed quantum of light energy should cause one molecule to undergo a change although the exact reaction undergone by the molecule after light absorption is neither specified nor need it be specified. In the ideal photochemical reaction, one molecule absorbs one quantum of light energy to produce one molecule of product. Such a process may only involve the electronic energy levels. The energy transmitted to the molecule in this light absorption is proportional to the wavelength of light being absorbed and is related to the frequency and hence the wavelength of the absorbed radiation, eq. (4):

(4) $E = h\nu = hc/\lambda$

E = energy in ergs, h = Planck's constant (6.62×10^{-27} erg sec), ν = frequency of light absorbed in cm^{-1}, and λ = wavelength of absorbed radiation.

Putting eq. (4) in molar terms and making the appropriate conversions, one finds that the absorption of 1 einstein of light (6.023×10^{23} quanta or 1 mole of light quanta) of 5000 Å (20,000 cm^{-1}) imparts an equivalent of 56.9 kcal/mole to the system by energy absorption, while absorption of 1 einstein of light of 3000 Å (33,333 cm^{-1}) imparts 94.6 kcal/mole to the absorbing molecule.* Since bond dissociation energies for carbon

*In the general case, $E = hc/\lambda$ or $(hc/\lambda)\,N$ for 1 einstein of absorbed radiation. Applying the necessary conversion factors, $E = (2.86 \times 10^5)/\lambda$ in Å kcal/mole; N = Avogadro's number.

covalent bonds are generally in the range of 100 kcal/mole,[1] absorption of ultraviolet radiation of wavelength 3000 A is often sufficient to cause the dissociation of single carbon covalent bonds.

Many photochemical reactions involve the homolytic cleavage of carbon covalent bonds. Since the occurrence of most photochemical processes is caused by ultraviolet rather than visible or infrared radiation, the question, why do not all covalently bound carbon compounds decompose when illuminated with radiation of these wavelengths, becomes then a question of light absorption and energy degradation. Since light absorption is a pre-requisite to photochemical reaction, some compounds do not photochemically decompose because they fail to absorb light. Other molecules fail to undergo rapid photochemical dissociation because stable excited states are formed. Energy degradation and reaction from these stable excited states is often the preferred mode of energy dissipation.

The practical applicability of the Einstein law of photochemical equivalence, that one molecule reacts chemically per absorbed quantum, has been tested frequently. It has been found that few compounds react ideally to give at least one, but only one, molecule of reaction product per absorbed quantum. Instead, chemical reactions have been found that give both many more than a molecule of product per absorbed energy quantum or much less than a molecule of product per absorbed energy quantum.

Due principally to the efforts of Bodenstein and co-workers, a revised version of the Einstein law of photochemical equivalence has been proposed. Essentially, this revised version states that even though photochemical processes may require but 1 quantum of absorbed radiation per molecule, the overall yield of products derived from a photochemical reaction depends on the secondary reactions of the system involved. Therefore, a new term is defined, the quantum yield, ϕ, from the revised photochemical equivalence law of Einstein:

$$\phi = \frac{\text{No. of moles of product produced (or reactant consumed)}}{\text{No. of einsteins of light absorbed}}$$

In a practical sense, the concept of the quantum yield is more meaningful than the law of photochemical equivalence because one can easily measure the concentration of reactants or products. Quantum yields can be observed that actually vary from 10^{-2} to 10^4. Illustrations of the significance of the quantum yield to mechanistic photochemical interpretations will appear later.

Quantum mechanical interpretations of molecular spectra were necessary prerequisites to the development of mechanistic organic photochemistry. By the 1940's the groundwork of quantum mechanics had been laid, and some photochemical occurrances could be interpreted in quantum mechanical terms. In essence, not only could the photochemist devise reaction pathways describing species by species transformations from reactants to products, but in the very simplest cases, the possibility of following the reaction electron by electron also existed. With the aid of the molecular spectroscopist and quantum mechanician, the photochemist could envision the microscopic process involved in the light absorption and the resulting energy transformations. For example, photochemists knew that absorption in the central ultraviolet region of the spectrum by ketones and aldehydes results in the promotion of one particular electron to a higher energy state. From an understanding of these electronic transitions, the photochemist was now able to predict which reactions would occur to degrade the excited states of an aldehyde or ketone back to a normal ground electronic state.

Because most photochemical reactions require radiation of sufficiently short wavelength to cause electronic transitions, photochemical reaction mechanisms generally involve free radical intermediates. Photochemical acceleration has long been accepted as criterion for a free radical chain process, and analogies between "ground state" free radical processes initiated by normal free radical initiators, such as peroxides and azo compounds, and photochemical reaction processes are valid.

As mentioned, the ultimate goal of the mechanistic photochemist is to describe the total species by species changes from the initial light absorption to product formation. Arbitrarily, the processes occurring during a photochemical reaction can be thought of in two groupings. Those processes that involve the actual initiation of the photochemical reaction, that is, the processes of excited state formation due to light absorption, are called *primary processes*. In practice, primary photochemical processes are those which can occur only as a direct result of absorption of a photon by the molecule. The primary photochemical process is said to end when the molecule dissociates or is returned to a normal state, reactive, but not excessively, toward its surroundings.[2] *Secondary processes* are those reactions involving the fragments from the primary process or those spectroscopic transpositions of the excited molecule which ultimately result in ground state, normally reactive products.

The remainder of this volume will be divided into two major parts. In the first few chapters, the electronic excitation processes will be discussed. This discussion will include light absorption, both on a partially quantum mechanical basis and from an empirical observation standpoint. In the second division, the actual observed secondary photochemical reactions will be discussed. Emphasis will be placed initially upon the processes of light absorption and formation of excited chemical states. Secondly, energy degradation from chemically excited states will be covered. Finally, specific photochemical reactions, for which reaction mechanisms have been postulated or are being postulated will be treated.

References

1. Walling, C., *Free Radicals in Solution*, New York, Wiley, 1957.
2. Noyes, W. A., Jr., G. Porter, and J. E. Jolley, *Chem. Rev.*, **56,** 49 (1956).

General References

Calvert, J. G., and J. W. Pitts, Jr., *Photochemistry*, New York, Wiley, 1966.

Gillam, A. E., and E. S. Stern, *An Introduction to Electronic Absorption Spectroscopy in Organic Chemistry*, London, Arnold, 1958.

Jaffé, H., and M. Orchin, *Theory and Applications of Ultraviolet Spectroscopy*, New York, Wiley, 1964.

Murrell, J. N., *The Theory of Electronic Spectra of Organic Molecules*, London, Methuen, 1963.

Turro, N. J., *Molecular Photochemistry*, New York, Benjamin, 1965.

CHAPTER
2

The Absorption Process

Atomic Spectra

A photochemical reaction is caused by the absorption of electromagnetic radiation by a molecule. The adsorption of light from 6000 Å to 2000 Å in wavelength may cause certain electronic transitions within a species. The ultimate result of these electronic processes may be the homolytic cleavage of a covalent bond. Many photochemical processes involve free radical intermediates, and an analogy between those processes initiated by the absorption of electromagnetic radiation and by other means of free radical initiation may often be drawn.

In 1900 Max Planck first suggested that a molecule could acquire energy only in discrete units called *quanta*. Planck's proposal precipitated a new way of thinking about processes involving light and absorption of light, this new method being called quantum mechanics.

According to Planck, the absorption of electromagnetic energy by a molecular (or atomic) species involves only stepwise transitions. The famous Planck equation, $E = h\nu$, shows that the energy of these stepwise or quantized absorptions is related directly to the excitation frequency, ν, (and hence the wavelength). It was proposed that during the process of electromagnetic radiation absorption, the energy of the electromagnetic wave is transferred to the molecule by a mechanism involving excitation of the overall molecule to some higher motional frequency and (or) electronic energy state. These processes are quantum processes, energetically distinct and stepwise, and as such require radiation of a particular wavelength.

Experimental confirmation of Planck's postulates followed shortly. As the techniques, instrumentation, and apparatus of emission spectroscopy became more sophisticated, it became possible to measure the actual energies of these quantized transitions. Emission techniques involved the excitation of the molecule to some higher energy state (generally by methods other than photochemical). The experimenter observed the wavelengths of the emitted radiation, and from Planck's postulate, calculated the energy of the transition. The number of molecules actually populating the excited state was related to the emission intensity of the line. The energetic assignment of the excitation transitions depended upon the quality of the available spectrographic equipment since the frequency, ν, is the simple reciprocal of the wavelength observed for the emission line. As the spectrographic equipment became more accurate, the wavelength of the line and energy associated therewith became better defined.

The Rutherford atomic model, a massive positive nucleus about which negatively charged electrons revolve, was unable to explain quantized light absorption and emission. There should be no discrete atomic emissions unless electrons are bound in specific energy levels surrounding the atom's positive nucleus, for classical electromagnetic theory demands that an accelerated charged particle emit only radiation of continuous wavelength. Such continuous emission would result in a loss of energy by the charged particle. As energy is lost, the particle will necessarily slow down, the end result being that the negatively charged electron approaches the positively charged nucleus more and more closely because of the decrease in acceleration. Eventually, the positive charge will overpower the electron and force it into the nucleus.

A solution to this problem was found in the theory that the electrons surrounding the nucleus are located in successively energetic orbital levels. This suggestion, made originally by Niels Bohr, presumed that the energy transitions observed in either absorption or emission spectroscopy are the result of electronic interchange between the atomic orbital levels. The observed spectroscopic transitions occur because the energy required to excite an electron from one energy level to another is furnished by some outside source. If one measures this energy by means of absorption techniques, one is observing the excitation process. On the other hand, observation of light emission requires that the excitation be provided by some outside source and that the observer look at the deactivation process.

The Atom

Bohr undertook to solve the problem of atomic structure by using a solar model for orbital motion. The simplest electronic orbitals (corresponding to energy levels) are those orbitals in which the electron moves circularly about the positive nucleus. Treating the moving electron as a singly charged particle and using the laws of classical mechanics, Bohr postulated that only those orbitals whose angular momentum, mvr, is an integral multiple of $h/2\pi$ are allowed. He called the integral multiplier, n, the quantum number. That is,

$$mvr = nh/2\pi$$

where m = mass of moving particle, v = velocity of particle, r = radius of circular pathway, h = Planck's constant, and $n = 1, 2, 3 \ldots$. The force of attraction, f, between the charged electrons and the positive nucleus is given by $f = Ze^2/r^2$ where Z is the number of charges, and e the magnitude, and r the distance between the charges. The magnitude of the accelerative force is given classically by $a = v^2/r$. Substituting into $f = ma$, $Ze^2/r^2 = mv^2/r$ or $r = Ze^2/mv^2$. However, according to the Bohr postulate, the angular momentum $mvr = nh/2\pi$ is quantized and given by discrete, integral energy units. Upon substitution for v, $r = n^2h^2/4\pi^2me^2Z$. This equation, a direct result of Bohr's postulates, states that the orbital radius is proportional to the square of some integer. This integer is called a *quantum number*. One could easily construct a calculated energy diagram for each of the principal orbitals of an atom as determined by the value of n and compare the so obtained values with the experimental quantities obtained for the energies of the various electronic levels from the emission spectrogram of an atom. The calculated energy diagrams have been found to agree, qualitatively at least, with the values observed. However, modification of the original Bohr atom to include elliptical orbits is required in order to make the agreement more quantitative. Since mathematically the ellipse requires the specification of two axes, a major axis and a minor axis, the introduction of elliptical electronic orbitals into the Bohr atom necessitates a second quantum number, the value of which is related to the first.

The spectra of the simplest atoms indicate that absorption of electromagnetic radiation does indeed cause stepwise transitions of electrons between energy levels. From the positions and splittings of spectral lines, energy levels can be assigned to particular transitions. Spectral emission lines appear, in the simplest cases, to occur in several series. These series are called *sharp* (*s*), *principal* (*p*), *diffuse* (*d*), and *fundamental* (*f*), and each is associated with excitation to or emission from a specific energy level. The energies related to the line positions increase regularly, and it is implied that in the ground, unexcited state, the electrons of a particular atom rest in the level of lowest energy. The alkali metals, which possess a single loosely bound outer electron easily excited by electromagnetic radiation, show spectral lines corresponding to each of a number of quantized energy states. These lines are sharp, amply spaced, and unique. The simplest of the alkali metals, lithium, has a ground state electronic configuration with two electrons in the 1s orbital and a third electron, the valence electron, in the 2s orbital. This orbital electron can be excited from the ground state, the 2s level, to any one of a number of higher levels, the 2p orbital, the 3s orbital, the 3p orbital, and so on. Each of these successive transitions requires an amount of energy that can be quantitatively assessed from the wavelength position of the absorption (or emission) band.

The Bohr theory gives a fairly accurate description of the orbital atomic picture, especially for the simple elements such as the alkali metals and the hydrogen atom. Calculated results deviate seriously from experimental results however, if systems having more than one electron of nearly equivalent energy are considered. When spectroscopic instruments of sufficient resolving power became available, it became apparent that some lines, once thought to be single lines, are indeed multiplets, and certain groups of lines are not all overlapping. To account for these discrepancies, it was proposed that the electrons revolve not in circular orbit, but in elliptical orbit, and that another quantum number related to the angular velocity of the electron is required. As experimental techniques improved, it became apparent that four quantum numbers are actually required to describe completely an electron's energy state.

It was de Broglie who first propounded the wave theory of electronic motion. According to de Broglie, it is possible to associate the properties of an ordinary standing (not progressive) wave with every moving electronic particle. Therefore, for each moving electron, one can speak meaningfully of an amplitude, a wavelength, and a frequency of motion. As for the standing wave, interference involving electronic charge is experimentally observed so that only certain motion frequencies are allowed. This reinforcement condition, namely that only electronic frequencies of certain specific integral multiples of one another are allowed, is qualitatively correlative, at least, with the Bohr atomic theory, and the integral multipliers of standing wave reinforcement are simply the principal quantum numbers postulated by Bohr.

Schrödinger attempted to treat the problem of the atom quantitatively and in three dimensions. He assumed, first, that electronic motion is analogous to the motion of a standing wave and, furthermore, that one can calculate the principal frequency and various overtone frequencies of electronic motion by assuming standing wave character (the reinforcement condition).

As a result, Schrödinger was able to replace the classical mechanical Bohr picture of electronic motion with his now famous equation for the amplitude of this standing electronic wave:

$$(1) \qquad \frac{\partial^2 \psi}{\partial x^2} + \frac{\partial^2 \psi}{\partial y^2} + \frac{\partial^2 \psi}{\partial z^2} + \frac{8\pi^2 m}{h^2}(E - V)\,\psi = 0$$

where m is the mass of the particle, E is the total energy of the particle, and V is the potential energy. If, like the standing wave resulting when a string is caused to vibrate, ψ is everywhere single valued, finite, and continuous, eq. (1) can be solved for specific values of E, called *eigenvalues*. Physically, the value of ψ gives some measure of the probability that the particle, an electron, will be found at a point in space (x, y, z). In order to keep this probability positive, one generally talks about the square of ψ, and the Schrödinger equation says that if ψ is a solution to the equation, the probability of finding an electron in the space $(x, y, z) \rightarrow (x + dx,\ y + dy,\ z + dz)$ is given by ψ^2.

Solutions to the Schrödinger equations are not simple. As a matter of fact, the Schrödinger wave equation defies any solution but an approximate one for systems with more than one electron. Its great utility is derived from the fact that even the approximate solutions obtained from using it are better than what was previously available for spectral correlations. However, it must be recognized that solutions to the Schrödinger equation still give only a probability.

Classical mechanics failed in its description of the atom principally because the Bohr theory tried to be exact. All atomic theories based on classical mechanical principles require that the position of an electron be exactly known at any particular time. The electron is so small, however, that any known measuring technique, of necessity, alters the electron's position. This principle, the Heizenberg uncertainty principle, forced the development of the Schrödinger wave mechanics based on the postulate that although absolute electronic position cannot be specified, the probability of finding an electron in a specific position can.

Regardless of the various philosophical differences between the clear-cut atomic model devised by Bohr and the more nebulous atomic model implied by Schrödinger, the fact still remains that significant and useful general conclusions may be obtained from either approach. It is apparent that every electron surrounding the nucleus of an atom can be represented by quantum numbers, the combination of which is unique. These quantum numbers are the principal quantum number, n, the azimuthal quantum number, l, the angular momentum quantum number, m and the spin quantum number, s. Specifically, the principal quantum number, n gives some picture of electron cloud area and has integral values ($n = 1, 2, 3....$). The letter l represents the orbital direction and has values from 0 to n-l. m Represents the orientation of the electron cloud about the Cartesian coordinates and has values from $-l$ to $+l$, and s, the direction of the spin, has values of $+\frac{1}{2}$ and $-\frac{1}{2}$. The Pauli exclusion principle states that no two electrons (in a single atomic representation) can have all four quantum numbers exactly the same. Therefore, the quantum mechanical electron picture is unique for each individual electron, and each of these electrons belong to one, and only one, energy level in the atomic ground state. The term ground atomic state necessarily implies that each individual electron within the atom is placed in the orbital of lowest energy.

From the quantum number rules described above, one can produce a quantum picture of the elements in the periodic table. This process, called the *aufbau* process, requires simply that one strip an atom of each of its electrons and replace them in the electronic orbital of lowest energy so that they will obey the Pauli exclusion principle. Statistically, as the values of n are assigned, the limiting values of the other three quantum numbers are fixed, as are the total quantum number combinations for any particular value of n. In practice, one assigns values to n, the principal quantum number, and gives l, m, and s the smallest possible values. For successive electrons, all possible combinations of l, m, and s are included. When no more combinations of these three quantum numbers remain, n is increased by one and the process repeated until electrical balance is attained. Table 2-1 shows the quantum numbers for the outermost electron of the first ten elements in the periodic table.

Table 2-1

Orbital Pictures of the Elements

Element	Atomic Number	Quantum Picture (n, l, m, s)	Valence Orbital Shorthand
H	1	$(1,0,0,-\frac{1}{2})$	$1s$
He	2	$(1,0,0,+\frac{1}{2})$	$1s^2$
Li	3	$(2,0,0,-\frac{1}{2})$	$2s$
Be	4	$(2,0,0,+\frac{1}{2})$	$2s^2$
B	5	$(2,1,-1,-\frac{1}{2})$	$2p_x{}^1$
C	6	$(2,1,0,-\frac{1}{2})$	$2p_y{}^1$
N	7	$(2,1,1,-\frac{1}{2})$	$2p_z{}^1$
O	8	$(2,1,-1,+\frac{1}{2})$	$2p_x{}^2$
F	9	$(2,1,0,+\frac{1}{2})$	$2p_y{}^2$
Ne	10	$(2,1,1,+\frac{1}{2})$	$2p_z{}^2$

All electrons with the same value for the principal quantum number, n, have approximately similar energies and are said to belong to the same shell, while all electrons having similar values of l are said to belong to the same subshell. Both electrons in helium, for example, are said to belong to the l shell, s subshell. The outer electron of boron is a $2p$ electron and so on. Representation of the shell, subshell, and direction of the electron cloud results if electrons with values of $l = 0$ are said to belong to the s subshell, $l = 1$ to the p subshell, $l = 2$ to the d subshell, and $l = 3$ to the f subshell. The orbitals in which s electrons are contained are nondirectional or spherical. p Electrons may be found in one of three orbitals; the major probability of their location is in orbitals of dumbbell shape lying along the cartesian coordinates. Shapes of d and f electronic orbitals have been determined and are discussed elsewhere.[1,2]

Carbon—The Covalent Bond

Carbon has an electronic configuration in the ground state of two $1s$ electrons, two $2s$ electrons, and two $2p$ electrons, and its ground electronic state (all electrons designated) may be pictured in shorthand notation as $1s^2 2s^2 2p^2$. According to the Lewis picture, the formation of covalent bonds results from electron-sharing between the two atoms being bonded so that the outer shells of all atoms attain a stable rare gas configuration. More modern theories indicate that the covalent bond results because of atomic orbital overlap. When this overlap is sufficient, a covalent bond is formed. In covalent bond formation, two electrons of opposite spin are placed together in a single bonding energy level called a *molecular orbital*.

From the ground state electron configuration of carbon, $1s^2 2s^2 2p^2$, one would expect the atom to form four covalent bonds in order to satisfy the octet rule, which predicts that the outer shell attains the rare gas configuration of eight electrons. One would also expect that the two $2s$ electrons and the two $2p$ electrons would be shared with electrons to form four covalent bonds, two formed from the p electrons that are similar in every respect, but different from two other orbitals formed from the s electrons.

Experimental observations indicate that carbon, contrary to the above thinking, forms four equivalent covalent bonds. For example, the four carbon-hydrogen bonds in methane are found to be equivalent in distance, bond strength, and bond direction. To account for carbon's ability to form four equivalent bonds rather than two different pairs of covalent bonds, it is proposed that the actual bonding configuration of carbon is a hybrid combination of one s and three p electrons. This situation is realized by promotion of one of the $2s$ electrons of atomic carbon to the $2p$ level. If the electronic orbitals are now hybridized to form equivalent orbitals, it is possible for carbon to form four equivalent bonds. These bonds are not formed by overlap of a pure p or pure s electron from the carbon atom with the bonding atom, but instead are formed as a combination or *hybrid bond* resulting from the mixture of the one s and three p electronic energy levels. Four new energy levels equivalent in all respects are formed by this hybridization process. The energy required to promote a $2s$ electron to the p energy level is apparently more than regained by the formation of four equivalent bonds.

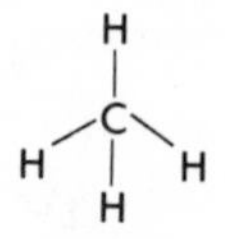

$$
\begin{array}{c}
\text{H} \\
| \\
\text{H} - \text{C} - \text{H} \\
| \\
\text{H}
\end{array}
$$

Methane

When carbon-carbon double bonds and carbon-carbon triple bonds are formed, one or two of the carbon's p electrons are utilized directly. By overlap of the directional p electrons of one carbon atom with another, a new bond weaker and more directional than the hybrid bonds discussed above is formed. This bond, called a π bond to distinguish it from those bonds resulting from overlap of hybridized s containing orbitals can be directed along any one of the three cartesian axes. In compounds containing carbon-carbon triple bonds, two π molecular orbitals are formed, and two p electrons from each carbon are utilized in the process. In either case, the remaining bonds are formed from hybrid atomic orbitals resulting from promotion of

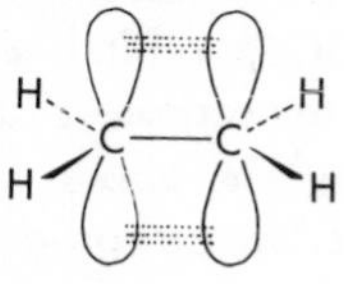

Ethylene

one of the $2s$ electrons of the ground state carbon atom to the p electronic level and subsequent hybridization of the remaining total electrons. Thus, the bonding in ethylene involves a π bond between the two carbon atoms, but, in addition, it involves a carbon-carbon single bond formed by overlap of electrons from two sp^2 hybrid orbitals and called a σ (sigma) bond. The two other sp^2 hybrid orbitals overlap with hydrogen atoms. The three hybrid bonds are formed at equivalent, 120° angles. With acetylene, electron promotion and hybridization results in the formation of two equivalent orbitals, sp hybrids. The bonding in acetylene involves 2π bonds and a sigma bond between the carbon atoms, while the remaining sp hybrid overlaps with an s orbital from hydrogen to form a sigma carbon-hydrogen bond.

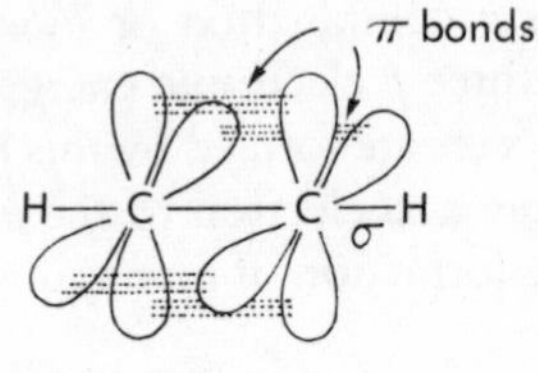

Acetylene

Formaldehyde

Molecular orbital approaches to more complex systems are also interesting, and it will be extremely useful later in our discussion of photochemical processes if we consider orbital structure of another simple organic molecule, formaldehyde. Oxygen has a ground state electronic configuration of $1s^2 2s^2 2p^4$. Use of one p electron on carbon and one p electron on oxygen results in the formation of a carbon-oxygen π bond. Hybridization of the electronic levels of the carbon atom results in three equivalent sp^2 hybrid electronic levels. Filling one p orbital on the oxygen with two electrons, and hybridization of the electrons remaining with use of two of these hybrid electrons to form another nonbonded pair on oxygen and the other to form the sigma bond to carbon results in one representation of the ground state of formaldehyde.

Energetically oxygen sp^2 hybridization may not be correct. The promotion of an oxygen $2s$ electron to a $2p$ orbital requires 15.66 ev, whereas the analogous electron promotion for carbon requires but 9.34 ev[3]. As a result, electron hybridization requiring the above transition is less favorable for oxygen than for carbon. Hence, the carbon-oxygen sigma bond of formaldehyde is, under the most limiting conditions, formed by overlap of almost pure p orbitals on oxygen. An alternative representation of formaldehyde would suggest that the sigma oxygen-carbon bond forms by overlap of an sp^2 carbon hybrid with the $2p$, electron of oxygen, and the π carbon-oxygen

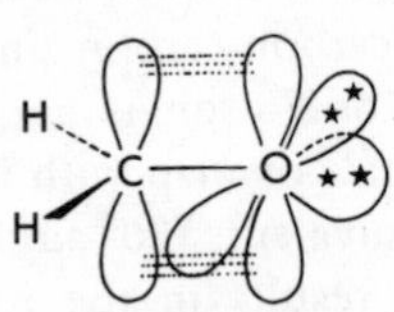

Formaldehyde

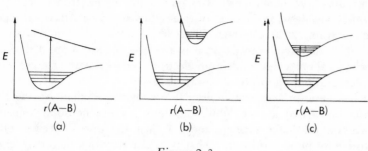

Figure 2-3

takes from 10^{-13} to 10^{-15} sec for the resulting transitions to occur), it can be assumed that the process of light absorption is *vertical*. This assumption, known as the *Franck-Condon principle*, says that the process of light absorption and the electronic changes that this process initiates are so rapid that they occur without change of atomic position.

In Figure 2-3a, the Franck-Condon diagram is shown for excitation to a dissociative excited state. An excited state of this type, typical to photochemical dissociation or decomposition reactions, is such that in the excited state the atoms A and B are repulsive to one another at the distance of separation $r(A-B)$, and the molecule is dissociated. Figure 2-3b illustrates excitation to an excited state of highly energetic character. Because the interatomic A—B distance is small, nuclear repulsions are very large and the atoms are thrown vigorously from one another. Figure 2-3c illustrates excitation to a nondissociative, relatively stable excited state. The lifetime of this excited state may be sufficiently long for secondary reactions and transformations other than molecular dissociation to occur. Unlike the situation in which dissociative excited states are formed (Figure 2-3a and b), there is no reason to assume that the transition to a bonded excited state (Figure 2-3c) is irreversible. A considerable portion of this and subsequent chapters will deal with the reverse transformation and others like it.

Electronic Transitions—The π-π^* Excitation

To this point, our discussion of the light absorption processes has been highly general. Of necessity, we must make application of the principles discussed to specific molecular cases in order to gain some appreciation of the relationship between spectroscopy and mechanistic photochemistry. In addition, it is imperative that we make some correlation between molecular structure and spectroscopic behavior so that we can attempt to follow more closely photochemical processes.

Generally, photochemical processes are initiated by electromagnetic radiation with wavelengths in the short wavelength, visible and ultraviolet regions of the spectrum (2000–7000 Å). Since it is known that in this spectral region electronic excitations occur, it is a reasonable assumption that most photochemical processes result from electronic energy state changes within the molecule although this is not always necessary.

It is a basic principle of molecular orbital theory that, by the linear combination of two atomic orbitals to form a covalent bond, one must produce two molecular orbitals and not just the one molecular orbital responsible for bond formation. That is, when electrons of certain energy levels are placed in a bonding situation of lower energy, an unfilled non-bonding orbital of higher energy also results. The second molecular orbital resulting from the linear combination of two atomic p orbitals of carbon is, unlike the molecular orbital that is responsible for the formation of the π bond, essentially antibonding in nature, i.e. the two electrons contained in this orbital would have no attraction for one another. It is of substantially higher energy than the filled, bonding π molecular orbital and in the ground state is unoccupied. This orbital is called a π^* energy level and may be pictured as in Figure 2-4b. Light absorption by the molecule results in the

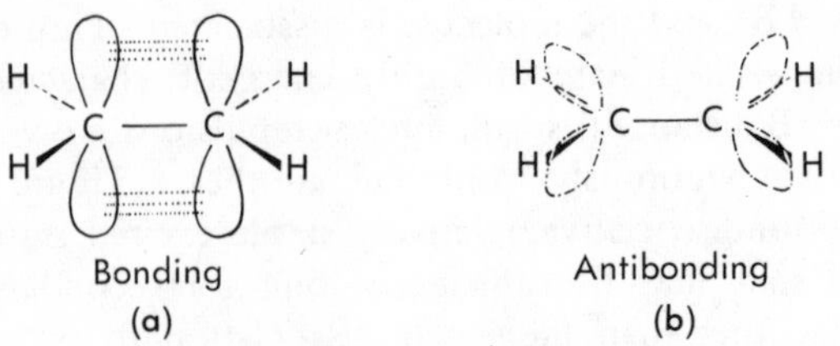

Bonding
(a)

Antibonding
(b)

Figure 2-4

promotion of one electron from the bonding π level to the essentially antibonding π^* level. This spectroscopic transition is called a π-π^* transition and, for ethylene, occurs at approximately 1800 Å.

Similar π-π^* absorption can be envisioned for most olefinic substances. The position of the π-π^* transition is controlled by many factors, including the strength of the π bond and the stability of the excited state, and quantitatively these factors are manifested in the energy level difference between the ground and excited states.

When excitation of a bonding π electron to an antibonding π^* state occurs as in ethylene, two possible spin configurations may be produced. If the electronic excitation occurs with complete retention of electron spin, the excited state is called a *singlet* state. In the excited singlet state, all spins are paired as they were in the molecule of ground state ethylene. If, on the other hand, excitation occurs with resultant spin inversion, the excited state is called a *triplet* state. Direct excitation to the triplet excited state, an excited state with spins unpaired, is a quantum mechanically forbidden process, and population of the triplet excited state must result from some secondary process.

Quantum mechanics shows that the most stable configuration of ethylene with one electron in the π^* state, that is, excited-state ethylene, is one in which the planes defined by the hydrogens and carbon of the two methylene groups are at right angles. Unlike ground state ethylene, which is a planar molecule, the excited state is nonplanar. Therefore, regeneration of ground state ethylene from excited state ethylene requires rotation about the sigma bond of the carbon skeleton, and a case can be made for the free radical character of excited state olefins resulting from the "isolation" of the methylenes by this rotation. It would be of interest to determine whether or not an electron in the excited π^* state is responsible for photochemical reaction of olefins or if the reactions of these excited states are of a concerted character. More will be said of these problems in a later chapter.

The *n-π** Excitation

For molecules containing heteroatoms such as sulfur, oxygen, or nitrogen, another electronic transition becomes possible. This electronic transition is a direct result of the fact that, for the most part, when these atoms are present in organic molecules, they possess unshared electron pairs. Ultraviolet absorptions may result by excitation of one of these nonbonded electrons to some higher energy level.

A good illustrative case is formaldehyde. As already discussed, it has the ground state configuration shown in the following structure. Just as linear combination of two carbon atomic orbitals in ethylene resulted in two molecular orbitals, one bonding and filled, the other antibonding and unfilled, so does linear combination of the atomic orbitals of carbon and oxygen form a bonding π and an antibonding π^* molecular orbital. Absorp-

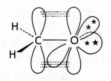

Formaldehyde

tion of ultraviolet radiation by formaldehyde produces at least two transitions. The first transition results from the excitation of one of the nonbonded electrons of the oxygen atom to the antibonding π^* state. This transition, which is of low probability, is called an n-π^* transition. Because of the nonbonded character of the oxygen electrons, the transition requires comparatively small amounts of energy, but the excited state is still essentially planar since two electrons still remain in the bonding carbon-oxygen π orbital.

The n-π^* transition of formaldehyde can be shown pictorially as in Figure 2-5. The antibonding π^* orbital is vacant in the ground state, but

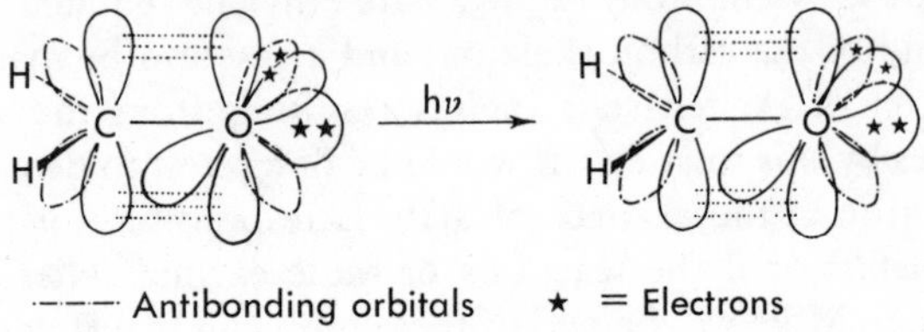

------ Antibonding orbitals   ★ = Electrons

Figure 2-5

occupied with one electron in the excited state. With carbonyl compounds such as formaldehyde, the characteristics of the excited state derived by n-π^* excitation are decidedly different from those of the ground state. In addition to the change brought about by the redistribution of electrons, it has been found[4] that the dipole moment of the excited state of formaldehyde is somewhat less than that of ground state formaldehyde, and that the carbon-oxygen bond is considerably lengthened. Thus, the n-π^* excited state of carbonyl compounds is less polar than the ground state, and less polar selectivity would be expected from either the excited carbon or excited oxygen atoms.

Excitation of one of the bonding π electrons of formaldehyde to the π^* state is also possible. This π-π^* transition is highly probably, but requires somewhat higher energies than the n-π^* transition. Like the π-π^* transition of ethylene, however, the π-π^* absorption of formaldehyde produces an excited state in which twist about the carbon-oxygen bond has occurred. Since the n-π^* transition of formaldehyde is an improbable excitation while the π-π^* transition is a probable one, the latter occurs for many more molecules per mole than does the former, if the excitation energy is sufficient to cause both transitions. However, n-π^* transitions are of lower energy and hence occur at longer wavelength than do the corresponding π-π^* transitions for the same chromophore.

Excited States—Spin Considerations

Just as in the case of ethylene, excitation can occur with electron spin retention or resultant electron spin inversion in both the n-π^* and π-π^* formaldehyde excitation. Quantum mechanics tells us that singlet-triplet spectroscopic transitions are forbidden (of low probability). Since the ground state for most organic molecules (unless the ground state is a stable free radical or diradical) is necessarily singlet, that is, all electronic spins are paired, direct excitation to the triplet state does not occur. In addition, since singlet-triplet excitation is a process of low probability, the reverse triplet-singlet transition is also forbidden. As a result, the excited triplet state of a molecule is substantially longer lived than the excited singlet state and is unable to be degraded to normal bonding ground states with facility.

The Jablonski Diagram

Figure 2-6 is the well-known Jablonski diagram.[5] The Jablonski diagram is a pictorial representation of the energy transitions that result from the simple absorption by a molecule of ultraviolet radiation. The molecule is

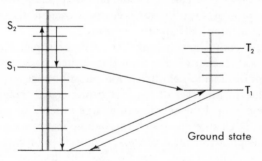

Figure 2-6

excited to one of the excited singlet electronic states (s_1 or s_2), and through a series of radiationless transitions called *internal conversions*, it drops back to the excited singlet state of lowest energy. As a general rule, resulting transitions occur from this lowest energy excited singlet level. The whole excitation process requires less than 10^{-12} sec. From the first excited singlet level, the molecule may decay by one of three major pathways: it may drop back to the ground electronic state by emitting radiation of a wavelength exactly the same as that of the absorption; it may drop back without emitting radiation, or it may undergo crossing to the first excited triplet state (t_1). The first process is an important spectroscopic process requiring about

10^{-9} sec and is called *fluorescence*. The important distinguishing feature of fluorescence is that it occurs from the first excited singlet state. The transition from excited singlet to excited triplet states is radiationless and requires less than 10^{-9} sec. It is called a process of *intersystem crossing*.

The first excited triplet state is generally of lower energy than the first excited singlet state; therefore, intersystem crossing is an energetically downhill process. Since singlet-triplet conversions are low probability transitions, the triplet state is decidedly more stable (longer lived) than the singlet state. However, after a time period, which varies from 10^{-4} sec to several minutes, the triplet state also decays to the ground state. When it does so, a photon of light may be emitted, but its wavelength is substantially longer than the wavelength of the radiation initially absorbed (because of the lower energy of the triplet state). This process is called *phosphorescence*. The important distinguishing feature of phosphorescence is that it occurs from the triplet excited state. That the transition is a quantum mechanically forbidden one means that experimentally the process is comparatively slow and occurs for only a few molecules at any one time. Both excited singlets and excited triplets can decay to the ground state by radiationless processes as well. These processes result because of collision with solvent, with the vessel walls, or with other molecules and are not well understood. Obviously, since radiative processes can be observed spectroscopically, we know much more about them empirically and theoretically.

Because of the comparatively long lifetime of the triplet state, the majority of photochemical reactions occur from this excited state. By evaluation of the wavelength of radiation emitted upon phosphorescence, one can assign an energy value to the level of the first triplet state. Hammond and co-workers[6] have obtained the energies of a large number of triplet states, and these are listed in Chapter 4. Much can be implied concerning the mechanism of certain photochemical processes from these triplet state energies. Similarly, from Planck's equation, $E = h\nu$, the level of the first singlet state can be assigned if the wavelength of fluorescence is known.

Since we have already established that gross bond dissociation generally results when radiation of wavelengths much shorter than 2500 Å is absorbed, molecules that absorb in this spectral region generally fail to fluoresce; instead they decompose. In addition, since singlet-triplet transitions are quantum mechanically forbidden, the occurrence of phosphorescence is often improbable, and the number of molecules per unit volume actually phosphorescing is generally quite small. The experimental observation of phosphorescence depends upon the limiting of other modes of deactivation to the molecule by freezing the compound from which phosphorescence is expected into a rigid matrix at low temperatures so that collisional deactivation is prevented.

References

1. Jaffé, H., and M. M. Orchin, *Theory and Application of Ultraviolet Spectroscopy*, p. 31, New York, Wiley, 1963.
2. Becker, C., *J. Chem. Educ.*, **41**, 358 (1964).
3. Murrell, J. N., *The Theory of Electronic Spectra of Organic Molecules*, p. 158, London, Methuen, 1963.
4. Freeman, D. E., and W. Klemperer, *J. Chem. Phys.*, **40**, 604 (1964).
5. Jablonski, A., Z. *Phyzik*, **94**, 38 (1935).
6. Herkstroeter, W., A. A. Lamola, and G. S. Hammond, *J. Am. Chem. Soc.*, **86**, 4537 (1964).

General References

Ballhausen, C. J., and H. B. Gray, *Molecular Orbital Theory*, New York, Benjamin, 1964.

Herzberg, G., *Atomic Spectra and Atomic Structure*, New York, Dover, 1944.

Jaffe, H., and M. Orchin, *Theory and Applications of Ultraviolet Spectroscopy*, New York, Wiley, 1963.

Mason, S. F., *Quart. Rev.*, **15**, 287 (1961).

Moore, W. J., *Physical Chemistry*, Englewood Cliffs, N. J. Prentice-Hall, 1955.

Murrell, J. N., *The Theory of the Electronic Spectra of Organic Molecules*, New York, Wiley, 1963.

Reid, C., *Excited States in Chemistry and Biology*, London, Butterworths, 1957.

Reid, C., *Quart. Rev.*, **12**, 205 (1958).

Simons, J. P., *Quart. Rev.*, **13**, 3 (1959).

Streitwieser, A., *Molecular Orbital Theory for Organic Chemists*, New York, Wiley, 1961.

Walling, C., *Free Radicals in Solution*, New York, Wiley, 1957.

Weissberger, A., ed., *Techniques of Organic Chemistry*, Vol. II, New York, Interscience, 1956.

CHAPTER

3

Organic Molecules— Spectra

Color Theory

In the laboratory, the photochemist faces two problems. First, he must get radiative energy into a molecule. Second, he must determine what happens to the molecule after it accepts the electromagnetic radiation.

To this point, our discussion has been centered around theoretical aspects of absorption spectroscopy. To the practicing photochemist, however, those empirical relationships that have developed after many years of studying ultraviolet and visible light absorption are of great importance.

Every organic chemist realizes the influence that the dye and color industry has had on his discipline. The early successes of Perkin and Hofmann in preparing synthetic dyestuffs stimulated the experimental and theoretical development of organic chemistry substantially. Realizing the monetary value of synthetic dyes, early German chemists were quick to ask questions about the relationship of color to molecular constitution. Due primarily to their efforts, certain functional groups were found to be prevalent in highly colored molecules. These groups, azo, nitro, nitroso, sulphone, sulfoxide, sulfonic acid, and others, are called *chromophoric* or color producing. Other groups, hydroxyl, amino, and alkyl amino to mention a few, although they do not serve alone to produce a colored molecule, serve to enhance and deepen the color caused by an already existing chromophore. These groups are called *auxochromes* or color enhancing.

As more and more compounds were synthetically prepared, more correlations of structure and color became apparent. It became clear that not only is the color of a molecule dependent upon the existence of a chromophore in the molecule, but the position and number of these chromophores also affects the strength and position of the light absorption and hence the molecule's color. The number and the position of the unsaturated groups were found to be important to a molecule's light absorption properties. More highly unsaturated molecules were observed to be more highly colored.

Modern electronic theory explains these observations by demonstrating that in more highly conjugated molecules there is a lower antibonding π^* level, excitation to which requires less energy. Therefore, while conjugated molecules require excitation energies of a relatively low magnitude to excite electrons to antibonding energy levels, unconjugated molecules require excitation energies of a higher magnitude. Conjugated molecules generally absorbed in the red and yellow and appear blue in color, while many nonconjugated molecules absorb in the blue or ultraviolet region and appear yellow or colorless. The auxochromic effect of the hydroxyl or amino groups can be interpreted either as an inductive electron donation to the chromophore or as a resonance stabilization of the excited state of the molecule. Neither effect is independent of the other, and strictly speaking, one can only say that the transition energy difference between ground and excited state is lowered by the auxochrome.

The effect of extended conjugation on the absorption process is a striking one and is of great importance to the photochemist. Unconjugated systems absorb ultraviolet radiation of short wavelength only. Absorbed radiation of 2500 Å or less imparts such large quantities of energy to the molecule that a great number of bond cleavages become possible. As a result, the number of simultaneously occurring processes make evaluation of the overall reaction mechanism difficult.

Ultraviolet Absorption

Organic chemists and spectroscopists working with organic molecules are concerned with two characteristics of the absorbing chromophore. First, they are concerned with the wavelength of maximum absorption (reported in units of length such as Å, mμ, μ) and second with, the strength of the absorption at the position of maximum absorption. Due to convention, one usually finds chemical compounds characterized by ϵ, the molar extinction coefficient, already defined in Chapter 1, at $\lambda_{max.}$, the position of maximum absorption. The units of ϵ are in absorbance per mole.

Traditionally, ultraviolet spectroscopy has been most useful as a tool for structural diagnosis. Since electronic absorption is always accompanied by changes in vibrational and rotational molecular energy levels, the ultraviolet spectrum of a molecule is generally band-like. The position and intensity of ultraviolet absorption bands are characteristic of the extent of unsaturation and the conjugation of unsaturated centers within a particular molecule. Since electronic energy changes are involved, generally only those molecules with unsaturated linkages have sufficiently low lying excited (π^*) states for spectral observation. In making use of ultraviolet spectroscopy to determine the structure of an unknown compound, one compares the ultraviolet spectrum of the unknown with a known compound of similar structure. Since similar chromophores that are similarly conjugated have similar absorption spectra, one can narrow down the structure of an unknown compound by a process of elimination. Such a process is necessarily tedious, since generally an educated guess must be made as to what the unknown structure is. However, in the days before the advent of nuclear magnetic resonance such an elimination technique often proved to be exceedingly useful.

Ultraviolet absorption maxima and their corresponding molar extinction coefficients for typical compounds are shown in Table 3-1. Each of the molecules for which the ultraviolet absorption properties are listed contain but one single chromophore. The absorptions listed are, therefore, wholly characteristic of the molecule's functional group. Notice that the absorption maxima of the simplest olefin, ethylene, and the simplest alkyne, acetylene, are at a significantly shorter wavelength than are the maxima for almost any of the other chromophores listed. The energy necessary for the excitation of a π electron of ethylene to an antibonding π^* state is about 149 kcal/mole, while a similar excitation for acetylene requires about 166 kcal/mole. Absorption of such an amount of energy is sufficient to cleave any single bond in either molecule.

The n-π^* Absorption

The data in Table 3-1 indicate that aldehydes and ketones absorb at far longer wavelengths than do most of the other simple single chromophores. Thus, absorption of an einstein of light by a mole of acetone imparts 106.9 kcal of energy to the sample. This amount of energy is sufficient to rupture any of a number of single bonds in acetone so that a great number of photochemical processes have been observed for this molecule. To acetaldehyde is imparted 99.0 kcal/mole upon absorption of light energy at its

Table 3-1

Ultraviolet Absorptions of Simple Chromophores

Compound Type	Example	$\lambda_{max.}$ (mμ)	Δ E trans. (kcal/mole)	ϵ	Solvent
$\overset{\text{O}}{\overset{\|}{\text{RCR}}}$	$\overset{\text{O}}{\overset{\|}{CH_3CCH_3}}$	270.6	106.9	15.8	EtOH
$\overset{\text{O}}{\overset{\|}{\text{RCR}}}$	$\overset{\text{O}}{\overset{\|}{tBuCtBu}}$	295.0	97.0	20.0	EtOH
$\overset{\text{O}}{\overset{\|}{\text{RCH}}}$	$\overset{\text{O}}{\overset{\|}{CH_3CH}}$	293.4	99.0	11.8	hexane
$\overset{\text{O}}{\overset{\|}{\text{RCOH}}}$	$\overset{\text{O}}{\overset{\|}{CH_3COH}}$	204.0	140.0	60.0	H_2O
$\overset{\text{O}}{\overset{\|}{\text{RCCl}}}$	$\overset{\text{O}}{\overset{\|}{CH_3CCl}}$	235.0	121.5	53.0	hexane
$\overset{\text{O}}{\overset{\|}{\text{RCOR}'}}$	$\overset{\text{O}}{\overset{\|}{CH_3COEt}}$	204.0	140.0	60.0	H_2O
$\overset{\text{O}}{\overset{\|}{\text{RCNH}_2}}$	$\overset{\text{O}}{\overset{\|}{CH_3CNH_2}}$	214.0	134.0	—	H_2O
$\overset{\text{O}}{\overset{\uparrow}{\text{RSR}'}}$	$\overset{\text{O}}{\overset{\uparrow}{C_6H_5SCH_3}}$	210.0	136.5	1,500	EtOH
$\overset{\text{O}}{\underset{\text{O}}{\overset{\uparrow}{\underset{\downarrow}{\text{RSR}'}}}}$	$CH_3SO_2CH_3$	180.0	159.2	—	—
RCH=CHR	$CH_2{=}CH_2$	193.0	149.0	10,000	vapor
RC≡CR	CH≡CH	173.0	166.0	6,000	vapor
$R_1R_2N_2$	CH_2N_2	410.0	70.0	1,200	vapor
RC≡N	CH_3CN	160.0	179.0	—	—
RNO	$n\text{-}C_4H_9NO$	300.0	95.7	120.0	ether
		665.0	42.8	20.0	—
RNO_2	CH_3NO_2	271.0	106.0	18.6	EtOH
$RONO_2$	$EtONO_2$	270.0	106.2	12.0	dioxane
RONO	n-octyl nitrite	230.0	125.0	2,200	hexane

position of maximum absorption. Since the extinction coefficient gives a rough measure of absorption probability per unit concentration, the relative probability of the absorption of light by ethylene at its position of maximum absorption compared to that of acetaldehyde at its $\lambda_{max.}$ clearly shows that the former, a π-π^* excitation, is more probable than the latter, an n-π^* process.

Table 3-1 also indicates that compounds other than simple aldehydes and simple ketones exhibit n-π^* absorption maxima. For example, the nitrates, nitro compounds, and nitroso compounds all show a relatively weak absorption maxima at comparatively long wavelength positions. As in the case of the aldehydes and ketones, absorption of electromagnetic radiation by nitro compounds, nitroso compounds, and nitrate esters at their ultraviolet maximum results in an energy acceptance, by the absorbing molecule, of between 95 and 110 kcal/mole.

All of the carbonyl compounds listed in Table 3-1 show an n-π^* absorption maximum. This absorption maximum, characterized by its improbability, is always represented by a small molar extinction coefficient. Except for the aldehydes and ketones, all the other carbonyl compounds show n-π^* maxima at relatively short wavelengths. The amides, the acids, the esters, and the acyl halides all absorb in the 205–230 mμ region of the ultraviolet spectrum. This substantial blue shift (hypsochromic shift in the older literature) results from the greater electronegativity of the adjacent halogen, nitrogen, or oxygen in the comparison to carbon. The highly electronegative atoms cause electron withdrawal from the chromophoric carbonyl group, and the energy gap between ground state and π^* excited state is widened. Practically, the observed shorter wavelength absorption maximum of acids, anhydrides, esters, acyl halides, and amides has caused photochemists to examine the more convenient aldehydes and ketones first although acid chlorides and amides have received some recent attention. Work at shorter wavelengths than 3100 Å requires all quartz apparatus, for Pyrex absorbs substantially below this wavelength. Quartz itself becomes unusable below about 2200 Å, and reactions requiring absorption at wavelengths shorter than this require sophisticated vacuum techniques. In addition, most ultraviolet solvents, such as chloroform, cyclohexane, methanol, carbon tetrachloride, and others, absorb substantially in these regions.

The data in Table 3-1 further indicate that compounds containing multiply bonded nitrogen atoms also absorb in an accessible region of the spectrum. Photochemical reactions of diazo compounds such as diazomethane are well known, and even though at its absorption maximum only 69 kcal of energy are imparted to a mole of diazomethane, formation of nitrogen is such a favorable process that diazomethane decomposes readily. Absorption at the ultraviolet maximum of n-octyl nitrite is relatively strong, and photochemical decompositions of nitrite esters, such as *n*-octyl nitrite, are experimentally convenient.

Finally, the data in Table 3-1 illustrate why photochemical reactions of single simple chromophores, such as sulfoxide and cyano, are not well classified or understood. Absorption by these chromophores occurs at such a short wavelength that, at least in solution, photochemical reactions of compounds containing these simple chromophores involve too much experimental difficulty, and too many different reaction processes occur.

The Effect of Unsaturation

Most of the chemical compounds with which photochemists are involved contain more than just a single isolated chromophore. If the unsaturation of an organic molecule is isolated from the absorbing chromophore by methylene groups or more highly substituted carbon atoms, the effect of the unsaturation on the absorption maximum is relatively small and results primarily from simple electrostatic effects. On the other hand, if the unsaturated linkages are conjugated with the absorbing chromophore, shifts of substantial magnitude and increases in extinction coefficient often result. As a general rule, shifts in the position of the absorption maximum are bathochromic (toward longer wavelengths) when a chromophore is placed in conjugation with unsaturated centers. Both n-π^* and π-π^* electronic transitions are shifted toward longer wavelengths by an increase in the number of carbon-carbon double bonds (or other unsaturated linkages) in conjugation with the chromophore undergoing the transition.

Empirical Prediction of The π-π^* Maximum

Through the years, several empirical relationships have resulted which correlate, nearly quantitatively, the position of the absorption maximum of a chromophore with the degree of unsaturation in conjugation with the chromophore and with the number, the type, and the position of substituents located on the unsaturated linkage. These empirical relationships, developed by R. B. Woodward and by L. F. Fieser, predict ultraviolet absorption maxima with some accuracy. The major purpose that the relationships serve is simply that from the position of the absorption maximum and from some knowledge about molecular structure, the exact position and nature of substituent groups can be predicted.

Table 3-2 lists empirical rules for predicting the position of the π-π^* transitions of alkyl-substituted dienes. Table 3-3 gives some illustrative examples of the use of the Woodward empirical rules. The observed π-π^* absorption maxima are also given for comparison.

Table 3-2 [a]

Woodward-Fieser Rules for Alkyl Substituted Dienes

The Diene	$\lambda_{max.}$, mμ
diene system base	217
each alkyl substituent M, N, X, or Y	add 5 mμ to base
if exocyclic double bond to six-membered ring is part of the conjugated system	add 5 mμ to base

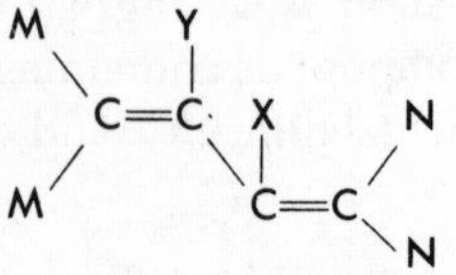

[a] R. B. Woodward, *J. Am. Chem. Soc.*, 64, 72 (1942).

The calculation of the predicted maximum ultraviolet absorption of 2,3-dimethylbutadiene, for example, is obtained by adding 10 mμ for the two alkyl substituents to the base butadiene absorption of 217 mμ. Calculation of the predicted absorption maximum of cyclohexylidinepropene results from adding 10 mμ for two alkyl substituents and 5 mμ for the exocyclic double bond to the 217 mμ base. The predicted absorption maxima is 232 mμ.

Woodward's rules[1] for calculation of the absorption maximum of diene systems is particularly useful when applied to steroid systems. Fieser[2] has found that alkyl substituents affect the absorption maxima of a steroidal diene system, but acetoxy and ether substituents do not. In addition, homoannular dienes always have a substantially higher absorption maxima than similarly substituted heteroannular dienes. Table 3-4 gives Fieser's

Table 3-3

Examples of Woodward-Fieser Calculations for Alkyl-Substituted Dienes

Diene	$\lambda_{max.}$ Calculated mμ	$\lambda_{max.}$ Observed mμ
butadiene	—	217
2,3-dimethylbutadiene	227	226
2,4-hexadiene	227	227
isoprene	222	220
3-cyclohexylidinepropene	232	236.5
3-methylene-6-isopropylcyclohexene	232	232
1,1-bicyclohexenyl	237	236
3-methylenecyclohexene	232	231

Table 3-4

Empirical Rules for Calculation of Absorption Maxima of Cyclic Dienes

Group	$\lambda_{max.}$, mμ
heteroannular diene base	214
homoannular diene base	253
double bond extending conjugation	add 30
alkyl substituent	add 5
exocyclic double bond	add 5
groups OAc or OR on the diene system	0

empirical ultraviolet absorption maxima rules for cyclic diene systems. Table 3-5 gives some typical examples. Calculation of the predicted $\lambda_{max.}$ follows from Fieser's rules (Table 3-4). When, for example, the system

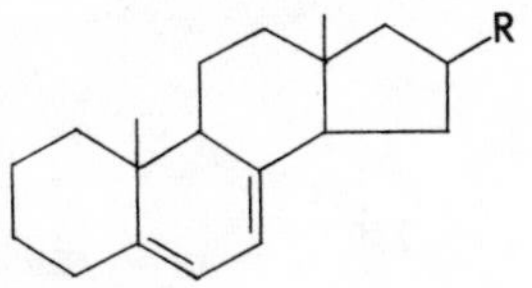

is chosen, the base absorption is 253 mμ because the diene is contained in only one carbocyclic system. Counting each ring residue as an alkyl substituent adds 20 mμ, and 10 mμ are added for the two exocyclic double bonds. The calculated total is 283 mμ. Calculating in a similar manner for 1-ethyl-5,5-dimethylcyclohexadiene-1,3 leads to a predicted value of 258 mμ, 253 base absorption plus 5 mμ for the ethyl group. Calculation of the absorption maxima for the monocyclic dienes requires the further modification that the entire cyclohexadiene system be responsible for the base absorption. No ring residue alkyl groups are counted.

The effect of alkyl substituents on the diene system results in either an increased stability of the excited state because of a combination of resonance and inductive effects or a decreased stability of the ground state (an increase in energy level of the bonding molecular orbital of the ground state). In general, the more highly substituted an olefinic center, the less is the energy required for the π-π^* transition, and the longer is the wavelength of the absorption due to this transition. The highly ordered ground state is destabilized by the steric repulsions of tri- or tetra-substituted olefinic centers. Since π-π^* excitation appears to involve some twisting about the central carbon-carbon bond, π-π^* excitation is a favorable process in systems where twisting relieves substituent group interactions.

Table 3-5

Ultraviolet Maxima of Cyclic Dienes

Compound	$\lambda_{max.}$ Calculated mν	$\lambda_{max.}$ Observed mν
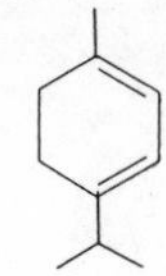	263	265
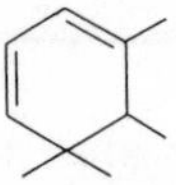	258	263
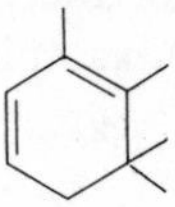	263	264
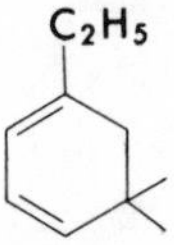 C₂H₅	258	260
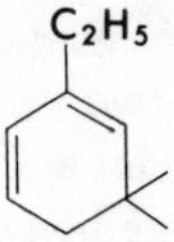 C₂H₅	258	261
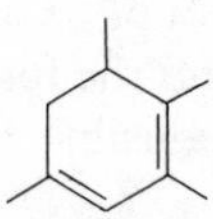	268	265
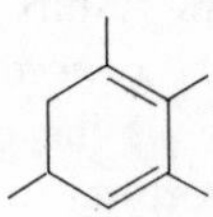	268	265

In some systems, large groups so destabilize the ground state that conjugation is destroyed. For example, 2,3-di-*t*-butylbutadiene-1,3 has none of the spectral or chemical properties of a conjugated diene.[3] The molecule is so forced out of a common plane by the interactions of the neighboring

Table 3-6

Prediction of Absorption Maxima of α, β-Unsaturated Ketones

Substituent	Probable $\lambda_{max.}$, mμ
base system	215
per substituent	Add 10 mμ to base
for each exocyclic bond to a six-membered ring	Add 5 mμ to base

t-butyl groups that the two double bonds act independently in spite of their apparent conjugation.

Rules have also been proposed for predicting the π-π^* absorption maxima of α,β-unsaturated ketones. Again these rules are useful in structure proof and are most beneficial when applied to steroidal systems. These rules are summarized in Table 3-6, and a few typical examples of the accuracy of these rules are shown in Table 3-7.

In 3,4-dimethyl-3-pentene-2-one, a typical example, the base is 215 mμ, and 30 mμ is added to the total because of the three alkyl substituents. The total calculated value is 245 mμ.

The n-π^* absorption maxima of aldehydes and ketones is also shifted to longer wavelength by increased conjugation. For example, although the n-π^* transition of formaldehyde occurs at 270 mμ, the same transition for benzaldehyde occurs at 312 mμ and in benzophenone at 328 mμ. Probably, this shift to longer wavelength results from a resonance stabilization of the excited state, but no quantitative empirical relationships for calculation of the position of n-π^* maxima exist.

Table 3-7

Example Calculations for α, β-Unsaturated Ketones

Compound	$\lambda_{max.}$ Calculated mμ	$\lambda_{max.}$ Observed mμ
2-acetobutene-1	225	221 or 220
1-acetocyclohexene	235	233.5
1-acetoisobutylene	235	235
1-methyl-3-acetobutene-2	245	249
2-cyclohexylidinecyclohexanone	255	257.5
1-acetocyclopentene	235	239
1-aceto-2-methylcyclopentene	245	253
1-aceto-2-methylcyclohexene	245	249

When two separate chromophores exist in the same compound, absorption maxima due to each of the chromophores are observed. If the chromophores are completely unconjugated, little relative difference between the observed absorption due to the chromophore in the dual system and the same chromophores in isolated systems is observed. Thus, unsaturated ketones and aldehydes show absorption maxima due to both an n-π^* transition of the carbonyl system and a π-π^* transition of the olefinic system. Classically, it was observed that unsaturated aldehydes and ketones display two absorption bands. The former was observed at comparatively long wavelength and was of relatively low extinction. In the original classification by Burawoy, this band was called the *radikal* or R band. It is, of course, the n-π^* transition.[4] The other band was at shorter wavelengths, but of high intensity, and was called a K (*konjugiert*) absorption band. It corresponds to π-π^* excitation.

In borderline cases, distinguishing between K and R absorption bands is a difficult process. Polar solvents, however, cause the π-π^* absorption band to occur at longer wavelengths, while the position of the n-π^* absorption is shifted toward shorter wavelengths by more polar solvents. For example, the n-π^* band of acetone occurs at 279 mμ in n-hexane; it occurs at 272 mμ in ethanol, and at 264.5 mμ in water. In hydroxylic solvents, the nonbonded electron pairs of the oxygen atoms are associated with a hydrogen of the solvent by a hydrogen bond and excitation is a comparatively difficult process. The strength of this hydrogen bond determines the position of the n-π^* absorption maxima. The observed difference in the effect of polar solvents on π-π^* and n-π^* absorption maxima makes distinguishing between them possible. This process can be carried to its logical extreme by examining the ultraviolet absorption maximum in acid solution. In acid, chromophores giving rise to n-π^* absorptions are generally destroyed because of the addition of the proton to the chromophore's most electronegative atom. An absorption disappearing in acid solution is generally an n-π^* absorption band.

Benzene Absorptions

With aromatic systems, other electronic transitions become possible, and the absorption spectra of aromatic molecules are decidedly more complicated than those of their aliphatic counterparts. In general, a new series of bands appears in aromatic systems. These bands occur at shorter wavelengths than R bands, but at longer wavelengths than K bands; they have larger extinction coefficients than typical R bands, but smaller extinction coefficients than typical K bands. These bands are called B (benzenoid) bands. In simple aromatic systems, they are characterized by a large degree of fine structure. They generally occur between 250 and 280 mμ and are called secondary aromatic bands.

Benzene and its derivatives also show other absorption maxima. The second general absorption of benzene derivatives shows properties typical of π-π* bands. These bands occur in the middle ultraviolet, near the limit of quartz apparatus, and are of extinction between 5000 and 10,000. Doub and VandenBelt classified them as primary aromatic bands. Table 3-8 lists the absorption maxima of benzene and several of its monosubstituted derivatives. Doub and VandenBelt[5] found that a good correlation between the

Table 3-8

Absorption Maxima of Benzene Derivatives

Substituent	$\lambda_{max.}$ K mμ	ϵ	$\lambda_{max.}$ B mμ	ϵ
H	203.5	7,400	254	204
NH$_3$	203.0	7,500	254	160
CH$_3$	206.5	7,000	261	225
Cl	209.5	7,400	263.5	190
OH	210.5	6,200	270	1450
OMe	217.0	6,400	269	1480
CN	224.0	13,000	271	1000
NH$_2$	230	8,600	280	1430
CHO	249.5	11,400	—	—
NO$_2$	268.5	7,800	—	—

[a]From L. Doub and J. M. VandenBelt, *J. Am. Chem. Soc.*, **69**, 2714 (1947).

position of the primary band of the benzene system and the Hammett sigma substituent constants can be obtained if one considers electron withdrawers and electron donors separately. Their results demonstrated that both electron-donating and electron-withdrawing substituents cause a bathochromic shift in the absorption maximum, but the amount of the shift varies regularly with the relative strength of the substituent as either an electron withdrawer or donor.

Recent results suggest strongly that electronic interactions are significantly different in the first excited states of many aromatic systems. In many cases, substituents on the aromatic nucleus affect photochemical reactions far differently from the way that they affect chemical reactions initiated by other methods. Examples will be discussed in Chapter 9. Furthermore, from a study of fluorescence spectra, acidities of excited state molecules can be determined. In many cases, marked changes in a molecule's acidity or basicity occur because of electronic excitation.[6] A recent study has shown that, at least in the case of phenols, the excited state acidities can be correlated with the Hammett substituent constants, but that conjugative effects are decidedly more important than inductive effects in excited species. Direct resonance interactions with *meta* (rather than *ortho* or *para* substituents as in ground state systems) substituents are observed.[7]

The n-π^* excitation of carbonyl compounds and nitro compounds creates an excited molecule that reacts much like a free radical on oxygen. A majority of the photochemical reactions of carbonyl compounds occur from the excited triplet state with the oxygen atom of the carbonyl moiety behaving like an alkoxy radical. Once the free valence of the carbonyl oxygen has been effectively used, various electron spin demotions occur so as to create a free radical species on the carbonyl carbon as well. Whether photochemical reactions of carbonyl compounds occur in the stepwise fashion described or not depends upon the specific photochemical reaction in question, but in most instances the alkoxy radical comparison is valid. The π-π^* excited state of olefins behaves like a di-free radical on carbon. Cycloadditions initiated photochemically also may occur in a stepwise or concerted fashion. These reactions will be discussed in detail in Chapter 6.

Although a formal analogy of photochemical reaction processes to free radical reactions initiated by other sources exists, there are also instances that require ionic intermediates in photochemical processes. Clearly, photochemical excitation results initially in bond homolysis, but oxidation or reduction of the radical formed may subsequently occur. In such cases, bond homolysis resembles bond heterolysis, and products such as solvolysis products take the place of the species typically observed in free radical reactions. Polar intermediates do have a place in some photochemical reactions although for the most part as secondary species only.

The specific values of absorption spectroscopy to organic photochemistry are varied and numerous. The first and most obvious utility of the absorption spectrum of a molecule is to give some clue as to whether the excited state results from an n-π^* absorption or a π-π^* absorption so that reactivity or lack of it can be understood. In organic molecules where both possibilities exist, definitive questions about the reaction mechanism can be answered if the n-π^* and π-π^* absorptions are separable.

The practicing photochemist attempting to determine the mechanism of a photochemical reaction is concerned with several questions after he is sure the molecule absorbs light. He must know whether the excitation is an n-π^* or π-π^* process, how efficient the photochemical reaction is, and whether the excited states responsible for chemical reaction are singlets or triplets. Concomitant with the above questions are questions concerning the lifetime of the excited states and the efficiency of energy degradation processes.

Quantum Yield

All of the various electronic excitation processes can be related in terms of their efficiencies by measuring the number of chemical reactions per impingent light quantum. The tendency of a molecule to undergo a chemical reaction after the absorption process has occurred gives rise to the concept of the quantum yield. As mentioned earlier, the quantum yield of a photochemical reaction is defined as either the number of moles of reactant consumed or products produced per einstein of absorbed radiation. The primary quantum yield ϕ, measures the number of species that disappear directly as a result of the molecular absorption. It must have values between the limits of 0 and 1.

The primary quantum yield as distinguished from the total quantum yield, Φ, of a photochemical reaction is illustrated diagrammatically in Figure 3-1. The primary quantum yield of a photochemical reaction measures efficiency of the one step process giving reaction products immediately from the excited state (Fig. 3-1a). The total reaction quantum yield, on the other hand, measures the efficiency of a multiple step process (Fig. 3-1b). In prac-

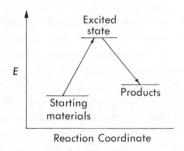

Figure 3-1a

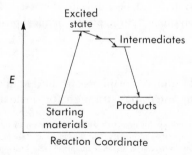

Figure 3-1b

tice, the quantum yield for the primary process often cannot be successfully separated from the quantum yield for the total process, and ϕ and Φ become indistinguishable.

For diagnosis of reaction mechanism, the quantum yield is a useful concept. For example, by observing that the quantum yield for product formation in the photochemical chlorination of hydrocarbons is far greater than one, photochemists have proposed a chain reaction sequence. On the other hand, the relative inefficiency of the reactions of certain azo compounds indicates that rearrangements are necessary before decomposition can occur.

Measurement of the quantum yield of a photochemical reaction is generally accomplished by comparison with some standard quantum process. This technique is called *actinometry* and is more convenient than the direct quantum output measurement of lamp output by photoelectric or thermopile methods.* Because the output intensity of most lamps varies with time, the photochemist must either measure the total quanta incident upon a reacting solution or average the output with time. In addition, with many commercial lamps the output is not regular from each position around the lamp. The radiation incident upon the sample is, therefore, best averaged by rotating the samples and the actinometric standards around the light source.

Chemical actinometers are many and varied. Organic chemists find that the photoreduction of benzophenone by benzhydrol developed by Hammond and co-workers is convenient[8], while Pitts and co-workers[9] have reported that the photochemical oxygen transfer reaction of o-nitrobenzaldehyde is also a suitable photochemical standard reaction. Another popular actinometer utilizes the photochemical decomposition of oxalic acid in the presence of uranyl oxalate, while ferrioxalate solutions are most often used.

With each individual actinometer the experimenter must carefully control the temperature of the reaction and must isolate the desired wavelength for reaction by means of filter systems. In addition, it is frequently necessary for the actinometer systems to be carefully degassed, for particularly with benzophenone, oxygen quenches the photochemical process.

Light Sources

The lamps generally utilized for photochemical studies are mercury resonance lamps of varying intensities although for qualitative studies ordinary

*A discussion of electrical methods for detection and measurement of light energy may be found in W. West, "Spectroscopy and Spectrophotometry," in *Technique of Organic Chemistry*, A. Weissberger, ed., Interscience, London, 1949. Of course, absolute quantum yield measurements were initially necessary for comparative standards to be defined originally. A more recent discussion may be found in *Photochemistry*, J. G. Calvert and J. N. Pitts, Jr., New York, Wiley, 1966.

sunlamps or just sunlight are sometimes adequate. With most lamps, large quantities of thermal energy are generated, and careful temperature control is necessary. The mercury resonance lamp generally consists of a sealed quartz tube containing mercury, liquid and vapor, and a rare gas. An arc is struck through the gas by means of an applied potential. After an initial warm-up period, the discharge produces excited mercury atoms. Emission is predominantly of 2537 Å wavelength although significant 3130 and 3660 Å emissions are also observed. Particularly with medium and high pressure mercury lamps, the 2537 Å line is generally reversed. That is, the observed emission is produced by absorption by and emission of the mercury contained in the lamp proper. For work in the shorter ultraviolet region, cadmium and xenon arc discharge lamps are generally preferred.

Filters

When radiation of a specific wavelength is desired, several alternative procedures are applicable. The least accurate, but often satisfactory, results are obtained using filter systems. Filter systems make use of a process of selective absorption. By combining certain filters, wavelength bands can be isolated. These bands are 200 or more Å wide although somewhat narrower bands may be isolated by using certain filter combinations at a limited number of wavelengths. The simplest filter is "Pyrex" glass, which absorbs most radiation of less than 3100 Å. Noyes and Leighton[10] as well as Calvert and Pitts[11] discuss a number of other filter systems. If narrower bandwidths are desired, monochromators are commerically available. Monochromators have the disadvantage, however, of emitting only low intensities at any one individual wavelength. The mechanistic photochemist anxiously awaits the development of a blue or ultraviolet laser, a high intensity, monochromatic source.

Flash Photolysis

The technique of flash photolysis provides the photochemist with an adequate method for preparing highly unstable intermediates in high concentrations. In essence, the technique involves the creation of a nonequilibrium condition in a system in an extremely short period of time by rapidly irradiating the sample with high intensity radiation. If the intensity of the flash is large enough, high concentrations of reactive intermediates can be obtained. Providing that suitable detection devices are available, these reactive intermediates can actually be observed, and the rates of decay of the reactive intermediates can be measured. Detection of the intermediates is, generally, but not always, accomplished by spectroscopic techniques. Intermediates in photochemical reactions that have been detected by means of flash photolysis include free radicals, monovalent carbon intermediates, transient enols, triplet states, etc.

References

1. Woodward, R. B., *J. Am. Chem. Soc.*, **64**, 72 (1942).
2. Fieser, L. F., and M. Fieser, *Steroids*, p. 15, New York, Reinhold, 1959.
3. Huyser, E. S., private communication.
4. Burawoy, A., *Chem. Ber.*, **63**, 3155 (1930).
5. Doub, L., and J. M. VandenBelt, *J. Am. Chem. Soc.*, **69**, 2714 (1947) et seq.
6. Weller, A., *Progr. Reaction Kinetics*, **1**, 189 (1961).
7. Wehry, E. L., and L. B. Rogers, *J. Am. Chem. Soc.*, **87**, 4234 (1965).
8. See, for example, W. M. Moore, G. S. Hammond, and R. Foss, *J. Am. Chem. Soc.*, **83**, 2789 (1961).
9. Pitts, J. N., Jr., J. K. S. Wan, and E. A. Schuck, *J. Am. Chem. Soc.*, **86**, 3606 (1964).
10. Noyes, W. A., Jr., and P. A. Leighton, *The Photochemistry of Gases*, p. 68, New York, Reinhold, 1941.
11. Calvert, J. G. and J. N. Pitts, "Photochemistry," p. 686, New York, Wiley, 1966.

General References

Bowen, E. J., *The Chemical Aspects of Light*, Oxford, Clarendon, 1946.

Calvert, J. G., and J. N. Pitts, *Photochemistry*, New York, Wiley, 1966.

Gillam, A. R., and E. S. Stern, *An Introduction to Electronic Absorption Spectroscopy in Organic Chemistry*, London, Arnold, 1958.

Jaffé, H. H., and M. Orchin, *Theory and Applications of Ultraviolet Spectroscopy*, New York, Wiley, 1962.

Masson, C. R., W. A. Noyes, Jr., and V. Boekelheide, in *Technique of Organic Chemistry*, Weissberger, A., ed., Vol. II, New York, Interscience, 1956.

Murrell, J. N., *The Theory of Electronic Spectra of Organic Molecules*, New York, Wiley, 1964.

Porter, G., in *Technique of Organic Chemistry*, Weissberger, A., ed., Vol. VIII, Part 2, New York, Interscience, 1955.

Reid, C., *Excited States in Chemistry and Biology*, London, Butterworths, 1957.

CHAPTER

4

Photochemical Processes

Although physical chemists have tried to understand the intricacies of photochemical reactions for many years, organic chemists have been essentially content to describe a photochemical reaction only in terms of the reactants and the products. Organic chemists made little or no step by step examination of those reactions of organic molecules resulting from the absorption of a light quantum until the late 1950's.

Ultimately, a complete microscopic description of any reaction must include a discussion of three general steps: the initiation of the reaction sequence, the continuation or propagation of the reaction sequence, and the termination of the reaction sequence.

A complete description of photochemical processes requires just such an evaluation. The photochemist must first ask the question, what is the absorption process like for the molecule? Having answered this question, the photochemist can then ask, what happens to cause the reaction to continue after the light absorption? Finally, having answered both of these questions, he can ask, how do all the molecules return to a normally reactive state?

Noyes et al.[1] define the primary photochemical process as "the series of events beginning with light absorption by a molecule and ending either with the disappearance of the molecule or with a return of the molecule to some ground electronic state." Secondary photochemical processes are said to include chemical reactions of the excited state or the fragments produced therefrom.

After light absorption, molecules find themselves in states of shorter lifetime than normal. Molecules in excited states generally are highly reactive, and they tend to revert to normally reactive ground states as soon as possible. On a molecular basis, a single chemical species can degrade itself to a normally reactive ground state by one of three general pathways. First, the molecule can undergo chemical reaction from the excited state to give ground state products. Second, the excited molecule can lose its energy by a process exactly the opposite of light absorption. This process may be a radiative process in which light of the same, or nearly the same wavelength as that absorbed is emitted, or the process may occur without radiation via collisional or other deactivation pathways. Finally, the molecule can simply transfer its excess energy to another molecule in the solution. This process is called *energy transfer*.

Photochemical secondary processes appear to divide themselves into six general areas. Arbitrarily, the six general types of photochemical reactions include photochemical elimination and decomposition reactions, photochemical addition and dimerization reactions, photochemical atomic abstraction reactions, photochemical rearrangement reactions, photochemical substitution reactions, and finally, photochemically induced chain reactions. In subsequent chapters, each of these general types of secondary photochemical reaction processes will be treated in detail and current trends and results discussed.

The information gathered from photochemical processes occurring in lieu of chemical reaction is useful in understanding excited state behavior. Processes of radiative excited state decay include phosphorescence, fluorescence, and slow fluorescence.

The First Excited Singlet State

Emissions from irradiated organic molecules are of several kinds. Many years ago it was recognized that most substances emit light of a wavelength similar to the wavelength of the radiation absorbed. This emission, termed *fluorescence*, results from the excited to ground state singlet-singlet radiative transition. Qualitatively, the fluorescence spectrum is the mirror image of the absorption spectrum. However, since absorption may occur to any one of a number of excited states above the first, the absorption spectrum of a molecule generally contains some structure on the short wavelength side of the absorption maximum. Since thermal deactivation to the lowest vibrational level of the excited state is rapid, fluorescence occurs when an electron drops from the lowest vibrational level of the excited state to any of the vibrational levels of the ground state. The result is that emissions of lower energy (longer wavelength) than the principal emission are observed. The principal emission from the lowest vibrational level of the excited state to the lowest energy vibrational level of the ground state is termed the zero-zero (0-0) emission band.

Degradation from the first excited singlet state is not limited to fluorescence. Generally, the potential energy surfaces associated with the first singlet state and with the excited triplet state intersect. At some time, the nuclear configuration of the first singlet state and the first triplet state as well as the potential energy of the two states are exactly the same. At this instant, the molecule may cross, without radiation, from the first excited singlet state to the first excited triplet state. This radiationless conversion is termed *intersystem crossing*.

To get to the point of potential energy equality of the first excited singlet and first excited triplet state requires that the vibrational energy associated with the singlet state cascade downward. In other words, since the excitation process leaves the majority of molecules in a variety of excited vibrational levels, most molecules must be able to degrade themselves by thermal transfer of vibrational energy to the surroundings and place themselves in the vibrational energy level of the excited singlet state corresponding exactly to an energy level of the triplet excited state. Much of the thermal energy transfer by the excited molecule is by *solvent quenching*, a radiationless transfer of excited state energy to the solvent.

The First Excited Triplet State

The triplet state of a molecule is in the general case of lower energy than the corresponding singlet state. Hund's first rule states that molecules having electrons with parallel spins are of higher energy than those with nonparallel spins. This is probably a result of the fact that the unpaired electrons repel one another in the triplet state, thus minimizing unfavorable electronic and nuclear interactions. The triplet state of a molecule is generally longer lived than the singlet state because under normal circumstances conversion of the triplet state to the ground state singlet is improbable; therefore, it is in the triplet state that the molecule sits waiting for chemical reaction. If no reaction possibility presents itself, the molecule eventually will phosphoresce or decay radiationlessly to the ground state.

Lewis and Kasha[2] investigated the phosphorescence spectra of some 79 organic materials. These workers and others[3] observed two major wavelengths of light emission from samples maintained in a rigid matrix at low temperatures. The first emission is called α phosphorescence and is proposed to result from the triplet to ground state emission. The second emission spectrum is very similar in structure to the fluorescence emission spectrum. Its lifetime, however, is characteristic of a phosphorescence, and it is thought to result from an excited singlet state to ground state transition. These workers reasoned that thermal reactivation of the molecule in the triplet state to the excited singlet state permits this process, *slow fluorescence*. Lewis proposed that the triplet state is a biradical state, and he obtained the triplet state energy from the wavelength of phosphorescence by means of the Planck equation.

Lewis had convincing evidence supporting his postulate that the triplet state is solely responsible for the phosphorescent behavior of molecules. The energy level of a molecule's lowest lying triplet is related to the molecule's chemical structure. Auxochromic groups cause the frequency of the emission, v, to decrease. Roughly the decrease in the frequency of the phosphorescence caused by an auxochromic group depends on the ability of the auxochrome to enhance longer wavelength absorption, that is, on its ability to function as either an electron withdrawer or an electron donor. The stronger the electron withdrawer, the lower is the frequency of the emission and the energy of the triplet state. In addition, thermal activation from the triplet to the singlet state significantly decreases the probability of the existence of the triplet state at higher temperatures. Therefore, the triplet state is generally observable at low temperatures. Triple state energies of a variety of compounds have been reevaluated by several workers. Representative triplet state energies of compounds, as obtained by Lewis and Kasha are listed in Table 4-1. The greater portion of these values were obtained at liquid nitrogen temperatures in ether-pentane-ethanol glass. Recent results indicate that the triplet state energy of a compound is somewhat dependent upon the solvent that is used to form the glassy matrix.[4] Different triplet state energies were obtained in all hydrocarbon matrices although the differences are small numerically.

Energy Transfer

In the presence of suitable acceptor molecules, a third alternative for decay of an excited molecule back to a ground electronic state is presented. This alternative is that of *energy transfer*. Theoretically, the process of energy transfer can occur either from the excited singlet state or the excited triplet state of the donor molecule. Furthermore, energy transfer can result either in an excited singlet or excited triplet state of the acceptor molecule. The acceptor molecule may be either a ground state triplet or singlet. The only

Table 4-1

Triplet State Energies of Selected Compounds[a]

Compound	ν_p, cm^{-1}	E_t, kcal/mole
cis-stilbene	21,700	62
benzene	29,800	85
naphthalene	21,300	61
anthracene	14,700	42
biphenyl	22,800	65
diphenylamine	25,200	72
triphenylamine	24,500	70
α-naphthylamine	20,100	58
aniline	26,800	77
carbazole	24,500	70
nitrobenzene	21,100	60
α-nitronaphthalene	19,200	55
4-nitrostilbene (trans)	17,400	50
p-nitroaniline	19,300	55
m-nitroacetophenone	20,300	58
benzaldehyde	25,200	72
acetophenone	26,500	74
benzophenone	24,400	70
thiobenzophenone	14,100	40
benzil	21,600	62
biacetyl	19,700	56
diisopropyl ketone	25,900	74
toluene	28,900	83
phenol	28,500	82
benzonitrile	27,000	77
benzoic acid	27,200	78
p-dichlorobenzene	26,000	74
methyl-α-naphthyl ether	20,900	60
α-bromonaphthalene	20,700	59
α-naphthol	20,500	59

[a] Lewis and Kasha, *J. Am. Chem. Soc.*, **66**, 2100 (1944).

condition necessary for energy transfer is that the energy state to which the acceptor is excited be of a lower level than the excited state energy of the donor molecule. An important result of energy transfer is that the donor molecule is degraded to the ground electronic state, whether this is singlet or triplet. Table 4-2 shows some of the energy transfer possibilities between a donor excited state, D, and an acceptor ground state, A. Some of these

Table 4-2

Some Possible Energy Transfer Processes

(1)	D* (singlet)	+	A (singlet)	→	D (singlet)	+	A* (singlet)
(2)	D* (triplet)	+	A (singlet)	→	D (singlet)	+	A* (singlet)
(3)	D* (singlet)	+	A (triplet)	→	D (singlet)	+	A* (triplet)
(4)	D* (triplet)	+	A (singlet)	→	D (singlet)	+	A* (singlet)
(5)	D* (triplet)	+	A (triplet)	→	D (singlet)	+	A* (singlet)
(6)	D* (singlet)	+	A (singlet)	→	D (singlet)	+	A* (triplet)
(7)	D* (triplet)	+	A (singlet)	→	D (singlet)	+	A* (triplet)

processes are of low probability and have not been observed experimentally. Of the processes listed, singlet-singlet energy transfer, 1, and triplet-triplet energy transfer, 7, are best known.

There are at least four theoretical mechanisms of energy transfer. The first of these, a trivial example, suggests that energy transfer occurs by donor emission and acceptor absorption of the radiative energy. Experimentally, such a process is not uncommon and is governed by Beer's law. The second general mechanism suggests that energy transfer occurs by collision. Presumably, exchange of radiative energy occurs upon collision between donor and acceptor molecules. Energy transfer of the third type results from dipole-dipole interactions between the donor and the acceptor. This is most probable when there is a large overlap in the emission spectrum of the donor and the absorption spectrum of the acceptor for, at some time, the potential energy surfaces of the excited state donor molecule and the excited state acceptor molecule are nearly the same. Finally, the fourth type of energy transfer is probable in rigid media and results from the migration of "excitons." This energy transfer is thought of as nonradiative, noncollisional crossing of energy from the excited state of the donor to the excited state of the acceptor.

Experimentally, one observes energy transfer in a number of ways. The classical spectroscopic method involves, for singlet excited states, measurement of the quenching of fluorescence of the donor as a function of the concentration of the acceptor. Concomitant with the quenching of donor fluorescence is the appearance of acceptor fluorescence. A dramatic example of this process visible to the eye, is the green fluorescence of commercial anthracene and the blue-violet fluorescence of pure anthracene. Experimentally, it has been shown that commercial anthracene contains minute quantities of another aromatic hydrocarbon, napthacene, and its fluorescence is actually observed even though anthracene is, undoubtedly, absorbing most of the incident radiation.

Triplet-triplet energy transfer is observed in a similar fashion. By observing phosphorescence from solid solutions of naphthalene and carbonyl sensitizers, such as benzophenone and benzaldehyde, Terenin and Ermolaev[5,6,7] observed that under conditions where absorption is solely due to the benzophenone or benzaldehyde, phosphorescence due to the naphthalene appears. Since the triplet energies of both benzophenone $(E_t = 68.9$ kcal/mole) and benzaldehyde $(E_t = 72.0$ kcal/mole) lie above that of naphthalene $(E_t = 61$ kcal/mole), a transfer of energy from carbonyl compound to naphthalene would be downhill. Furthermore, both benzaldehyde and benzophenone undergo rapid intersystem crossing to the triplet state so that energy transfer must be from the triplet state of the donor and yield the triplet state of the acceptor. These data are shown diagrammatically in Figure 4-1.

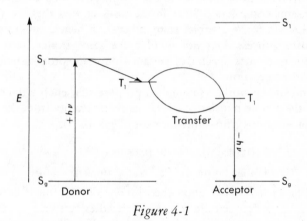

Figure 4-1

More recent experiments by Porter and Wilkinson[8] have demonstrated that triplet energy is exchanged between donor and acceptor upon every collision, providing the triplet state of the acceptor lies significantly below the triplet energy state of the donor. Bäckström and Sandros[9,10] have observed triplet-triplet energy transfer to take place in solution. They found that benzene solutions of benzophenone and biacetyl show phosphorescence due to biacetyl even when benzophenone absorbs most of the incident radiation. In cases where the triplet energy of the donor and the triplet energy of the acceptor are quite different, the rate of the transfer process will depend only on the rate of thermal diffusion of donor to acceptor. In solid matrix, energy transfer from singlet donor to give singlet acceptor molecules occurs far more rapidly than does similar transfer of triplet energy. The rate constants for singlet transfer are around 10^{11} sec^{-1}, but for the triplet state process, are only 10^3 sec^{-1}. Such an observation again reflects the stability of the triplet state compared to the singlet state.

The exact nature of collisional energy transfer between triplet donor and acceptor is open to question. Two distinct theories have been suggested. Schenck suggests that energy transfer takes place by formation of a covalent bond between the donor and the acceptor, eqs. (1–3).[11–18]

(1)   D $\xrightarrow{h\nu}$ D* (singlet) $\rightarrow$ D* (triplet)

(2)   D* (triplet) + A $\rightarrow$ ·A—D·

(3)   ·A—D· + y $\rightarrow$ Ay + D

The diradical complex, · A—D ·, is called an "excito" dimer, and the evidence for its formation is twofold. First, products formed in certain photosensitized reactions differ from the products formed by direct irradiation of the same compound. Since in the cases chosen the direct radiation process is known to be a triplet state process, Schenck suggests that the energy transfer process does not involve the same triplet state. Second, electron spin resonance spectra of certain donor-acceptor systems suggest "excito" dimer formation.

Hammond and co-workers in contrast propose that energy transfer occurs directly by the simple transfer of electromagnetic energy from the donor to the acceptor without excito dimer formation, eqs. (4–5).

(4)   D $\xrightarrow{h\nu}$ D* (singlet) $\rightarrow$ D* (triplet)

(5)   D* (triplet) + A $\rightarrow$ D + A* (triplet)

Hammond bases his theory upon the observation that most differences in products resulting between direct and sensitized excitation processes can be accounted for by other explanations, and that in all cases the different products in the sensitized and direct excitation result from different excited states not from different chemical reaction intermediates.[19–23]

Transfer of triplet energy need not be a bimolecular process. Significant energy transfer can occur if a suitable donor and acceptor are located in the same molecule. As an example, Leermakers, Byers, Lamola, and Hammond[24] have observed that 4-(1-naphthylmethyl)benzophenone (I) causes the isomerization of *cis* to *trans* piperylene and vice versa and gives a product ratio of *cis* to *trans* piperylene similar to that of naphthalene even when the light absorption takes place via the n-π^* transition of the carbonyl chromophore. Leermakers and co-workers assumed that an intramolecular energy transfer from the benzophenone moiety to the naphthalene moiety takes place and the triplet state of I is naphthalene-like when it transfers its triplet energy to piperylene.

Naturally and synthetically, energy transfer plays an important role in chemical reactions of organic materials. One of the many exciting natural uses of energy transfer is in photosynthesis. In the light-induced reversal of cellular respiration, energy transfer processes allow absorbed energy to be carried to reactive enzymatic sites. Since only a very small number of chlorophyll molecules absorb radiation, it is probable that other pigments contained in the cell contribute to the photosynthetic process by absorbing and transferring energy to the active chlorophyll molecules.

4-(1-naphthylmethyl)benzophenone

In the laboratory as well as in nature, energy transfer is extremely useful. It finds its greatest laboratory application by providing the chemist with a method of populating excited states not easily populated by direct radiation processes. Since the photochemical behavior of certain molecules is better understood than the behavior of other molecules, use of the understood donor to study new molecules provides a handle for initial investigation of excited state behavior of the acceptor. Use of carbonyl compounds to sensitize *cis-trans* isomerization in cyclopropanes and olefins, decomposition of certain azo compounds, ring closures, and cycloaddition reactions has been reported in recent years. Discussion of these reactions will be presented in later chapters.

As has been implied, singlet-singlet and triplet-triplet energy transfer processes are experimentally the most common. Some other energy transfer processes are also known; however, their experimental observation is not as common. These processes include energy transfer reactions in which triplet donors produce singlet acceptors and vice versa. The former process has been observed;[25] the latter process has not been detected.

The electronic structure of the ground state of either the donor or the acceptor need not be specified. Energy transfer from excited singlet states to ground state triplet molecules has recently been proposed as an important step in certain sensitized oxidation sequences.

Foote and Wexler,[26,27] as well as Corey and Taylor,[28] have proposed that the photooxidation of anthracene involves excitation of anthracene to its excited singlet state, followed by reaction of the excited singlet with ground state triplet oxygen to give ground state anthracene and singlet oxygen. The singlet oxygen reacts independently with ground state anthracene. A similar reaction mechanism is proposed for allylic oxidation. These experiments will be discussed in greater detail later.

References

1. Noyes, W. A., Jr., G. B. Porter, and J. E. Jolley, *Chem. Rev.*, **56**, 49 (1956).
2. Lewis, G. N., and M. Kasha, *J. Am. Chem. Soc.*, **66**, 2100 (1944).
3. Lewis, G. N., T. T. Magel, and D. Lipkin, *J. Am. Chem. Soc.*, **64**, 1774 (1942).
4. Herkstroeter, W. G., A. A. Lamola, and G. S. Hammond, *J. Am. Chem. Soc.*, **86**, 4537 (1964).
5. Terenin, A., and V. Ermolaev, *Doklady Akad. Nauk. S. S. S. R.*, **85**, 547 (1952).
6. Ermolaev, V., and A. Terenin, *J. chim. phys.*, 698 (1958).
7. Terenin, A., and V. Ermolaev, *Trans. Faraday Soc.*, **52**, 1042 (1956).
8. Porter, G., and F. Wilkinson, *Proc. Roy. Soc.*, **A264**, 1 (1961).
9. Bäckström, H. L. J., and K. Sandros, *Acta Chem. Scand.*, **12**, 823 (1958).
10. Bäckström, H. L. J., and K. Sandros, *Acta Chem. Scand.*, **14**, 48 (1960).
11. Schenck, G. O., and R. Steinmetz, *Tetrahedron Letters*, **21**, 1 (1960).
12. Schenck, G. O., and R. Wolgast, *Naturwissenschaften*, **49**, 36 (1962).
13. Schenck, G. O., *Z. Elektrochem.*, **64**, 997 (1960).
14. Schenck, G. O., K. G. Kinkel, and H. J. Mertens, *Ann. Chem.*, **584**, 125 (1953).
15. Schenck, G. O., H. Eggert, and W. Denk, *Ann. Chem.*, **584**, 177 (1953).
16. Schenck, G. O., and K. H. Schulte-Elte, *Ann. Chem.*, **618**, 185 (1958).
17. Schenck, G. O., *Ind. Eng. Chem.*, **55**, 40 (1963).
18. Schenck, G. O., and K. Gollnick, Forschungberichte Des Landes Nordhein-Westfalen, No. 1256, Westdeutscher Verlag, Köln and Opladen (1963).
19. Hammond, G. S., J. Saltiel, A. A. Lamola, N. J. Turro, J. S. Bradshaw, D. O. Cowan, R. C. Counsell, V. Vogt, and C. Dalton, *J. Am. Chem. Soc.*, **86**, 3197 (1964).
20. Hammond, G. S., and R. S. Liu, *J. Am. Chem. Soc.*, **85**, 477 (1963).
21. Hammond, G. S., N. J. Turro, and P. A. Leermakers, *J. Am. Chem. Soc.*, **83**, 2396 (1961).
22. Hammond, G. S., N. J. Turro, and P. A. Leermakers, *J. Phys. Chem.*, **66**, 1144 (1962).
23. Hammond, G. S., and J. Saltiel, *J. Am. Chem. Soc.*, **84**, 4983 (1962).
24. Leermakers, P. A., G. W. Byers, A. A. Lamola, and G. S. Hammond, *J. Am. Chem. Soc.*, **85**, 2670 (1963).
25. Ermolaev, V., and E. B. Sveshnikova, *Dokl. Akad. Nauk. S. S. S. R.*, **149**, 1295 (1963).
26. Foote, C. S., and S. Wexler, *J. Am. Chem. Soc.*, **86**, 3879 (1964).
27. Foote, C. S., and S. Wexler, *J. Am. Chem. Soc.*, **86**, 3880 (1964).
28. Corey, E. J., and W. C. Taylor, *J. Am. Chem. Soc.*, **86**, 3881 (1964).

General References

Bowen, E. J., *Advances in Photochemistry*, Vol. I, p. 23 ff., New York, Interscience, 1963.
Gollnick, K., and G. O. Schenck, *Pure Appl. Chem.*, **9**, 507 (1964).
Livingston, R., *J. Phys. Chem.*, **61**, 860 (1957).
Rabinowitch, E., *J. Phys. Chem.*, **61**, 870 (1957).
Robinson, G. W., *Ann. Rev. Phys. Chem.*, **15**, 311 (1964).
Wilkinson, F., *Advances in Photochemistry*, Vol. III, p. 241 ff., New York, Interscience, 1964.

CHAPTER

5

Decomposition Reactions

Photochemical elimination or decomposition reactions include all photo-chemical reactions in which the absorbing material loses one or more fragment species. Lost fragments may be gaseous and chemically inert, or they may be a stable compound, an unstable compound, an ion, or a free radical. Specific photochemical decomposition reactions which have been observed include reactions in which aldehydes or ketones lose molecular carbon monoxide, reactions during which azo, diazo, and azido compounds lose molecular nitrogen, reactions of organic nitro compounds from which nitric oxide is evolved, and reactions of nitrite esters in which the nitric oxide moiety undergoes decomposition and intramolecular rearrangement. Sulfur dioxide and alkenes also are produced in some photochemical elimination reactions.

Elimination of Carbon Monoxide

Decarbonylation processes involving aldehydes and ketones have been studied extensively both in vapor and condensed phases. The photolytic decomposition of simple aldehydes and ketones has been the subject of a great number of papers in the scientific literature and several excellent reviews on the photochemical behavior of simple aldehydes and ketones in the vapor phase have appeared. The reader interested in a more detailed evaluation of the reactions of these materials is referred to these reviews.[1-6]

The photochemistry of acetone has been studied extensively in the vapor phase. Acetone is known, among other things, to lose carbon monoxide photochemically and produce ethane, eq. (1).

$$(1) \qquad CH_3\overset{\displaystyle O}{\overset{\|}{C}}CH_3 \xrightarrow{h\nu} CH_3CH_3 + CO$$

The process shown in eq. (1) is highly efficient, particularly at slightly elevated temperatures; the quantum yield for formation of carbon monoxide, Φ = moles CO/quanta absorbed, has been measured by Noyes[7] and found to be essentially unity. The major mode of photodecomposition of acetone at elevated temperatures is postulated by Noyes to be:

$$(2) \qquad CH_3\overset{\displaystyle O}{\overset{\|}{C}}CH_3 \xrightarrow{h\nu} 2CH_3\cdot + CO$$

$$(3) \qquad 2CH_3\cdot \longrightarrow C_2H_6$$

At lower temperatures the situation becomes more complex because secondary processes begin to occur. A stepwise decomposition of acetone to methyl radicals and acetyl radicals, eq. (4), is proposed. Decarbonylation

$$(4) \qquad CH_3\overset{\displaystyle O}{\overset{\|}{C}}CH_3 \xrightarrow{h\nu} CH_3\overset{\displaystyle O}{\overset{\|}{C}}\cdot + \cdot CH_3$$

of the acetyl radical can occur to produce carbon monoxide and a second methyl radical; however, reactions of the methyl radical with acetone and of the acetyl radical with acetone are also observed. The products at lower temperatures include smaller amounts of acetaldehyde, methane, biacetyl, and probably 2,5-hexanedione. A chain sequence accounting for these products is given in eqs. (5–9).

$$(5) \qquad CH_3\overset{\displaystyle O}{\overset{\|}{C}}CH_3 \xrightarrow{h\nu} CH_3\overset{\displaystyle O}{\overset{\|}{C}}\cdot + \cdot CH_3$$

$$(6) \qquad CH_3\overset{\displaystyle O}{\overset{\|}{C}}\cdot + CH_3\overset{\displaystyle O}{\overset{\|}{C}}CH_3 \longrightarrow CH_3\overset{\displaystyle O}{\overset{\|}{C}}H + \cdot CH_2\overset{\displaystyle O}{\overset{\|}{C}}CH_3$$

$$(7) \qquad \cdot CH_3 + CH_3\overset{\displaystyle O}{\overset{\|}{C}}CH_3 \longrightarrow CH_4 + CH_3\overset{\displaystyle O}{\overset{\|}{C}}CH_2\cdot$$

$$(8) \qquad 2CH_3\overset{\displaystyle O}{\overset{\|}{C}}\cdot \longrightarrow CH_3\overset{\displaystyle O\ O}{\overset{\|\ \|}{C\ C}}CH_3$$

(9)
$$2CH_3\overset{O}{\underset{\|}{C}}CH_2\cdot \longrightarrow CH_3\overset{O}{\underset{\|}{C}}CH_2CH_2\overset{O}{\underset{\|}{C}}CH_3$$

The excited state from which the decomposition of acetone takes place probably depends on a number of variables. Both singlet and triplet excited acetone can lead to decomposition. However, the amount of triplet acetone present depends on the temperature, the incident radiation wavelength, the pressure, and a number of other things. Caldwell and Hoare[8] have shown that the triplet state decomposes more efficiently than the singlet state or vibrationally excited analogs thereof.

A complicating facet of acetone photochemistry is a photooxidation reaction. Quenching of the triplet state of acetone by oxygen has been demonstrated by Pearson.[9] From the photooxidation of acetone, one obtains formaldehyde, carbon dioxide, and methanol as well as methane, ethane, and carbon monoxide.

Since one of the primary decomposition modes of aliphatic ketones involves the cleavage of a carbonyl-carbon alkyl group carbon single bond, structural considerations play an important role in the primary mode of photochemical decomposition reactions of mixed aliphatic ketones. It is observed that although the carbon-carbon bond dissociation energy of acetone is low (71 kcal/mole), the carbon-carbon bond dissociation process leading to acetyl radicals and ethyl radicals from methyl ethyl ketone is preferred over the competing carbon-carbon cleavage with formation of methyl radicals and propionyl radicals, eq. (10) and (11).

(10)
$$CH_3\overset{O}{\underset{\|}{C}}C_2H_5 \rightarrow CH_3CH_2\cdot + CH_3\overset{O}{\underset{\|}{C}}\cdot$$

(11)
$$CH_3\overset{O}{\underset{\|}{C}}CH_2CH_3 \rightarrow CH_3\cdot + CH_3CH_2\overset{O}{\underset{\|}{C}}\cdot$$

Such an outcome is clearly the result of increased stability of ethyl radicals compared to methyl radicals due to either inductive or hyperconjugative resonance factors. Experimentally, the effect of structure on the photochemical decarbonylation reactions of alkyl ketones has been measured by photolysis in the presence of added iodine. The bond dissociation energy of the iodine-iodine bond in molecular iodine is 36 kcal/mole, whereas carbon-iodine bonds are valued near 60 kcal/mole. As a result, chain transfer on molecular iodine is a particularly efficient process, and iodine serves as a rather good free radical scavenger, eq. (12).

(12) $I_2 + R\cdot \rightarrow RI + I\cdot$

Analysis of the alkyl iodides formed gives some measure of the alkyl radical concentrations available in reaction mixture. For methyl ethyl ketone, the quantum yield for ethyl iodide formation using incident radiation of 3130 Å is some six times the quantum yield for methyl iodide formation. If the radical scavenger is completely effective, the data indicate the stability of methyl radicals to be some six times less than the stability of ethyl radicals.[10]

As the size of the alkyl groups of alkyl ketones becomes larger, the photochemical behavior of the ketones becomes more complicated. Photodissociation to yield carbon monoxide and alkyl radicals no longer is an important mode of reaction. Secondary reactions of the radicals make the product mixtures complicated and the reaction pathways more difficult to understand.

When hydrogen atoms are suitably positioned six atoms from the carbonyl oxygen, intramolecular hydrogen abstraction becomes a very important mode of decomposition. This process, called the *Norrish Type II process*, can be illustrated with methyl neopentyl ketone, eq. (13).[11-13] The proposed mechanism for the photodecomposition of methyl neopentyl

$$(13) \quad (CH_3)_3CCH_2\overset{\displaystyle O}{\overset{\|}{C}}CH_3 \xrightarrow{h\nu} (CH_3)_2C{=}CH_2 \ + \ CH_3\overset{\displaystyle O}{\overset{\|}{C}}CH_3$$

ketone involves a cyclic six-membered transition state, eqs. (14–15). Some typical examples of Norrish Type II rearrangements along with the quantum yields for carbon monoxide formation and intramolecular rearrangement are shown in Table 5-1.

Table 5-1[a]

Comparative Quantum Yields for Rearrangement and Carbon Monoxide Elimination of Aliphatic Ketones

Ketone	$\phi_{\sim}$[b]	ϕ_{CO}[c]	$\phi_{\sim}/\phi_{CO}$
$CH_3\overset{O}{\overset{\|}{C}}CH_3$	0.0	1.00	—
$CH_3COCH_2CH_3$	0.0	0.84	—
$CH_3\overset{O}{\overset{\|}{C}}(CH_2)_3CH_3$	0.48	0.11	4.4
$CH_3\overset{O}{\overset{\|}{C}}CH_2CH(CH_3)_2$	0.35	0.15	2.3
$CH_3COCH_2C(CH_3)_3$	0.23	0.04	5.8

[a]From W. A. Noyes, Jr., G. B. Porter, and J. E. Jolley, *Chem. Rev.*, **56**, 49 (1956).
[b]$\phi_{\sim}$ = quantum yield for rearrangement.
[c]ϕ_{CO} = total quantum yield for carbon monoxide production.

(14) $(CH_3)_3CCH_2\overset{\overset{\displaystyle O}{\|}}{C}CH_3$ $\xrightarrow{h\nu}$

(15) $CH_3\overset{\overset{\displaystyle OH}{|}}{C}=CH_2$ + $(CH_3)_2C=CH_2$

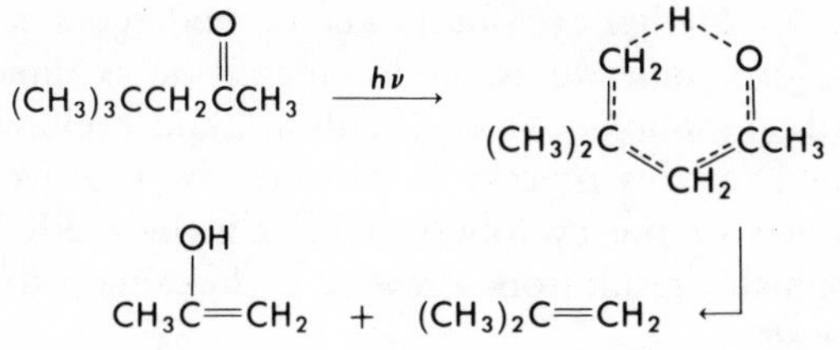

Photodecomposition reactions of cycloalkyl ketones, of alkyl alkenyl ketones, and of haloketones have been reported in the gas and condensed phases. The primary decomposition processes of methyl cyclopropyl and methyl cyclobutyl ketone have been reported by Pitts and Norman.[14,15] Due to the stability differences between the cyclopropyl and the cyclobutyl radical, photodecarbonylation of methyl cyclobutyl ketone is a more efficient process at 100° than is the corresponding decarbonylation of methyl cyclopropyl ketone, eqs. (16–17).

(16) 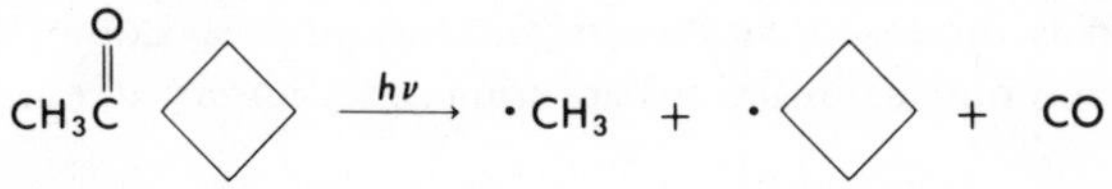 $CH_3\overset{\overset{\displaystyle O}{\|}}{C}$ ◇ $\xrightarrow{h\nu}$ $\cdot CH_3$ + $\cdot$ ◇ + CO

(17) 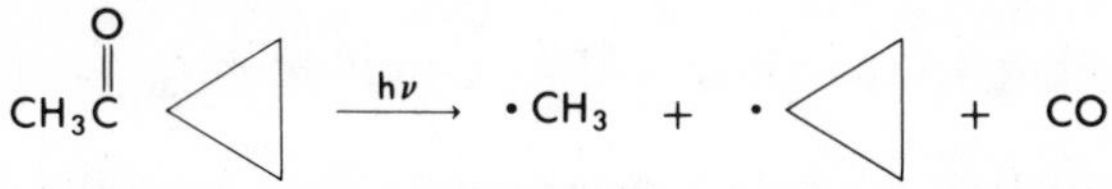 $CH_3\overset{\overset{\displaystyle O}{\|}}{C}$ ◁ $\xrightarrow{h\nu}$ $\cdot CH_3$ + $\cdot$ ◁ + CO

In both cases, little or no recombination of the two alkyl radicals is observed. Methyl cyclopropyl ketone undergoes an interesting photorearrangement, which apparently is its major mode of photo behavior, eqs. (18–19).

(18) 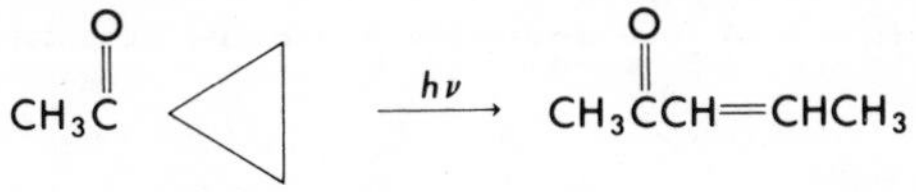 $CH_3\overset{\overset{\displaystyle O}{\|}}{C}$ ◁ $\xrightarrow{h\nu}$ $CH_3\overset{\overset{\displaystyle O}{\|}}{C}CH=CHCH_3$

(19) 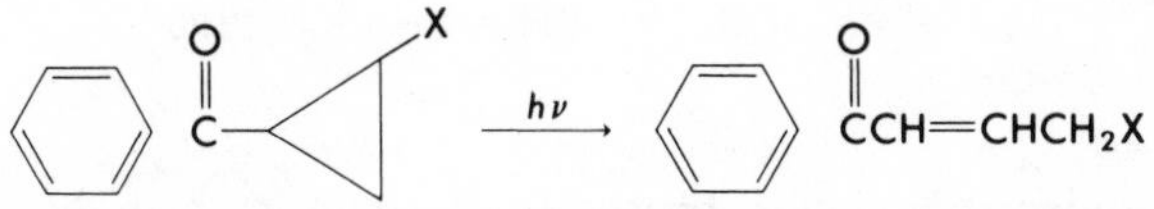   ⬡$\overset{\overset{\displaystyle O}{\|}}{C}$◁$-X$ $\xrightarrow{h\nu}$ ⬡$\overset{\overset{\displaystyle O}{\|}}{C}CH=CHCH_2X$

Brown[16] as well as Roberts and co-workers[17,18] report that in solution such rearrangements occur for substituted cyclopropyl ketones. Resistence to decarbonylation forces the cyclopropane ring to undergo preferential ring opening rather than decarbonylation. Quantum yields for the formation of methyl propenyl ketone in the gas phase have been measured as a function of temperature and are seemingly unaffected by temperature rises of 150°. At 25° the quantum yield for methyl propenyl ketone formation is 0.30, whereas at 170° its value is 0.39. Methyl cyclobutyl ketone undergoes no similar rearrangement. Its major manner of photodecomposition is direct decarbonylation to yield carbon monoxide, methyl radicals, and cyclobutyl radicals. The quantum yield for this process as measured by CO evolution is 0.35. Secondary products of the cyclobutyl radical include ethylene and butadiene. These presumably result from a reverse cycloaddition to produce ethylene and vinyl radicals.

Cis-trans isomerization is also an important reaction of cyclopropyl ketones.[19] Initially reported by Griffin and co-workers,[20,21], the reaction probably proceeds by ring opening to a diradical with subsequent ring closure in a nonstereospecific fashion. Pitts' ring opening rearrangement reaction probably involves similar diradical intermediates.

Unsaturated alkyl ketones undergo a variety of reactions.[22] When the olefinic linkage is directly conjugated to the carbonyl carbon, the major photochemical reaction involves only isomerization about the carbon-carbon double bond when 3130 Å incident radiation is used. As the energy of the incident radiation is increased, homolytic dissociations become more and more important, and unusual reactions are sometimes observed, eq. (20).

$$(20) \quad CH_3\overset{O}{\overset{\|}{C}}CH=CHCH_3 + \cdot CH_3 \xrightarrow{h\nu} CH_3CH=CHCH_3 + CH_3\overset{O}{\overset{\|}{C}}\cdot$$

Cyclic ketones undergo homolytic decarbonylation in both the vapor and liquid phases. In the vapor phase, cyclobutanone, cyclopentanone, cyclohexanone, and cycloheptanone are all observed to eliminate carbon monoxide. Ring opening, resulting in formation of an unsaturated aldehyde, is also common to all the cyclic ketones, eq. (21). Table 5-2 lists the quantum yields for the decarbonylation and ring opening processes as a function of ring size.[23]

$$(21) \quad \underset{\underset{\displaystyle C=O}{\big|\underline{\qquad}}}{(CH_2)_n\rceil} \xrightarrow{h\nu} CO + CH_2=CH(CH_2)_n CHO$$

Like the photodecarbonylation processes of straight chain ketones, the decarbonylation reactions of cyclic aliphatic ketones are thought to involve radical intermediates.[24] The photolysis of cyclopentanone in the vapor phase gives the major products, as shown in eq. (22).[25] The mechanism involves

$$(22) \quad \overset{\displaystyle \square\!\!>}{}=O \xrightarrow{h\nu} C_2H_4 + CO + \square + CH_2=CHCH_2CH_2CHO$$

carbonyl carbon bond cleavage as the initial step subsequent to light absorption, eq. (23).

(23)

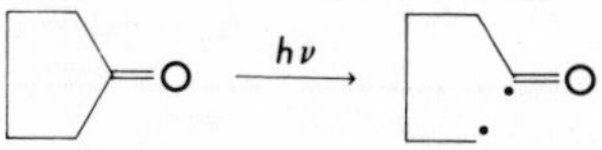

Recent evidence suggests that decarbonylations of cyclic ketones are nonstereospecific.[26] For example, *cis* or *trans* 2,6-dimethylcyclohexanone gives the same mixture of *cis* and *trans* cyclopentanes upon decarbonylation, eq. (24).

(24)

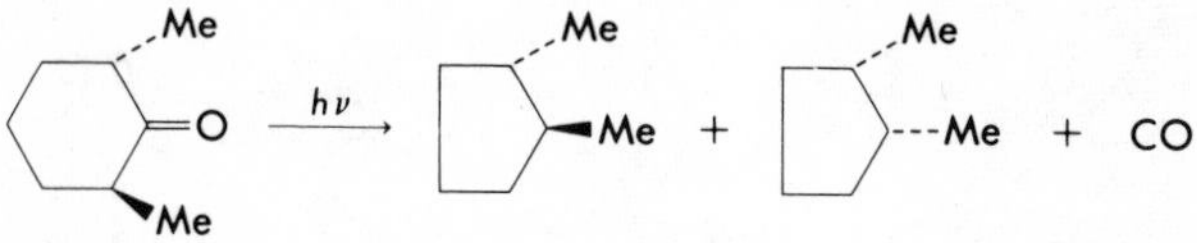

The authenticity of a diradical mechanism, eqs. (23) and (25–28), is suggested although a concerted process also has been proposed.[24,27]

(25)

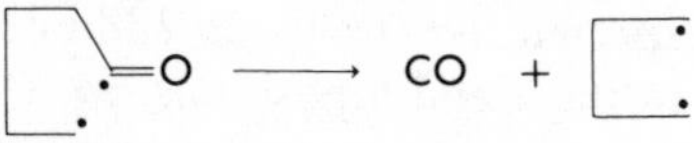

(26)

(27)

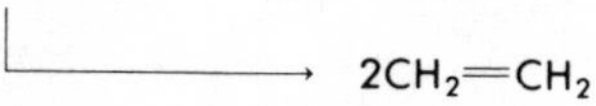

(28)

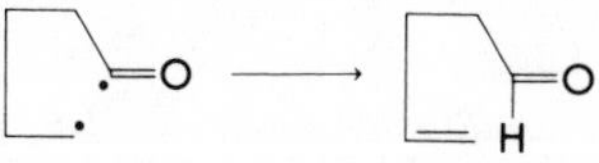

Following cleavage of the carbonyl carbon bond, decarbonylation or intramolecular hydrogen abstraction may occur. The former process leads to cyclobutane or, subsequently, to ethylene, the latter to 4-pentenal. That ethylene is formed from the cyclobutane diradical, eq. (27), and not from subsequent photolysis of cyclobutane can be shown from photolysis of cyclopentanone 2,2,5,5,d$_4$. The only ethylenic product observed is 1,1-dideuteroethylene. No 1,1,2,2-tetradeuteroethylene or normal ethylene is observed, eq. (29). A nearly random thermal or photodecomposition of

(29)

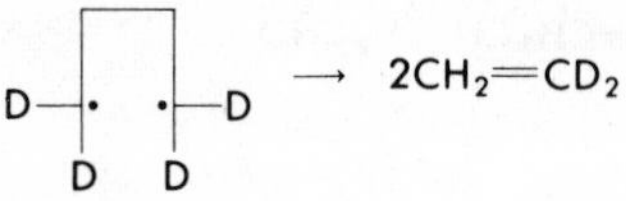

Table 5-2

Quantum Yields for Ring Opening of Cyclic Ketones at 100°C

Ketone	ϕ_{CO}	ϕ CH$_2$=CH(CH$_2$)$_n$CHO
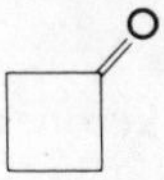	0.35	0.004
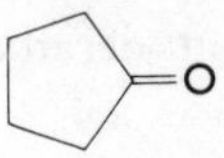	0.18	0.04
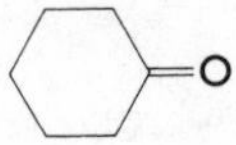	0.11	0.12
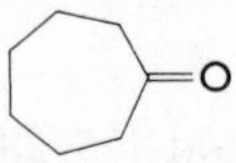	0.14	0.15

tetradeuterocyclobutane would be expected, eq. (30). In addition, the 4-pentenal formed has deuterium only in the 2 and 5 positions, eq. (31). The ring-opened species are formed nonstereospecifically also and probably from

(30) $\xrightarrow{\quad}$ H$_2$C=CD$_2$ + CD$_2$=CD$_2$ + CH$_2$=CH$_2$

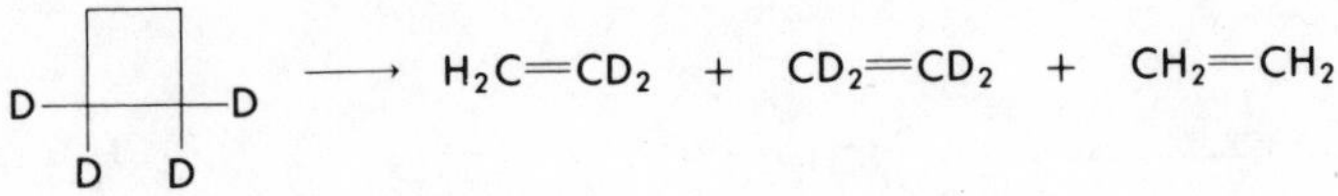

(31) $\xrightarrow{h\nu}$ CO + CD$_2$=CHCH$_2$CD$_2$CHO +

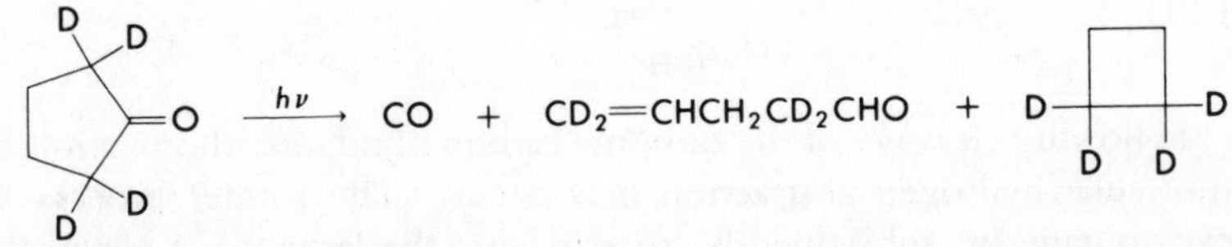

the triplet state of the ketone carbonyl group. Thus, photolysis of 2-methyl-cyclohexanone gives a mixture of isomeric 5-heptenals,[26] discounting the possibility of a concerted ring opening-hydrogen migration, eq. (32). Dunion and Trumbore[28] have observed that the ring opening process is

(32) $\xrightarrow{h\nu}$ CH$_3$CH=CHCH$_2$CH$_2$CH$_2$CHO

(*cis* + *trans*)

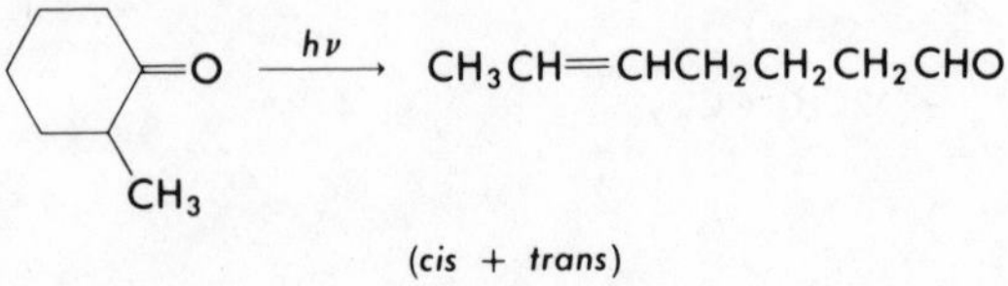

significantly retarded by triplet state quenchers like piperylene and oxygen. Photolysis of cyclopentanone in the presence of either piperylene or oxygen decreases the yield of 4-pentenal.

Photolysis of cyclohexanone in the vapor phase leads to similar products. Cyclopentane, ethylene, propylene, carbon monoxide, and 5-hexenal are all observed, eq. (33).[29,30,31] 2-Methylcyclohexanone produces 5-heptenal as the

(33)

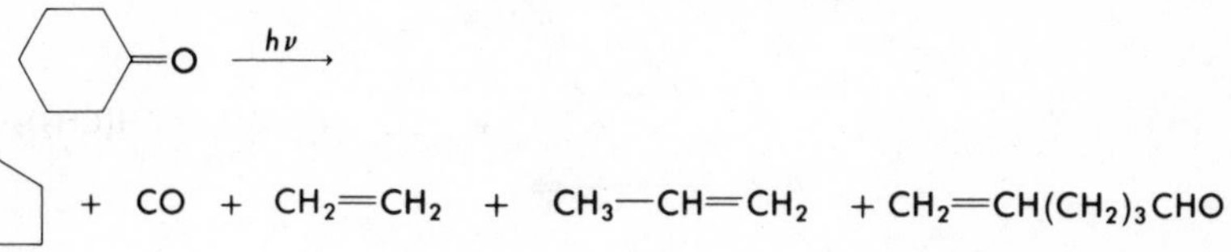

$$\text{(cyclohexanone)} \xrightarrow{h\nu}$$

$$\text{(cyclopentane)} + CO + CH_2{=}CH_2 + CH_3{-}CH{=}CH_2 + CH_2{=}CH(CH_2)_3CHO$$

major olefinic product, eq. (34).[31] Cyclobutanone decomposes to ethylene,

(34)

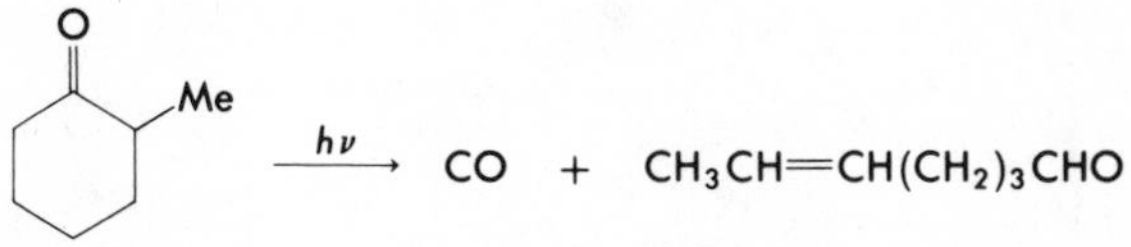

$$\text{(2-methylcyclohexanone)} \xrightarrow{h\nu} CO + CH_3CH{=}CH(CH_2)_3CHO$$

ketene, cyclopropane, carbon monoxide, and propylene, eq. (35). Some

(35)

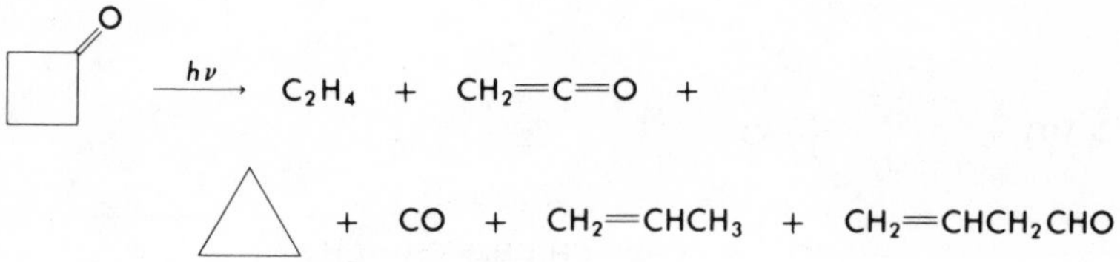

$$\text{(cyclobutanone)} \xrightarrow{h\nu} C_2H_4 + CH_2{=}C{=}O +$$

$$\text{(cyclopropane)} + CO + CH_2{=}CHCH_3 + CH_2{=}CHCH_2CHO$$

3-butenol has been observed.[32,33] Cycloheptanone produces propylene, carbon monoxide, cyclohexane, 1-hexene, and 5-hexenal, eq. (36).[23,33] Examples of substituted cycloalkyl ketones that have been examined are 2- and 3-methylcyclopentanone,[34] menthone,[29] and 2-ethylcyclohexanone.

(36)

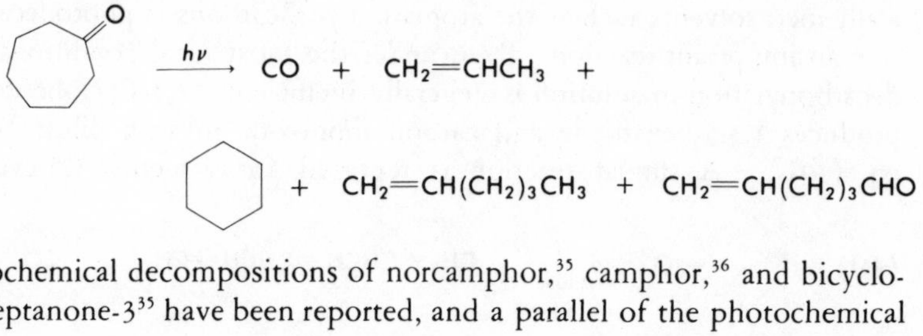

$$\text{(cycloheptanone)} \xrightarrow{h\nu} CO + CH_2{=}CHCH_3 +$$

$$\text{(cyclohexane)} + CH_2{=}CH(CH_2)_3CH_3 + CH_2{=}CH(CH_2)_3CHO$$

Photochemical decompositions of norcamphor,[35] camphor,[36] and bicyclo-[3.2.0]heptanone-3[35] have been reported, and a parallel of the photochemical behavior of these compounds to that of cyclopentanone has been reported, eqs. (37, 38, 39).

(37)

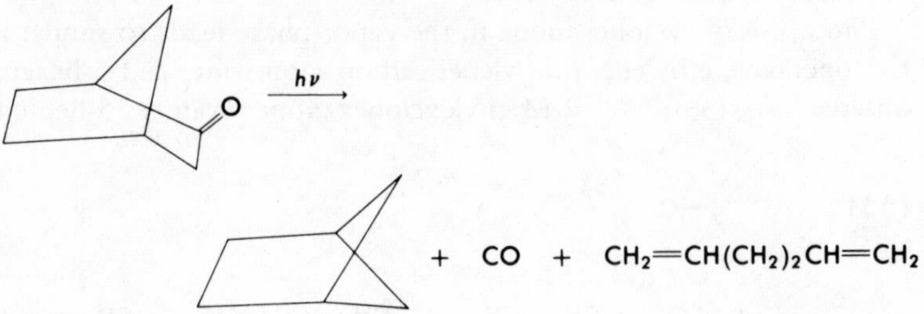

(38)

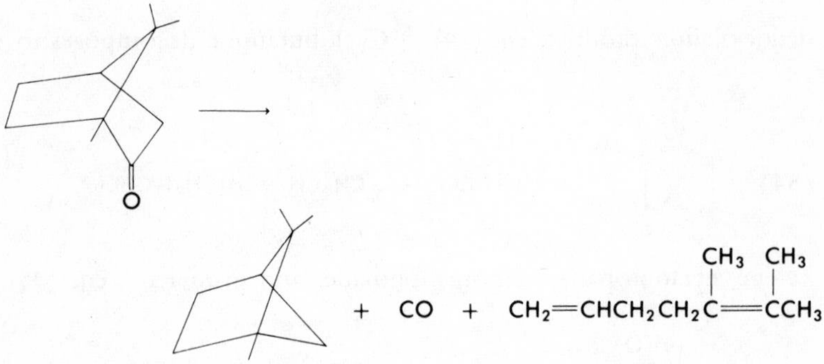

(39)

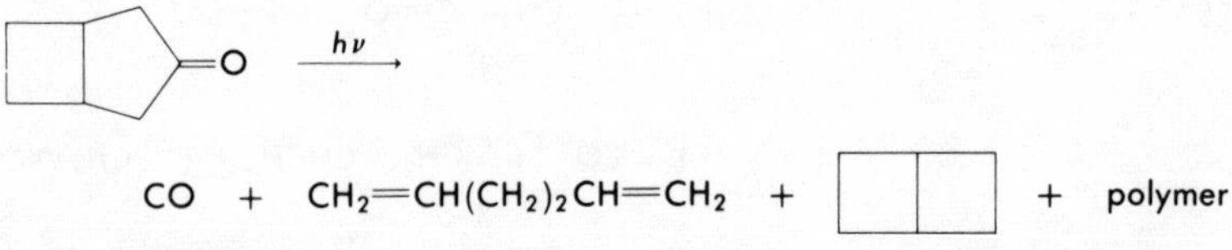

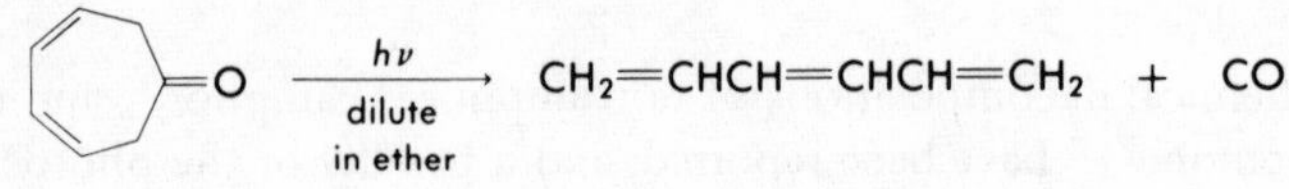

In solution, the behavior of ketones varies markedly with the solvent. In hydrogen-donor solvents such as alcohols and some hydrocarbons, photoreduction generally occurs, whereas in aqueous media, carboxylic acids indicative of ketene intermediates are the major products. Only in chemically inert solvents such as the aromatic hydrocarbons is photodecarbonylation an important reaction. Even under the most ideal conditions, photodecarbonylation in solution is generally inefficient. 3,5-Cycloheptadienone produces 1,3,5-hexatriene and carbon monoxide in very dilute solutions, eq. (40).[37] A similar reaction is reported for 2-methyl-3-5-cycloheptadienone.[38] Dihydrocarvone, eq. (41),[39] and menthone, eq. (42),[40] are said to

(41)

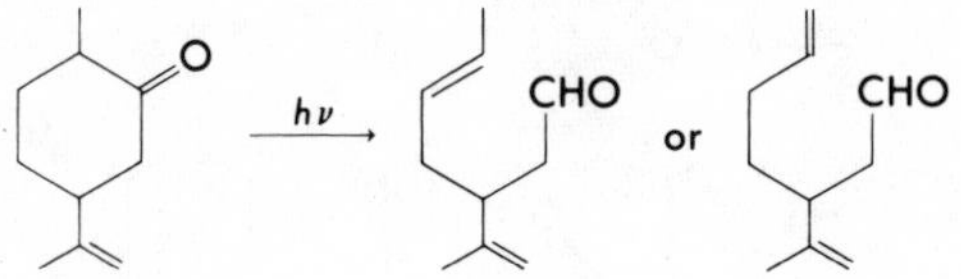

(42)

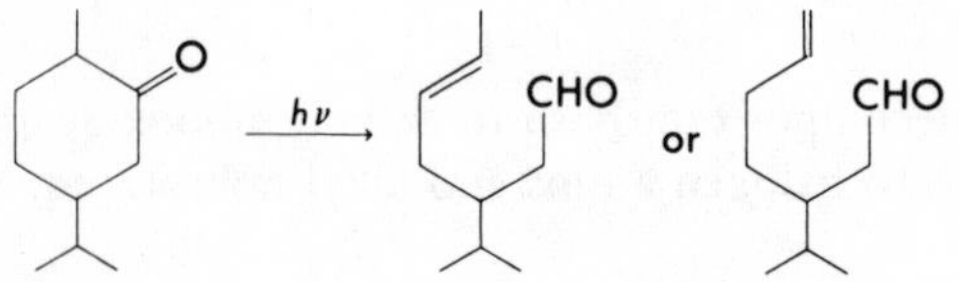

undergo ring opening to unsaturated aldehydes in aqueous ethanol solution.

Schuster, Lee, Padwa, and Gassman[41] have recently reported that 7-keto-norbornene undergoes a facile decarbonylation. Two olefins, cyclohexa-diene-1,3 and hexatriene-1,3,5, are the major products from the reaction, eq. (43). A singlet mechanism is tentatively proposed.

(43)

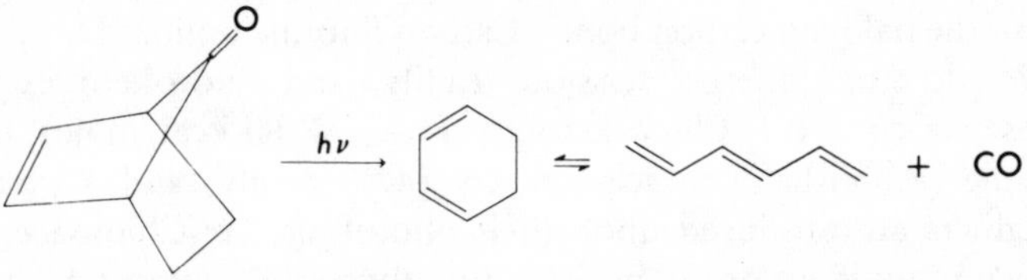

Decarbonylation of 1-phenylindanone in ether produces high yields of *cis* and *trans*-1,2,5,6-dibenzo-3,4-diphenylcyclooctane, eq. (44).[42]* Hostettler[43]

(44)

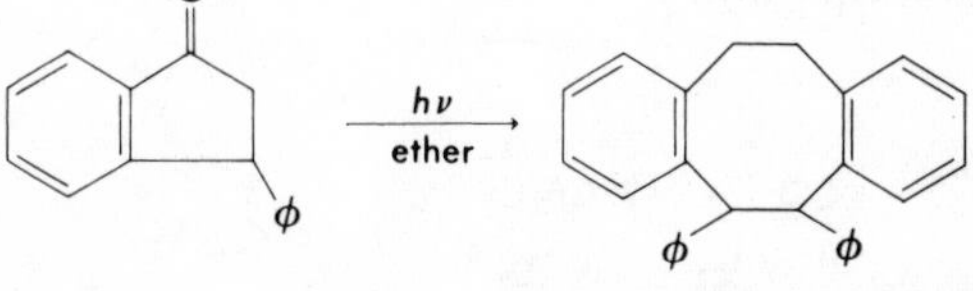

and Yates[44] report reactions of bicyclic ketones that give intermediate car-benes. Thus, 7,7-dimethyl[3.2.0]bicyclohept-2-ene-6-one gives a cyclic acetal and an ester when photolyzed in methanol via the carbene shown in eq. (45).

*Diphenyl-2-indanone, 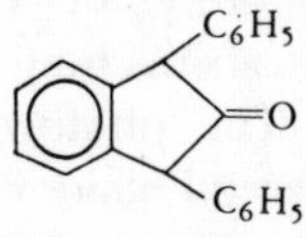 , is reported to react similarly, G. Quinkert, K. Opitz,
W. W. Wiersdorff, and M. Finke, *Ann. Chem.*, **963**, 44 (1966).

(45)

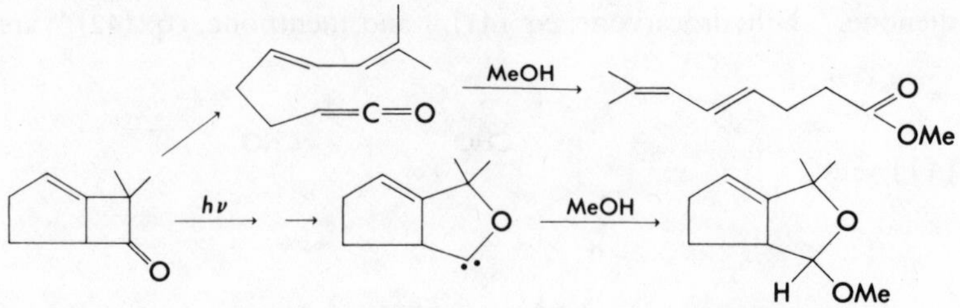

Haloketones undergo decomposition both to carbon monoxide and alkyl radicals, eq. (46), and also to halogen atoms and alkyl radicals, eq. (47), in

$$\text{(46)} \quad CX_3\overset{\displaystyle O}{\overset{\displaystyle \|}{C}}CX_3 \xrightarrow{h\nu} CO + 2 \cdot CX_3$$

$$\text{(47)} \quad CX_3\overset{\displaystyle O}{\overset{\displaystyle \|}{C}}CX_3 \xrightarrow{h\nu} CX_3\overset{\displaystyle O}{\overset{\displaystyle \|}{C}}CX_2 \cdot + X \cdot$$

vapor phase reactions. The importance of the latter process depends on the strength of the halogen carbon bond. Carbon fluorine bonds ($D_{C-F} = 115.0$ kcal/mole) do not undergo scission readily, and fluoroketones tend to decompose via eq. (46). Chloroketones ($D_{C-Cl} = 80$ kcal/mole), however, undergo the carbon-halogen scission, eq. (47), readily, and a great many more products are produced upon their photolysis. α-Chloroacetone has been shown to undergo decomposition by process (47) almost exclusively,[45] while trifluroacetone and hexafluoroacetone behave in a manner much like that of acetone.[46,47] With mixed fluorochloroketones such as 1,1,3,3-tetrafluoro-1,3-dichloropropanone, carbon-halogen bond scission and decarbonylation are competitive, eq. (48).[48]

$$\text{(48)} \quad CF_2ClCCF_2Cl \xrightarrow{h\nu} CO + 2 \cdot CF_2Cl$$
$$\xrightarrow{h\nu} CF_2ClCCF_2 \cdot + \cdot Cl$$

Chain sequences, to be discussed in a later chapter, also become important when chloro, bromo, and iodoketones are photolyzed. The weakness of the carbon-halogen bond allows halogen atom abstraction to become an important complicating secondary process. The photolysis of hexachloroacetone, for example, produces trichloroacetyl chloride and octachloropropane as major products, eq. (49).[49]

(49) $\quad CCl_3\overset{\displaystyle O}{\overset{\displaystyle \|}{C}}CCl_3 \xrightarrow{h\nu} CCl_3CCl_2CCl_3 + CCl_3\overset{\displaystyle O}{\overset{\displaystyle \|}{C}}Cl$

Of the aromatic halogenated alkyl ketones, only trifluoroacetophenone seems to behave like the simple alkyl ketones. Trifluoroacetophenone has been shown[50] to be a source of trifluoromethyl radicals, eq. (50).

(50) ![benzene ring]—$\overset{\displaystyle O}{\overset{\displaystyle \|}{C}}CF_3 \xrightarrow{h\nu}$![benzene ring]—$\overset{\displaystyle O}{\overset{\displaystyle \|}{C}}\cdot + \cdot CF_3$

Fluoroform is an observed reaction product, and polymeric products resulting from homolytic aromatic substitution by trifluoromethyl have been postulated, eq. (51).[51]

(51) ![benzene ring]—$\overset{\displaystyle O}{\overset{\displaystyle \|}{C}}$—$CF_3 + \cdot CF_3 \rightarrow$![cyclohexadienyl ring with H and CF₃]—$\overset{\displaystyle O}{\overset{\displaystyle \|}{C}}$—$CF_3 \rightarrow$ polymer

Alpha diketones, beta diketones, and even some triketones have been shown to undergo decarbonylation and related decompositions both in the vapor phase and in solution. The simplest α diketone, biacetyl, has been the subject of extensive investigations. In the vapor phase, biacetyl undergoes a facile decarbonylation reaction, carbon monoxide and ethane being major products of the decomposition, eq. (52).[52,53] In all probability the first

(52) $\quad CH_3\overset{\displaystyle O}{\overset{\displaystyle \|}{C}}\!-\!\overset{\displaystyle O}{\overset{\displaystyle \|}{C}}CH_3 \xrightarrow{h\nu} 2CO + CH_3CH_3$

excited singlet state is dissociative, and significant decomposition occurs before intersystem crossing to the long-lived triplet state takes place. In solution, biacetyl undergoes a similar decomposition. The major products of the decomposition are carbon monoxide and ethane, and the mechanism for product formation at short wavelength incident radiation is essentially the same as in the gas phase.[54] The quantum yield for carbon monoxide formation appears to be dependent upon the viscosity of the solvent in which the photolysis is conducted. Decomposition from a high vibrational level of the excited singlet is not important in solution because of collisional deactivation. Some self-quenching of excited biacetyl molecules by unexcited biacetyl is observed. The mechanism for the decomposition is wavelength dependent.

Photodecomposition reactions for longer chained α-diketones have not been observed. The photochemical behavior of α-diketones often involves a gamma hydrogen abstraction reaction and will be discussed in a subsequent chapter.

Most β-diketones behave either as isolated keto chromophores or as enols. In the gas phase, the photochemical behavior of β-diketones is virtually uninvestigated. In solution, both decarbonylation and other decomposition pathways have been observed. For example, de Mayo and co-workers[55] have studied extensively the reactions of acetylacetone with certain olefins. From cyclohexene and acetylacetone, α-(2-acetocyclohexyl)acetone has been isolated, eq. (53). With cyclopentene, 1-methylcyclopentene and 1-octene, similar products have been isolated.

(53)

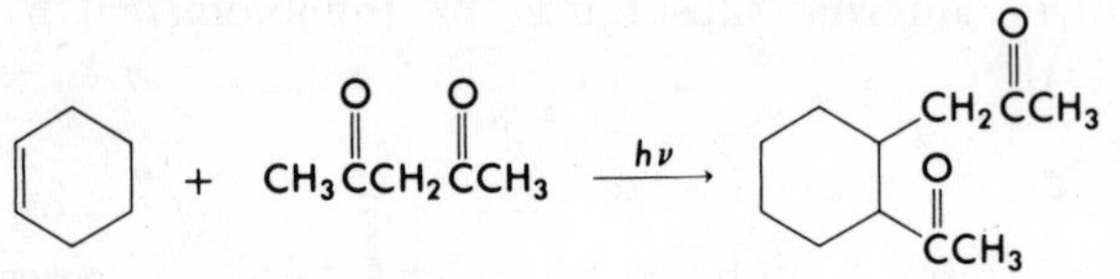

Other reactions of β-diketones include certain cycloaddition reactions. For example, de Mayo and co-workers[56] have observed that cyclohexane-dione-1,3 reacts with olefins to give cyclooctanedione derivatives, eq. (54).

(54)

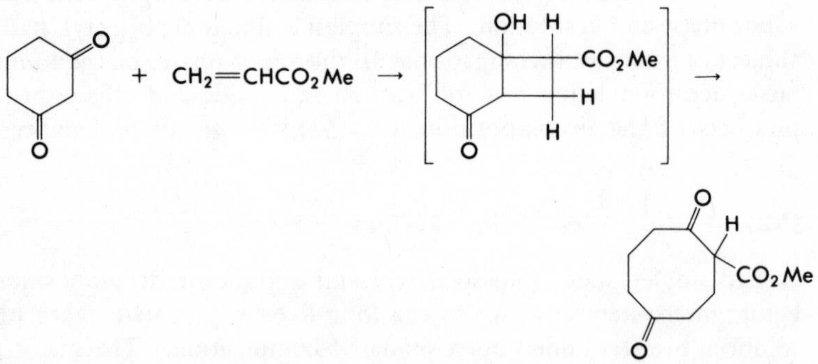

Similar reactions are observed with dimedone and certain enol acetates. The de Mayo method appears to have general utility as a method for ring enlargement. These reactions will be discussed in greater detail in Chapter 6.

Decarbonylation of cyclic β-diketones is one of the most efficient solution phase decarbonylation reactions. Loss of 1 mole of carbon monoxide from cyclobutane-1,3-diones offers a synthetic route to cyclopropanones.[57-59] Photolysis of tetramethylcyclobutanedione-1,3 under an argon atmosphere in methanol or isopropyl alcohol causes a rapid evolution of carbon mon-

oxide and formation of two esters. Some tetramethylethylene is also observed, eq. (55).

(55)

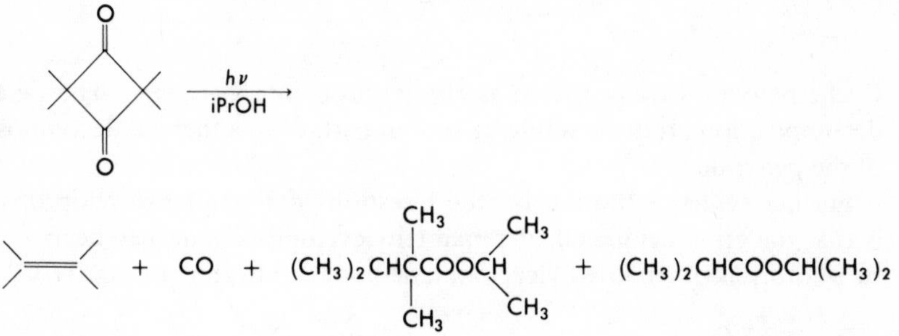

$$\diagup\!\!=\!\!\diagdown \quad + \quad CO \quad + \quad (CH_3)_2CHCCOOCH \quad + \quad (CH_3)_2CHCOOCH(CH_3)_2$$

Tetramethylcyclopropanone or a diradical analogous to tetramethylcyclopropanone has been proposed to account for the observed ester products,
eq. (56).

(56)

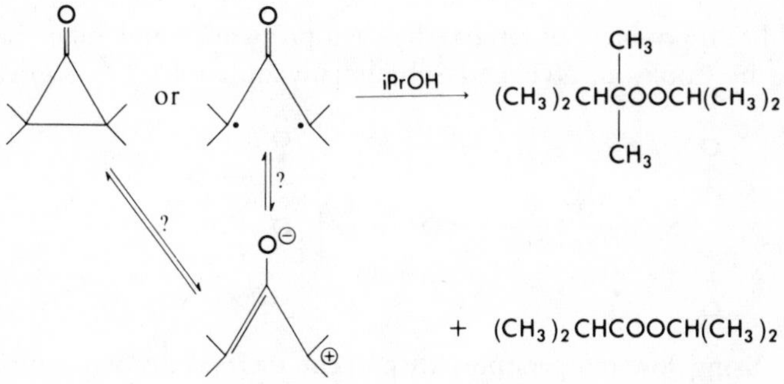

$$\xrightarrow{iPrOH} \quad (CH_3)_2CHCOOCH(CH_3)_2$$

$$+ \quad (CH_3)_2CHCOOCH(CH_3)_2$$

When oxygen is present, acetone, tetramethylethylene oxide, and carbon
dioxide become important reaction products. Addition of oxygen to tetramethylcyclopropanone or the analogous diradical accounts for the observed
products, eqs. (57–59).

(57)

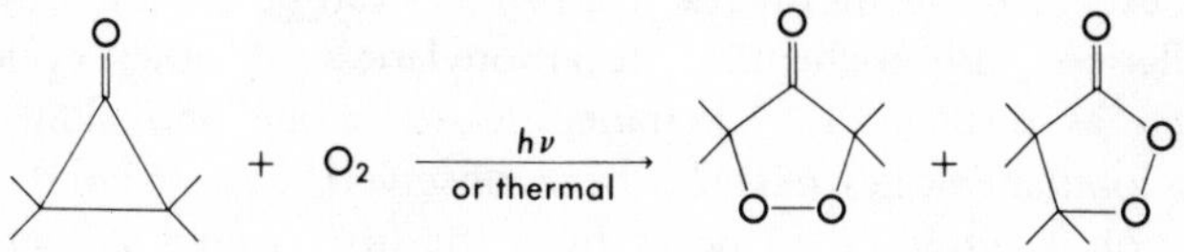

(58)

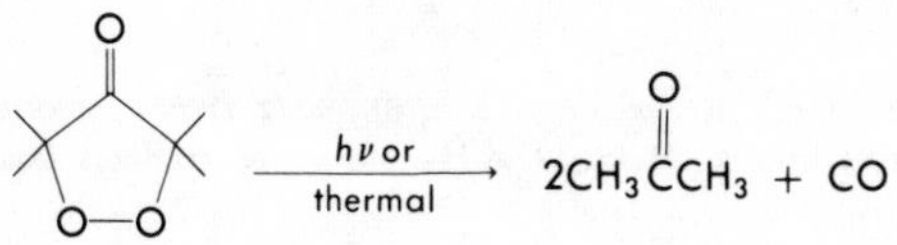

$$\xrightarrow[\text{thermal}]{h\nu\ or} \quad 2CH_3CCH_3 \quad + \quad CO$$

(59) $\xrightarrow[\text{thermal}]{h\nu \text{ or}}$ CO_2 +

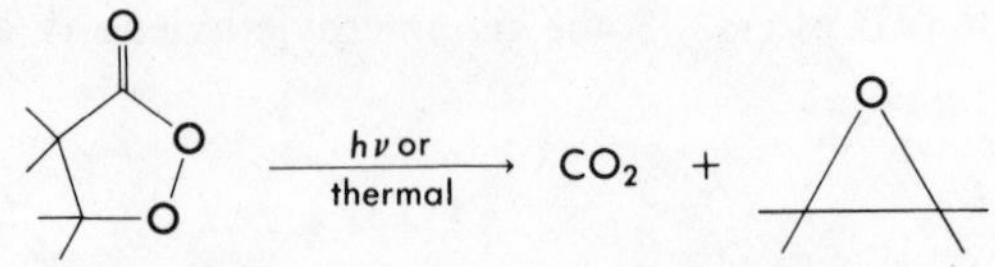

Cyclic peroxides are proposed as the reaction intermediates. The peroxide decomposition products result, at least in part, from a thermal decomposition of the peroxide.

Further evidence bearing on the question of tetramethylcyclopropanone is that the ethyl hemiketal of tetramethylcyclopropanone has been isolated by photolysis of tetramethylcyclobutanedione-1,3 in ethanol, eq. (60).[58,60]

(60) $\xrightarrow[\text{EtOH}]{h\nu}$ CO +

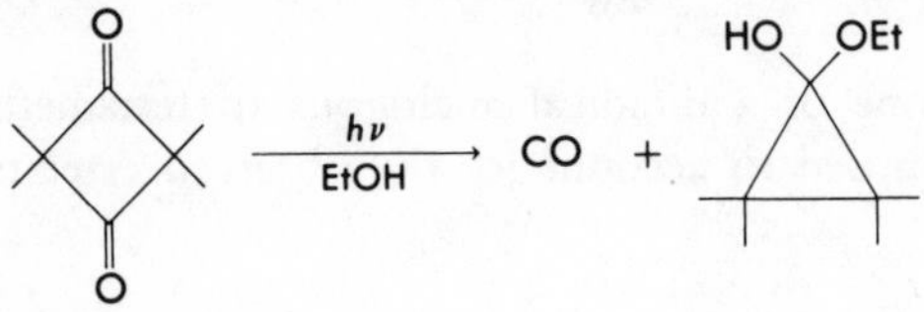

Cycloaddition products of tetramethylcyclopropanone and furan have been observed by Cookson, Nye, and Subrahmanyam, eq. (61).[61] Srinivasan and

(61) $\xrightarrow[h\nu, \text{reflux}]{}$ CO +

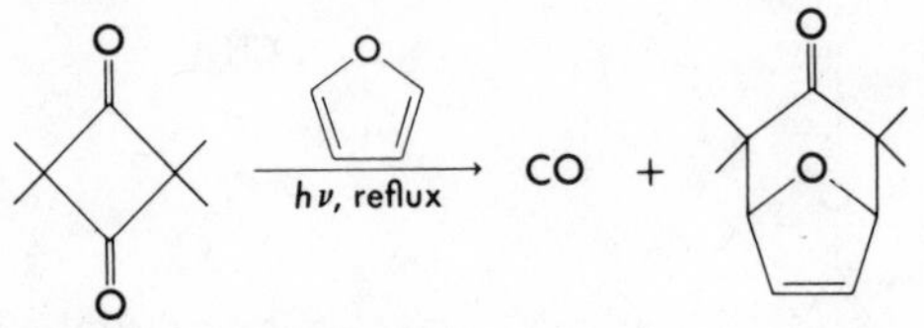

Haller,[62] using low temperatures to prevent thermal decomposition of the cyclopropanone, have been able to observe the intermediate spectrally. They have found that tetramethylcyclopropanone absorbs in the high frequency carbonyl region of the infrared spectrum as expected from its highly strained nature. Turro, Leermakers, and co-workers[63] have successfully isolated tetramethylcyclopropanone under carefully controlled conditions. When oxygen is carefully excluded, the highly reactive product can be obtained by bulb to bulb distillation. Photochemical decarbonylation of other cyclobutanediones such as dispiro[5.1.6.1.]tetradecane-1,14-dione and similarly substituted cyclobutanediones has also been observed, eqs. (62-63). Photodecomposition is proposed to occur from the first excited singlet state of these cyclobutane-1,3-diones.[59]*

*Wagner, Stout, Searles and Hammond, *J. Am. Chem. Soc.*, **88**, 1242 (1966), reported a similar process for the structurally analogans lactone, $H_3C$$CH_3$, the major products being acetone,

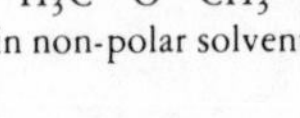

dimethylketone, and tetramethylethylene oxide in non-polar solvents.

(62)

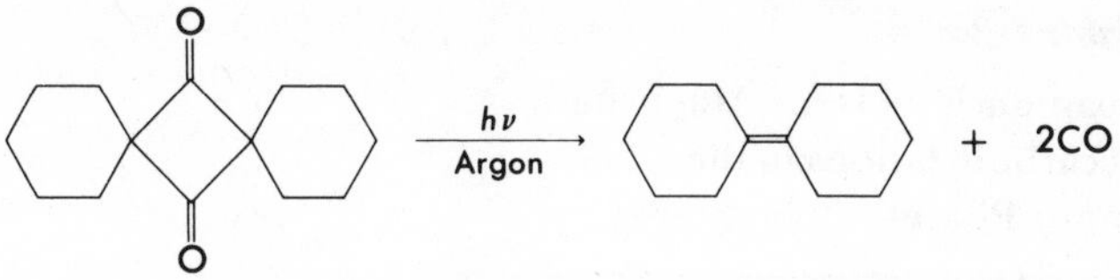

(63)

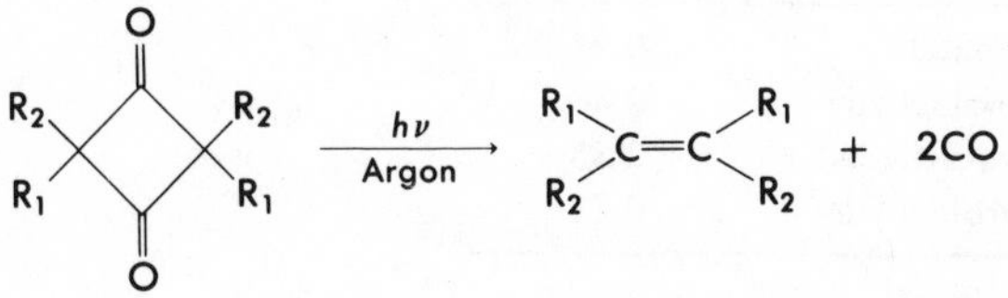

Decarbonylation reactions of the simplest of all β-diketones, carbon suboxide, leads to formation of something approaching atomic carbon atoms in the vapor phase, eq. (64).[64-67] Evidence for the formation of atomic carbon

$$(64) \quad O{=}C{=}C{=}C{=}O \xrightarrow{h\nu} 2CO + \cdot\overset{\cdot}{\underset{\cdot}{C}}\cdot$$

is the insertion reaction, eq. (65). Mullen and Wolf[66] have shown, using

$$(65) \quad \cdot\overset{\cdot}{\underset{\cdot}{C}}\cdot + CH_2{=}CH_2 \rightarrow CH_2{=}C{=}CH_2$$

isotopic carbon, that about 96% of the isotopic content occurs in the center carbon of the allenic product.

The photochemical decomposition of triones has been reported.[68] Triones appear to behave more like monoketones than like diketones when photo-lyzed in solution. Thus, although no substantial degree of decarbonylation is reported for the photolysis of alkyl triones, acyl radical interchange is observed, and no intramolecular hydrogen abstraction is noted, eq. (66).

$$(66) \quad R_1\overset{O}{\overset{\|}{C}}{-}\overset{O}{\overset{\|}{C}}{-}\overset{O}{\overset{\|}{C}}R_2 \rightleftharpoons R_1\overset{O}{\overset{\|}{C}}{-}\overset{O}{\overset{\|}{C}}{-}\overset{O}{\overset{\|}{C}}R_1 + R_2\overset{O}{\overset{\|}{C}}{-}\overset{O}{\overset{\|}{C}}{-}\overset{O}{\overset{\|}{C}}R_2$$

As a general rule, aromatic diketones such as benzil and acetylbenzoyl undergo no photochemical decarbonylation in solution. They are more inclined to undergo hydrogen abstraction from solvent rather than simple decomposition. In the vapor phase, however, α-diketones like benzil have been reported to lose carbon monoxide.

With aldehydes, the readily abstractable aldehydic hydrogen causes other chain processes to mask the simple decarbonylation reaction. Gas phase data indicate that the primary mode of photochemical decomposition of simple aliphatic aldehydes involves homolysis of the carbonyl carbon-alkyl carbon bond, eq. (67).[69] A summary of the effect of the structure of the alkyl por-

Table 5-3[a]

Quantum Yields for Aldehyde
Decarbonylations in the
Vapor Phase

Compound	ϕ_{CO}
acetaldehyde	0.21
propionaldehyde	0.48
n-butyraldehyde	0.35
isobutyraldehyde	0.72

[a]Data from F. E. Blacet and J. N. Pitts, Jr., *J. Am. Chem. Soc.*, 74, 3382 (1952).

tion of the aldehyde on the quantum yield of carbon monoxide has appeared,[70] and these results are shown in Table 5-3.

$$(67) \quad RCH_2\overset{O}{\overset{\|}{C}}H \xrightarrow{h\nu} RCH_2\cdot \ + \ \cdot\overset{O}{\overset{\|}{C}}H$$

As in the case of ketone decarbonylations, alkyl group structure affects the decarbonylation process. As the alkyl radical formed becomes more highly branched, the quantum yield for the homolytic process becomes higher. The major products of the reaction result from immediate decarbonylation of the formyl radical and recoupling to form the straight chain hydrocarbon, eqs. (68–69).

$$(68) \quad RCH_2CHO \xrightarrow{h\nu} RCH_2\cdot \ + \ \cdot CHO$$

$$(69) \quad RCH_2\cdot \ + \ \cdot CHO \longrightarrow RCH_3 \ + \ CO$$

Using both iodine scavenger techniques[70] and deuterium isotope methods,[71,72] one can show that more than 50% of the straight chain hydrocarbon is formed directly from the two free radicals resulting from the initial homolytic cleavage.

Crotonaldehyde and acrolein, the only two unsaturated aldehydes for which gas phase results are available, do not behave normally. Crotonaldehyde[73] is resistent to decarbonylation, presumably because of the lack of stability of the 1-propenyl radical. Acrolein undergoes photopolymerization.[74]

Halogenated aldehydes such as trifluoroacetaldehyde, perfluoropropionaldehyde, and perfluoro-n-butyraldehyde undergo normal decarbonylation.[75,76]

With aromatic aldehydes, hydrogen abstraction becomes the major process, and products resulting from acyl radicals, the chief product of hydrogen abstraction, become important. Facile oxidation of aromatic aldehydes requires thorough degassing procedures before meaningful results can be obtained.

Other Carbonyl Derivatives

Schmidt has found that 2540 Å radiation provides the necessary energy to cleave the carbon chlorine bonds of acyl chlorides. Photolysis of acetyl chloride in hydrocarbons and in ethers produces ketones in 10–15% yield. Thus, photolysis of acetyl chloride in diethyl ether gives 3-ethyoxy-2-butanone and in cyclohexane gives acetocyclohexane, eq. (70).[77,78]

$$(70) \quad CH_3\overset{O}{\overset{\|}{C}}Cl \; + \; \bigcirc \quad \xrightarrow{h\nu} \quad \bigcirc\text{-}\overset{\overset{\displaystyle O}{\|}}{C}CH_3 \quad + \quad HCl$$

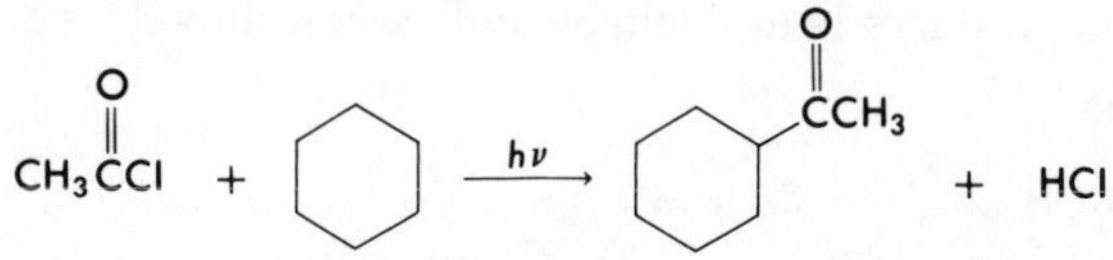

Recently, Schmidt and co-workers have reported observing an acyl radical spectrum in acyl halide photolyses by electron spin resonance methods. At lower temperatures, both benzoyl bromide and benzoyl chloride give spectral patterns attributable to an acyl radical.[79]

Elad and co-workers have reported studies of photochemical decompositions of amides. They propose cleavage of the nitrogen-carbon bond. Decompositions of formamide in olefins with acetone as a photosensitizer give amides by addition of an amido radical to the carbon-carbon double bond, eq. (71).[80]

$$(71) \quad HCONH_2 \; + \; RCH{=}CHR' \quad \xrightarrow{h\nu} \quad \underset{\underset{NH_2}{\overset{|}{C}{=}O}}{RCH_2CHR'} \quad + \quad \underset{\underset{NH_2}{\overset{|}{C}{=}O}}{RCHCH_2R'}$$

Decomposition of anilides in alcohols gives aniline and the corresponding acid. Certain aromatic rearrangement products are also isolated, eq. (72).[81,82]

$$(72) \quad C_6H_5NH\overset{O}{\overset{\|}{C}}R \quad \xrightarrow[EtOH]{h\nu} \quad C_6H_5NH_2 \; + \; RCOOH \; + \; \text{(o-aminophenyl ketone)} \; + \; \text{(p-aminophenyl ketone)}$$

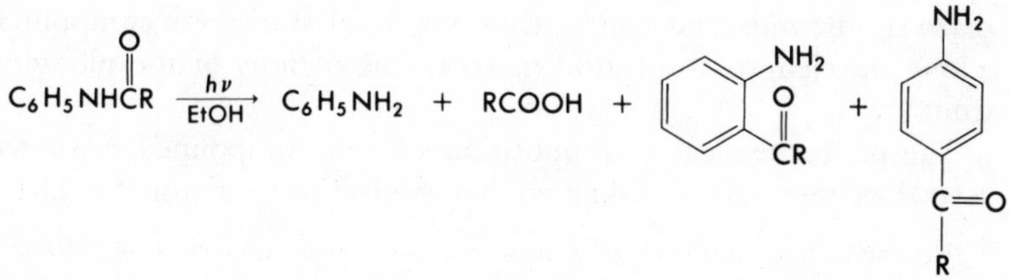

Earlier, Walling and Naglieri[83] reported the smooth, homolytic decomposition of N,O-dibenzoylhydroxylamine when photolyzed in acetone. Since some photolysis of the solvent acetone also was reported, it is not clear whether the decomposition resulted from a direct or a sensitized process.

The photochemical decomposition of α-keto acids has been examined. In aqueous media, the major products obtained from the photolysis of pyruvic acid are acetoin, acetaldehyde, and carbon dioxide, eq. (73), whereas

$$(73) \quad CH_3\overset{O}{\overset{\|}{C}}-\overset{O}{\overset{\|}{C}}OH \xrightarrow{h\nu} CO_2 + CH_3\overset{O}{\overset{\|}{C}}H + CH_3\overset{O}{\overset{\|}{C}}-\underset{H}{\overset{OH}{\underset{|}{C}}}CH_3$$

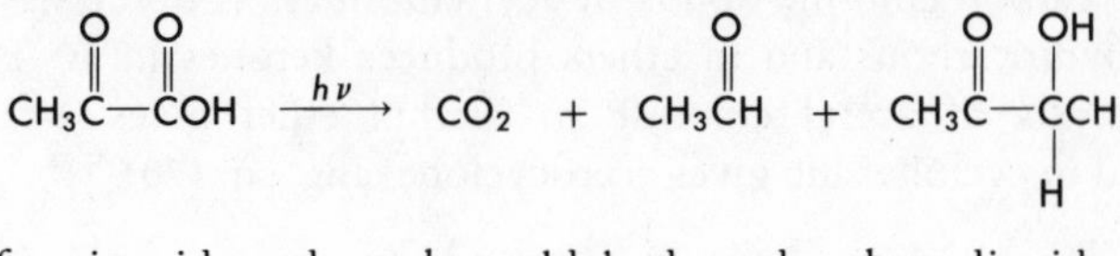

benzoylformic acid produces benzaldehyde and carbon dioxide, eq. (74).[84,85]

$$(74) \quad C_6H_5\overset{O}{\overset{\|}{C}}-\overset{O}{\overset{\|}{C}}OH \xrightarrow{h\nu} C_6H_5CHO + CO_2$$

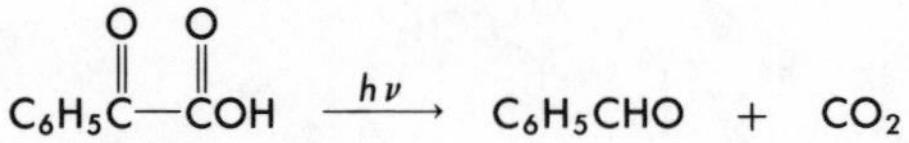

An intramolecular decomposition mechanism in which a carbene plays an important role is proposed, eq. (75).

$$(75) \quad CH_3\overset{O}{\overset{\|}{C}}-\overset{O}{\overset{\|}{C}}OH \xrightarrow{h\nu} \quad \longrightarrow CH_3\overset{OH}{\overset{|}{C}}: + CO_2$$

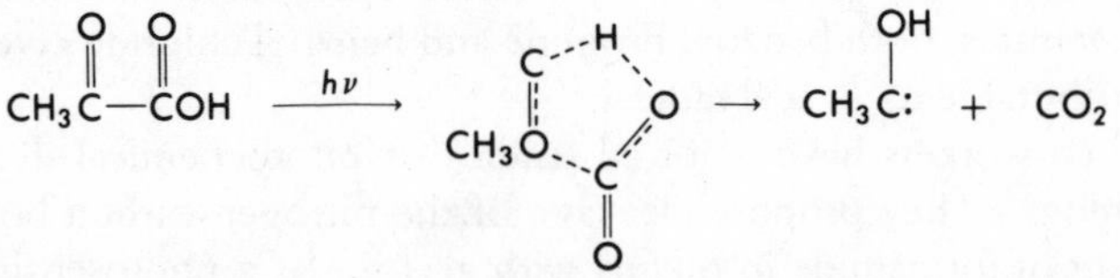

Evidence supporting the mechanism is the observation that the quantum yield for sodium pyruvate is less than 1/20 that of pyruvic acid itself. Other derivatives of α-keto acids such as α-keto esters tend to undergo interesting intramolecular hydrogen abstraction reactions and will be discussed later.

Elimination of Nitrogen

Compounds containing nitrogen-nitrogen double bonds are extremely photoreactive because of the great driving force for decomposition imparted to the molecule by the possibility of formation of molecular nitrogen. Specific classes of compounds that fall into this category are azo compounds, diazo compounds, and azides. Even the simplest of these compounds shows a long wavelength absorption in accessible regions of the ultraviolet spectrum.[86]

The photochemical decomposition of azo compounds is so facile that several of them are well-known polymerization initiators.* The simplest

*Generally, the thermal cleavage of these initiators is more convenient and cleaner and hence preferred.

member of the series, azomethane, has been investigated extensively in the gas phase.[87] The quantum yield for the decomposition to N_2 and methyl with incident radiation of 3660 Å is nearly unity, eq. (76). In solution, the quantum yield for decomposition of azomethane is lowered substantially and

$$(76) \quad CH_3N{=}NCH_3 \xrightarrow{h\nu} 2CH_3\cdot \ + \ N_2, \phi = 1$$

is often less than 0.02. Hutton and Steel[88] suggest that one of the reasons for this lowered quantum yield is *cis-trans* isomerization about the nitrogen-nitrogen double bond. *Trans*-azomethane is the stable configuration under normal conditions.

Photolysis of azomethane in a variety of solvents such as ether or water or even in a solid film produces a new material, isomeric with *trans*-azomethane. Hutton and Steel conclude that the new compound is *cis*-azomethane, eq. (77), from nuclear magnetic resonance, mass spectral, and ultra-

$$(77) \quad \begin{array}{c} CH_3 \\ \diagdown \\ N{=}N \\ \diagdown CH_3 \end{array} \rightleftharpoons \begin{array}{c} CH_3 \diagdown \qquad \diagup CH_3 \\ N{=}N \end{array}$$

violet spectral evidence. Since the quantum yield for decomposition to nitrogen and methyl radicals is lower in solution than in the gas phase, it may be concluded that isomerization precludes the decomposition process. Perhaps the data indicate that decomposition occurs preferentially from one of the stereoisomeric forms of azomethane. Whether decomposition is from the singlet excited or from the triplet excited state of azomethane is unknown from the current data.

Lyon[89] has calculated the recombination rate constant for methyl radicals produced from the photolysis of azomethane in the gas phase. His results indicate that the entire yield of ethane obtained from photolysis in the presence of excess propane occurs before the two methyl radicals become distinct and separate. Pressure dependence data of Rebbert and Ausloos[90] illustrate the efficiency of formation of ethane via a cage recombination process.

The popular radical initiator azo-bis-isobutyronitrile (AIBN) leads to different decomposition products when photolyzed in benzene at 25° than when decomposed thermally in inert solvents. Photolysis of AIBN in benzene at 25° produces dimethyl(N-2-cyano-2-propyl)ketenimine in good yield, eq. (78).[91,92]

$$(78) \quad \begin{array}{c} CN \quad CN \\ | \qquad | \\ CH_3\overset{|}{\underset{|}{C}}N{=}N\overset{|}{\underset{|}{C}}CH_3 \\ CH_3 \quad CH_3 \end{array} \xrightarrow{h\nu} N_2 \ + \ \begin{array}{c} CN \quad CH_3 \\ | \qquad | \\ CH_3\overset{|}{\underset{|}{C}}N{=}C{=}CCH_3 \\ CH_3 \end{array}$$

A possible mechanism for the production of the ketenimine involves selective unsymmetrical coupling of the 2-cyanoisopropyl radicals produced from AIBN decomposition, eq. (79).

$$
(79) \quad
\begin{array}{c} CN \\ | \\ CH_3C\cdot \\ | \\ CH_3 \end{array}
\rightarrow
\begin{array}{c} N\cdot \\ \| \\ C \\ \| \\ H_3CC \\ | \\ CH_3 \end{array}
+
\begin{array}{c} CN \\ | \\ CH_3C\cdot \\ | \\ CH_3 \end{array}
\rightarrow
\begin{array}{cc} CN & CH_3 \\ | & | \\ CH_3CN\!\!=\!\!C\!\!=\!\!CCH_3 \end{array}
$$

Whether or not this unsymmetrical coupling results from a concerted process in which cyclic intermediates are involved, eq. (80), is not known.

$$
(80) \quad
\begin{array}{cc} CN & CN \\ | & | \\ CH_3CN\!\!=\!\!NCCH_3 \\ | & | \\ CH_3 & CH_3 \end{array}
\rightarrow
\begin{array}{cc} N\cdot & \\ \| & \\ C & CN \\ | & | \\ CH_3C & \cdot N_2CCH_3 \\ | & | \\ CH_3 & CH_3 \end{array}
\rightarrow
N_2 +
\begin{array}{cc} CN & CH_3 \\ | & | \\ CH_3\,CN\!\!=\!\!C\!\!=\!\!CCH_3 \\ | & \\ CH_3 & \end{array}
$$

Electron spin resonance evidence[93] suggests that, at least in solid matrix at $-196°$, the photodecomposition of AIBN is a stepwise process, eq. (81).

$$
(81) \quad
\begin{array}{cc} CN & CN \\ | & | \\ CH_3CN\!\!=\!\!NCCH_3 \\ | & | \\ CH_3 & CH_3 \end{array}
\xrightarrow{h\nu}
\begin{array}{cc} CN & CN \\ | & | \\ CH_3C\cdot + \cdot N_2CCH_3 \\ | & | \\ CH_3 & CH_3 \end{array}
$$

Kinetic evidence bearing on the thermal decomposition of the azo compound appears to show that the decomposition occurs by simultaneous evolution of nitrogen and production of two 2-cyanoisopropyl radicals. Temperature probably influences the nature of the decomposition. Leermakers and co-workers[94] have shown that the photochemical decomposition of AIBN is significantly different when the AIBN is adsorbed on silica gel surface. In a typical experiment, Leermakers isolated only tetramethylsuccinonitrile from the decomposition of AIBN when absorbed on silica gel. No dimethyl(N-2-cyano-2-propyl)ketenimine was produced.

Perfluoroazomethane undergoes a simple decomposition to trifluoromethyl radicals in the gas phase,[95,96] but complex products result from the addition of trifluoromethyl radicals to unreacted azo compound, eq. (82).

$$
(82) \quad 2\cdot CF_3 + CF_3N\!\!=\!\!NCF_3 \rightarrow (CF_3)_2NN(CF_3)_2
$$

The great majority of mechanistic studies of alkyl azo compounds and their decomposition reactions has been on thermal reactions, however, and the reader is referred to other sources for a more complete discussion.[97]

Photochemical decomposition of ethyl-2,2'-azo-bis-isobutyrate leads to nitrogen and ethyl-2-isobutyrate radicals; however, the process is quite inefficient, eq. (83).[98] Even though the quantum yield for the decomposition

(83)
$$CH_3\underset{\underset{CO_2Et}{|}}{\overset{\overset{CH_3}{|}}{C}}N\!=\!N\underset{\underset{CO_2Et}{|}}{\overset{\overset{CH_3}{|}}{C}}CH_3 \xrightarrow{h\nu} 2CH_3\underset{\underset{CO_2Et}{|}}{\overset{\overset{CH_3}{|}}{C}}\cdot + N_2$$

in benzene is quite high ($\phi = 0.416$), the quantum yield for scavenger consumption is relatively low ($\phi = 0.156$). The small quantity of scavengeable radicals can be attributed to solvent cage recombination of the two 2-ethyl isobutyrate radicals. They never become wholly free from one another's influence. The large amount of radical cage recombination requires that decomposition be from the singlet excited state of the azo compound or that spin inversion of the radical be rapid in comparison to recombination. Bond formation would otherwise be impossible.

Aromatic azo compounds such as azobenzene have been observed to undergo photochemical *cis-trans* isomerization, but because of the inherent instability of phenyl radicals, no decomposition is observed.

The simplest diazo compound, diazomethane, undergoes facile photo-decomposition in the gas phase. The primary products of the photochemical decomposition are nitrogen and methylene, eq. (84).[99] Methylene, a divalent

(84) $\quad CH_2N_2 \xrightarrow{h\nu} :CH_2 + N_2$

carbon species, is detectable by a variety of methods including insertion into carbon-hydrogen and some carbon-carbon bonds, cycloaddition to olefins, and solution of metallic mirrors. Two recent reviews containing exhaustive literature searches are available[100,101] for the interested reader.

The nature of photochemically produced methylene has been a constant source of discussion. Some workers contend that methylene is diradical in nature and hence approximates a triplet state species. Others propose that the two electrons of methylene are essentially paired, and a singlet state description of methylene is more accurate.[102]

Recent evidence favors the singlet state picture of photochemically produced methylene. Skell and Woodworth[103,104] found that photolysis of diazomethane either in the gas phase or in solution in the presence of excess *cis*- or *trans*-2-butene causes no isomerization about the carbon-carbon double bond of the butene and produces cyclopropane products in which the *cis* or *trans* stereochemical relationship is retained, eq. (85). Even the insertion products of the methylene in a carbon-hydrogen bond in the olefinic system retain their stereochemistry, eq. (86). Skell argues that such stereo-

(85) 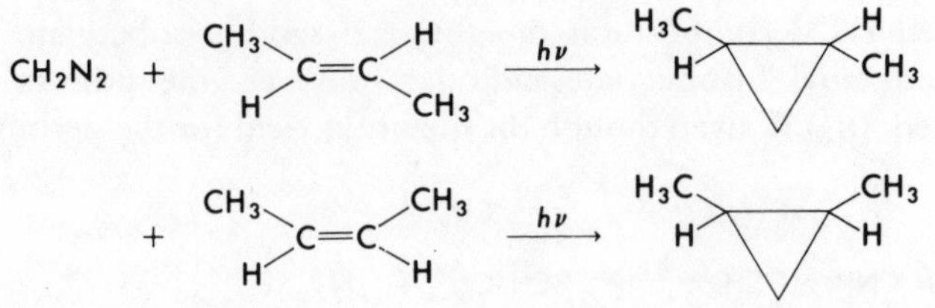 CH_2N_2 +   (structure) $\xrightarrow{h\nu}$ (structure)

+   (structure) $\xrightarrow{h\nu}$ (structure)

(86) 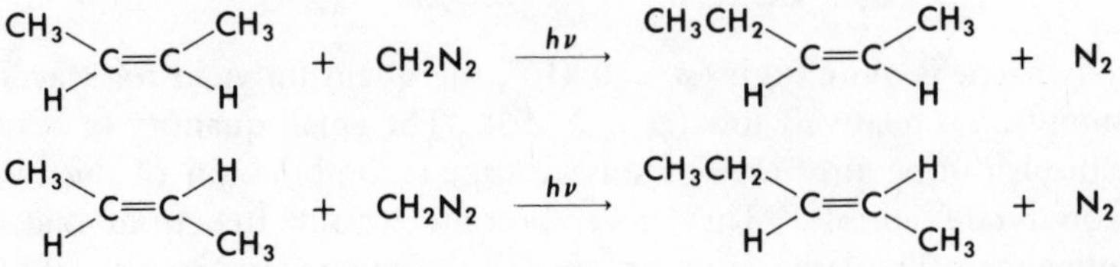   (structure) + CH_2N_2 $\xrightarrow{h\nu}$ (structure) + N_2

(structure) + CH_2N_2 $\xrightarrow{h\nu}$ (structure) + N_2

specificity can result only if the reactive state of methylene is singlet rather than triplet, for addition of a diradical (triplet) methylene to the olefinic center would be stepwise and so slow as to permit isomerization about the carbon-carbon double bond.

Additional evidence favoring the singlet state of photomethylene is that methylene produced by energy transfer decomposition with benzophenone adds nonstereospecifically to olefins. Kopecky, Hammond, and Leermakers[105] have observed that a variety of decompositions of diazomethane in cyclohexene lead to norcarane, 1-methylcyclohexene, and 3- and 4-methyl-cyclohexene. The relative product yields for the different methods of methylene production are shown in Table 5-4.

The products obtained by the benzophenone-sensitized decomposition of diazomethane in either cis- or trans-2-butene fail to retain stereoregularity. Cis- and trans-dimethylcyclopropane are produced in a ratio of 1.9 to 1.0.

Table 5-4[a]

Relative Yields for Insertion and Addition by Methylene

	Norcarane	1-Methyl-cyclohexene	3-, 4-Methyl-cyclohexene
neat photolysis	1.0	0.24	1.3
thermal, 265°	1.0	0.43	1.7
benzophenone-sensitized photolysis	1.0	—	0.42
thermal decomposition catalyzed by Cu powder	1.0	0.0	0.0

[a]Data from K. R. Kopecky, G. S. Hammond, and P. A. Leermakers, *J. Am. Chem. Soc.*, **84**, 1015 (1962).

That the nonstereospecific addition results from triplet methylene rather than singlet methylene was shown by Frey[106] who found that increasing the lifetime of the divalent carbon intermediate by diluting diazomethane with argon in the gas phase causes nonstereospecific addition to occur. At high dilution, singlet-triplet intersystem crossing becomes more probable.

The total reaction sequence for the photosensitized decomposition of diazomethane is shown in eqs. (87–89).

$$(87) \quad C_6H_5\overset{O}{\overset{\|}{C}}C_6H_5 \xrightarrow{h\nu} C_6H_5\overset{O^{*1}}{\overset{\|}{C}}C_6H_5 \longrightarrow C_6H_5\overset{O^{*3}}{\overset{\|}{C}}C_6H_5$$

$$(88) \quad C_6H_5\overset{O^{*3}}{\overset{\|}{C}}C_6H_5 + CH_2N_2 \longrightarrow CH_2N_2^{*3} + C_6H_5\overset{O}{\overset{\|}{C}}C_6H_5$$

$$(89) \quad CH_2N_2^{*3} \longrightarrow :CH_2^3 + N_2$$

Several groups have proposed that cyclodiazoethane (3-methyldiazerine) undergoes photochemical decomposition to nitrogen and ethylidine, eq. (90).[107,108]

$$(90) \quad CH_3CH\overset{N}{\underset{N}{\big<\|}} \xrightarrow{h\nu} CH_3CH: + N_2$$

Since the products of the reaction depend on the pressure of added gases, it has been proposed that a concerted loss of nitrogen and formation of ethylene occurs. Facile hydrogen migration to form ethylene makes this carbene difficult to trap.

Another useful methylene produced by photodecomposition of a diazo compound is carboethoxymethylene. Doering and Knox[109] have observed that ethyl diazoacetate produces a methylene capable of insertion into the carbon-hydrogen bond of cyclohexane, eq. (91). Doering and Knox[110] also

$$(91) \quad \bigcirc + N_2CHCO_2Et \xrightarrow{h\nu} \bigcirc^{CH_2CO_2Et} + N_2$$

observed that the ability of a methylene to insert in a carbon-hydrogen bond is decreased (the insertion reaction becomes more selective) when an α-carboxy substituent is present in the methylene. Insertion by simple methylene into the carbon-hydrogen bonds of 2,3-dimethylbutane favors the tertiary hydrogen over the primary hydrogens by a ratio of 1.2 to 1, whereas carboxymethylene inserts into the tertiary carbon-hydrogen bonds 2.9 times as often as the primary carbon-hydrogen bonds. Part of this increased stereoselectivity may be due to polar factors.

Diazo ketones also are known to lose molecular nitrogen photochemically. Wolfe rearrangement processes complicate the nitrogen elimination process, however. A critical review of the synthetic uses of diazoketones has recently appeared.[111] Generally, these decompositions can be envisioned as proceeding through methylene intermediates, eq. (92). Frequently, Arndt-Eistert type rearrangements of the intermediate methylene follow the rate-determining loss of nitrogen so that ketene trapped products may be isolated.

$$(92) \qquad -\overset{\overset{\displaystyle O}{\|}}{\underset{|}{C}}CN_2 \xrightarrow{h\nu} -\overset{\overset{\displaystyle O}{\|}}{C}\overset{..}{C}- \ + \ N_2$$

A typical example is azibenzil, eq. (93).[112] Photolysis causes nitrogen evolution with methylene formation; the methylene, subsequently, rearranges to

$$(93) \qquad \begin{matrix} C_6H_5 \\ \diagdown \\ \diagup \\ C_6H_5 \end{matrix} \begin{matrix} C=O \\ | \\ CN_2 \end{matrix} \xrightarrow{h\nu} \begin{matrix} C_6H_5 \\ \diagdown \\ \diagup \\ C_6H_5 \end{matrix} \begin{matrix} C=O \\ | \\ C: \end{matrix} \rightarrow$$

$$\begin{matrix} C_6H_5 \\ \diagdown \\ \diagup \\ C_6H_5 \end{matrix} C=C=O \xrightarrow{H_2O} \begin{matrix} C_6H_5 \\ \diagdown \\ \diagup \\ C_6H_5 \end{matrix} CHCO_2H$$

the ketene, which reacts with water to form an acid. The rearrangement process is favored at higher temperatures.

Table 5-5 lists some of the diazo compounds that have been observed to undergo photodecomposition. Generally, the products can be interpreted in terms of methylene intermediates.

Triplet, diradical intermediates have been observed spectroscopically from the photolysis of some diazoketones in rigid matrix at 77°K. Unlike the photolysis of diazomethane, phenyl- and diphenyldiazomethane have been shown to produce triplet methylene under the above conditions.[134,135] A relatively stable divalent carbon intermediate with unpaired electrons may be observed by electron spin resonance techniques, and the rate of decay of the ground state triplet can be followed spectroscopically. Similar results

for p-phenylene-bis-phenylmethylene, ![structure] ,[135]

have been obtained. Nitrene intermediates obtained by the photolysis of diazides have been observed by electron spin resonance techniques as well, eq. (94).[135] Recently, Trozzolo, Wasserman, and Yager[136] have observed

$$(94) \qquad N_3-\!\!\!\!\bigcirc\!\!\!\!-N_3 \xrightarrow{h\nu} \cdot N-\!\!\!\!\bigcirc\!\!\!\!-N\cdot \ + \ 2N_2$$

Table 5-5

Diazoalkane Decomposition Reactions

Compound	Methylene	Reference
2-diazobutane	$CH_3CH_2\ddot{C}CH_3$	113
diazotoluene	$C_6H_5\overset{H}{\underset{}{C}}{:}$	114
diazofluorene	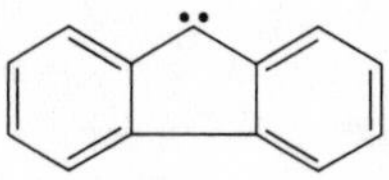	115
1,1-diphenyldiazomethane	$(C_6H_5)_2C{:}$	115
diazocyclopentadiene	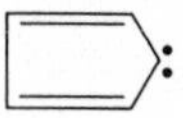	115
1-diazo-1,3-diphenylpropane	$C_6H_5\overset{.}{C}$ $CH_2CH_2C_6H_5$	116
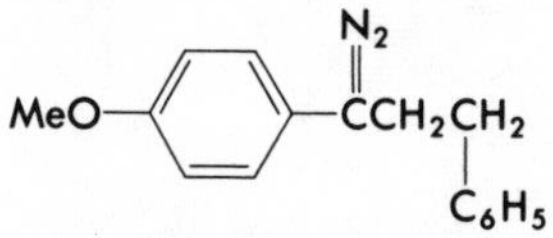 MeO—◯—$\overset{N_2}{\underset{C_6H_5}{C}CH_2CH_2}$	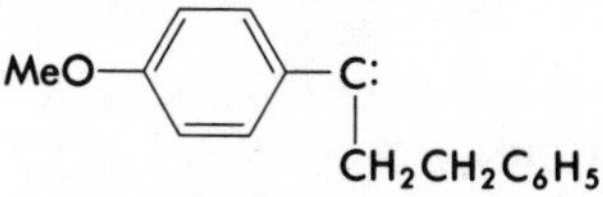 MeO—◯—$\overset{}{\underset{CH_2CH_2C_6H_5}{C}{:}}$	117
$CF_3\overset{O}{\overset{\|}{C}}{-}\overset{N_2}{\overset{\|}{C}}CO_2Et$	$CF_3\overset{O}{\overset{\|}{C}}\ddot{C}CO_2Et$	118
methyl diazoacetate	$:CHCO_2Me$	119
1-diazochloranil	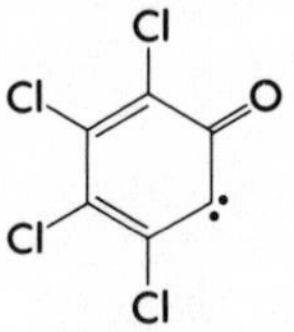	120
diazomethylacetylene	$CH{\equiv}CCH{:}$	121
diazocamphor	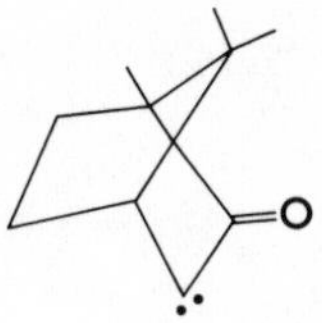	122

Table 5-5 (cont.)

Compound	Methylene	Reference
o-diazoquinone	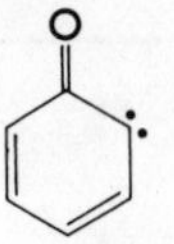	123
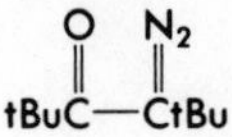 tBuC(O)—C(N₂)tBu	 tBuCCtBu (O)	124
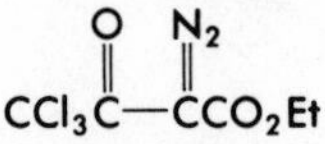 CCl₃C(O)—C(N₂)CO₂Et	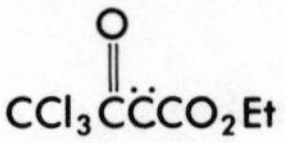 CCl₃CCCO₂Et (O)	125
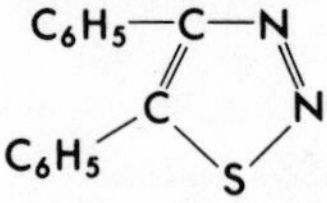 C₆H₅—C=N, C₆H₅—C—S—N (ring)	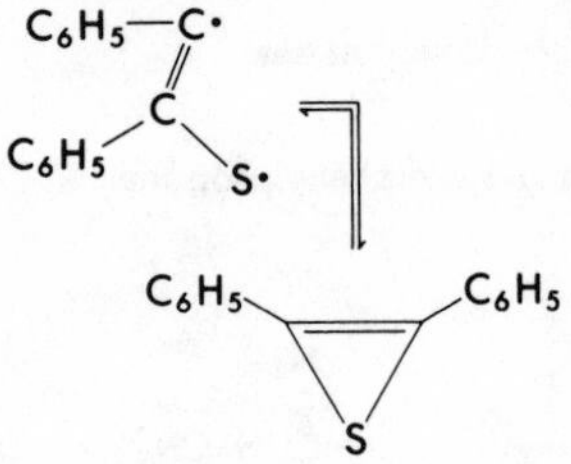 C₆H₅—C· , C₆H₅—C=S· and C₆H₅ C₆H₅ S (ring)	126
CH₃CHN₂	CH₃CH:	127
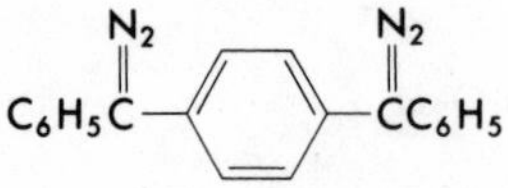 C₆H₅C(N₂)—C₆H₄—C(N₂)C₆H₅	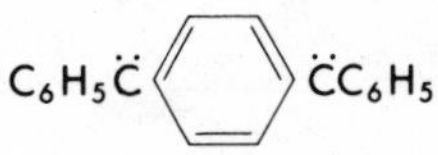 C₆H₅C̈ —C₆H₄— C̈C₆H₅	128
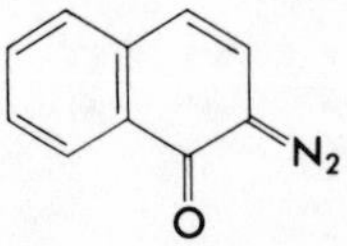	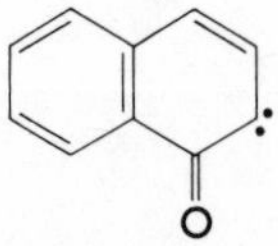	129
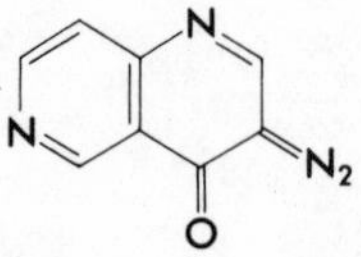	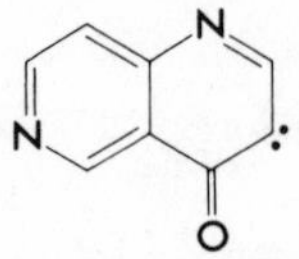	130
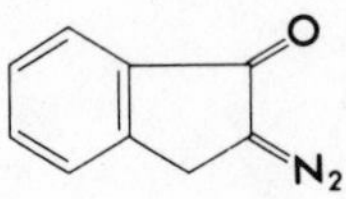	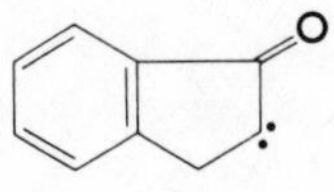	131

Table 5-5 (*cont.*)

Compound	Methylene	Reference
$tBu\overset{O}{\overset{\|}{C}}CHN_2$	$tBu\overset{O}{\overset{\|}{C}}CH:$	132
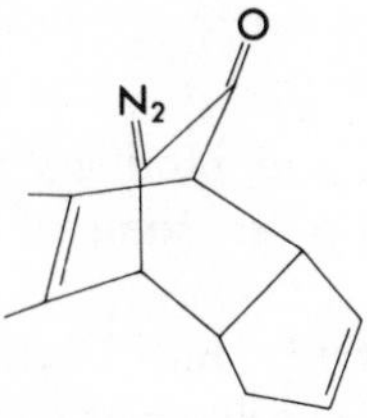	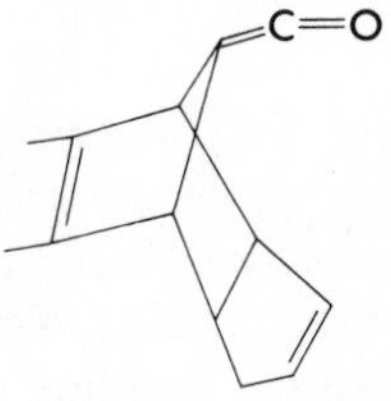	133

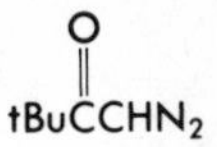

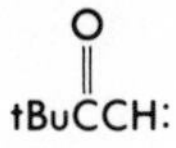

geometrically isomeric methylene intermediates in the 1- and 2-naphthyl-methylene series. Observation of these geometrical isomers suggests a bent rather than linear structure for methylene intermediates, formula (95).

(95) 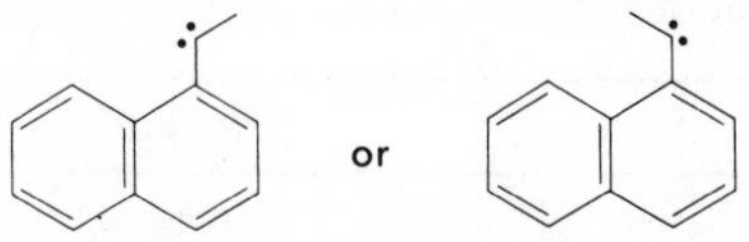   or

Padwa and Layton have observed that the photochemical decomposition of diazoacetophenone is solvent dependent. In the presence of solvents possessing readily abstractable hydrogen atoms, the yield of acetophenone is greater than 15%. In methanol, the acetophenone yield drops to about 1%, while the competitive Wolfe rearrangement becomes more important in methanol.[138]

Azides and diazonium salts generally decompose rapidly enough so that photolytic assistance is not needed. However, some reports of photode-compositions of azido compounds and of diazonium salts are in the literature. Generally, photolysis of azides leads to nitrene intermediates, eq. (96).[139] Nitrenes, like methylenes, are said to be diradical-like,[140] and they

(96) $RN_3 \xrightarrow{h\nu} N_2 + R\ddot{N}\cdot$

generally react via hydrogen abstraction or by isomerization to the imine. The hydrogen abstraction reaction may be intramolecular or intermolecular. Thus, *n*-butyl azide gives pyrrolidine by an intramolecular hydrogen abstraction reaction when photolyzed in ether for three hours, eq. (97). Similar reactions have been reported for *n*-octyl and hexyl azides. Cyclopentyl and

(97) 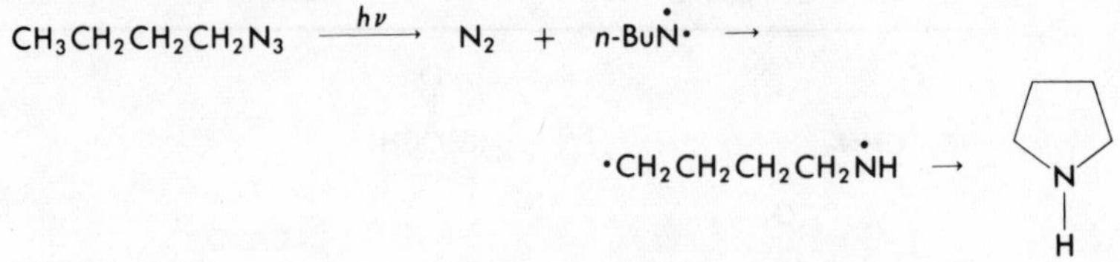 $CH_3CH_2CH_2CH_2N_3$ $\xrightarrow{h\nu}$ N_2 + *n*-BuṄ· →

·$CH_2CH_2CH_2CH_2\overset{.}{N}H$ →

cyclohexyl azides give the corresponding amines and products from the analogous imines upon similar photolysis. Table 5-6 lists some of the alkyl azides whose photolyses have been investigated.[141]

Nitrene trapping with olefins has been observed, and Lwowski and Mattingly have isolated the aziridine shown from photolyses of ethyl azido-formate in cyclohexene, eq. (98).[142,143]

(98) 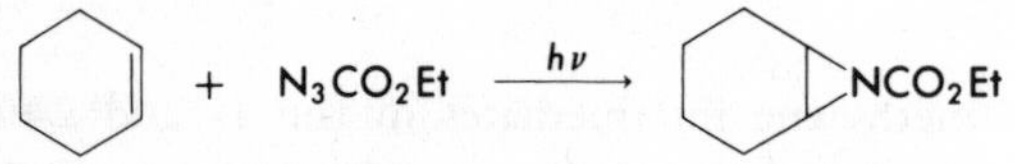   ⬡ + N_3CO_2Et $\xrightarrow{h\nu}$ ⬡NCO₂Et

Table 5-6

Azide Decomposition Reactions[a]

Azide	Products
butyl azide	pyrrolidine
n-octyl azide	N-butyl pyrolidine
propyl azide	propylimine
heptyl azide	2-propyl pyrollidine
cyclopentyl azide	cyclopentylimine[b]
cyclohexyl azide	cyclohexylamine + cyclohexylimine[b]
cycloheptyl azide	cycloheptylamine and imine[b]
(+) neomenthyl azide	imine[b] + neopentyl amine
ethyl-α-azido propionate	imine[b] from ethylpyruvate[b]
phenethyl azide	phenylethyl amine
allyl azide	acrylimine[b]
3-phenylpropyl azide	tetrahydroquinoline
4-methylhexyl azide	4-methylhexyl amine + 2-ethyl-2-methyl pyrrolidine
3-β-azido-5-cholestene	3-β-aminocholest (5) ene[b] + 3-iminecholest (5) ene

[a]Data from D. H. R. Barton and L. R. Morgan, *J. Chem. Soc.*, 622 (1962). See, however, D. H. R. Barton and A. N. Starratt, *J. Chem. Soc.*, 2444 (1965).
[b]Isolated as 2,4-dinitrophenylhydrazone of aldehyde after hydrolysis.

Recent results from the laboratories of Moriarty and Lwowski suggest that the decomposition of azides occurs via a singlet excited state and that 1,2-hydrogen migration is the predominant reaction pathway in the decomposition of alkyl azides.[143-146] The interested reader is advised to consult a recent review by Abramovitch and Davis[147] for a more complete discussion of azide decomposition processes.

Photolysis of diazonium salts in alcohols around 0° produces aromatic ethers and aromatic hydrocarbons in a pseudo-Gomberg Bachman reaction, eq. (99).[148]

(99)   Me⟨⟩N$_2^\oplus$, Cl$^\ominus$ $\xrightarrow[h\nu]{\text{MeOH}}$

⟨⟩Me + MeO⟨⟩Me + N$_2$ + HCl

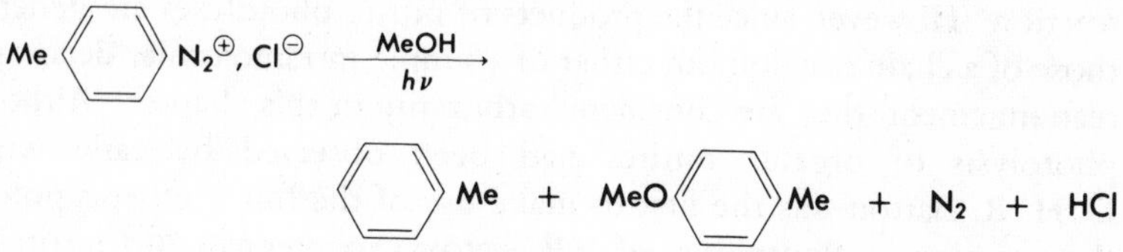

A possible mechanism involves either free tolyl radicals or ionic intermediates. Lee, Calvert, and Malmberg[149] have examined the decompositions of *m*- and *p*-nitrobenzene diazonium salts in aqueous and nonaqueous media. They have found, using radical scavengers, that the major decomposition process for diazonium salts with *m*- and *p*-nitro substituents is homolytic. In ethanol, nitrobenzene and the α and β-arylethanols along with butanediol are major reaction products, eqs. (100–102).

(100)   O$_2$N⟨⟩—N$_2^\oplus$ $\xrightarrow{h\nu}$ O$_2$N⟨⟩· $\xrightarrow{\text{EtOH}}$

O$_2$N⟨⟩ + CH$_3\overset{\cdot}{C}$HOH

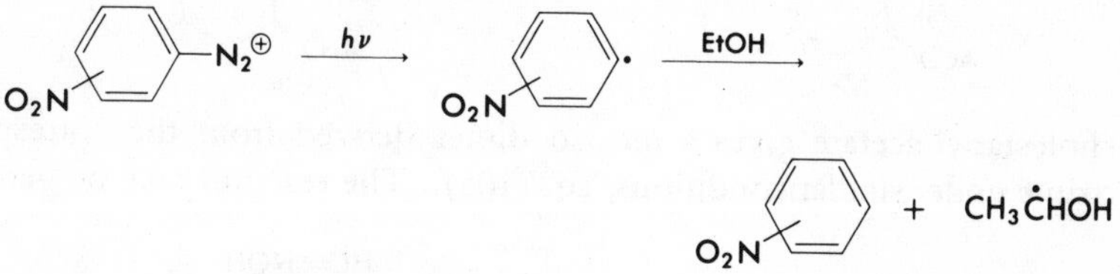

(101)   2CH$_3\overset{\cdot}{C}$HOH → CH$_3\underset{\underset{H}{|}}{\overset{\overset{OH}{|}}{C}}$—$\underset{\underset{H}{|}}{\overset{\overset{OH}{|}}{C}}CH_3$

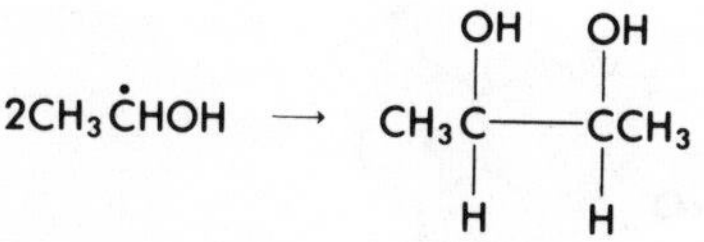

(102)   O$_2$N⟨⟩· + CH$_3\overset{\cdot}{C}$HOH → O$_2$N⟨⟩$\underset{\underset{H}{|}}{\overset{\overset{CH_3}{|}}{C}}$—OH

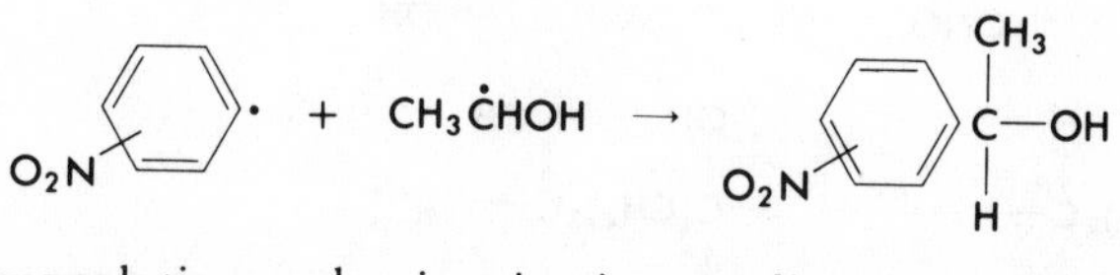

In aqueous solution, carbonium ion intermediates are suggested, eq. (103).

(103)   O$_2$N⟨⟩N$_2^\oplus$ → O$_2$N⟨⟩$^\oplus$ + N$_2$

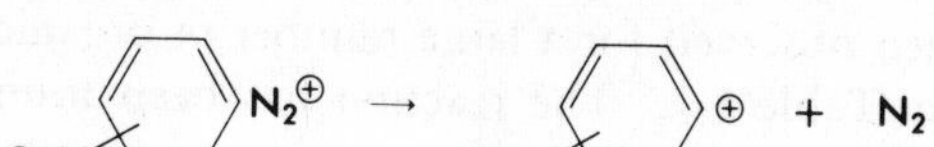

Photolysis in a rigid matrix suggests that triplet state intermediates are involved. Boudreaux and Boulet[150] have come to similar conclusions from magnetic susceptibility measurements. Quantum yield measurements for a variety of diazonium salts indicate that in nearly neutral media, nitrogen evolution may be nearly quantitative.[151,152]

Elimination of Nitric Oxide

Photochemical decomposition of alkyl nitrites can be considered as a chain reaction. However, since the products of nitrite photolyses are generally not those of a chain reaction but rather of a simple intramolecular decomposition rearrangement, they are considered arbitrarily in this chapter. Although the photolysis of organic nitrites had been observed by early workers,[153] D. H. R. Barton was the first to make use of the full synthetic potential of the reaction. Photolysis of 3β-acetoxy-5α-pregnan-20β-nitrite in dry benzene in the absence of oxygen gives 34% 18-oximino-5α-pregnane-3β-20β-diol-3-acetate, eq. (104).[154] Similarly, the nitrite of 6β-hydroxy-

(104)

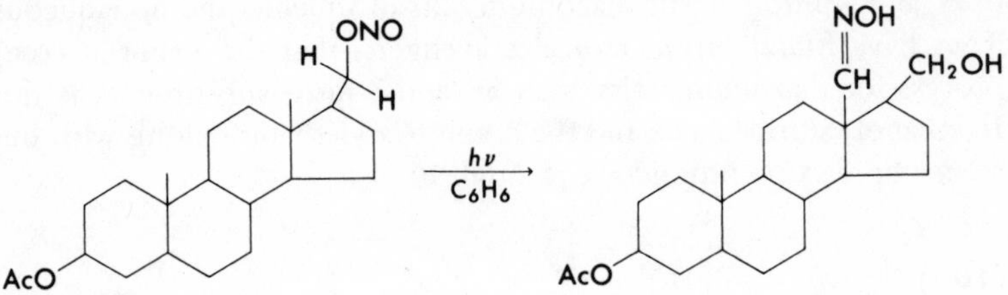

cholestanyl acetate gives a nitroso dimer derived from the corresponding oxime under similar conditions, eq. (105). The reaction may be generalized

(105)

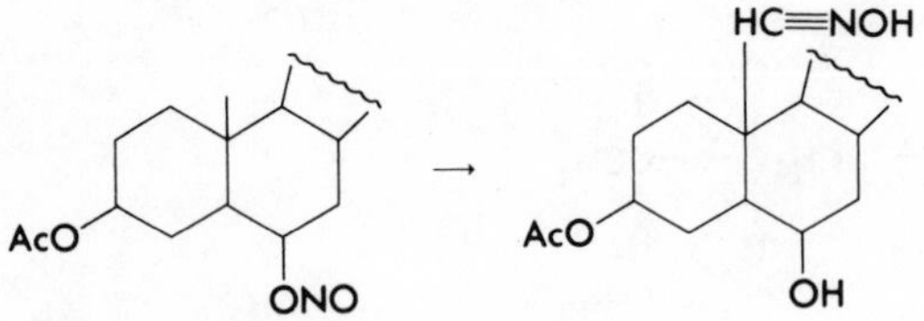

(106) $\quad -\overset{\text{ONO}}{\underset{|}{\text{C}}}(\text{CH}_2)_2\overset{\text{H}}{\underset{|}{\text{C}}}- \quad \xrightarrow{h\nu} \quad -\overset{\text{OH}}{\underset{|}{\text{C}}}(\text{CH}_2)_2\overset{\text{NOH}}{\underset{\|}{\text{C}}}-$

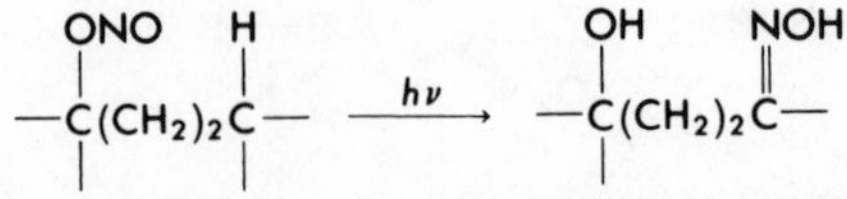

as in eq. (106) and has been observed for a large number of organic nitrites some of which are listed in Table 5-7. The reaction has been found to be solvent dependent with aromatic hydrocarbons being preferred. Large

Table 5-7

Decomposition Reactions of Alkyl Nitrites

Nitrite	Product	Reference
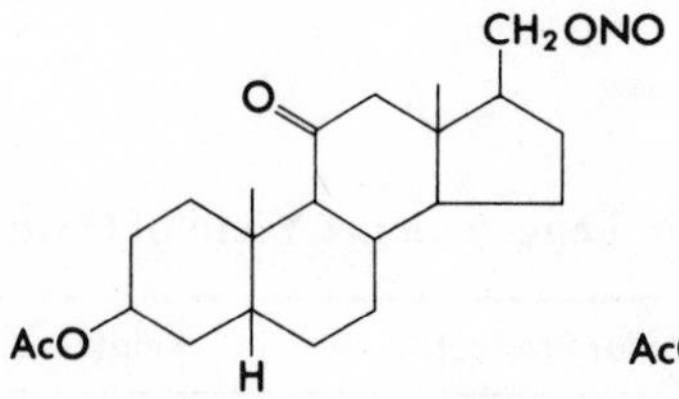	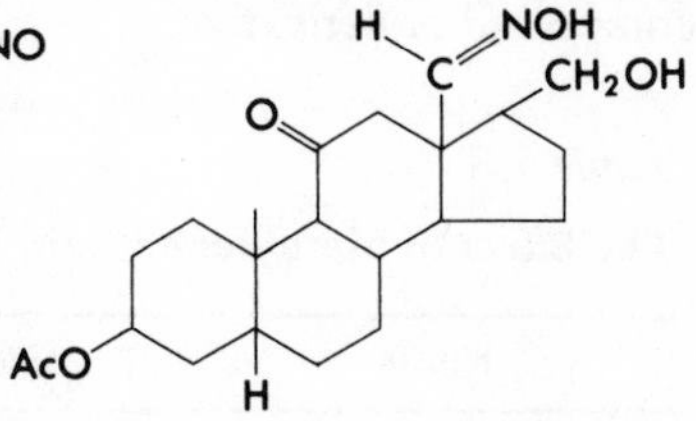	154
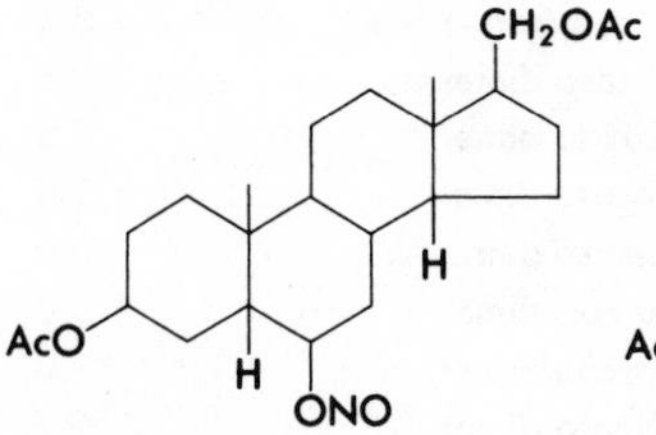	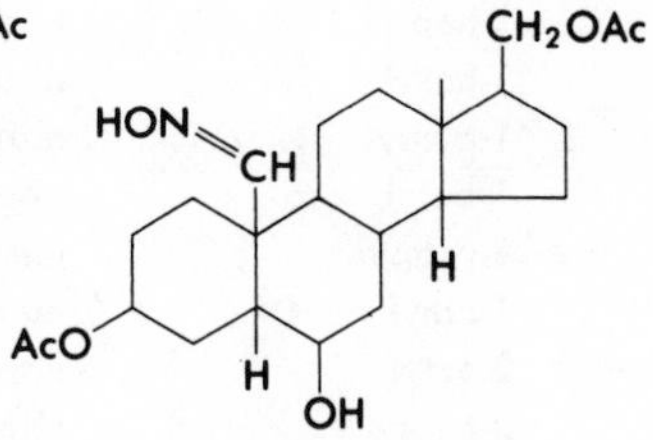	154
$CH_3(CH_2)_6CH_2ONO$	$CH_3(CH_2)_5\overset{NO}{\underset{H}{C}}CH_2CH_2OH$	155
$C_6H_5CH_2CH_2CH_2ONO$	no reaction	156
$C_6H_5CH_2ONO$	no reaction	156
$C_6H_5CH_2CH_2ONO$	$(C_6H_5CH{=}NOH)_2$	156
$C_6H_5CH_2CH_2CH_2CH_2ONO$	$(C_6H_5\overset{NOH}{C}CH_2CH_2CH_2OH)_2$	156
$C_6H_5CH_2CH_2CH_2CH_2CH_2ONO$	$(C_6H_5CH_2\overset{NOH}{C}CH_2CH_2CH_2OH)_2$	156
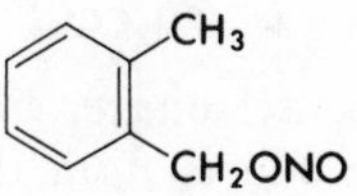	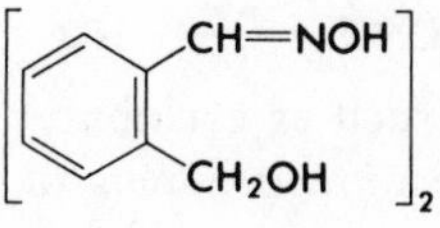	156

excesses of added nitric oxide cause a decrease in oxime yield, presumably because of either nitric oxide trapping of the intermediate radicals before hydrogen abstraction* can occur or quenching of the excited state of the nitrite ester responsible for reaction.[157]

Table 5-8 shows the effect of methylene chain length on the yield of nitroso compound or derivative.

Table 5-8

The Effect of Methylene Chain Length on the Yield of Oxime[a]

Nitrite	Major Products	Relative Yield
1-octyl	nitroso dimer	9.7
1-heptyl	nitroso dimer	8.5
1-hexyl	nitroso dimer	8.5
1-pentyl	nitroso dimer	7.5
1-butyl	nitroso dimer	1.0
1-propyl	nitroso dimer	0.0
1-ethyl	nitroso dimer	0.0
2-octyl	nitroso dimer	11.0
2-heptyl	nitroso dimer	9.75
2-hexyl	nitroso dimer	7.5
2-pentyl	nitroso dimer	4.2
2-butyl	nitroso dimer	1.7
2-propyl	nitroso dimer	—

[a]Data from P. Kabasakalian, E. R. Townley, and M. D. Yudis, *J. Am. Chem. Soc.*, **84**, 2716 (1962).

The major products resulting when nitrites not possessing γ hydrogens are photolyzed are the alcohol and carbonyl compound characteristic of the intermediate alkoxy radical. From 1-propyl nitrite, propionaldehyde and *n* - propyl alcohol are obtained in approximately equivalent yields, eq. (107).

(107) $CH_3CH_2CH_2ONO \xrightarrow{h\nu} NO + CH_3CH_2CH_2OH + CH_3CH_2CHO$

2-Propyl nitrite yields acetone and 2-propanol as well as nitric oxide, eq. (108).

(108) $(CH_3)_2CHONO \xrightarrow{h\nu} NO + (CH_3)_2CHOH + CH_3\overset{\displaystyle O}{\overset{\displaystyle \|}{C}}CH_3$

Cyclic nitrites such as cyclobutyl nitrite, cyclopentyl nitrite, and cyclohexyl nitrite give nitroso dimers of ring-opened products from the inter-

*The hydrogen abstracted is most often located at the γ position.

mediate alkoxy radical, eq. (109).[159] With cyclooctyl nitrite, transannular hydrogen abstraction is observed.[159]

$$(109) \quad (CH_2)_n \overset{}{\diamondsuit} ONO \quad \xrightarrow{h\nu} \quad (CH_2)_n \overset{NO}{\underset{CHO}{\diagup}}$$

$n = 1, 2,$ or 3

Cyclohexyl nitrites with suitably substituted alkyl groups such as 2-ethylcyclohexyl nitrite have been shown to undergo the expected γ hydrogen abstraction reaction.[160] Tertiary nitrites appear to behave in a manner analogous to primary and secondary nitrites with the intermediate tertiary alkoxy radical undergoing the expected radical elimination to produce alkyl radicals and a carbonyl product.[158,161]

The inferred mechanism for the photolysis of organic nitrites involves photolytic decomposition to an alkoxy radical and nitric oxide with rapid hydrogen abstraction and recombination. An alkyl nitroso compound, a tautomeric form of the oxime, is formed. This nitroso compound is isolated as a dimer, eqs. (110–112). Evidence supporting the proposed mechanism,

$$(110) \qquad RCH_2CH_2CH_2CH_2ONO \quad \xrightarrow{h\nu} \quad (RCH_2CH_2CH_2CH_2O\cdot, NO\cdot)$$

$$(111) \quad (RCH_2CH_2CH_2CH_2O\cdot \;+\; NO\cdot) \quad \longrightarrow \quad (R\overset{\cdot}{C}HCH_2CH_2CH_2OH, NO\cdot)$$

$$(112) \qquad \overset{NOH}{\overset{\|}{RCCH_2CH_2CH_2OH}} \;\rightleftharpoons\; \overset{NO}{\overset{|}{RCHCH_2CH_2CH_2OH}}$$

in addition to McMillan's interesting vapor phase results,[162-164] has been obtained by Akhtar and Pechet.[165] Based on the observation that photolysis of organic nitrite mixtures partially enriched with isotopic nitrogen affords products in which significant scrambling has occurred, these workers propose a free radical, noncage mechanism for the reaction. Photolysis of mixtures of two nitrites produces mixtures of nitroso dimers in which the ratios of heavy nitrogen are approximately equivalent, eq. (113).

$$(113) \quad A\overset{*}{NO} + BNO \quad \xrightarrow{h\nu} \quad \begin{array}{ccc} A\overset{}{NO} & & B\overset{}{NO} \\ + & + & + \\ B\overset{*}{NO} & & A\overset{*}{NO} \end{array}$$

Like all compounds containing nitrogen-oxygen double bonds, organic nitrites show a low intensity, relatively long wavelength absorption maximum, presumably an n-π^* transition. One can predict that the photolysis of organic nitrites under low energy radiation involves an n-π^* excitation to either a singlet or triplet state, followed by decomposition to nitric oxide and alkoxy radical products.

Nussbaum and co-workers have recently shown that the alkoxy radical formed can do things other than abstract hydrogens. For example, an allylic rearrangement can take place if a double bond is in proximity to the formed alkoxy radical, eq. (114).[166]

(114)

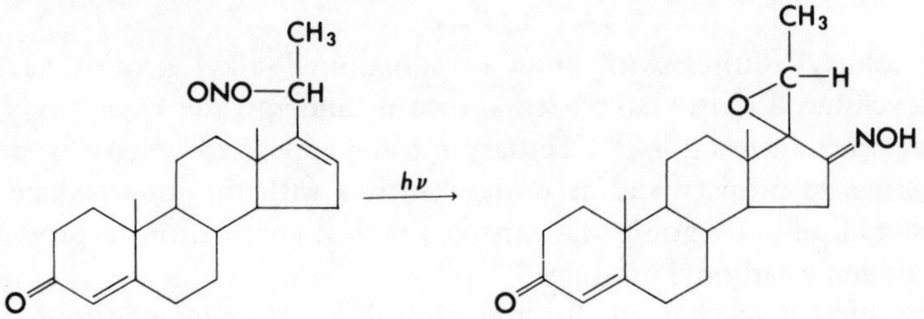

Organic Nitro Compounds

The photochemical behavior of organic nitro compounds is of interest because of the comparative similarity of their absorption characteristics to carbonyl compounds. Organic nitro compounds display short and long wavelength absorptions assigned to π-π^* and n-π^* transitions. Chapman has observed that organic nitro compounds undergo a photochemical elimination reaction in solution.[167] Photolysis of β-nitro-β-methylstyrene affords a high yield of a product identified as an oximo ketone, eq. (115). When aromatic nitro compounds such as 9-nitroanthracene are photolyzed under

$$(115) \quad C_6H_5CH = \overset{\overset{\displaystyle CH_3}{|}}{C}NO_2 \quad \xrightarrow{h\nu} \quad C_6H_5\overset{\overset{\displaystyle NOH}{\|}}{C} - \overset{\overset{\displaystyle O}{\|}}{C}CH_3$$

similar conditions, nitric oxide and quinoid products result. The yield of quinoid product is unaffected when degassed samples are irradiated. Excess nitric oxide, unlike the observed reaction depression in the photolysis of organic nitrites, serves to increase the rate of quinone formation.

Chapman proposes that these results are consistent with a nitro-nitrite[167] rearrangement. A mechanism for the conversion of β-methyl-β-nitrostyrene to an oximo ketone, eq. (115), involves the steps shown in eqs. (116–117). With aromatic nitro compounds, photolysis of the nitrite produces an aroxyl radical and a nitric oxide fragment. It is proposed that quinone formation results from continued reaction of the oximo product. A mechanism for the formation of anthraquinone from 9-nitroanthracene is shown in eqs. (118–120). No quinone could be isolated from the photolysis of nitrobenzene, presumably because of the relative reactivity of the phenoxyl radical

(116) 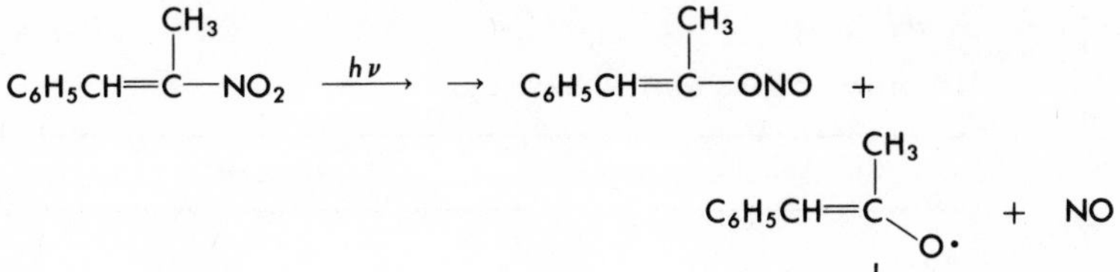 $C_6H_5CH=\overset{\underset{\displaystyle CH_3}{|}}{C}-NO_2$ $\xrightarrow{h\nu}$ $\rightarrow$ $C_6H_5CH=\overset{\underset{\displaystyle CH_3}{|}}{C}-ONO$ +

$C_6H_5CH=\overset{\underset{\displaystyle CH_3}{|}}{C}\diagdown_{O\cdot}$ + NO

(117) 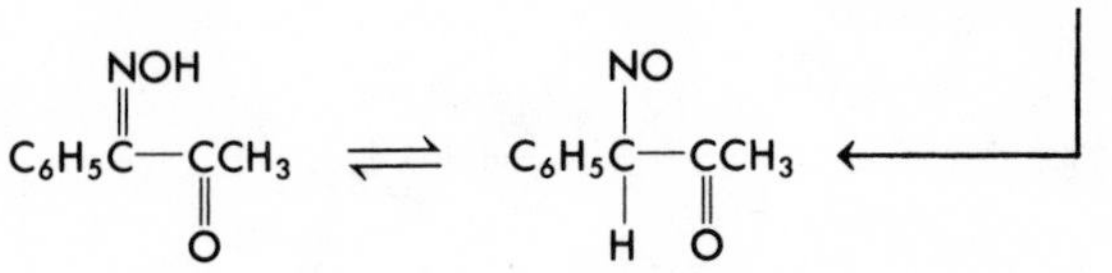 $C_6H_5\overset{\underset{\displaystyle C}{||}\,\underset{\displaystyle O}{|}}{\overset{NOH}{C}}-CCH_3$ $\rightleftharpoons$ $C_6H_5\overset{\underset{\displaystyle H}{|}}{\overset{NO}{C}}-\overset{\underset{\displaystyle O}{||}}{C}CH_3$ $\leftarrow$

(118)

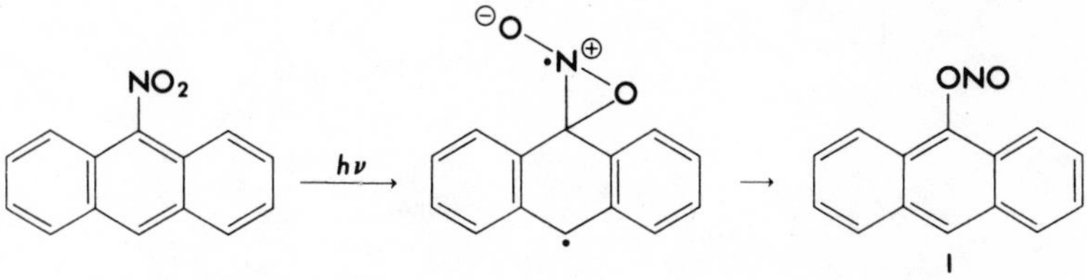

$\xrightarrow{h\nu}$ $\rightarrow$

I

(119) 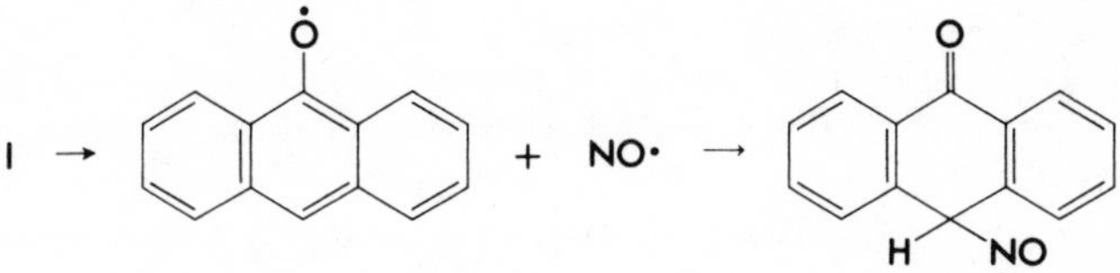   I $\rightarrow$

+ NO· $\rightarrow$

(120)

$\xleftarrow{?}$

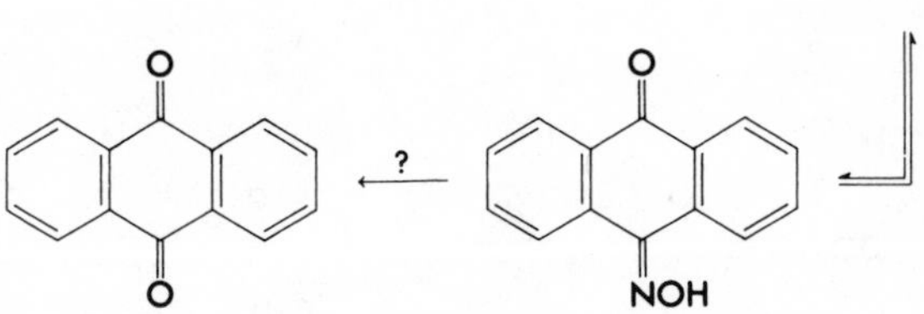

compared to the aroxyl radical obtained from 9-nitroanthracene. It has been reported that upon photolysis, the monooxime of benzoquinone is converted to benzoquinone in the presence of excess nitric oxide so that if the oxime is formed, it will lead to products.

Elimination of Sulfur Dioxide

Photochemical decomposition reactions of aryl sulfones to sulfur dioxide and hydrocarbons are another example of photochemically induced elimination reactions.[168] Table 5-9 lists the aromatic sulfones that have been observed to liberate sulfur dioxide when photolyzed with radiation of less than 2800 Å.

Table 5-9

Photoreactions of Aryl Sulfones [a]

Sulfone	Products	Yield, %
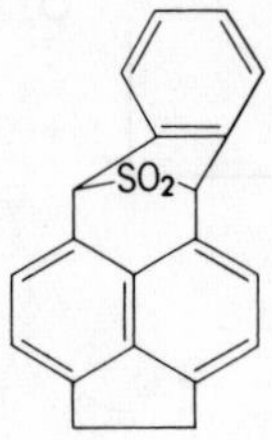 (1)	dimer	50
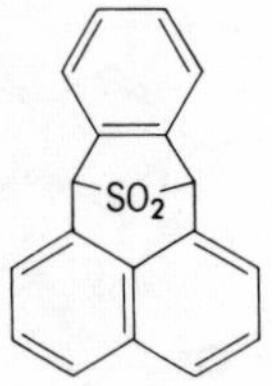 (2)	dimer	50
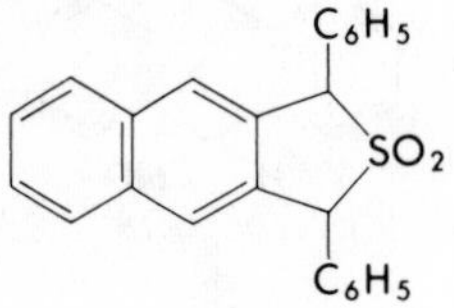	dimer + 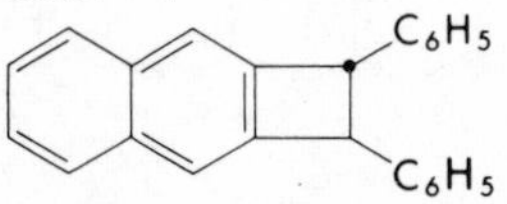	50
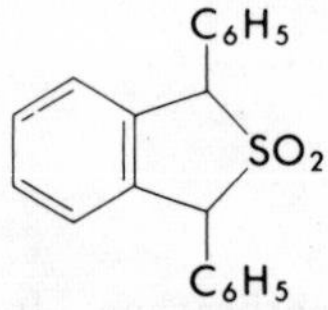	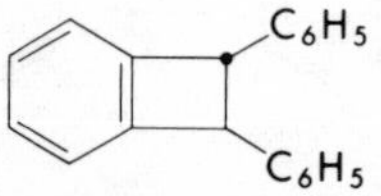	13

[a]From M. P. Cava, R. H. Schlessinger, and J. P. Van Meter, *J. Am. Chem. Soc.*, **86**, 3173 (1964).

Sulfone 1 and sulfone 2 will undergo energy transfer decompositions at longer wavelength when carbonyl sensitizers such as benzophenone and acetophenone are employed. Lower energy sensitizers such as fluorenone and 2-naphthaldehyde are ineffective.

Loss of Carbon Dioxide—Decompositions of Peroxides

The photochemically induced decomposition of diaryl peroxides and peresters represent another class of photochemical elimination reactions.

Walling and Gibian[169] have recently reported that carbonyl sensitizers readily promote the decomposition of hydroperoxides, diacyl peroxides, and peresters. The photochemical cleavage of these peroxy compounds appears to parallel the thermal cleavage giving oxygen-oxygen bond homolysis, eq. (121).

$$(121) \quad ROOR \xrightarrow[\text{sensitized}]{h\nu} 2RO \cdot$$

$$R = H, \text{alkyl, acyl}$$

Walling and Gibian report that all the peroxides investigated decompose homolytically. Even peroxides that undergo a thermal bond heterolysis undergo a photosensitized bond homolysis. Furthermore, from quantum yield studies, it appears that significant cage recombination may occur at least in the benzophenone-sensitized decomposition of dibenzoyl peroxide. Such a result is unusual in that most thermal peroxide decompositions proceed without cage recombination of the radicals produced.[170]

Disproportionation of Phosphines— Elimination of Aryl Radicals

Recent reports indicate that organo-phosphorous compounds undergo photodecomposition reactions. Horner and Dörges[171] and Griffin and Kaufman[172] have observed that triphenylphosphine decomposes photochemically to give diphenylphosphine, phenylphosphine, and tetraphenylphosphonium salts, eq. (122).

$$(122) \quad (C_6H_5)_3P \xrightarrow[\text{MeOH}]{h\nu} (C_6H_5)_2PH + (C_6H_5)_4P^{\oplus}, X^{\ominus}$$

Both research groups propose that the triarylphosphine photochemically eliminates phenyl radicals, which then may attack either solvent or residual triarylphosphine. The diarylphosphinyl radical is proposed to undergo a one electron transfer reaction with tetraarylphosphinyl radicals to give a phosphonium ion and phosphinium anion, eq. (123). Arylphosphonium salts also give aryl radicals photochemically. An initial electron transfer reaction

$$(123) \quad (C_6H_5)_2P \cdot + (C_6H_5)_4P \cdot \rightleftharpoons (C_6H_5)_2P:^{\ominus} + (C_6H_5)_4P^{\oplus}$$

between the phosphonium cation and anion is proposed, eq. (124).[173]

$$(124) \quad (C_6H_5)_4P^{\oplus}, Cl^{\ominus} \rightleftharpoons (C_6H_5)_4P \cdot + \cdot Cl \longrightarrow \text{Products}$$

Decompositions of Sulfur Compounds

Recent reports suggest that dithiocarbamic anhydrides undergo smooth photochemical decomposition. Tarbell and Hoffmeister[174,175] as well as other workers report that a number of dithiocarbamic anhydrides decompose homolytically when photolyzed in benzene. The products obtained include an acid, an amide, and various sulfur-containing dimers and polymers, eq. (125). Xanthates are also photolabile.[176]

(125)

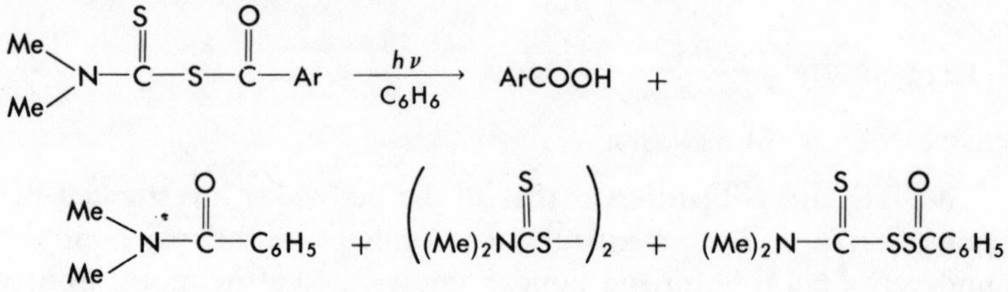

$$\underset{Me}{\overset{Me}{>}}N-\overset{\overset{S}{\|}}{C}-S-\overset{\overset{O}{\|}}{C}-Ar \quad \xrightarrow[C_6H_6]{h\nu} \quad ArCOOH \quad +$$

$$\underset{Me}{\overset{Me}{>}}N-\overset{\overset{O}{\|}}{\overset{\cdot}{C}}-C_6H_5 \quad + \quad \left(\overset{\overset{S}{\|}}{(Me)_2NCS-}\right)_2 \quad + \quad (Me)_2N-\overset{\overset{S}{\|}}{C}-SSCC_6H_5$$

Decompositions of Small Ring Compounds

Photolyses of three-membered compounds have recently been reported to yield carbenes. Richardson and co-workers[177] report that 9,10-dihydro-9,10-methanophenanthrene yields phenanthrene and methylene when photolyzed in cyclohexene, eq. (126).

(126)

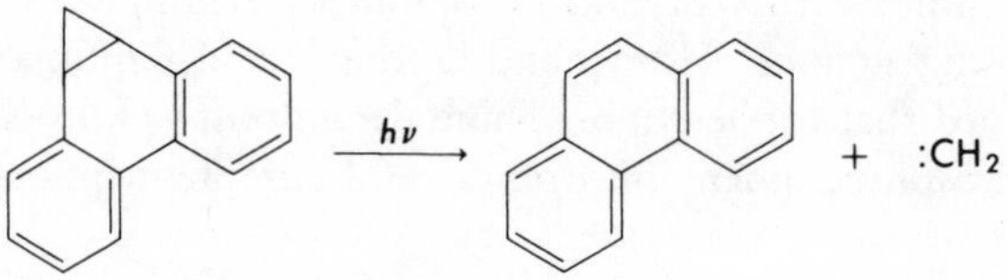

$$\xrightarrow{h\nu} \qquad + \quad :CH_2$$

The methylene generated adds stereospecifically to olefins. Phenylcyclopropane is observed to give styrene and methylene. Leermakers and co-workers[178] report that cyclopropylphenylmethane yields naphthalene upon photolysis in the vapor phase. A diradical mechanism involving cleavage of the cyclopropane ring is proposed, eq. (127).

(127) 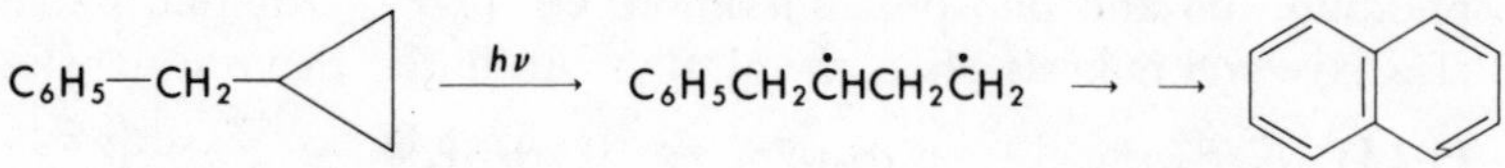 $C_6H_5-CH_2-\triangleleft \quad \xrightarrow{h\nu} \quad C_6H_5CH_2\overset{\cdot}{C}HCH_2\overset{\cdot}{C}H_2 \quad \rightarrow \quad \rightarrow$

Padwa and Hamilton have reported interesting decomposition reactions of benzoylaziridines. Irradiation of *trans*-1-cyclohexyl-2-phenyl-3-benzoylethyleneimine in aqueous ethanol gives a mixture of *cis* and *trans* benzalacetophenone and N-cyclohexylhydroxylamine as major products, eq. (128). A mechanism involving cleavage of the aziridine ring to an enolate anion is proposed.[179]

(128) C_6H_5 ⎯⎯⎯ CC_6H_5 $\xrightarrow{h\nu}$ $C_6H_5CH{=}CHCC_6H_5$ + $C_6H_{11}NHOH$

(with N–C_6H_{11} substituent on the ring; carbonyl oxygens shown)

Photolysis of certain epoxides has been observed by Griffin and co-workers. Epoxides such as tetraphenylethylene oxide are reported to give benzophenone and diphenylcarbene, eq. (129).[180]

(129) $\begin{array}{c} C_6H_5 \\ C_6H_5 \end{array} C{-}C \begin{array}{c} C_6H_5 \\ C_6H_5 \end{array}$ (with epoxide O bridging) $\xrightarrow{h\nu}$ $(C_6H_5)_2C{=}O$ + $(C_6H_5)_2C{:}$

References

1. Davis, W., Jr., *Chem. Rev.*, **40**, 201 (1947).
2. Noyes, W. A., Jr., and P. A. Leighton, *Photochemistry of Gases*, New York, Reinhold, 1949.
3. Rollefson, G. K., and M. Burton, *Photochemistry and the Mechanisms of Chemical Reactions*, Englewood Cliffs, N. J., Prentice-Hall, 1939.
4. Pitts, J. N., Jr., *J. Chem. Educ.*, **34**, 112 (1957).
5. Noyes, W. A., Jr., G. B. Porter, and J. E. Jolley, *Chem. Rev.*, **56**, 49 (1956).
6. Noyes, W. A., Jr., G. S. Hammond, J. N. Pitts, Jr., *Advances in Photochemistry*, Vol. I., New York, Interscience, 1963.
7. Herr, D. S., and W. A. Noyes, Jr., *J. Am. Chem. Soc.*, **62**, 2052 (1940).
8. Caldwell, J., and D. E. Hoare, *J. Am. Chem. Soc.*, **84**, 3987 (1962).
9. Pearson, G. S., *J. Phys. Chem.*, **67**, 1686 (1963).
10. Pitts, J. N., Jr., and F. E. Blacet, *J. Am. Chem. Soc.*, **72**, 2810 (1950).
11. Norrish, R. G., and M. E. S. Appleyard, *J. Chem. Soc.*, 874 (1934).
12. Davis, W., Jr., and W. A. Noyes, Jr., *J. Am. Chem. Soc.*, **69**, 2153 (1947).
13. Masson, C. R., *J. Am. Chem. Soc.*, **74**, 4731 (1952).
14. Pitts, J. N., Jr., and I. Norman, *J. Am. Chem. Soc.*, **76**, 4815 (1954).
15. Norman, I., and J. N. Pitts, Jr., *J. Am. Chem. Soc.*, **77**, 6104 (1955).
16. Brown, W. G., *U. S. Govt. Res. Rept.*, **38**(22), 25 (1963).
17. Roberts, R. M., and R. G. Landolt, *J. Am. Chem. Soc.*, **87**, 2281 (1965).
18. Roberts, R. M., R. N. Green, R. G. Landolt, and E. W. Heyer, *J. Am. Chem. Soc.*, **87**, 2282 (1965).
19. Neumar, J. F., Ph. D. thesis, University of Chicago, 1957.
20. Griffin, G. W., J. Covell, R. C. Petterson, R. M. Dodson, and G. Klose, *J. Am. Chem. Soc.*, **87**, 1410 (1965).
21. Griffin, G. W., E. J. O'Connell, and H. A. Hammond, *J. Am. Chem. Soc.*, **85**, 1001 (1963).
22. Pitts, J. N., Jr., R. A. Tolberg, and T. W. Martin, *J. Am. Chem. Soc.*, **79**, 6370 (1957).
23. Srinivasan, R., *J. Am. Chem. Soc.*, **81**, 5541 (1959).
24. Srinivasan, R., *Advances in Photochemistry*, Vol. I., p. 83 ff., New York, Interscience, 1963.

25. Srinivasan, R., J. Am. Chem. Soc., 81, 1546 (1959).
26. Alumbaugh, R. L., G. O. Pritchard, and B. Rickborn, J. Phys. Chem., 69, 3225 (1965).
27. Klemm, R. F., D. N. Morrison, P. Gilderson, and A. T. Blades, Can. J. Chem., 43, 1934 (1965).
28. Dunion, P., and C. N. Trumbore, J. Am. Chem. Soc., 87, 4211 (1965).
29. Bamford, C. H., and R. G. W. Norrish, J. Chem. Soc., 1521 (1938).
30. Benson, S. W., and G. B. Kistiakowsky, J. Am. Chem. Soc., 64, 80 (1942).
31. Srinivasan, R., J. Am. Chem. Soc., 81, 2601 (1959).
32. Blacet, F. E., and A. Miller, J. Am. Chem. Soc., 79, 4327 (1957).
33. Srinivasan, R., J. Am. Chem. Soc., 83, 4344 (1961).
34. Frey, H. M., Chem. Ind., 1367 (1961).
35. Srinivasan, R., J. Am. Chem. Soc., 83, 2590 (1961).
36. Srinivasan, R., J. Am. Chem. Soc., 81, 2604 (1959).
37. Cremer, S., and R. Srinivasan, Tetrahedron Letters, 21, 24 (1960).
38. Chapman, O. L., and G. W. Bordon, J. Org. Chem., 26, 4185 (1961).
39. Ciamician, G., and P. Silber, Chem. Ber., 41, 1928 (1908).
40. Ciamician, G., and P. Silber, Chem. Ber., 41, 1071 (1908).
41. Schuster, D. I., F. T. H. Lee, A. Padwa, and P. G. Gassman, J. Org. Chem., 30, 2262 (1965).
42. Quinkert, G., K. Opitz, and J. Weinlich, Angew. Chem., 74, 507 (1962).
43. Hostettler, H. U., Tetrahedron Letters, 687 (1965).
44. Yates, P., and L. Kilmurry, Tetrahedron Letters, 1739 (1964).
45. Strachan, A. N., and F. E. Blacet, J. Am. Chem. Soc., 77, 5254 (1955).
46. Sieger, R. A., and J. G. Calvert, J. Am. Chem. Soc., 76, 5197 (1954).
47. Tucker, B. G., and E. Whittle, Proc. Chem. Soc., 93 (1963).
48. Bowles, R., J. R. Majer, and J. C. Robb, Trans. Faraday Soc., 58, 1541 (1962).
49. Haszeldine, R. N., and F. Nyman, J. Chem. Soc., 3015 (1961).
50. Smith, R. M., and J. G. Calvert, J. Am. Chem. Soc., 78, 2345 (1956).
51. Charles, S. W., J. T. Pearson, and E. Whittle, Trans. Faraday Soc., 57, 1356 (1961).
52. Sheats, G. F., and W. A. Noyes, Jr., J. Am. Chem. Soc., 77, 1421 (1955).
53. Okabe, H., and W. A. Noyes, Jr., J. Am. Chem. Soc., 79, 801 (1957).
54. Greenberg, S. A., and C. S. Forster, J. Am. Chem. Soc., 83, 4339 (1961).
55. de Mayo, P., H. Takeshita, and A. B. M. A. Sattar, Proc. Chem. Soc., 119 (1962).
56. Hikino, H., and P. de Mayo, J. Am. Chem. Soc., 86, 3582 (1964).
57. Turro, N. J., G. W. Byers, and P. A. Leermakers, J. Am. Chem. Soc., 86, 955 (1964).
58. Leermakers, P. A., G. F. Vesley, N. J. Turro, and D. C. Neckers, J. Am. Chem. Soc., 86, 4213 (1964).
59. Turro, N. J., P. A. Leermakers, H. R. Wilson, D. C. Neckers, G. W. Byers, and G. F. Vesley, J. Am. Chem. Soc., 87, 2613 (1965).
60. Ritchey, H. G., Jr., J. M. Richey, and D. C. Clagett, J. Am. Chem. Soc., 86, 3906 (1964).
61. Cookson, R. C., M. J. Nye, and G. Subrahmanyam, Proc. Chem. Soc., 144 (1964).
62. Haller, I., and R. Srinivasan, J. Am. Chem. Soc., 87, 1144 (1965).
63. Turro, N. J., W. B. Hammond, and P. A. Leermakers, J. Am. Chem. Soc., 87, 2774 (1965).
64. Bayes, K. D., J. Am. Chem. Soc., 83, 3712 (1961).
65. Bayes, K. D., J. Am. Chem. Soc., 84, 4077 (1962).
66. Mullen, R. T., and A. P. Wolf, J. Am. Chem. Soc., 84, 3214 (1962).
67. Bayes, K. D., J. Am. Chem. Soc., 85, 1730 (1963).
68. Urry, W. H., M. H. Pai, and C. Y. Chen, J. Am. Chem. Soc., 86, 5342 (1964).
69. Blacet, F. E., J. Phys. Chem., 52, 534 (1948).

70. Blacet, F. E., and J. N. Pitts, Jr., *J. Am. Chem. Soc.*, **74**, 3382 (1952).

71. Zemany, P. D., and M. Burton, *J. Phys. Chem.*, **55**, 949 (1951).

72. Zemany, P. D., and M. Burton, *J. Am. Chem. Soc.*, **73**, 499 (1951).

73. Blacet, F. E., and J. G. Roof, *J. Am. Chem. Soc.*, **58**, 73 (1936).

74. Blacet, F. E., G. H. Fielding, and J. G. Roof, *J. Am. Chem. Soc.*, **59**, 2375 (1937).

75. Dodd, R. E., and J. Watson Smith, *J. Chem. Soc.*, 1465 (1957).

76. Pritchard, G. O., G. H. Miller, and R. Foote, quoted by Majer and Simons, *Advances in Photochemistry*, Vol. II, p. 181, New York, Wiley, 1964.

77. Schmidt, U., *Angew. Chem., Intern. Ed. Eng.*, **4**, 146 (1965).

78. Schmidt, U., *Angew. Chem., Intern. Ed. Eng.*, **4**, 239 (1965).

79. Schmidt, U., K. H. Kabitzhe, and K. Markau, *Angew. Chem., Intern Ed. Eng.*, **4**, 355 (1965).

80. Elad, D., and J. Rokach, *J. Org. Chem.*, **30**, 3361 (1965).

81. Elad, D., D. V. Rao, and V. I. Stenberg, *J. Org. Chem.*, **30**, 3252 (1965).

82. Elad, D., *Tetrahedron Letters*, 873 (1963).

83. Walling, C., and A. N. Naglieri, *J. Am. Chem. Soc.*, **82**, 1820 (1960).

84. Leermakers, P. A., and G. F. Vesley, *J. Org. Chem.*, **28**, 1160 (1963).

85. Leermakers, P. A., and G. F. Vesley, *J. Am. Chem. Soc.*, **85**, 3776 (1963).

86. Gillam, A. E., and E. S. Stern, *Electronic Absorption Spectroscopy*, p. 63, London, Arnold, 1958.

87. For a review see E. W. R. Steacie, *Atomic and Free Radical Reactions*, Vol. I, p. 376, New York, Reinhold, 1954.

88. Hutton, R. F., and C. Steel, *J. Am. Chem. Soc.*, **86**, 745 (1964).

89. Lyon, R. K., *J. Am. Chem. Soc.*, **86**, 1907 (1964).

90. Rebbert, R. E., and P. Ausloos, *J. Phys. Chem.*, **66**, 2253 (1962).

91. Smith, P., J. E. Sheats, and P. E. Miller, *J. Org. Chem.*, **27**, 4053 (1962).

92. Smith, P., and A. M. Rosenberg, *J. Am. Chem. Soc.*, **81**, 2037 (1959).

93. Ayscough, P. B., B. R. Brooks, and H. E. Evans, *J. Phys. Chem.*, **68**, 3889 (1964).

94. Leermakers, P. A., L. D. Weis, and H. T. Thomas, *J. Am. Chem. Soc.*, **87**, 4403 (1965).

95. Dacey, J. R., and D. M. Young, *J. Chem. Phys.*, **23**, 1302 (1955).

96. Pritchard, G. O., H. O. Pritchard, H. I. Schiff, and A. F. Trotman-Dickenson, *Trans. Faraday Soc.*, **52**, 849 (1956).

97. Walling, C., *Free Radicals in Solution*, pp. 511–517, New York, Wiley, 1957.

98. Hammond, G. S., and J. R. Fox, *J. Am. Chem. Soc.*, **86**, 1918 (1964).

99. Kirkbride, F. W., and R. G. W. Norrish, *J. Chem. Soc.*, 119 (1933).

100. de More, W. D., and S. W. Benson, in *Advances in Photochemistry*, W. A. Noyes, G. S. Hammond, and J. N. Pitts, Eds., Vol. II, New York, Wiley, 1964.

101. Hine, J., *Divalent Carbon*, New York, Ronald, 1964.

102. See, for example, R. G. W. Norrish, and G. Porter, *Discussions Faraday Soc.*, **2**, 97 (1947).

103. Skell, P. S., and R. C. Woodworth, *J. Am. Chem. Soc.*, **78**, 4496 (1956).

104. Woodworth, R. C., and P. S. Skell, *J. Am. Chem. Soc.*, **81**, 3383 (1959).

105. Kopecky, K. R., G. S. Hammond, and P. A. Leermakers, *J. Am. Chem. Soc.*, **84**, 1015 (1962).

106. Frey, H. M., *J. Am. Chem. Soc.*, **82**, 5947 (1960).

107. Brinton, R. K., and D. H. Volman, *J. Chem. Phys.*, **19**, 1394 (1951).

108. Frey, H. M., and I. D. R. Stevens, *J. Chem. Soc.*, 1700 (1965).

109. Doering, W. E., and L. H. Knox, *J. Am. Chem. Soc.*, **78**, 4947 (1956).

110. Doering, W. E., and L. H. Knox, *J. Am. Chem. Soc.*, **83**, 1989 (1961).

111. Weygand, F., and H. J. Bestmann, *Angew. Chem.*, **72**, 535 (1960).

112. Horner, L., E. Spietschka, and A. Gross, *Ann. Chem.* **573**, 17 (1951).

113. Frey, H. M., and I. D. R. Stevens, *J. Am. Chem. Soc.*, **84**, 2647 (1962).
114. Gutsche, C. D., G. L. Bachman, and R. S. Coffey, *Tetrahedron*, **18**, 617 (1962).
115. Kirmse, W., L. Horner, and H. Hoffmann, *Ann. Chem.*, **614**, 19 (1958).
116. Gutsche, C. D., and H. E. Johnson, *J. Am. Chem. Soc.*, **77**, 5933 (1955).
117. Gutsche, C. D., E. F. Jason, R. S. Coffey, and H. E. Johnson, *J. Am. Chem. Soc.*, **80**, 5756 (1958).
118. Weygand, F., H. Dworschak, K. Koch, and S. Konstas, *Angew. Chem.*, **73**, 409 (1961).
119. Doering, W. E., and T. Mole, *Tetrahedron*, **10**, 65 (1960).
120. Huisgen, R., H. König, G. Binsch, and H. J. Sturm, *Angew. Chem.*, **73**, 368 (1961).
121. Skell, P. S., and J. Klebe, *J. Am. Chem. Soc.*, **82**, 247 (1960).
122. Horner, L., and E. Spietschka, *Chem. Ber.*, **88**, 934 (1955).
123. Süs, O., *Ann. Chem.*, **556**, 65 (1944).
124. Newman, M. S., and A. Arkell, *J. Org. Chem.*, **24**, 385 (1959).
125. Weygand, F., and K. Koch, *Angew. Chem.*, **73**, 531 (1961).
126. Kirmse, W., and L. Horner, *Ann. Chem.*, **614**, 4 (1958).
127. Frey, H. M., *J. Chem. Soc.*, 2293 (1962).
128. Murray, R. W., and A. M. Trozzolo, *J. Org. Chem.*, **26**, 3109 (1961).
129. Süs, O., *Ann. Chem.* **579**, 133 (1953).
130. Süs, O., and K. Moller, *Ann. Chem.* **599**, 233 (1956).
131. Cava, M. P., R. L. Litle, and D. R. Napier, *J. Am. Chem. Soc.*, **80**, 2257 (1958).
132. Wiberg, K. B., and T. W. Hutton, *J. Am. Chem. Soc.*, **76**, 5367 (1954).
133. Horner, L., and D. W. Baston, *Chem. Ber.*, **98**, 1252 (1965).
134. Murray, R. W., A. M. Trozzolo, E. Wasserman, and W. A. Yager, *J. Am. Chem. Soc.*, **84**, 3213 (1962).
135. Trozzolo, A. M., R. W. Murray, and E. Wasserman, *J. Am. Chem. Soc.*, **84**, 4990 (1962).
136. Trozzolo, A. M., R. W. Murray, G. Smolinsky, W. A. Yager, and E. Wasserman, *J. Am. Chem. Soc.*, **85**, 2526 (1963).
137. Trozzolo, A. M., E. Wasserman, and W. A. Yager, *J. Am. Chem. Soc.*, **87**, 129 (1965).
138. Padwa, A., and R. Layton, *Tetrahedron Letters*, 2167 (1965).
139. Barton, D. H. R., and L. R. Morgan, *J. Chem. Soc.*, 622 (1962).
140. Smolinsky, G., E. Wasserman, and W. A. Yager, *J. Am. Chem. Soc.*, **84**, 3220 (1962).
141. Barton, D. H. R., and A. N. Starratt, *J. Chem. Soc.*, 2444 (1965). These authors report that the conditions necessary for the described azide photodecomposition ring closure are not always reproducible.
142. Lwowski, W., and T. Mattingly, *Tetrahedron Letters*, 277 (1962).
143. Lwowski, W., T. J. Maricich, and T. W. Mattingly, *J. Am. Chem. Soc.*, **85**, 1200 (1963).
144. Moriarty, R. M., and M. Rahman, *Tetrahedron*, **21**, 2877 (1965).
145. Moriarty, R. M., and M. Rahman, *J. Am. Chem. Soc.*, **87**, 2519 (1965).
146. Lwowski, W., and G. T. Tisue, *J. Am. Chem. Soc.*, **87**, 4022 (1965).
147. Abramovitch, R. A., and B. A. Davis, *Chem. Rev.*, **64**, 149 (1964).
148. Horner, L., and H. Stöhr, *Chem. Ber.*, **85**, 993 (1952).
149. Lee, W. E., J. G. Calvert, and E. W. Malmberg, *J. Am. Chem. Soc.*, **83**, 1928 (1961).
150. Boudreaux, E. A., and E. Boulet, *J. Am. Chem. Soc.*, **80**, 1588 (1958).
151. Schmidt, J., and J. Maier, *Chem. Ber.*, **64**, 767 (1931).
152. Baril, A., *J. Chem. Phys.*, **22**, 1275 (1954).
153. See, for example, A. L. Nussbaum and C. H. Robinson, *Tetrahedron*, **17**, 35 (1961).
154. Barton, D. H. R., J. M. Beaton, L. E. Geller, and M. M. Pechet, *J. Am. Chem. Soc.*, **82**, 2640 (1960).
155. Barton, D. H. R., J. M. Beaton, L. E. Geller, and M. M. Pechet, *J. Am. Chem. Soc.*, **83**, 4076 (1961).

156. Kabasakalian, P., and E. R. Townley, *J. Am. Chem. Soc.*, **84**, 2711 (1962).
157. Kabasakalian, P., E. R. Townley, and M. D. Yudis, *J. Am. Chem. Soc.*, **84**, 2716 (1962).
158. Kabasakalian, P., E. R. Townley, and M. D. Yudis, *J. Am. Chem. Soc.*, **84**, 2718 (1962).
159. Kabasakalian, P., and E. R. Townley, *J. Org. Chem.*, **27**, 2918 (1962).
160. Kabasakalian, P., and E. R. Townley, *J. Am. Chem. Soc.*, **84**, 2724 (1962).
161. Kabasakalian, P., and E. R. Townley, *J. Am. Chem. Soc.*, **84**, 2723 (1962).
162. McMillan, G. R., *J. Am. Chem. Soc.*, **84**, 2514 (1962).
163. Levy, J. B., *Ind. Eng. Chem.*, **48**, 762 (1956).
164. McMillan, G. R., *J. Am. Chem. Soc.*, **84**, 4007 (1962).
165. Akhtar, M., and M. M. Pechet, *J. Am. Chem. Soc.*, **86**, 265 (1964).
166. Nussbaum, A. L., R. Wayne, E. Yuan, O. Sarre, and E. P. Oliveto, *J. Am. Chem. Soc.*, **87**, 2451 (1965).
167. Chapman, O. L., A. A. Griswold, E. Hoganson, G. Lenz, and J. Reasoner, *Pure Appl. Chem.*, **9**, 585 (1964).
168. Cava, M. P., R. H. Schlessinger, and J. P. Van Meter, *J. Am. Chem. Soc.*, **86**, 3173 (1964).
169. Walling, C., and M. J. Gibian, *J. Am. Chem. Soc.*, **87**, 3413 (1965).
170. Herk, L., M. Feld, and M. Szwarc, *J. Am. Chem. Soc.*, **83**, 2998 (1961).
171. Horner, L., and J. Dörges, *Tetrahedron Letters*, 763 (1965).
172. Kaufman, M. L., and C. E. Griffin, *Tetrahedron Letters*, 769 (1965).
173. Griffin, C. E., and M. L. Kaufman, *Tetrahedron Letters*, 773 (1965).
174. Hoffmeister, E. H., and D. S. Tarbell, *Tetrahedron*, **21**, 2857 (1965).
175. Hoffmeister, E. H., and D. S. Tarbell, *Tetrahedron*, **21**, 2865 (1965).
176. Okawara, M., T. Nakai, Y. Otsuji, and E. Imoto, *J. Org. Chem.*, **30**, 2025 (1965).
177. Richardson, D. B., L. R. Durrett, J. M. Martin, W. E. Putnam, S. C. Slaymaker, and I. Dvoretzky, *J. Am. Chem. Soc.*, **87**, 2763 (1965).
178. Leermakers, P. A., and G. F. Vesley, *J. Org. Chem.*, **30**, 539 (1965).
179. Padwa, A., and L. Hamilton, *J. Am. Chem. Soc.*, **87**, 1821 (1965).
180. Kristinsson, H., and G. W. Griffin, personal communication.
181. Kristinsson, H., *Tetrahedron Letters*, 2343 (1966).

CHAPTER

6

Addition Reactions

Photochemical addition reactions include all photochemical reactions that involve the addition of an excited state molecule to an unsaturated linkage. These reactions may involve like molecules (dimerizations), unlike molecules, or they may be intramolecular. The initial products are almost always cyclic, and many important synthetic applications of photochemical cyclo-addition reactions have been made. Photochemical addition reactions provide magnificent methods for the synthesis of four-membered ring compounds, and they can be compared with the thermal 1,2 and 1,4 cycloaddition and Diels-Alder reactions in their utility. Like many photochemical reactions, additions can be made to occur both by direct irradiation and by sensitized methods.

Dimerizations of Aromatic Hydrocarbons

One of the oldest known photochemical addition reactions is the dimerization of anthracene. Fritzsche[1] and later Elbs[2] and others[3] recognized that anthracene forms an insoluble dimer when a benzene solution is exposed to sunlight for a period of days, eq. (1). A great variety of substituted anthracenes and analogous heteroatomic aromatic compounds also give rise to

(1)

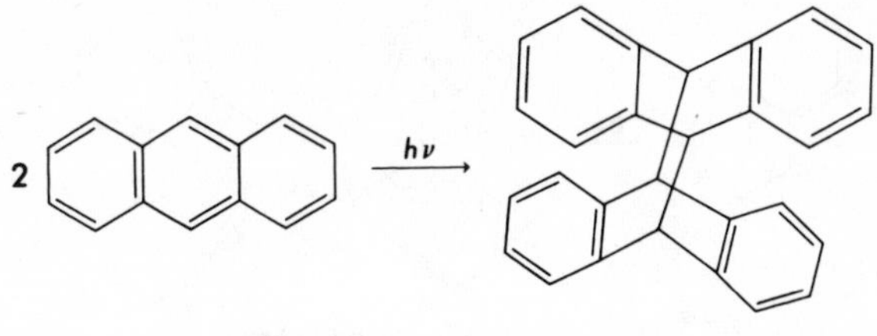

photodimers. Examples of polynuclear aromatic molecules that undergo dimerization are listed in Table 6-1.[15]

A proposed mechanism for the photochemical dimerization of anthracene and its derivatives must explain the experimental observations that although most of the nine substituted anthracenes form head to head dimeric materials, eq. (2), 9-haloanthracenes form head to tail dimers, eq. (3).

Table 6-1

**Substituted Anthracenes That Undergo
Photochemical Dimerization Reactions**

Anthracene	Comment
1-methylanthracene[4]	
2-methylanthracene[5]	
1-chloro-4-methylanthracene[4]	
1-chloroanthracene[4]	
9-bromoanthracene[4,6,16]	head to tail dimer
9-bromo-1-chloroanthracene[4]	
anthracene-9-carboxylic acid[7]	
9-methylanthracene[8]	
9-ethylanthracene[8]	
anthracene-9-carboxaldehyde[9-11]	head to head dimer
9-anthranoic acid, methyl ester[9]	head to head dimer
9-hydroxymethylanthracene[9]	head to head dimer
9-chloroanthracene[16]	head to tail dimer
1-azanthracene[12,13]	
9-chloro-1-azanthracene[13]	
2-phenyl-1-azanthracene[13]	
2-phenyl-9-chloro-1-azanthracene[14]	
2-azanthracene[13]	
1,3-diazanthracene[14]	

(2)

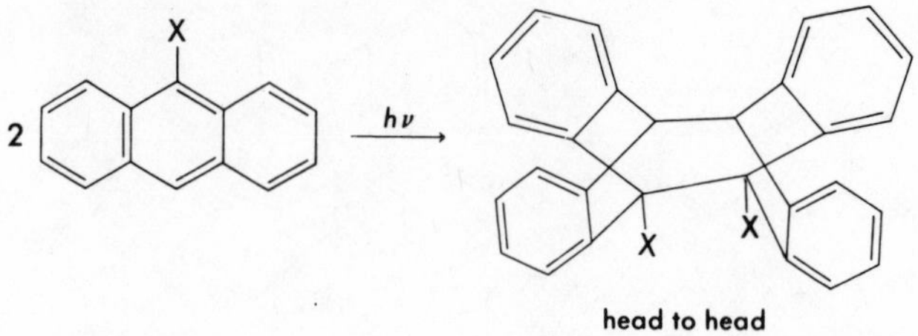

head to head

but...

(3)

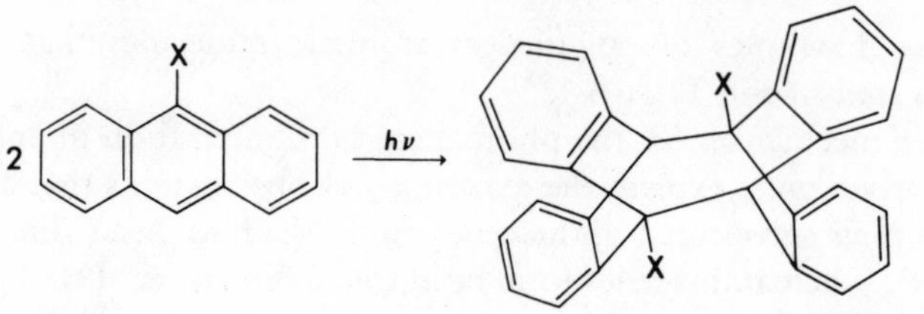

head to tail

In addition, the rate of anthracene dimer formation is independent of anthracene concentration between the limits of 6 and 17 mM in toluene,[17-19] and even though the quantum yields for anthracene dimer formation appear to be essentially independent of anthracene concentration, the quantum yields for fluorescence from anthracene and its nine substituted derivatives decrease over the same concentration region.[20-22]

Greene[9] and others[23,24] have proposed that the photochemical dimerization of anthracene involves free radical intermediates. Greene's evidence is based upon the observation that most often head to head dimers are formed. This evidence excludes polar intermediates since a consideration of polar contributors to the transition state indicates that head to tail dimerization would often be preferable. In the cases of 9-carboxyl derivatives, for example, the carboxyl group should function as an active electron withdrawer and serve to stabilize any developing negative charge at the 9 carbon, eq. (4). Coup-

(4)

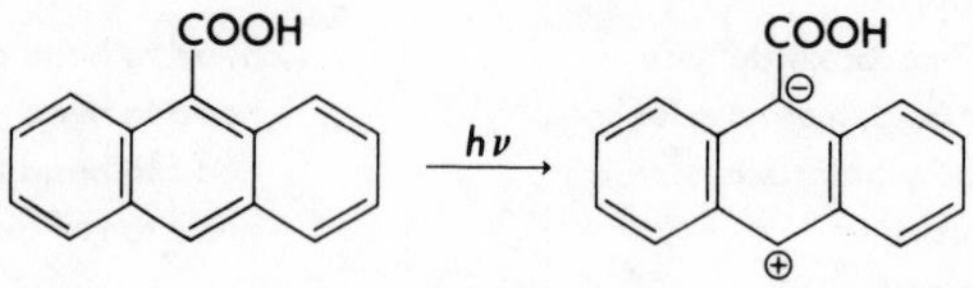

ling should then occur at the 10 position of another anthracene molecule, eq. (5). Greene argues that free radical intermediates would not be influenced by polar effects in the transition state for dimer formation to the same degree as would polar intermediates. Further, if the stepwise addition proceeds so as to favor the more stable diradical transition state, then initial coupling should occur more strongly between unsubstituted centers.

(5)

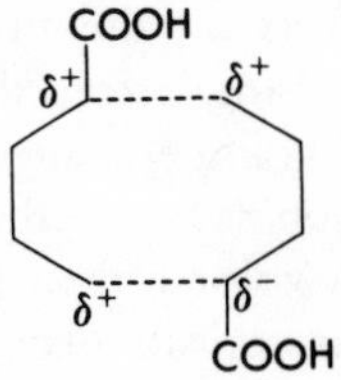

The dimerization of anthracene is thought to involve reaction of the photochemically excited singlet state of anthracene with a ground state molecule. The singlet mechanism is strongly suggested by the fact that as the concentration of anthracene in solution increases, the quantum yield of dimerization also increases, while the fluorescence efficiency of excited anthracene decreases. When the photodimerization is attempted in solvents which themselves serve to quench fluorescence, the quantum yield for the dimerization drops essentially to zero.[25]

Russian workers have obtained relative rate data and fluorescence quenching constants for a great number of substituted anthracenes. The data support the postulate that singlet anthracene is responsible for the dimerization reaction.[26,27]

The seemingly anomalous head to tail dimerizations of the 9-chloro- and 9-bromoanthracenes can be attributed to steric repulsions of the large halogen atoms as well as to larger contributions to the transition states for head to tail dimerizations by structures such as:

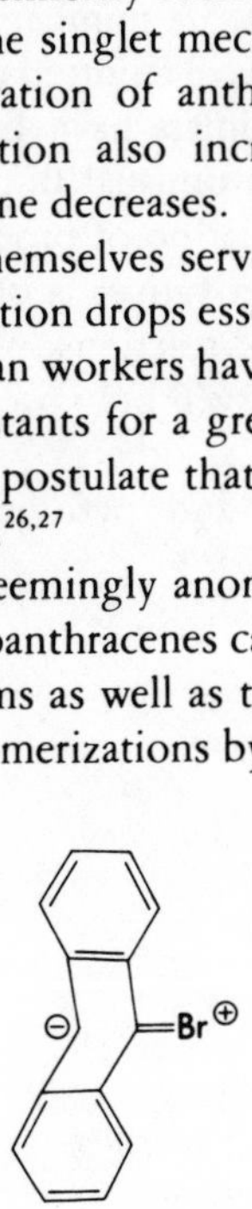

The total mechanism for the dimerization of anthracene probably involves reaction steps (6–8).

(6) $\qquad$ A $\xrightarrow{h\nu}$ A*'

(7) A*' + A $\xrightarrow{h\nu}$ dimer

(8) A*' + A $\longrightarrow$ 2A

Pitts and co-workers have reported studies of anthracene dimerization in an alkali halide matrix.[28] In a typical series of experiments, these workers observed that an increase in hydrostatic pressure affects the quantum yield of anthracene and 9-anthraldehyde dimerization. They interpreted this pressure effect on quantum yield as being the result of volume changes when going from starting materials to dimerization transition state. If the transition state necessary for dimer formation is larger in volume than the sum total volume of the reactants, an increase in pressure will decrease the quantum yield for the dimerization. If the transition state has a smaller volume, increases in pressure will decrease the quantum yield for dimerization.

Other polynuclear aromatics also form photodimers. A number of these are reviewed by Mustafa.[15] Bradshaw and Hammond have reported examples of naphthalene dimerization reactions.[29] Transient dimers have been proposed by Foerster and Doeller[30,31] to account for the unusual fluorescence spectra of concentrated pyrene solutions; however, isolation of products has been unsuccessful, and evidence for dimeric pyrene derivatives is only spectroscopic. Examples of photochemical dimerization reactions of mononuclear aromatic hydrocarbons are limited and are observed only for pyridine and its derivatives. Taylor and co-workers[32-35] as well as others[36,37] have reported dimerization reactions of 2-aminopyridines and pyridones, eqs. (9–10).

(9)

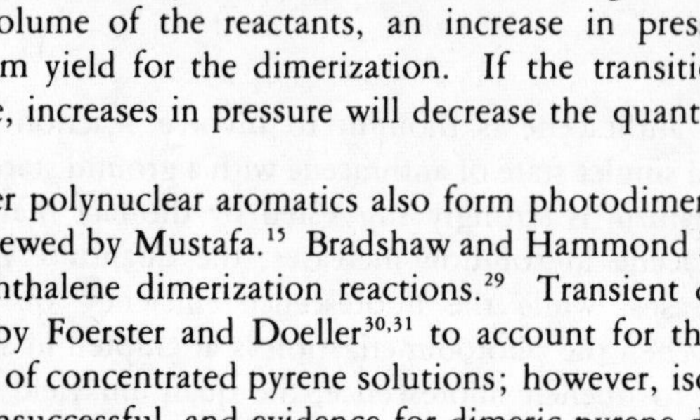

(10)

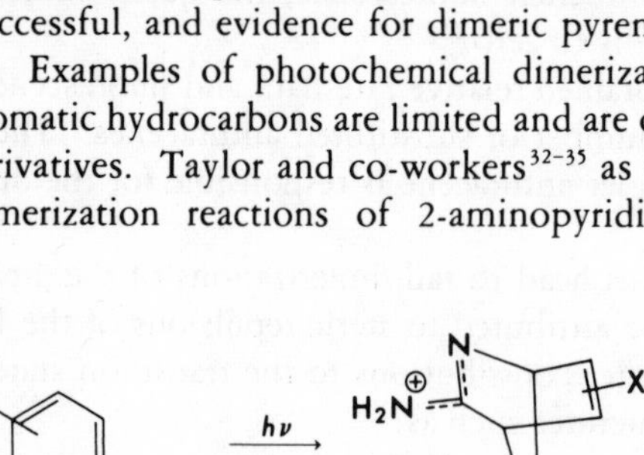

R = H, Me

Dimers have been obtained for a series of pyridines and for 2-pyridones including 2-aminopyridine, 2-amino-5-chloropyridine, 2-amino-3-methylpyridine, 4-methyl, 5-methyl and 6-methylpyridines, and N,6-dimethyl-2-iminopyridine. Irradiation of the pyridines and pyridones in hydrochloric acid solution gives a dimer to which a head to tail structure has been assigned on the basis of structural degradation and spectral evidence. Structure has been compared to the dimer of 2-pyridone to which the head to tail con-figuration was assigned previously.[38] De Mayo and Yip[39] report the forma-tion of three photodimers from the photolysis of 2,4-dimethylcoumalin in saturated benzene solution, eq. (11). The coumalin system represents the oxygen analog of 2-pyridone.

(11)

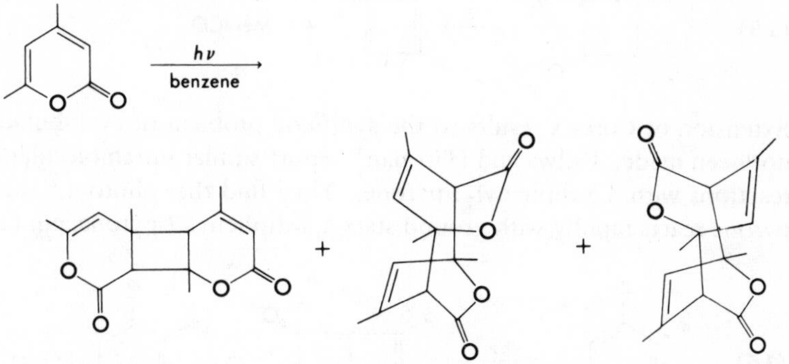

No mechanistic studies of the dimerization reactions of the above hetero-cycles and their derivatives have been reported. It might be assumed that π-π* singlet excitation is involved since the 2-pyridone, a ketone capable of n-π* excitation, and the pyridine hydrochloride, which is not capable of n-π* excitation, produce similar products. More evidence is required, how-ever, before the precise photochemical process can be determined.

Corey and co-workers[40] have observed intramolecular addition reactions with N-methyl-2-pyridone. 2-Pyrone behaves similarly and bicyclohexane-like derivatives are the resulting products. Corey prepared these photoaddi-tion products in an attempt to synthesize the elusive cyclobutadiene by using a nonpolar solvent (ether), eqs. (12–13). Mass spectrometric studies of both

(12)

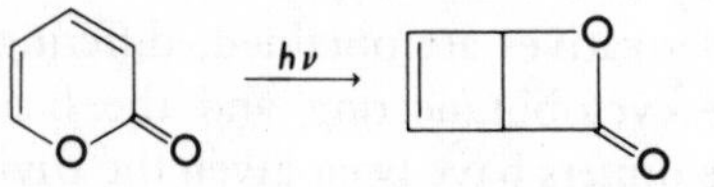

(13)

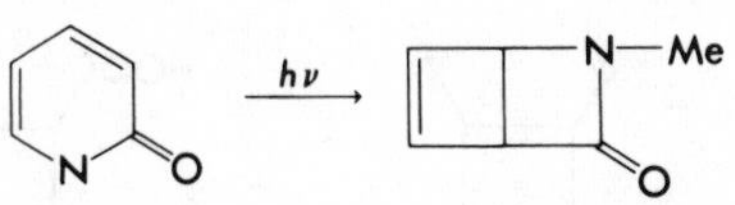

photoproducts show different fragmentation patterns. The photopyrone decarbonylates to yield furan-like fragments or open-chained derivatives analogous thereto, eq. (14),[41] whereas methyl isocyanate and a fragment corresponding to mass 52 (cyclobutadiene) are the predominant cracking modes of photopyridone, eq. (15).

(14)

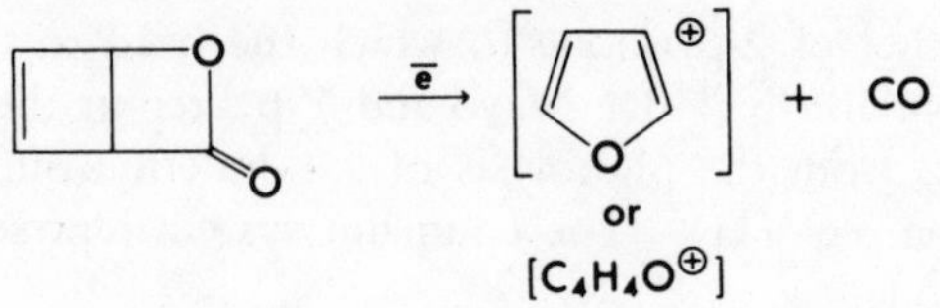

(15)

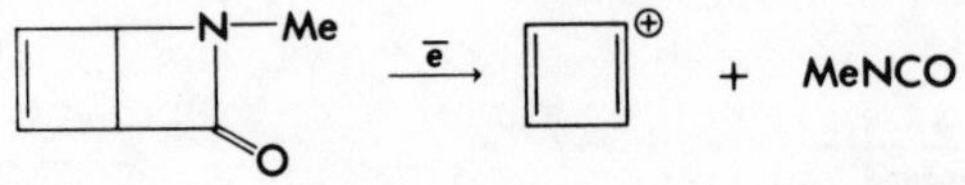

Extension of Corey's results to the synthetic problem of cyclobutadiene has not been made. Padwa and Hartman[42] report similar intramolecular addition reactions with 4,5-diphenyl-2-pyrone. They find that photo-4,5-diphenyl-2-pyrone reacts rapidly with ground state 4,5-diphenyl-2-pyrone, eq. (16).

(16)

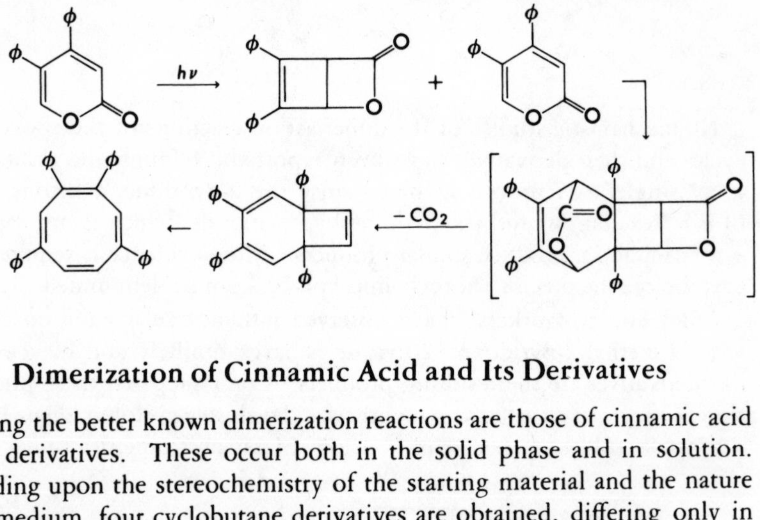

Dimerization of Cinnamic Acid and Its Derivatives

Among the better known dimerization reactions are those of cinnamic acid and its derivatives. These occur both in the solid phase and in solution. Depending upon the stereochemistry of the starting material and the nature of the medium, four cyclobutane derivatives are obtained, differing only in the stereochemical structure of the cyclobutane ring and the head to tail nature of the dimer, eq. (17). These dimers have been given the trivial names

(17) 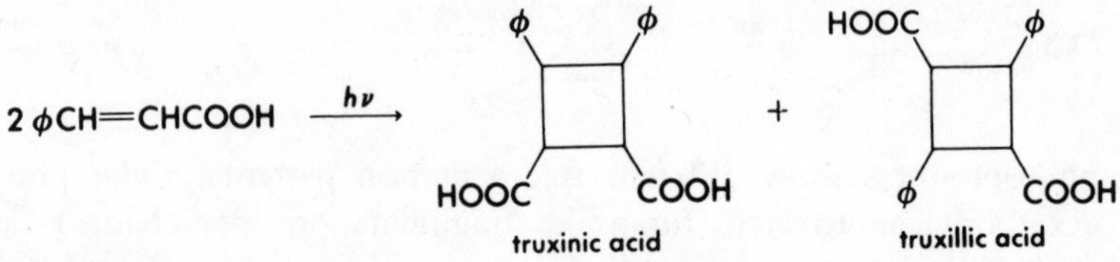 $2 \phi CH{=}CHCOOH \xrightarrow{h\nu}$

truxinic acid

truxillic acid

of truxinic and truxillic acids, truxinic being the head to head dimer, truxillic the head to tail dimer.[43,44] Table 6-2 lists some unsaturated aromatic deriva-

Table 6-2

Unsaturated Compounds Photochemically Forming Cyclobutane Dimers

Compound	Dimer	Reference
$C_6H_5CH=CHCH=C\begin{smallmatrix}CN\\C_6H_5\end{smallmatrix}$	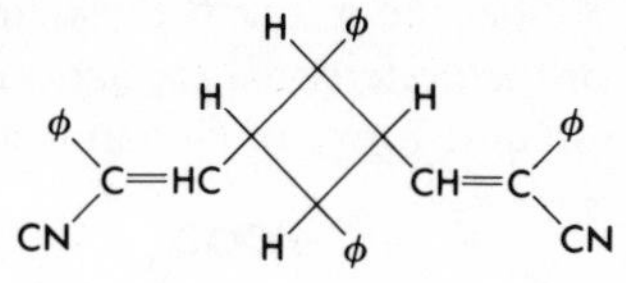	45, 46
$C_6H_5CH=CHCH=C\begin{smallmatrix}CN\\COOEt\end{smallmatrix}$	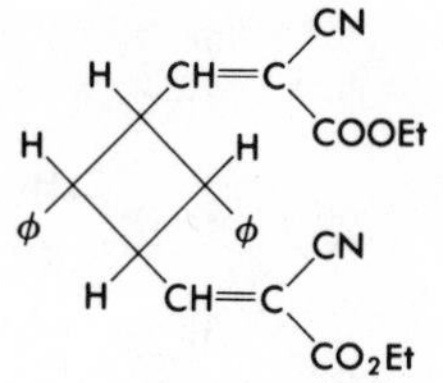	47
$C_6H_5CH=CHCH=CHCOC_6H_5$	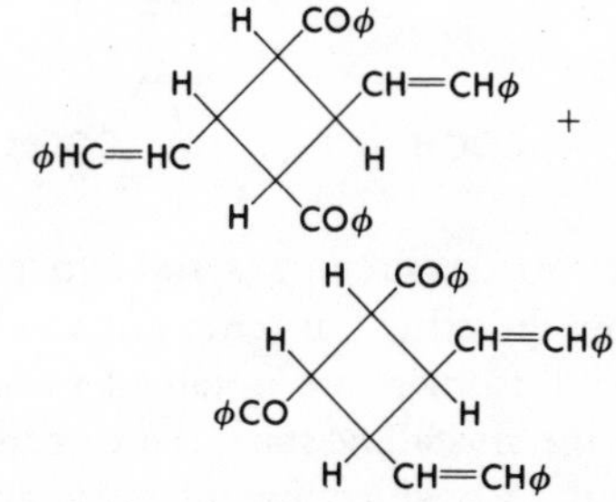 +	48, 49
$C_6H_5CH=CHCH=C(COOMe)_2$	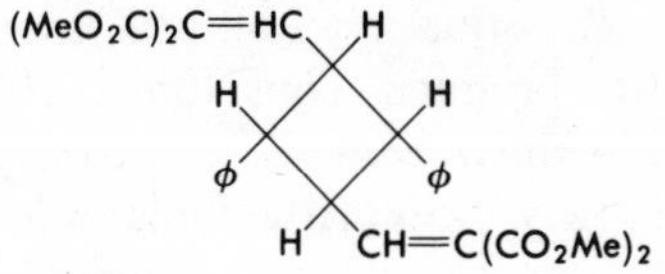	48, 50
$C_6H_5CH=CHCONHR$ $R = alkyl$	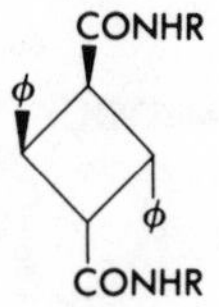	51
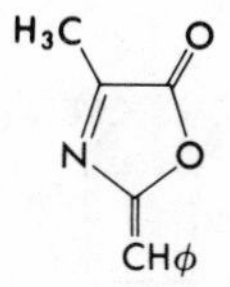	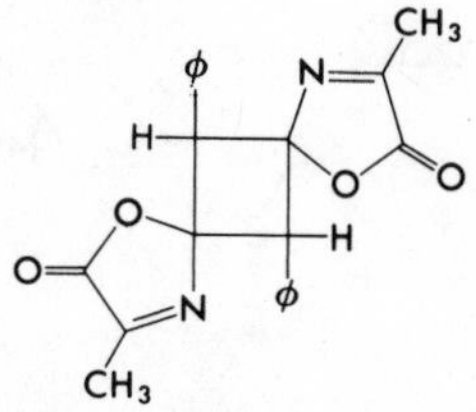	52

tives for which cyclobutane-like dimers have been obtained. A complete list of the early references has been reported by Mustafa.[15]

The solid state photodimerization of cinnamic acid and its derivatives has been investigated extensively. Schmidt has shown (by X-ray crystallography)[53,58-60,62-65] that the α and β crystalline modifications of *trans* cinnamic acid account for the preferential formation of α-truxillic and β-truxinic acids when these crystalline forms of cinnamic acid are photolyzed, eqs. (18–19).

(18)

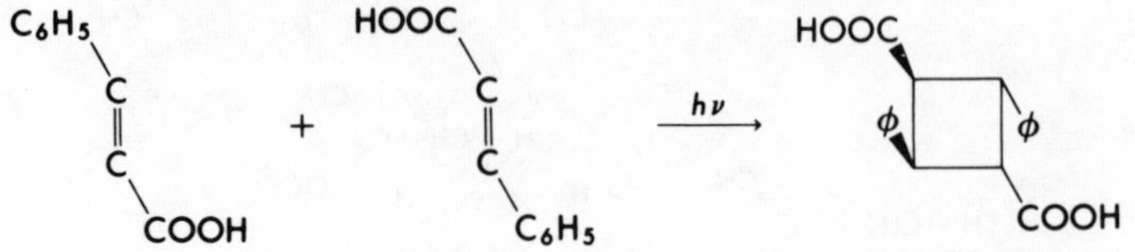

α-truxillic acid

(19)

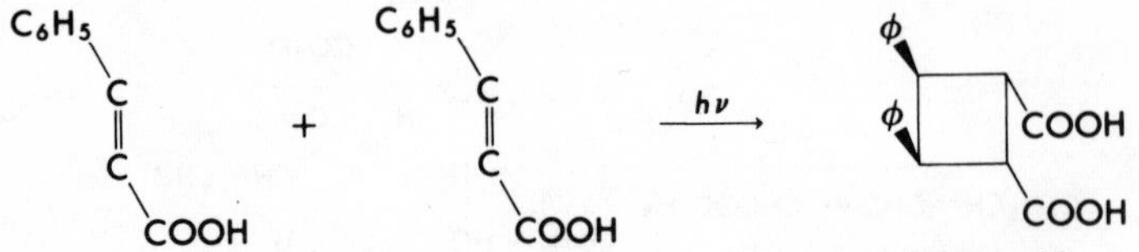

β-truxinic acid

Griffin and co-workers report crystal lattice control over the dimer structures obtained from dimethyl fumarate, fumaronitrile, and maleic anhydride. Since the least stable isomers are obtained generally when olefinic materials are irradiated in the crystalline state, these products must arise because of crystal lattice control. Consideration of polar and steric effects on the transition state for dimer formation leads to erroneous conclusions concerning the structure of the product. Thus, dimethyl fumarate yields but a single dimer, proposed to be the *cis-trans-cis* isomer from investigation of the crystal lattice structure, eq. (20).[54] Similarly, fumaronitrile produces a *cis-trans-cis* dimer, eq. (21).[55]

(20)

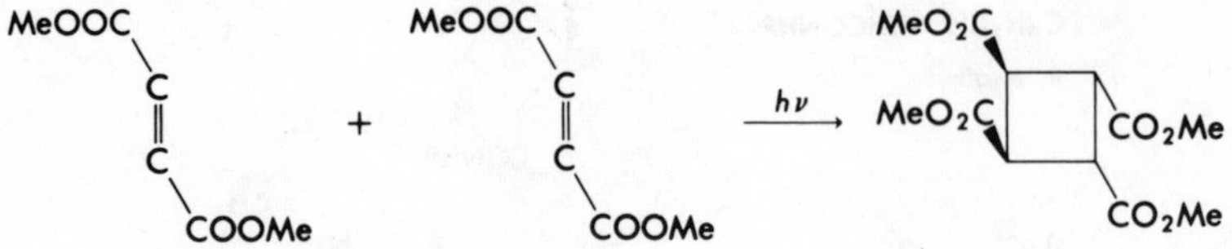

(21)

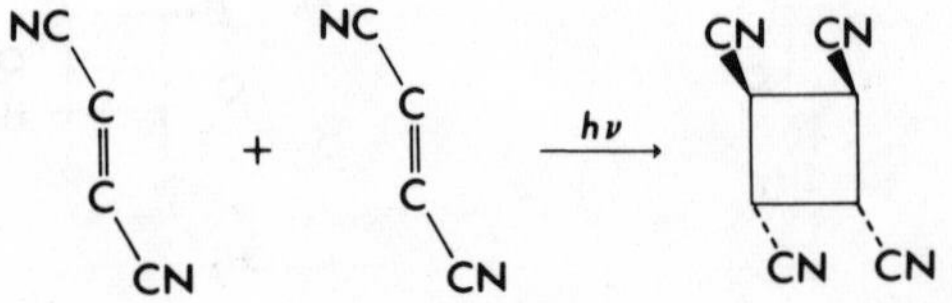

Photodimerization of maleic anhydride produces the *trans*-bis anhydride, eq. (22).[56,54]

(22)

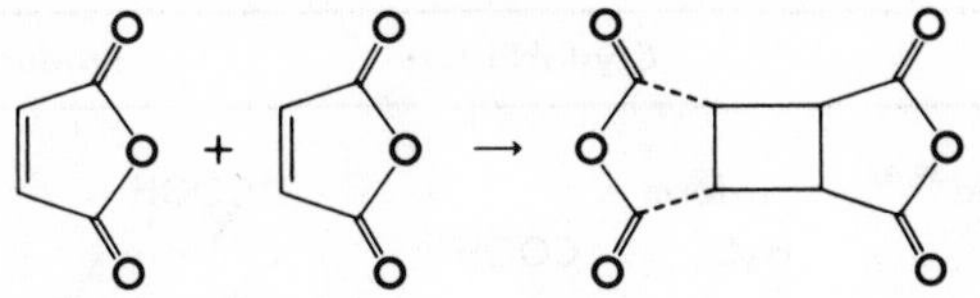

Photochemical dimerization of diethyl fumarate and of fumaronitrile produces the thermodynamically less stable dimer as determined by thermal equilibration experiments. A four center transition state involving the nearest neighbor carbon atoms in the crystal lattice of the olefinic material must account for the apparent nonthermodynamic reaction product control. Griffin has recently reported sensitizer evidence that would suggest, at least in some systems, that dimers are formed from the triplet excited state.[57] Relatively few excited state studies of direct irradiation dimerization reactions have been reported, however, and triplet state intermediates may or may not be involved in the majority of such reactions.

Topochemistry

Schmidt and co-workers[58-65] as well as others[66] have completed an elegant study of photochemical reactions in the solid phase. It is their thesis that "reaction in the solid state occurs with the minimum amount of atomic or molecular movement." They term this concern with crystal lattice geometry "topochemistry" and feel that in the crystalline state, all concern with electronic and steric effects and their contribution to transition state stabilization becomes somewhat less relevant. The importance of topochemical considerations is well illustrated by the results in Table 6-3 which demonstrate that in almost every case, the stereochemistry of the product may be predicted from the solid state structure.

The photochemical behavior of the *trans*-cinnamic acid derivatives is now well understood. In every investigated case, the crystal lattice geometry controls the structure of the dimer. *Cis*-cinnamic acids isomerize to *trans* derivatives and then cyclize. In 'addition, 2,5-dimethylbenzoquinone and 2,6-dimethyl-γ-pyrone also dimerize to give products controlled by the interatomic distance in the crystal lattice.

Photosensitized Dimerizations

It is clear that in solution the nature of the products obtained in dimerization reactions depends upon a variety of additional variables. By inference,

Table 6-3

Crystal Forms and Dimer Stereochemistry of Cinnamic Acids

Olefin	Crystal Picture	Product
trans-cinnamic acid[59,60]	α-form 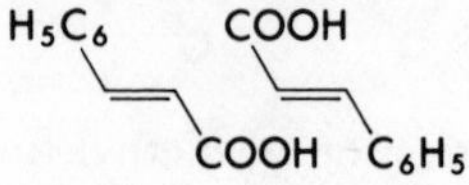	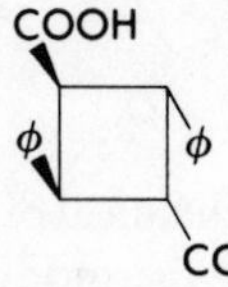
trans-cinnamic acid[59,60]	β-form 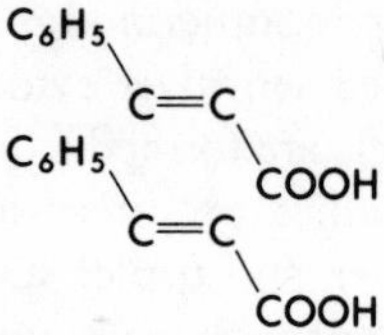	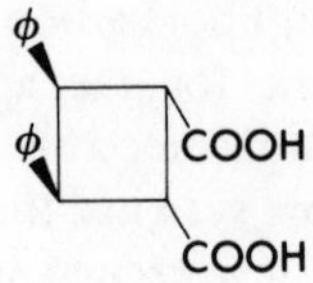
trans-2-alkoxy-cinnamic acid	α-form	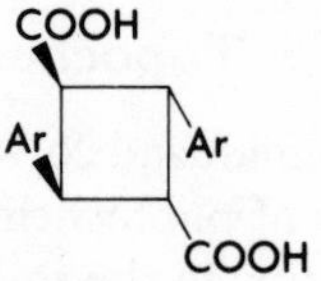
trans-2-alkoxy-5-bromo-cinnamic acid[59,60]	β-form	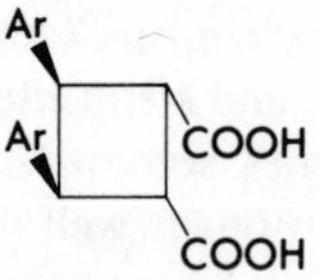
trans-m- or p-hydroxy-cinnamic acid[59,60]	α-form	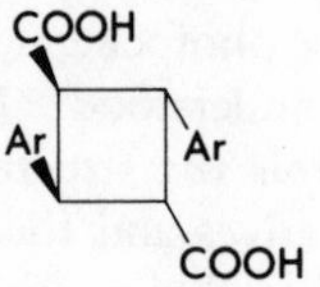
trans-o-, m-, or p-nitro-cinnamic acid[59,60]	β-form	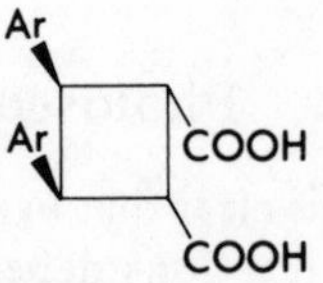

Table 6-3 (cont.)

Olefin	Crystal Picture	Product
trans-o-, m-, or *p*-halo-cinnamic acid [59,60]	β-form	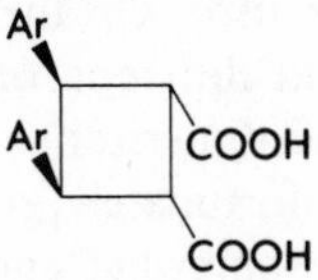
cis-o-, or *p*-halo-cinnamic acid [61]	α, and β-form	β-truxinic or α-truxillic acid derivative from the appropriate *trans* isomer
2,5-dimethyl-*p*-benzo-quinone [62]	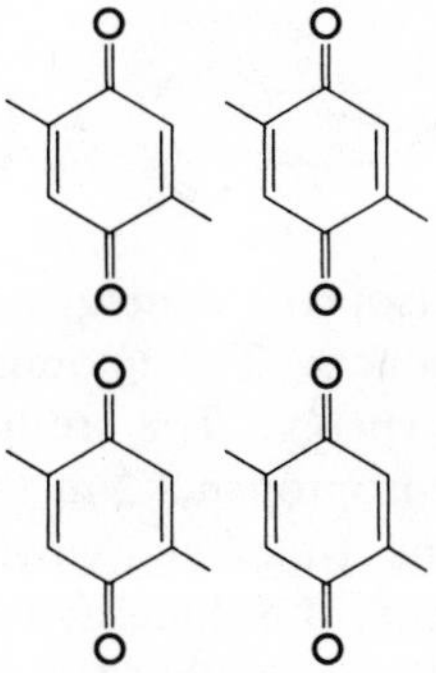	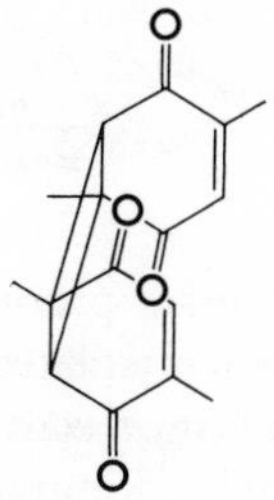
2,6-dimethyl-γ-pyrone [67]	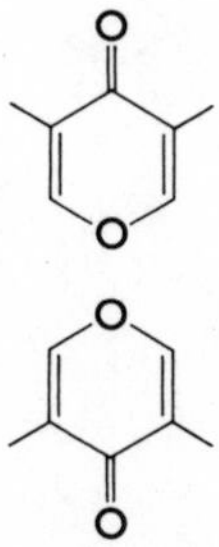	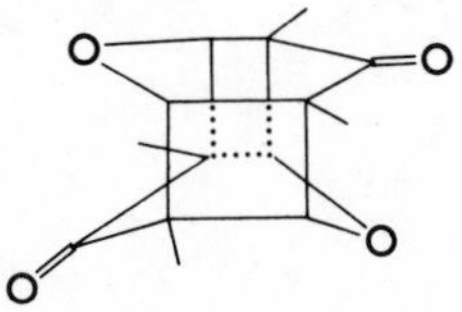

mechanisms for dimerization of olefinic substances are relatable to those proposed for an analogous photosensitized reaction since, if the products are the same in both the sensitized and direct irradiation processes, the reaction intermediates, spectroscopic and nonspectroscopic, are probably similar also. On the other hand, different products from the two processes demand different operative mechanisms. Mechanistic interpretations of olefinic dimerization reactions by comparison with energy transfer results are, unfortunately, somewhat tenuous since the mechanism of energy transfer is still somewhat uncertain. Experimentally, studies of the direct irradiation dimerization reactions of simple olefins and dienes are necessarily complicated by the fact that unsubstituted olefins and simple dienes absorb significantly only at very short wavelength spectral regions.

The photosensitized dimerization reactions of olefins and dienes have been extensively studied by Hammond and others.[68,69] The photodimer product distribution is affected by the triplet state energy of the photosensitizer. The sensitized photodimerization of butadiene, for example, produces three products, *trans*-1,2-divinylcyclobutane, *cis*-1,2-divinylcyclobutane, and 4-vinylcyclohexene, eq. (23). *Trans*-1,2-divinylcyclobutane is generally the

(23)

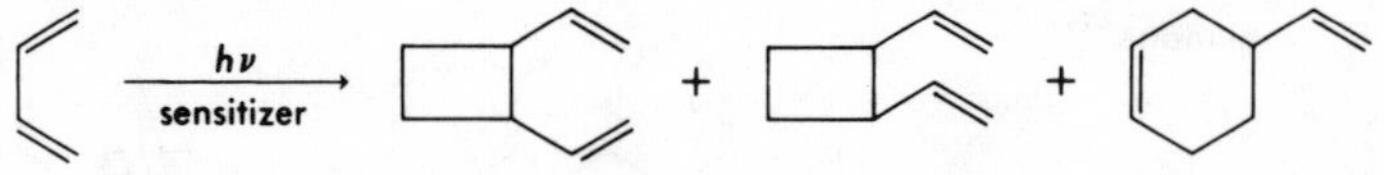

predominant product. Isoprene undergoes photosensitized dimerization to yield seven isolated products. The amounts of these products are also dependent upon sensitizer energy. The products identified are 1,2-divinyl-1,2-dimethylcyclobutane, 1-isopropenyl-2-methyl-2-vinylcyclobutane, *trans*-1,2-diisopropenylcyclobutane, 1-methyl-4-vinyl-4-methylcyclohexene, 1-methyl-4-isopropenylcyclohexene, 1,6-dimethylcyclooctadiene-1,5, 1,5-dimethyl-cyclooctadiene-1,4, and 1,5-dimethyl-5-vinylcyclohexene, eq. (24). Cyclo-

(24)

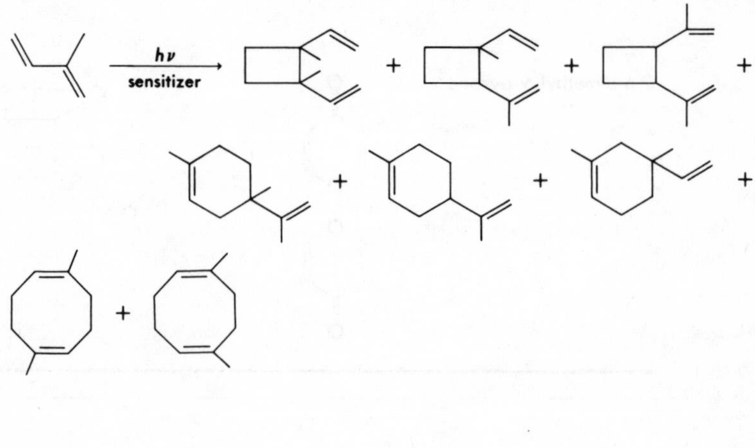

pentadiene undergoes a sensitized dimerization reaction yielding three products, *endo-* and *exo*-dicyclopentadiene and a tricyclo[3.3.0.0.]-decadiene, eq. (25).

(25)

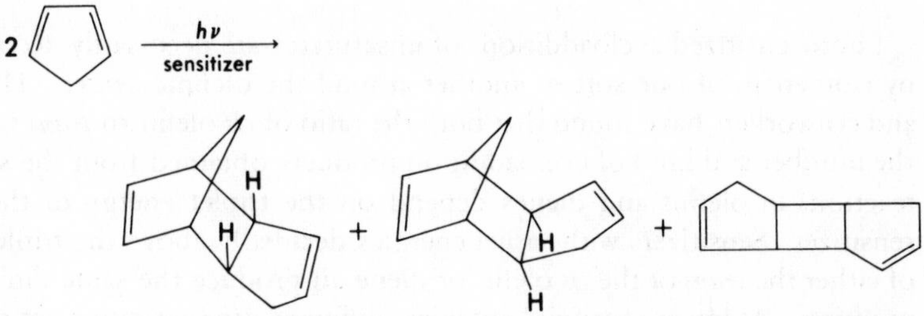

Mixtures of *cis* and *trans*-piperylene dimerized by energy transfer from a variety of sensitizers produces three products, *trans*-1,2-dipropenylcyclobutane, 1-methyl-*trans*-2-vinyl-3-propenylcyclobutane, and 1,2-dimethyl-*trans*-3,4-divinylcyclobutane, eq. (26). 2,3-Dimethylbutadiene produces a total of seven dimers, as yet uncharacterized, and norbornadiene undergoes

(26)

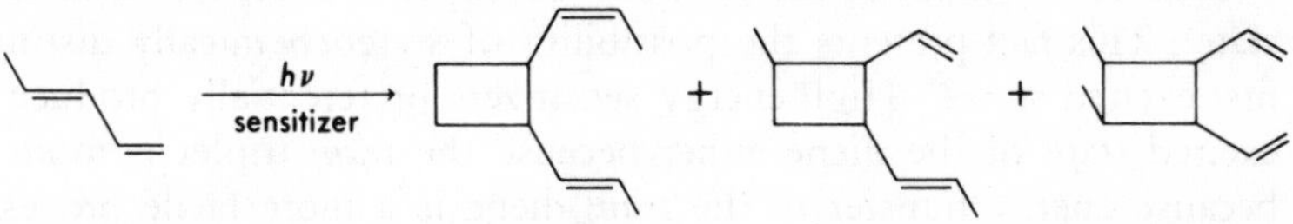

an intramolecular dimerization to yield quadricyclene, eq. (27).[68,69,112]

(27)

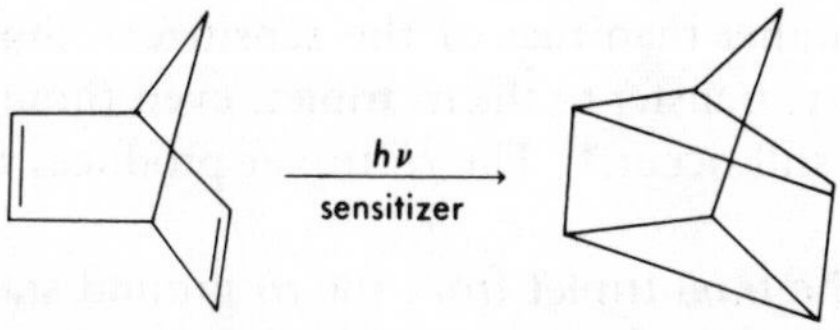

These results can be explained by a mechanism for triplet state energy transfer involving a spin conserved transfer of triplet energy from the donor molecule to the acceptor molecule. A triplet, higher energy state of the acceptor is thereby produced, while the donor molecule is deactivated to the ground state. This mechanism is shown for butadiene in eqs. (28–30).

(28) $\qquad\qquad\qquad S_{gr} \xrightarrow{h\nu} S' \rightarrow S^3$

(29) $S^3 + CH_2{=}CHCH{=}CH_2 \longrightarrow [CH_2{=}CHCH{=}CH_2]^3 + S_{gr}$
$\qquad\qquad\qquad\qquad\qquad\qquad\qquad\qquad A^3$

(30) A^3 + CH_2=$CHCH$=CH_2 $\longrightarrow$

$$\begin{array}{c} \overset{\bullet}{C}-C-C=CH_2 \\ | \\ \underset{\bullet}{C}-C-C=CH_2 \end{array} \quad \xrightarrow[\text{inversion}]{\text{spin}} \quad \text{coupling products}$$

Photosensitized cycloadditions of unsaturates are necessarily accompanied by isomerism of one sort or another around the olefinic center. Hammond and co-workers have found that both the ratio of *cis* olefin to *trans* olefin and the number and kind of cycloaddition products obtained from the sensitized reactions of olefins and dienes depend on the triplet energy of the photosensitizer. Sensitizers with triplet energies decidedly above the triplet energy of either the *trans* or the *cis* olefin or diene all produce the same dimerization products. At lower sensitizer energies, different product ratios are observed. In the dimerization of isoprene the greater quantities of cyclohexene products result when the triplet energy of the sensitizer is decreased. The cyclohexene products reach their highest absolute value when the triplet energy of the sensitizer exactly equals the triplet energy of the *cis* diene.

Hammond proposes that two or more processes are responsible for the variation in products with sensitizer energy. All of these processes result because rotation about the 2,3 bond of isoprene is restricted in the excited state. This fact presents the possibility of stereochemically distinguishable first excited states. High energy sensitizers preferentially produce the *trans* excited state of the diene either because the *trans* triplet is more stable or because energy transfer to the *trans* diene is a more facile process. *Trans* triplets selectively produce the cyclobutane and cyclooctane dimerization products. As the energy of the sensitizer is decreased, the possibility of energy transfer to form the *trans* triplet is also decreased because the triplet energy of the *trans* diene is higher than that of the sensitizer. Since the *cis* diene has a lower triplet energy, transfer to the *cis* triplet, even though a non-Franck-Condon process, can still occur.* The *cis* triplet produces the cyclohexene products.

The process of obtaining the *trans* triplet from the *cis* ground state or vice versa is one that formally violates the fundamental Franck-Condon principle. Photochemical excitations are so fast that nuclear motion during the processes is generally forbidden. It appears that the Franck-Condon principle is not so rigidly obeyed in energy transfer processes.

Miscellaneous Dimerizations

Olefins substituted with phenyl groups, nitro groups, or carbonyl groups may undergo similar photochemical addition reactions under conditions of

---

*This presumes that the ground state composition of the diene is predominantly *trans*.

direct irradiation, but the spectroscopic mechanisms for dimerizations of these compounds are, undoubtedly, quite different since n-π^* excitations become a possibility. Table 6-4 lists some examples of general compound types for which direct irradiation dimers have been observed.

Dimerization reactions of conjugated olefins involve π-π^* excitations of the conjugated olefinic chromophore. The excited multiple bond is free to

Table 6-4

Olefinic Materials that Undergo Photochemical Dimerization

Olefin	Dimer
α,β-unsaturated ketones and aldehydes	
quinones	
aromatic olefins	
carbon-heteroatom unsaturates	

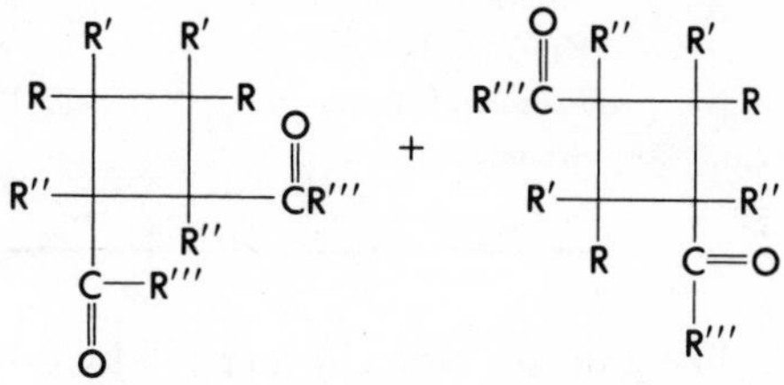

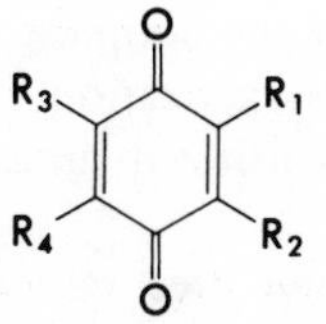

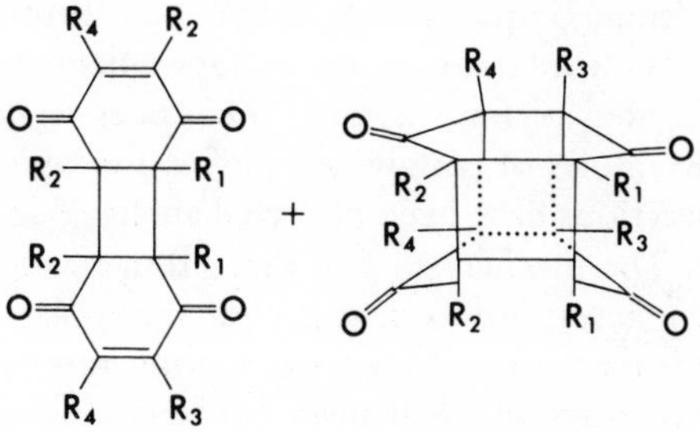

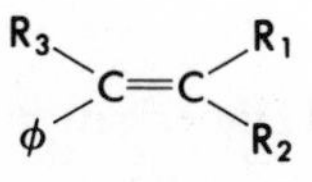

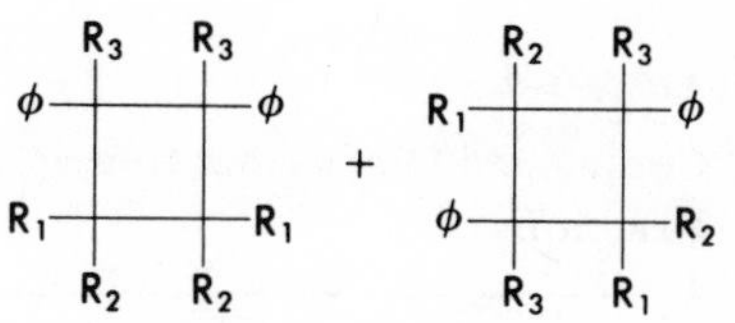

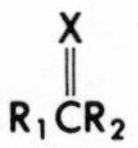

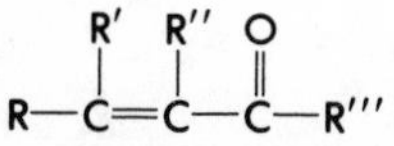

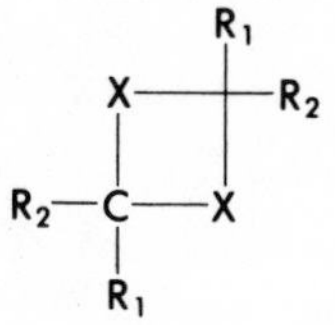

Table 6-4 (cont.)

Olefin	Dimer
$RC{\equiv}CR$ acetylenes	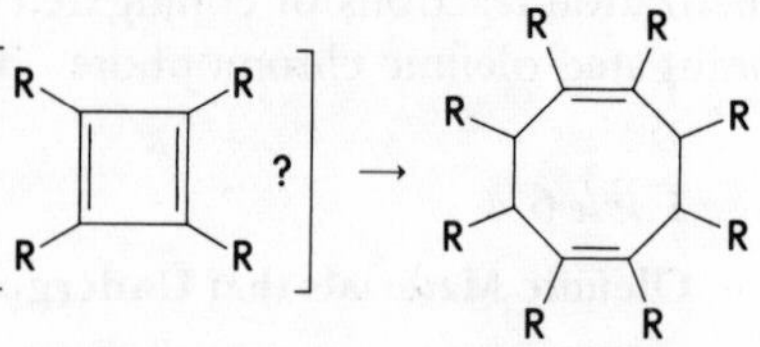
$R_1C{=}CNO_2$ with R_2, R substituents α,β-unsaturated nitro compounds	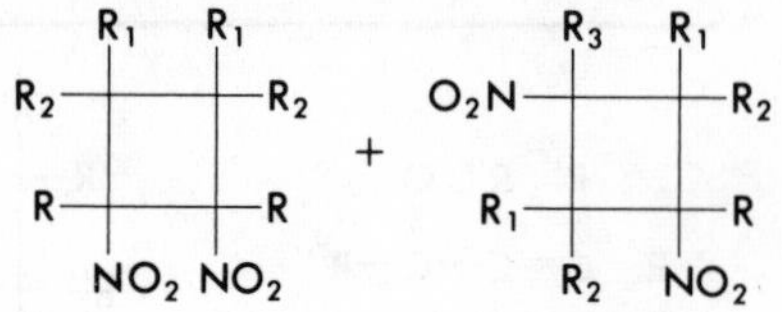

act like a di-free radical generated by other means. Free rotation about the carbon-carbon bond, addition to the carbon-carbon bonds of adjacent olefinic centers, and homolytic substitution of nearby aromatic nuclei are all feasible methods of excited state degradation. One of the simplest of conjugated olefins, styrene, undergoes a free radical polymerization reaction. Examples of conjugated olefins for which simple unsensitized dimerization reactions have been observed are listed in Table 6-5.

The mechanism for these dimerizations may involve free radical intermediates; however, it is clear that polar and steric effects play some role in the formation of products so ionic mechanisms are also possible. A dimerization reaction mechanism can be envisioned as in eqs. (31–33).

Table 6-5

Conjugated Olefins that Undergo Unsensitized Dimerization Reactions

Olefin	Dimer	Reference
acenaphthalene	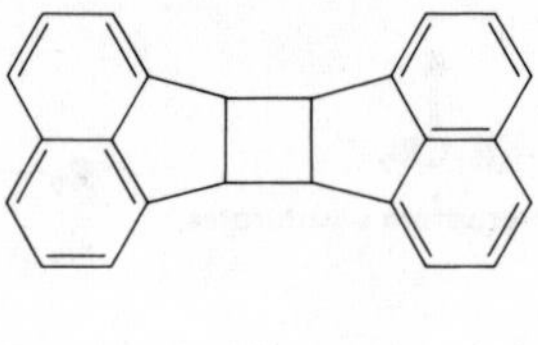	70, 79

Table 6-5 (*cont.*)

Olefin	Dimer	Reference
1,3-diphenylisobenzofuran	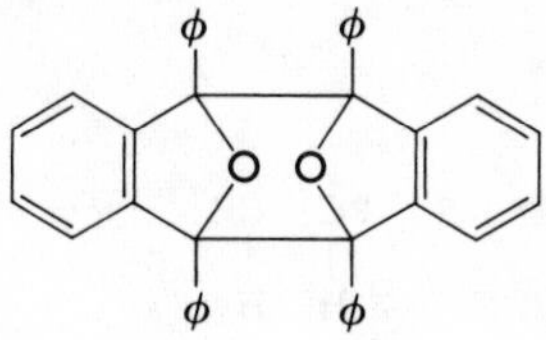	71
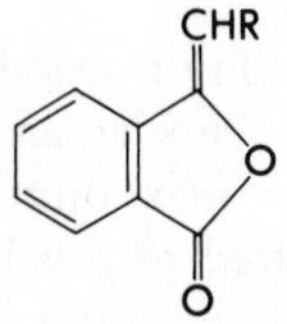	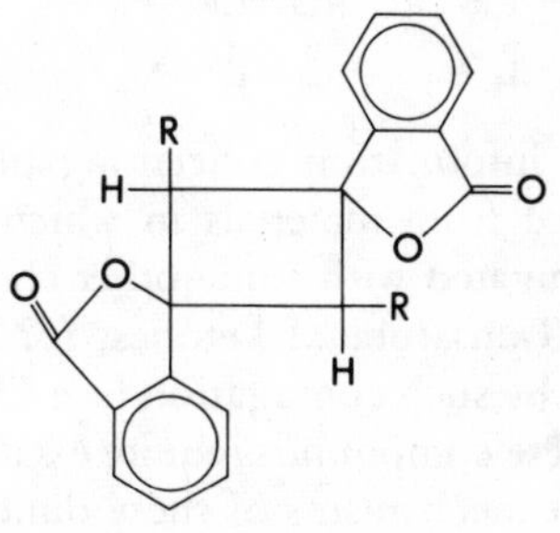	72, 75
stilbene and derivatives	tetraphenylcyclobutanes	73
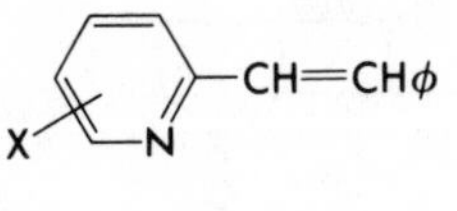	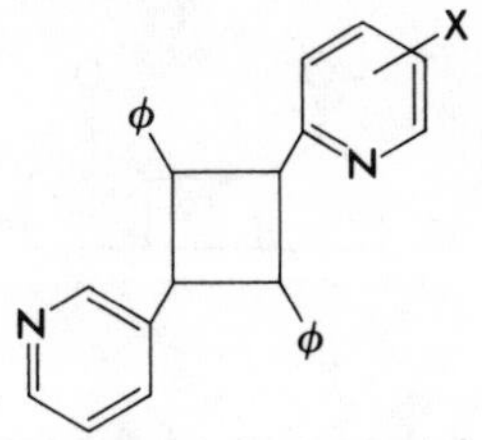	74, 76 77, 78
pyrene	none isolated	30, 31
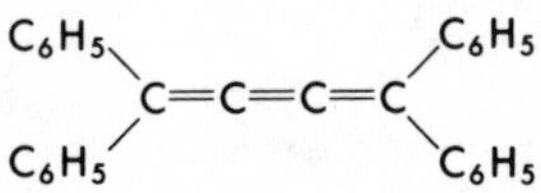	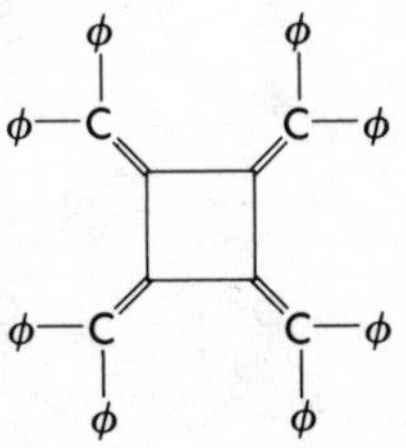	80

(31) 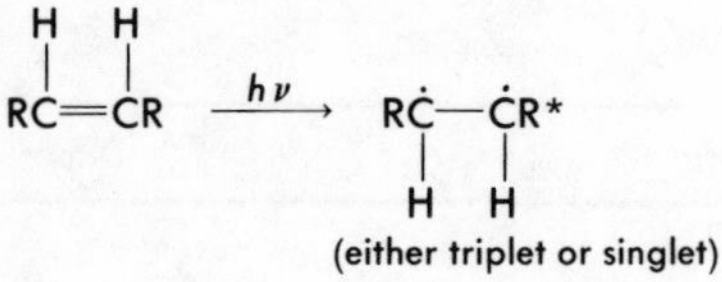
$$\underset{\substack{|\\H}}{RC}=\underset{\substack{|\\H}}{CR} \xrightarrow{h\nu} \underset{\substack{|\\H}}{R\dot{C}}-\underset{\substack{|\\H}}{\dot{C}R}*$$

(either triplet or singlet)

(32) 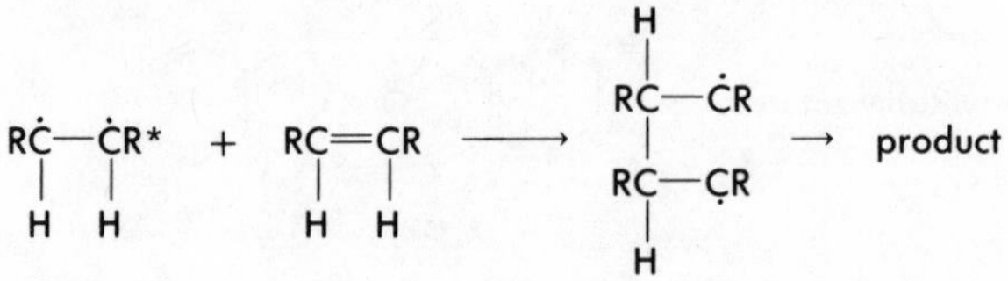
$$\underset{\substack{|\\H}}{R\dot{C}}-\underset{\substack{|\\H}}{\dot{C}R}* + \underset{\substack{|\\H}}{RC}=\underset{\substack{|\\H}}{CR} \longrightarrow \begin{matrix} \underset{\substack{|\\H}}{RC}-\dot{C}R \\ \underset{\substack{|\\H}}{RC}-\dot{C}R \end{matrix} \longrightarrow product$$

(33) 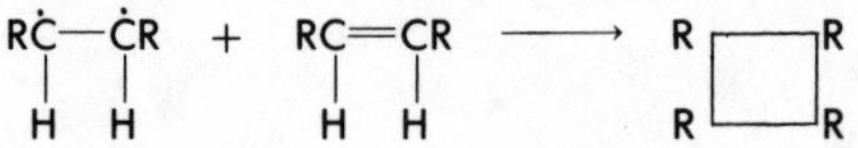
$$\underset{\substack{|\\H}}{R\dot{C}}-\underset{\substack{|\\H}}{\dot{C}R} + \underset{\substack{|\\H}}{RC}=\underset{\substack{|\\H}}{CR} \longrightarrow \begin{matrix} R \;\square\; R \\ R \;\;\; R \end{matrix}$$

Important information concerning photochemical addition reactions has been obtained from materials in which dimerization occurs at an olefinic linkage conjugated with some other chromophore. The maximum absorption of α-, β-unsaturated ketones, for example, is shifted to much longer wavelengths by such conjugation (see Chapter 3), and dimerization reactions involving these compounds require excitation energy of longer wavelengths. Although the mechanisms of these dimerizations in solution is still far from clear, Eaton[81,82] has observed that equal quantities of head to head and head to tail dimers are formed from the photochemical dimerization of cyclopentenone, eq. (34).

(34)

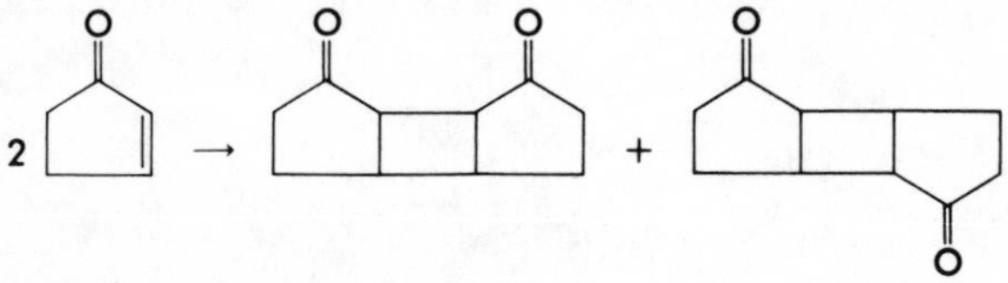

Diradical and dipolar forms of the intermediate excited state are shown in eq. (35). Addition of the intermediate, eq. (35), to ground state cyclopentenone, eq. (36), leads to both the head to head and head to tail dimer

(35)

or

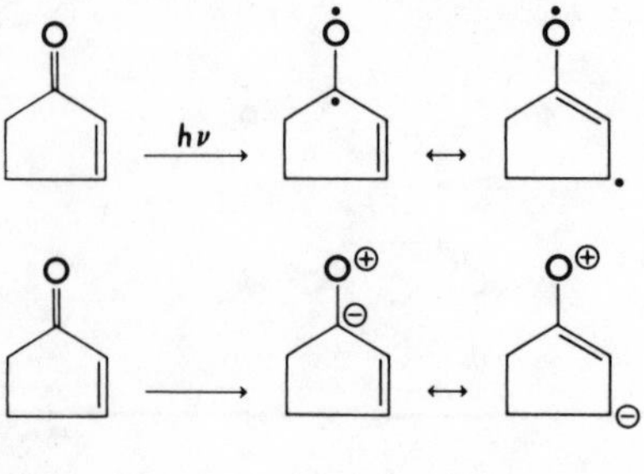

(36)

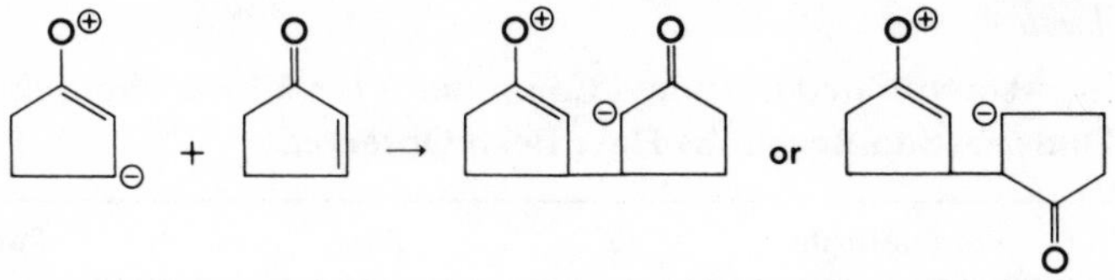

intermediate. In either a concerted or stepwise pathway, the intermediate leading to head to head dimerization would be expected to be preferred over that leading to head to tail dimerization because of the adjacent electron-withdrawing carbonyl group in the intermediate. Since this predicted polar preference is not observed, polar contributions from ground state cyclopentenone must be unimportant. In addition, cyclopentenone sensitizes photochemical reactions in a manner similar to benzophenone and acetophenone so that the dimerization reaction may utilize triplet state intermediates.

Many examples of dimerizations of α, β-unsaturated carbonyl compounds have been observed, and an early review can be found in Mustafa.[14] Since many of the structures reported were determined without the advantage of instrumental techniques, most of these reactions probably need to be re-examined. Schönberg's treatise[83] adds some examples as does that of de Mayo.[84] Table 6-6 lists some of the more recent examples of dimerization reactions of α, β-unsaturated carbonyl compounds.

Photochemical dimerization reactions have occasionally provided useful entrances into novel carbon skeletal systems. The photodimerization of certain p-quinones, for example, occurs either in solution or in the solid phase. Conversion of 2,3-dimethyl-p-benzoquinone to 2,5-dimethyl-p-benzoquinone is readily accomplished by a photodimerization of a p-benzoquinone and thermal cleavage of the dimeric adduct, eqs. (37) and (38).[103]

(37)

(38)

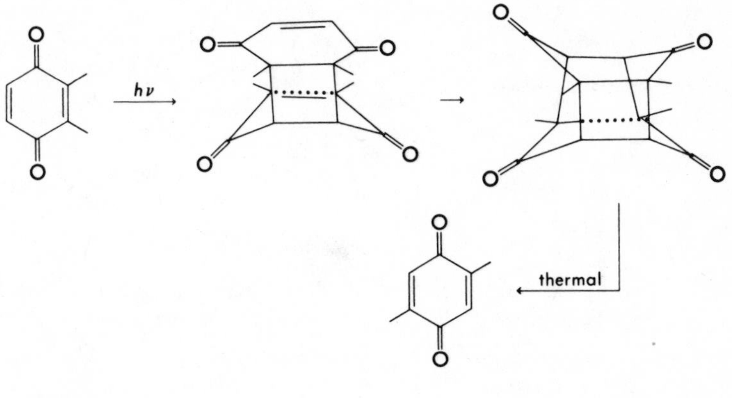

Table 6-6

α-, β-Unsaturated Carbonyl Compounds for Which Photochemical Dimerization Reactions Have Been Observed[a]

Substrate	Dimer	Reference
2-acetostyrene	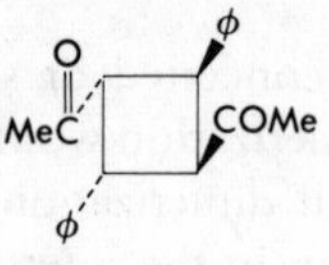	85
2,6-dimethyl-4-pyrone	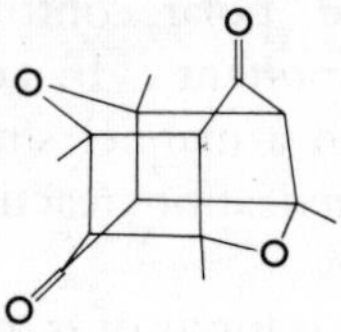	86, 87
distyrylketone	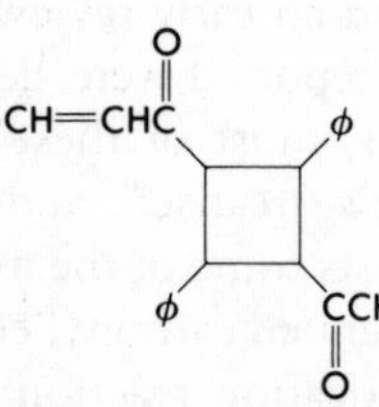	89
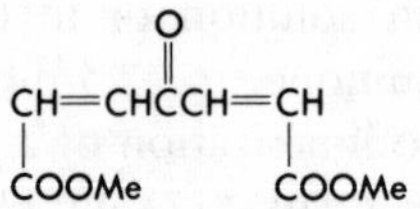	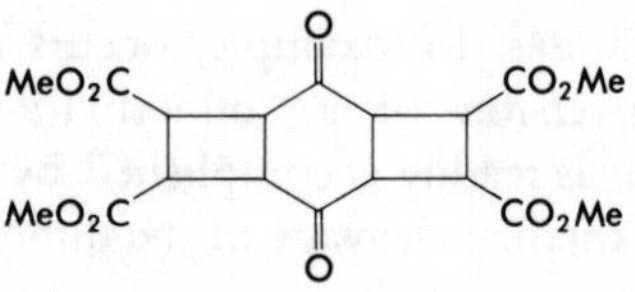	88
4-methyl-2-pyridone	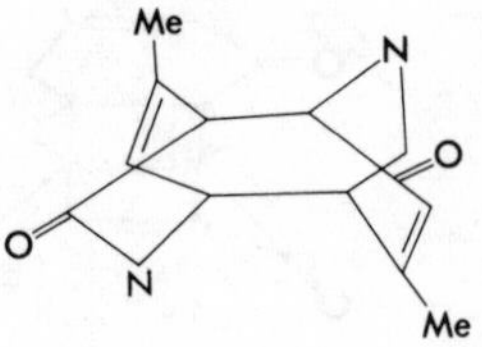	38
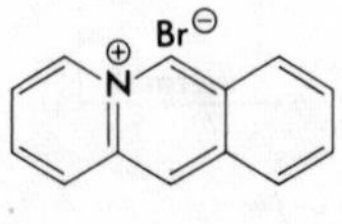	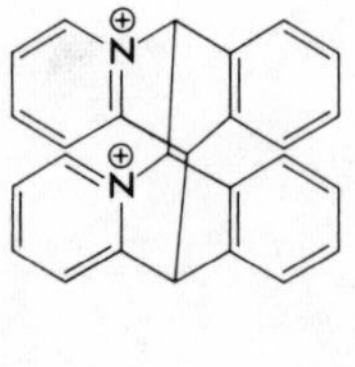	90

Table 6-6 (cont.)

Substrate	Dimer	Reference
colchicine	colchicine dimer (α-lumicolchicine)	91
2-pyridone	dimer	37
N-methyl-2-pyridone	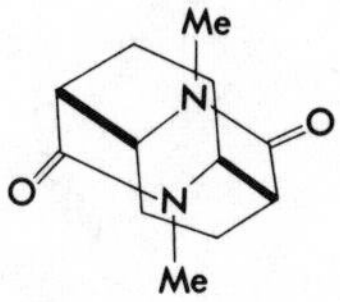	92
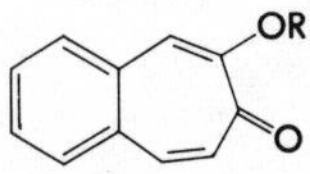	several	93
coumarin	several	94, 95, 96
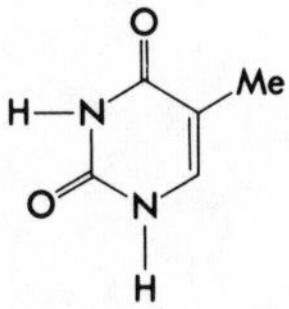	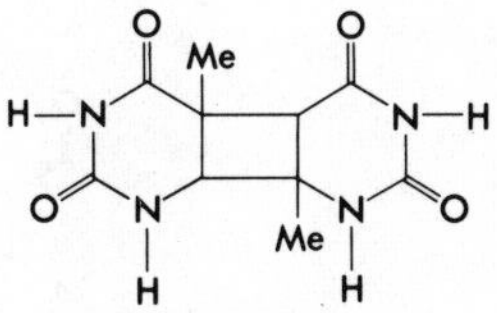	97, 107, 98
β-nitrostyrene	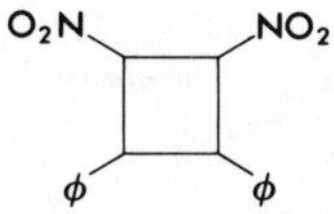	99
2-nitro-1,4-dithianaphthalene	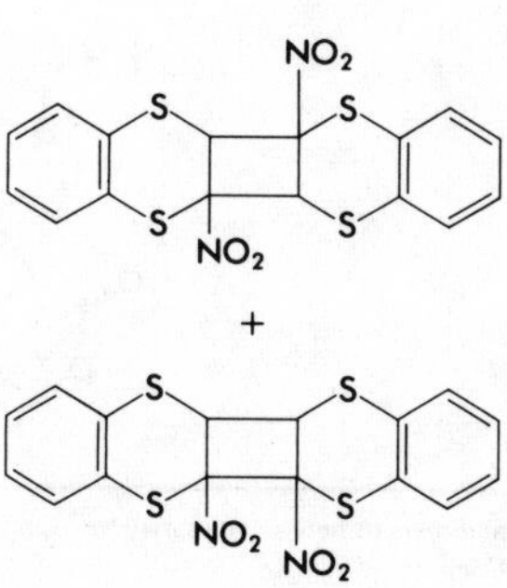	100

Table 6-6 (cont.)

Substrate	Dimer	Reference
benzoquinone	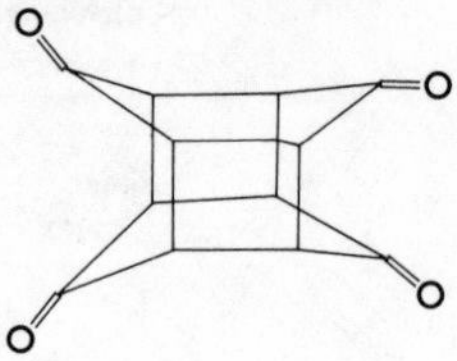	101
thymoquinone	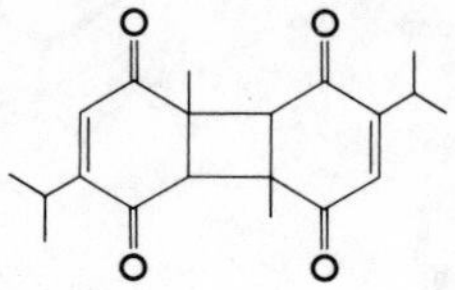	102
2,3-dimethylbenzoquinone	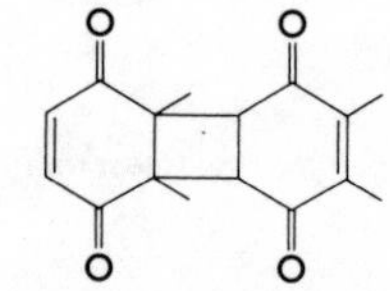 + 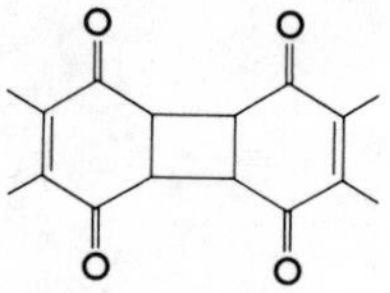	103, 108
2,3-dialkylbenzoquinones	dimers	104, 105
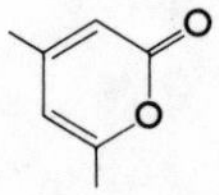	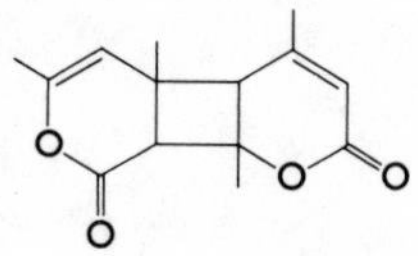 + 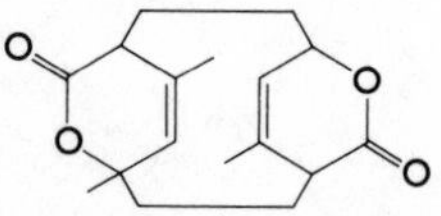	106

[a]Additional dimers of heterocycles may be found in A. Mustafa, *Advances in Photochemistry*, Vol. II, New York, Wiley, 1964.

De Mayo and co-workers[109] have observed what appears to be a photochemical dimerization of an enol. Photolysis of dibenzoylmethane gives a cyclobutane dimer derived from the enol, eq. (39). Additionally, application of photochemical dimerization sequences to a perplexing synthetic problem

(39)

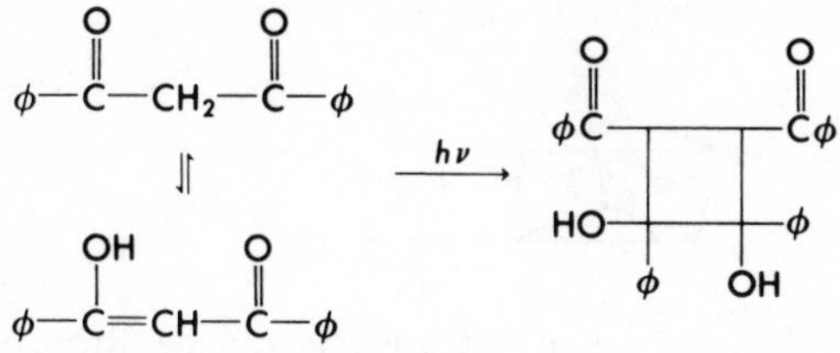

has been made by Eaton in his synthesis of cubane.[110,111] Photolysis of the spontaneously formed Diels-Alder adduct of 2-bromocyclopentadienone provided the cubane nucleus, eq. (40), from which cubane was prepared in

(40)

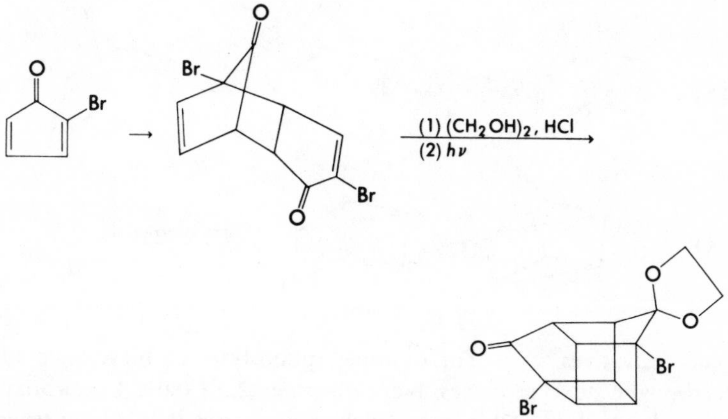

good yield by successive hydrolyses, Favorskii cyclizations, peresterifications, and decarboxylations, eq. (41).

(41)

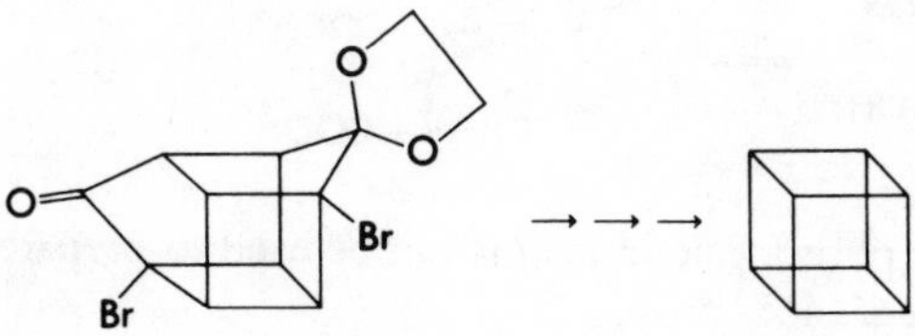

Intramolecular Photoadditions

Some of the most interesting examples of addition reactions initiated by light quanta occur intramolecularly. Of these the intramolecular addition reaction resulting in the formation of quadricyclene from norbornadiene,

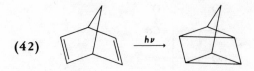

(42)

eq. (42),[112] is an unusual example. Since this reaction can be photosensitized by ordinary triplet state sensitizers such as benzophenone and acetophenone,[113] triplet state intermediates of the olefinic bond are presumed to be involved in the formation of the quadricyclene, and the following mechanism for its formation can be written as in eqs. (43) and (44). Cristol has observed a similar intramolecular photoaddition reaction of bicyclohepta-

(43)

(44)

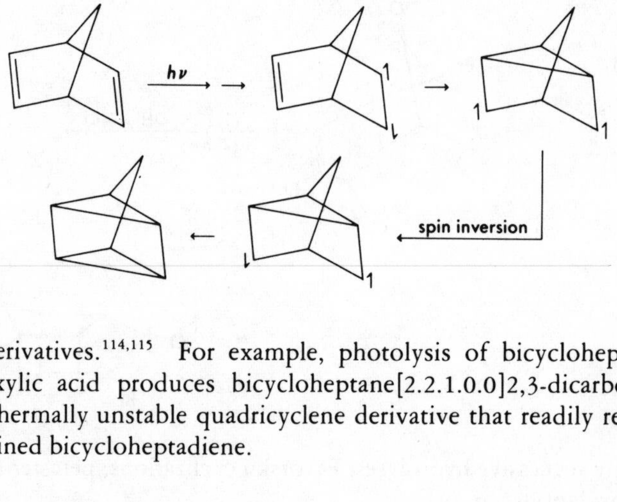

diene derivatives.[114,115] For example, photolysis of bicycloheptadiene-2,3-dicarboxylic acid produces bicycloheptane[2.2.1.0.0]2,3-dicarboxylate, eq. (45), a thermally unstable quadricyclene derivative that readily reverts to the less-strained bicycloheptadiene.

(45)

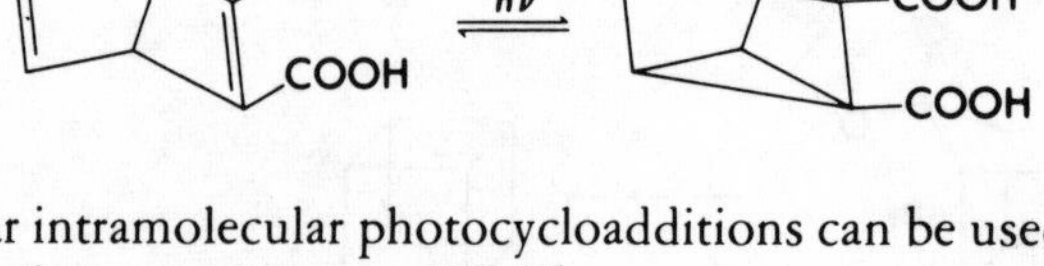

Similar intramolecular photocycloadditions can be used to prepare carvone camphor from carvone, eq. (46).[116]

(46)

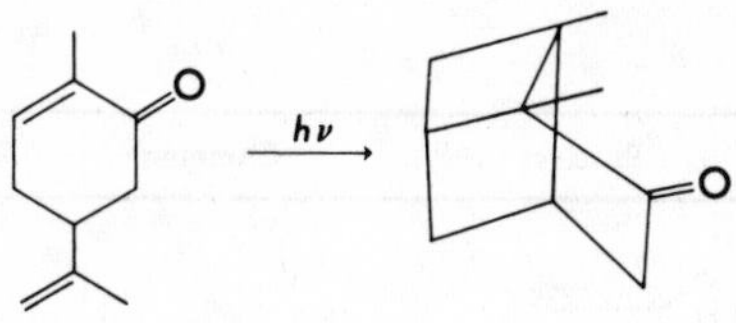

Other observed photointramolecular addition reactions are summarized in Table 6-7.

Intramolecular photoadditions need not involve the addition of both ends of but one double bond. These additions may take place across a conjugated system such as in a diene or triene with a cyclic system of more than three or four members resulting. These additions, recently called *electrocyclic* by Woodward and Hoffman,[130] sometimes take place in a stereospecific fashion, eq. (47).[131,132] Electrocyclic reactions of this type owe their stereospecificity

(47)

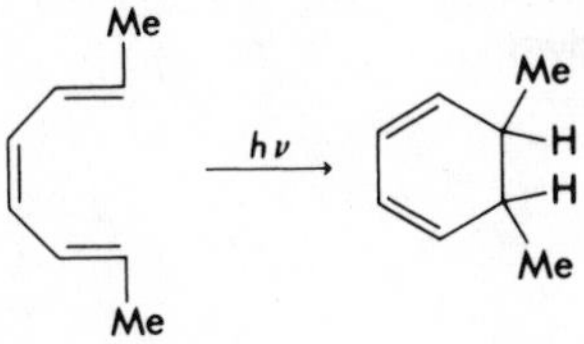

to the necessity for overlap of like orbital lobes in the formation of the carbon-carbon single bond. With photochemical processes, stereospecificity

Table 6-7

Intramolecular Photochemical Addition Reactions[a]

Olefin	Product	Comment	Reference
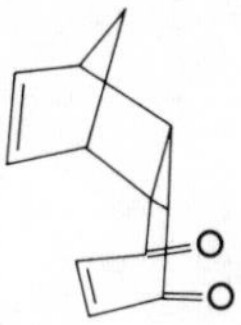	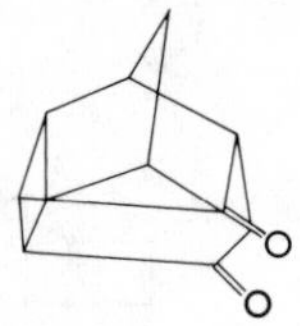		117
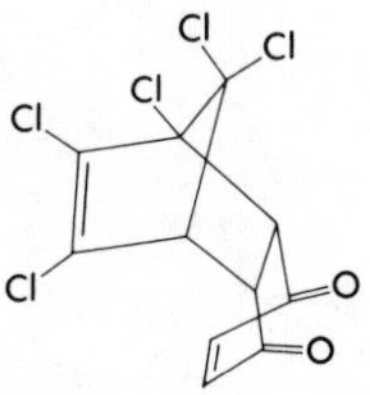	similar adduct (cage product)		117

Table 6-7 (*cont.*)

Olefin	Product	Comment	Reference
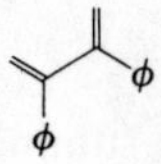	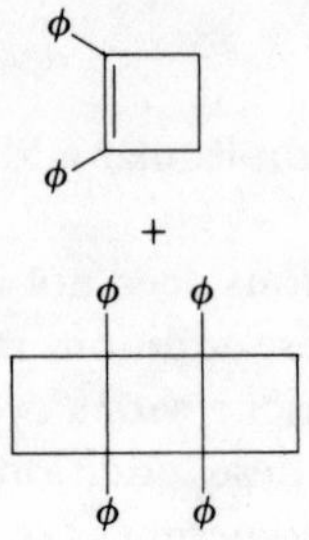		118
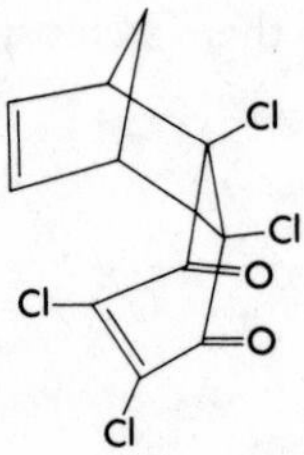	similar adduct (cage product)		117
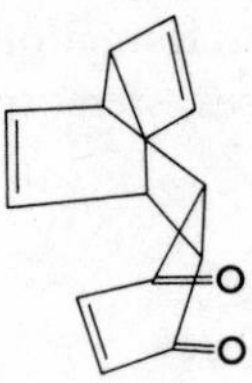	similar adduct (cage product)		117
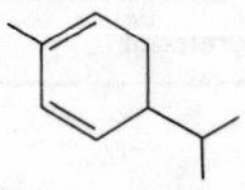	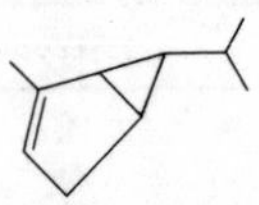		119, 120
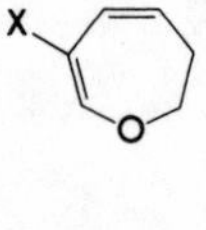	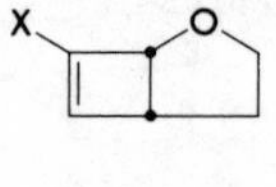		121
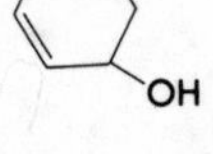	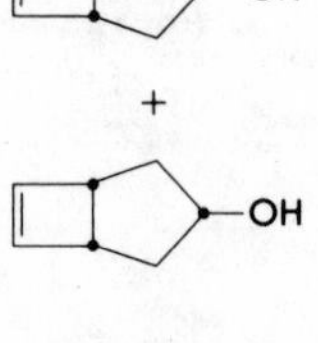		122

Table 6-7 (*cont.*)

Olefin	Product	Comment	Reference
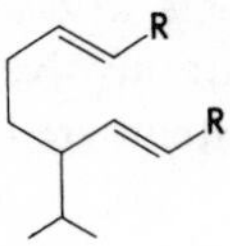	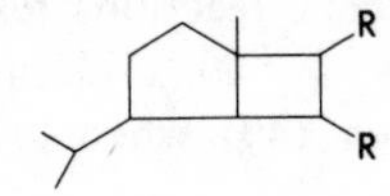		123
1,5-hexadiene	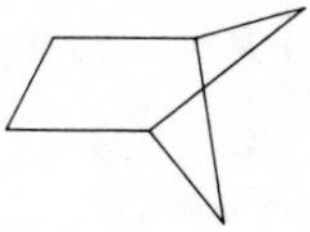	Hg sensitized	124
	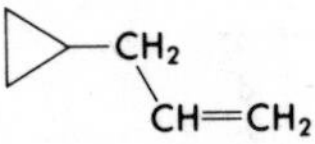		
1,5-cyclooctadiene	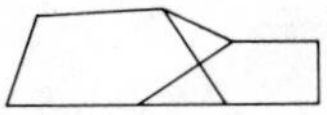	Hg sensitized	125
1,3,5-3,8-dimethyloctatriene	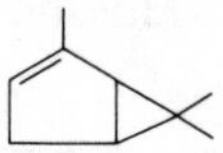		126, 127
isodrin	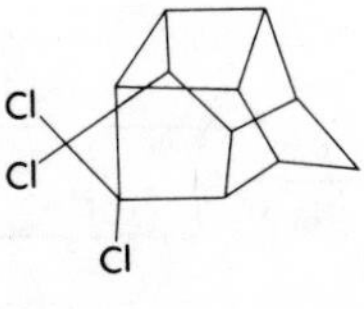		128
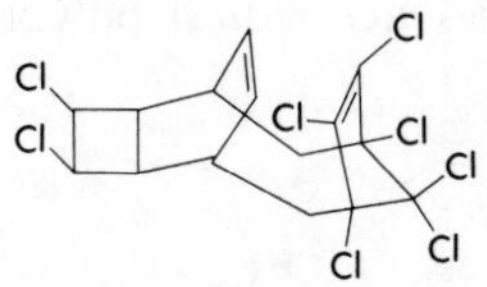	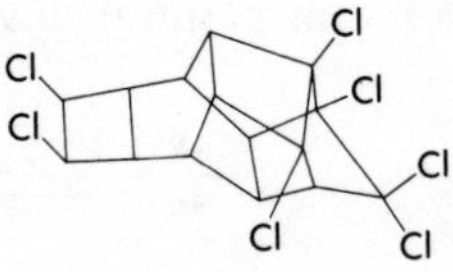		129

[a]Earlier references can be found in J. Meinwald, *Record Chem. Progress*, 22, 39 (1961). Earlier reviews of photocyclizations of this type may be found in O. L. Chapman, *Advances in Photochemistry*, Vol. I, New York, Wiley, 1963.

results, presumably, from the same orbital overlap necessity, but complicating factors of photochemical reactions such as multiple excited states and possibility for molecular dissociation prevent a uniquely accurate description of the nature of each reacting state. Be that as it may, Woodward and Hoffman propose that electrocyclic reactions result in products *disrotatory*, eq. (48), when conjugated $(4n + 2)$ π electron systems are involved in the cyclization and *conrotatory*, eq. (49), when $4n$ π electron systems are involved.

(48)

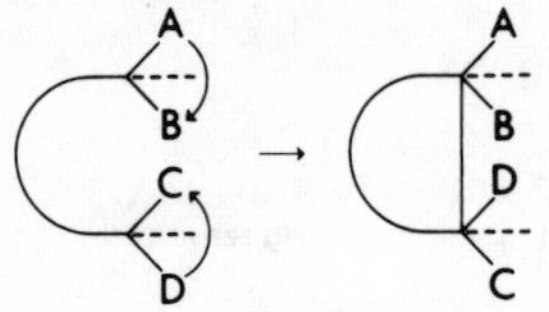

$(4n + 2)$ π electrons—disrotatory

(49)

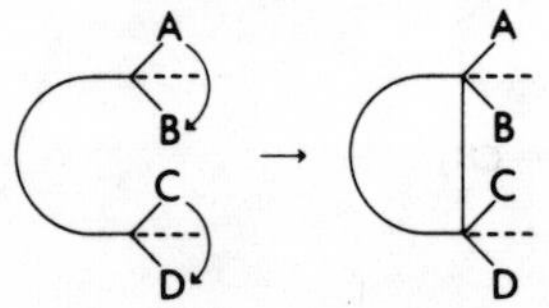

$4n$ π electrons—conrotatory

The mercury-sensitized preference of 1,5 internal rather than 1,6 internal addition to olefinic bonds in diene and triene systems[125,126,119] illustrates another type intramolecular photoaddition reaction, eqs. (50) and (51).

(50)

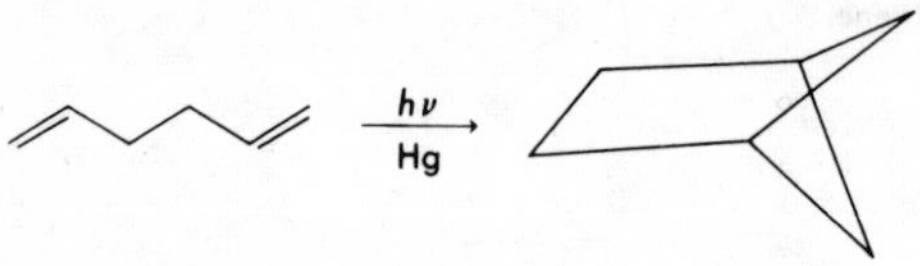

rather than

(51)

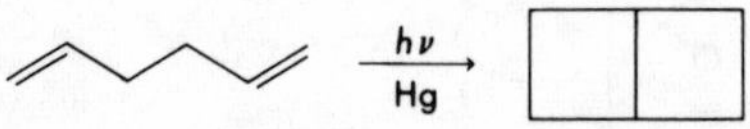

With 1,6 heptadiene, Srinivasan and Hill find four products of ring closure although the major reaction pathway involves free radical polymerization, eq. (52).[133]

(52)

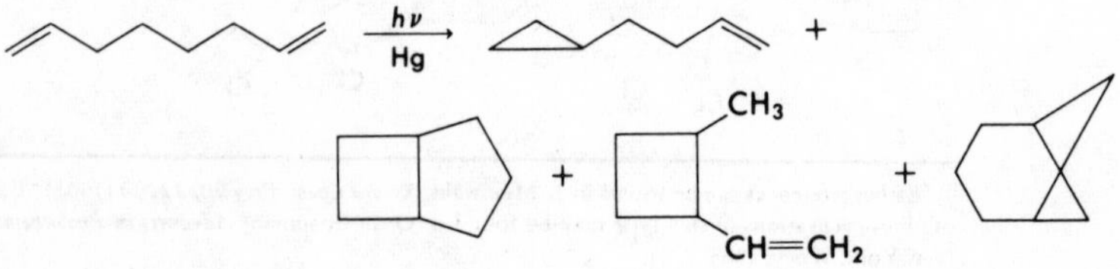

Baldwin and Greely[134] have observed a similar product from 3-deutero-1,5-cyclooctadiene when the photolysis was performed in solution in the presence of cuprous chloride, eq. (53). Srinivasan[124] also reports that the

(53) 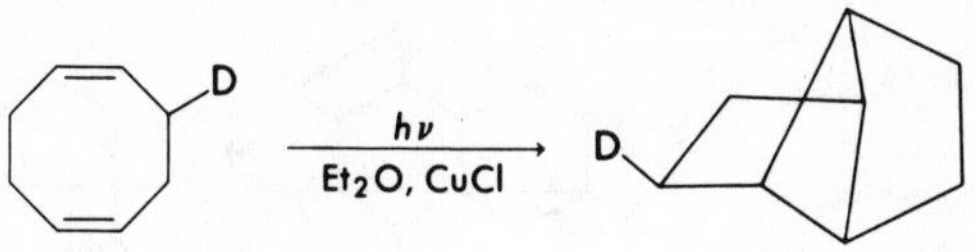
$$\xrightarrow[\text{Et}_2\text{O, CuCl}]{h\nu}$$

mercury-sensitized photolysis of 1,5-cyclooctadiene produces a strikingly unique tricyclooctane, eq. (54).

(54) 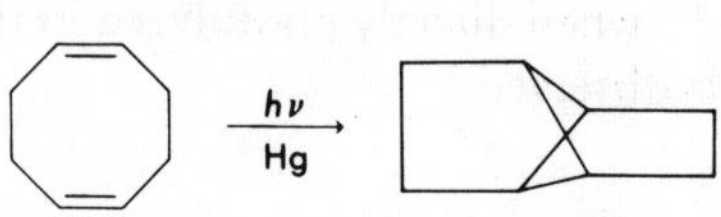
$$\xrightarrow[\text{Hg}]{h\nu}$$

One of the very useful and interesting aspects of photochemical reactions can be illustrated by some intramolecular photoaddition reactions. The versatility of photochemical methods provides the organic chemist with a practical tool for the synthesis of unusual compounds. Winstein and Zwiner[135] as well as Roth and Pelyer[136] have reported very unusual products from the photolysis of 1,3,5-cyclooctatriene, eq. (55), and 1,3,6-cyclo-

(55) 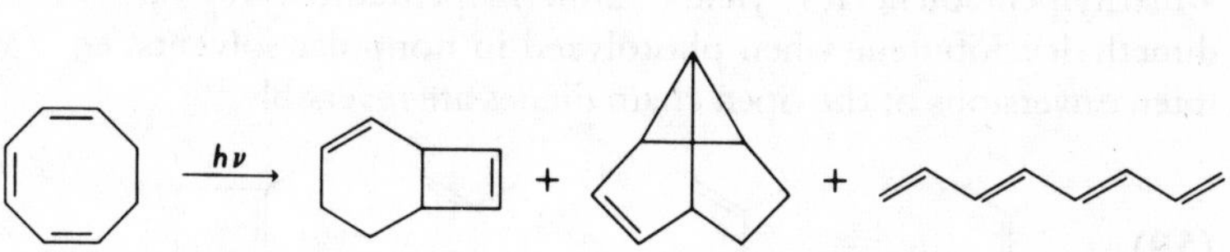
$$\xrightarrow{h\nu}$$

octatriene, eq. (56). We pity the poor organic chemist who would have to prepare such a variety any other way.

(56) 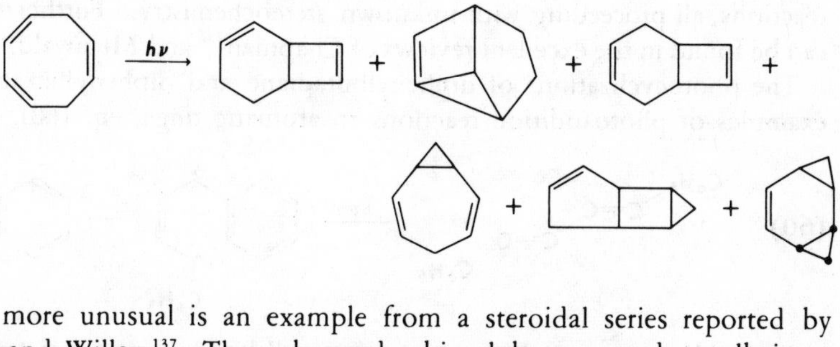
$$\xrightarrow{h\nu}$$

Even more unusual is an example from a steroidal series reported by Dauben and Willey.[137] They observed a bicyclobutane product, albeit an unstable one, in the photolysis of a 2,5 steroidal diene, eq. (57).

(57)

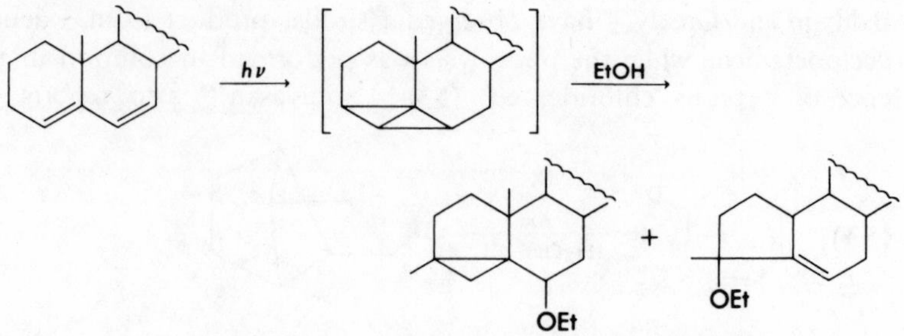

Although the solution phase photolysis of bicyclo[2.2.1]heptadiene-2,5 is reported to yield 67% quadricyclene,[111] when directly photolyzed in the vapor phase, eq. (58), little quadricyclene is observed.[138]

(58)

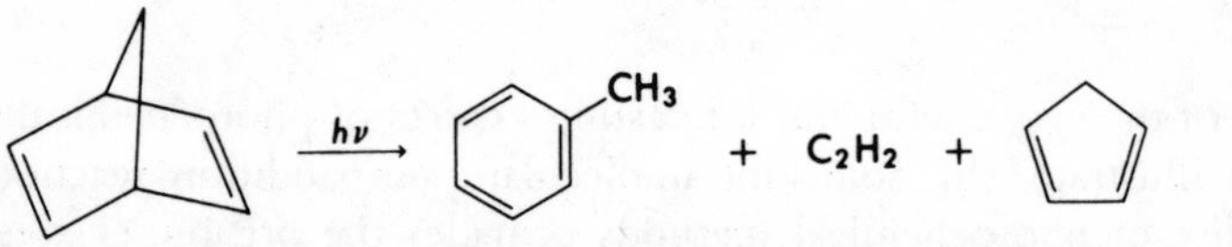

Crowley has reported that certain dienes undergo a hydrogen atom migration as well as ring closure to form cyclobutene derivatives. For example, 4-methylpentadiene-1,3 yields 2-methylpentadiene-1,3 as well as 1,3-dimethylcyclobutene when photolyzed in nonpolar solvents, eq. (59). The interconversions of the open chain dienes are reversible.[139]

(59)

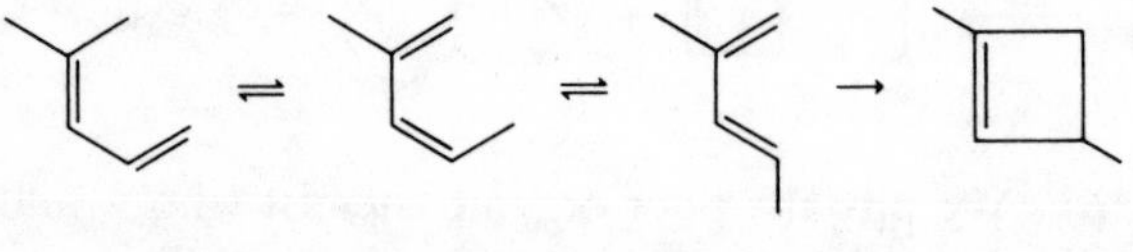

Table 6-8 gives other examples of electrocyclic photochemical addition reactions, all proceeding with unknown stereochemistry. Further examples can be found in the excellent reviews of Chapman[140] and Meinwald.[141]

The photocyclizations of diphenylbutadiene and diphenylhexatriene are examples of photoaddition reactions to aromatic rings, eq. (60). Carbon

(60)

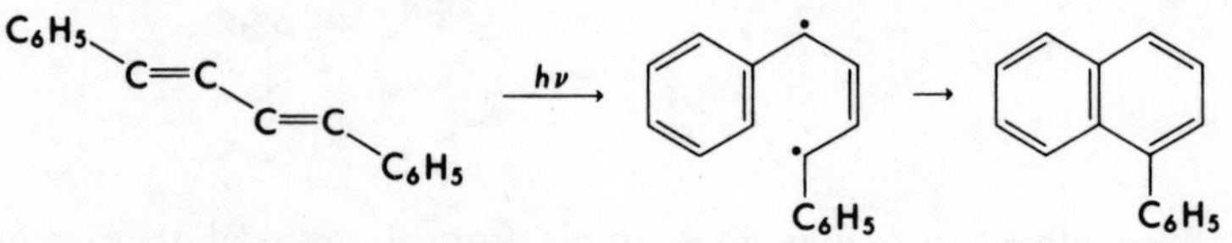

radical additions to aromatic systems are well known in normal free radical reactions where the radical on the γ carbon is generated by alkoxy radical

Table 6-8

Intramolecular Electrocyclic Photochemical Addition Reactions

Substrate	Product	Reference
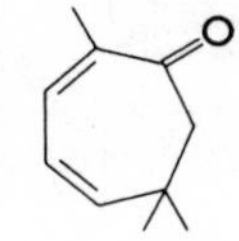	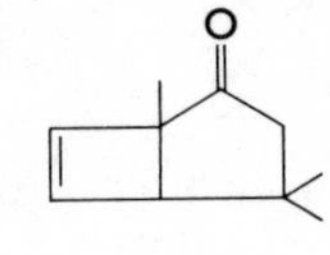	142
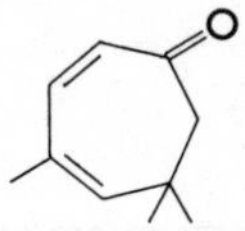	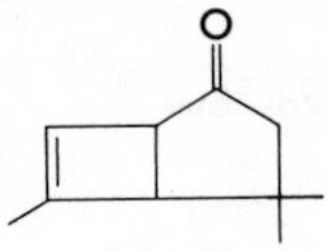	142
1,4-diphenylbutadiene	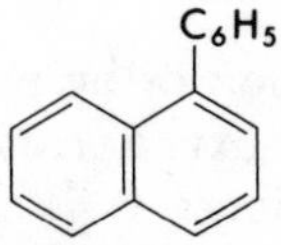	143
1,6-diphenylhexatriene	Chrysene	143
1,2,3,4,5-pentaphenylcyclo-hexadiene-1,3	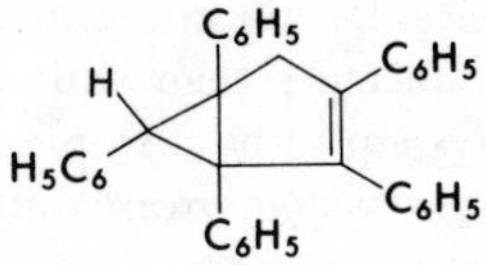	144
$(CH_3)_2C=CHCH_2CH_2\overset{\underset{\textstyle CH_3}{\mid}}{C}=CHCHO$ citral	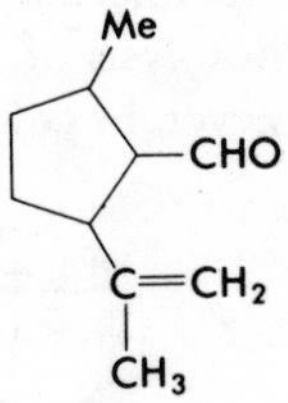 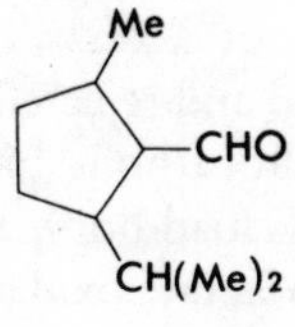 + 	145

Table 6-8 (cont.)

Substrate	Product	Reference
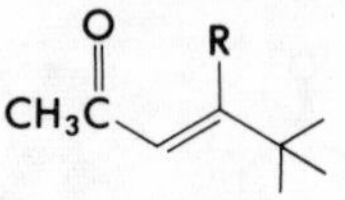 R = H, me	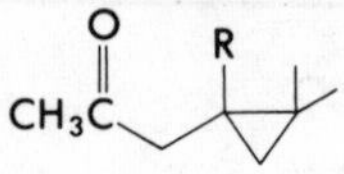	146
cycloheptatrienone	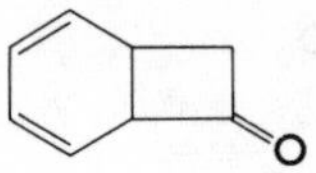	147

hydrogen abstraction or by perester decomposition. Wilt and co-workers have observed that oxygen radical addition to aromatic rings occurs in certain Hunsdiecker reactions.

Photoadditions Within Aromatic Molecules

Intramolecular photochemical addition reactions are less facile with aromatic molecules than with olefins. In order for the highly stabilized aromatic system to be disrupted photochemically, an impetus must be provided to the system from outside sources. Inordinate steric repulsions can provide the necessary ground state destabilization. An elegant example of an aromatic intramolecular photoaddition reaction was reported by van Tamelen.[148] Photolysis of 1,2,4-tri-*t*-butylbenzene in dilute ether solution produces a bicyclohexadiene, eq. (61). Bicyclohexadienes are the

(61)

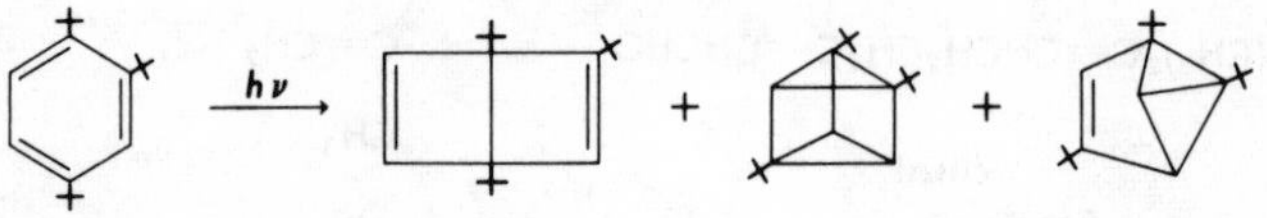

simplest members of a class of unique compounds, which resemble the classically proposed and rejected Dewar representation of benzene. Synthesis of the parent hydrocarbon, bicyclohexadiene, has been accomplished by utilizing a photocycloaddition reaction of 1,2-dihydrophalic anhydride followed by lead tetraacetate oxidation, eq. (62).[149]

(62)

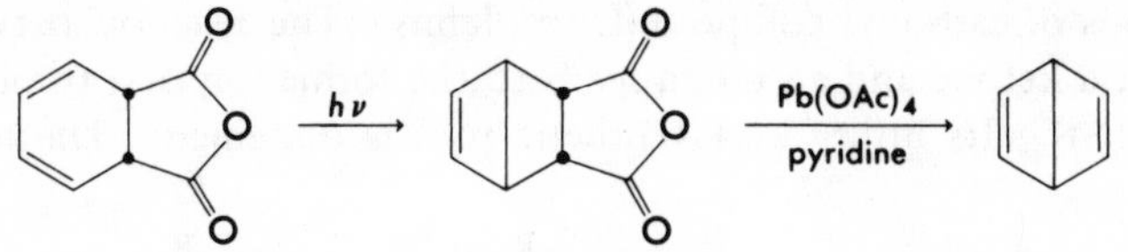

Wilzbach and Kaplan[150] as well as others[151, 152] have presented evidence pointing to the intermediacy of Ladenburg benzene structures in photochemical rearrangements of aromatic alkylated hydrocarbons, eq. (63). Carbon-14

(63)

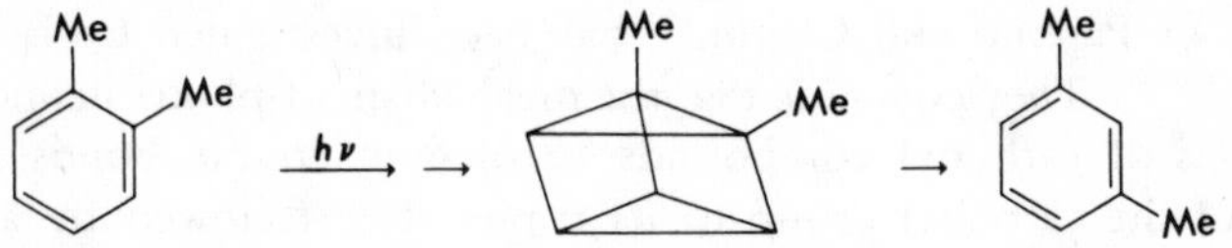

labeling experiments using labeled mesitylenes[153] have shown that ring carbon rather than alkyl carbon migrations occur, hence adding validity to the proposed intermediates. Rearrangement to the *para* isomer also is observed so that each of the possible decomposition modes of the Ladenburg form occurs. Ladenburg intermediates are not the only intermediates that can explain the observed results. Kaplan, Wilzbach, and co-workers propose that tricyclohexenes can also account for the observed products. In a recent publication, they report isolation of tricyclohexene intermediates in the Dewar benzene photolysis.[154] Wynberg and van Driel have reported similar rearrangements among phenylthiophenes. They suggest, although cautiously, that Dewar and Ladenberg structures may also be important in the thiophene series.[155]

Recent isotope-marking experiments verify the postulate that Dewar, valene, and perhaps Ladenburg structures are intermediates in thiophene ring rearrangements also.[156]

Additions of Carbonyl Compounds to Unsaturates

Photoaddition reactions of unlike molecules may take place between carbonyl compounds and olefins or acetylenes, aromatic compounds and olefins, thiocarbonyls and olefins, hydrocarbons and olefins, diones and olefins, quinones and olefins, olefins and other olefins, and oxygen or sulfur dioxide and carbonyl compounds. The mechanisms for these reactions are many and varied and not well understood in most cases.

The most completely studied of photochemical cycloaddition reactions is that of carbonyl compounds to olefins. Both de Mayo[157] and Masson, Noyes, and Boekelheide[158] provide extensive early examples of photoaddition reactions of carbonyl compounds to olefins. The reaction between an aldehyde or a ketone and an olefin leads to the formation of a trimethylene oxide, eq. (64). Its utility as a synthetic tool is undenied. The reaction,

(64)

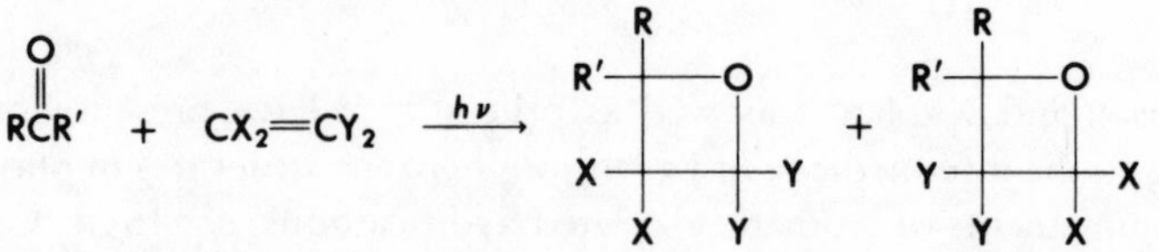

$$RCR' + CX_2=CY_2 \xrightarrow{h\nu}$$

a discovery of Paterno and Chieffi,[159] has been investigated by Büchi and co-workers.[160-162] They conclude that the mechanism of photochemical addition reactions of carbonyl compounds to olefinic double bonds involves excitation of the carbonyl group to its triplet state followed by addition, probably in a stepwise fashion with oxygen first, to the unsaturated center, eqs. (65–67). Büchi's evidence rests predominantly on the observation

(65) $RCR' \xrightarrow{h\nu} \rightarrow R\dot{C}R'$

(66) $R\dot{C}R' + R_1C=CR_4 \rightarrow$

(67)   products ⟵

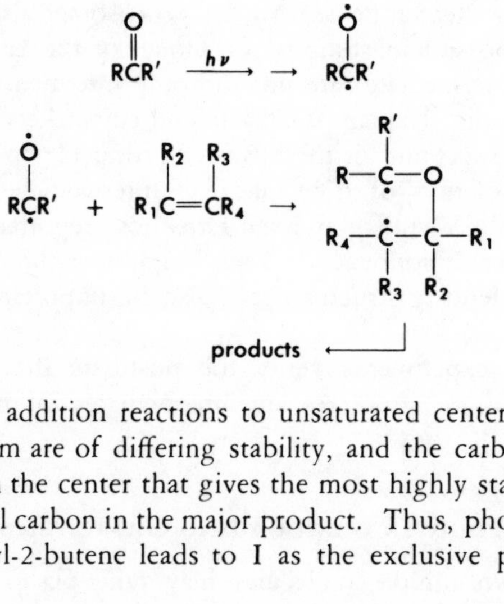

that for addition reactions to unsaturated centers, the free radicals derived therefrom are of differing stability, and the carbon-carbon bond is formed between the center that gives the most highly stabilized free radical and the carbonyl carbon in the major product. Thus, photolysis of acetophenone in 2-methyl-2-butene leads to I as the exclusive product, eq. (68), and the

(68) 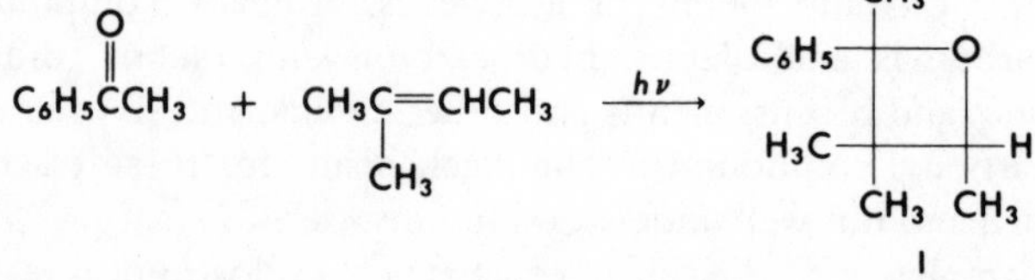 $C_6H_5CCH_3 + CH_3C=CHCH_3 \xrightarrow{h\nu}$
                                    $|$
                                   CH_3

I

major product from photolysis of benzaldehyde in 2-methyl-2-butene is II, eq. (69).

(69) 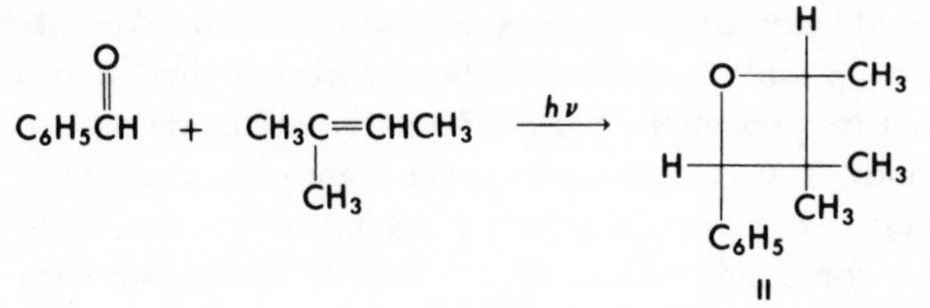 $\quad C_6H_5\overset{\overset{\displaystyle O}{\|}}{C}H \;+\; CH_3\underset{\underset{\displaystyle CH_3}{|}}{C}{=}CHCH_3 \;\xrightarrow{\;h\nu\;}$

Arnold and co-workers[163] have substantiated the fact that the triplet state of the carbonyl compound is involved in the addition reaction by showing that only those aromatic carbonyl compounds that undergo facile photoreduction in hydrogen donor solvents (Chapter 7) add smoothly to olefins. Since photoreduction is known to be a triplet state process (Chapter 7), photoaddition must also be a triplet state process. Yang has extended the investigation of isomer distribution in adduct formation with 2-methyl-2-butene and confirmed Büchi's prediction that radical intermediates are probably involved.[164] Some of Yang's results are listed in Table 6-9.

Yang's results confirm those of Arnold, Hinman, and Glick and show that all those carbonyl compounds for which very low quantum yields of adduct formation are observed fail to undergo rapid photoreduction in donor solvents. 9-Anthraldehyde, however, is an unusual case. It fails to undergo photoreduction, but adds 2-methyl-2-butene with a rather high quantum yield.

Table 6-9

The Addition of Carbonyl Compounds to 2-Methylbutene-2[a]

Carbonyl Group	Yield Adduct, %	$\dfrac{\text{2,3,3-Trimethyloxetane}}{\text{2,2,3-Trimethyloxetane}}$	Φ
benzaldehyde	64	1.6:1	0.45
anisaldehyde	50	2:1	—
acetophenone	65	>9:1	0.1
benzophenone	80	>9:1	0.5
1-naphthaldehyde	72	2:1	0.05
2-naphthaldehyde	70	1.6:1	0.05
2-acetonaphthone	0	—	—
2-benzonaphthone	62	>9:1	very low
fluorenone	68	>9:1	very low
cinnamaldehyde	50	1:1	very low
4-phenylcrotonaldehyde	50	1:1	very low
9-anthraldehyde	70	>9:1	0.1

[a]Data from N. C. Yang, *Pure Appl. Chem.*, **9**, 591 (1964).

Although the addition of an olefin to a quinone often takes place across the carbon-carbon double bond, it has been reported that, if troublesome side reactions can be prevented, the addition can be made to occur across the carbonyl bond.[165] Charge transfer spectra are observable spectroscopically for such systems; however, selective excitation studies show that the formation of the conjugate adduct of 2,3-dimethylbutadiene with the carbonyl group of benzoquinone does not result from a charge transfer complex, eq. (70).

(70)

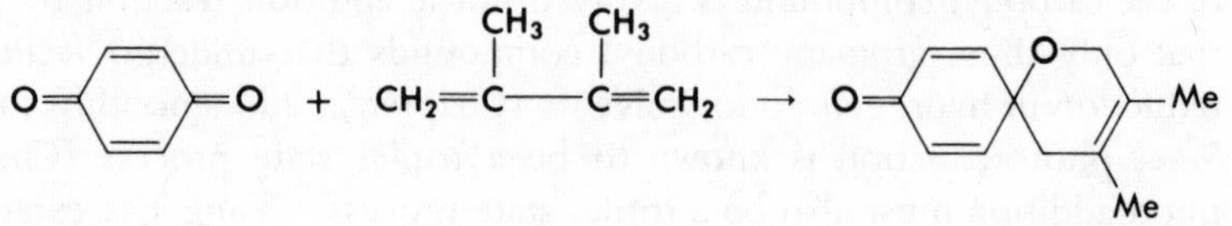

$$O{=}\langle\ \rangle{=}O\ +\ CH_2{=}C{-}C{=}CH_2\ \rightarrow$$

(with CH_3 substituents on the central carbons)

Barltrop and Hesp[166] have also reported that excitation of the $n\text{-}\pi^*$ transition of p-quinones in the presence of butadiene and isoprene gives spiropyrans. These systems, unlike the same reaction processes initiated thermally, lead to reaction of the carbonyl system with the conjugated olefin. Barltrop and Hesp propose a free radical mechanism for the addition of dienes to quinones, eq. (71).

(71)

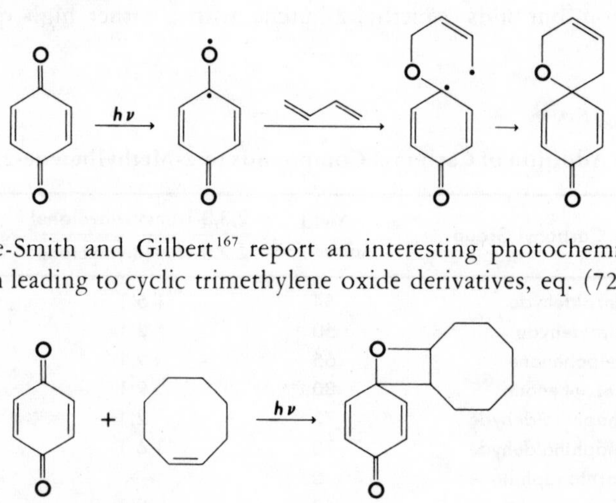

Bryce-Smith and Gilbert[167] report an interesting photochemical addition reaction leading to cyclic trimethylene oxide derivatives, eq. (72). Yields of

(72)

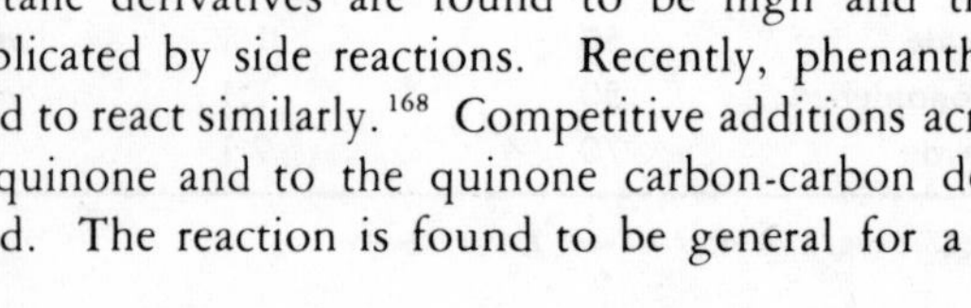

the oxetane derivatives are found to be high and the reaction pathway uncomplicated by side reactions. Recently, phenanthraquinone has been observed to react similarly.[168] Competitive additions across the two oxygens of the quinone and to the quinone carbon-carbon double bond are also observed. The reaction is found to be general for a variety of quinones and olefins. The mechanism for the reaction probably involves n-π^* excitation of the carbonyl group rather than π-π^* excitation of the ethylenic chromophore and probably results because the n-π^* triplet is energetically the lower lying of the pair.

Table 6-10 lists a variety of carbonyl compounds and olefins for which photocycloaddition reactions have been observed.

The products observed by Kharasch and co-workers (Table 6-10) result from a radical chain mechanism although the difference between the conditions used by Kharasch and those used by Büchi are not immediately obvious. De Mayo and co-workers[172] observe yet a different product from the reaction of cyclohexene and acetone. This product results from hydrogen abstraction from the allylic position of the olefin. Acetone undergoes at least three different photochemical reactions with olefins to give products indicative of free radical chain reactions in two cases and a cycloaddition reaction in the third case.

Bradshaw has shown that acetone and cyclohexene give an oxetane, an alcohol, and a hydrocarbon dimer in the following yields, eq. (73).[173]

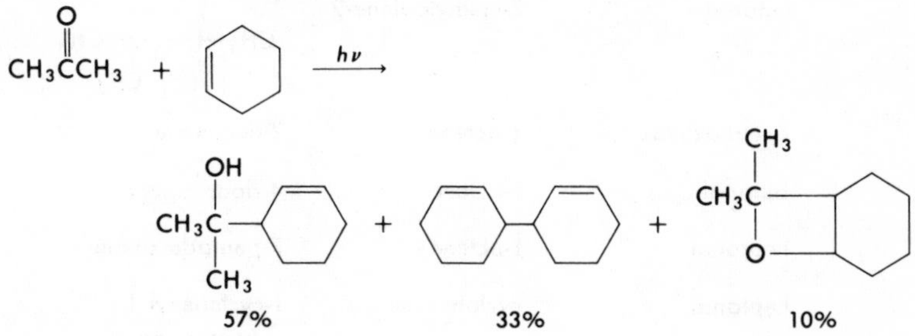

Addition reactions of ketones to acetylenes[161] lead to cycloadducts in the initial step of the sequence, but these adducts, cyclic enol ethers, decompose to α,β-unsaturated ketones, eq. (74). Benzaldehyde and acetophenone

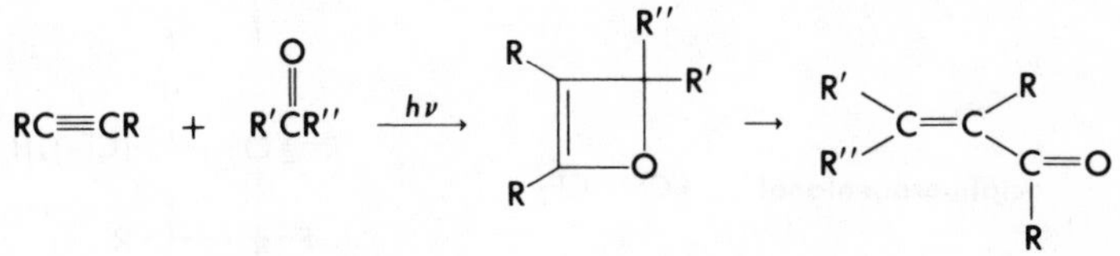

both add to 5-decyne in this manner. A mechanism similar to that proposed for the additions of olefins to ketones can be proposed to account for these products.

Thioketones suffer from a variety of complicating photochemical side reactions including exchange of sulfur for oxygen and polymerization across

Table 6-10

The Addition of Aldehydes and Ketones to Olefins

Carbonyl Compound	Olefin	Adduct	Reference
benzaldehyde	2-methylbutene-2	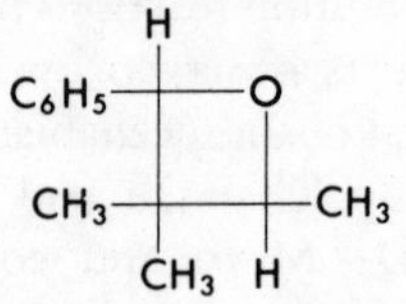 [oxetane ring: top C bearing H and C_6H_5 and O; bottom carbons CH_3—, —CH_3, CH_3 H]	160, 163, 164
acetophenone	2-methylbutene-2	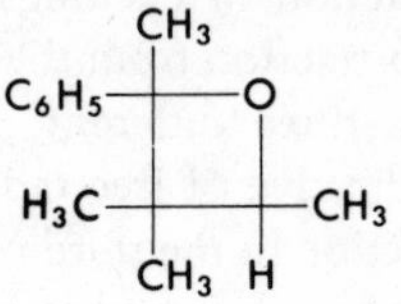 [oxetane ring: top C bearing CH_3 and C_6H_5 and O; H_3C—, —CH_3, CH_3 H]	160, 163, 164
butanal	2-methylbutene-2	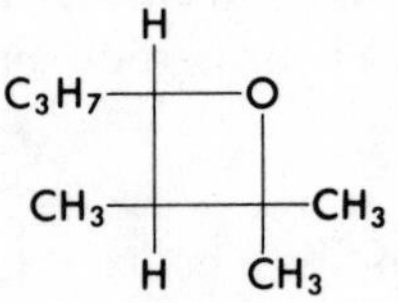 [oxetane ring: top C bearing H and C_3H_7 and O; CH_3—, —CH_3, H CH_3]	160
acetaldehyde	1-octene	2-decanone	169
butanal	1-octene	4-dodecanone	169
heptanal	1-octene	7-pentadecanone	169
heptanal	cyclohexene	1-cyclohexyl-1-heptanone	168
trifluoroacet-aldehyde	$RCF{=}CF_2$ R = fluoroalkyl	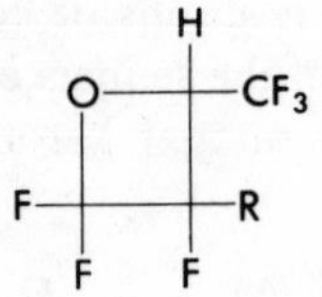 [oxetane ring: O, top C bearing H and CF_3; F—, —R; F F]	170
octafluoropentanal	$RCF{=}CF_2$	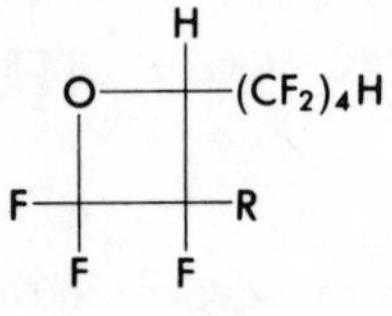 [oxetane ring: O, top C bearing H and $(CF_2)_4H$; F—, —R; F F]	170
octafluoropentanal	$CF_2{=}CFCl$	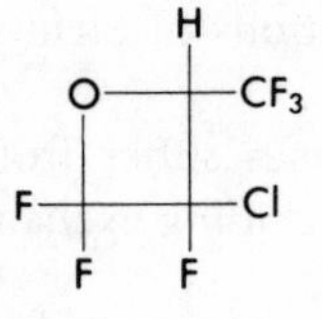 [oxetane ring: O, top C bearing H and CF_3; F—, —Cl; F F]	170

Table 6-10 (cont.)

Carbonyl Compound	Olefin	Adduct	Reference
sym-tetrafluorodi-chloroacetone	$CF_2{=}CFCl$	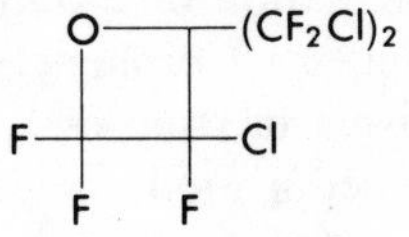 (oxetane ring) top: O—$(CF_2Cl)_2$; bottom: F—Cl; ring carbon: F, F	170
hexafluoroacetone	$CF_2{=}CFCF_3$	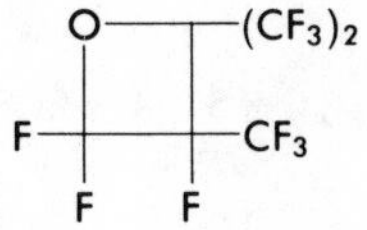 (oxetane ring) top: O—$(CF_3)_2$; bottom: F—CF_3; ring carbon: F, F	170
perfluoro-4-heptanone	$CF_2{=}CFC_5F_{11}$	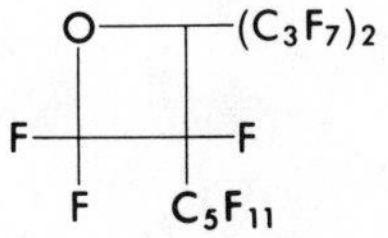 (oxetane ring) top: O—$(C_3F_7)_2$; bottom: F—F; ring carbon: F, C_5F_{11}	170
perfluorocyclo-butanone	$CF_2{=}CFCF_3$	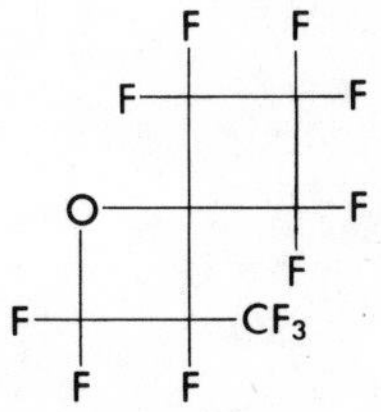 (spiro cyclobutane/oxetane) cyclobutane: $F, F / F—F / F / F$; oxetane: O—; bottom: F—CF_3; ring carbon: F, F	170
perfluoroacet-aldehyde	$CF_2{=}CFCF_3$	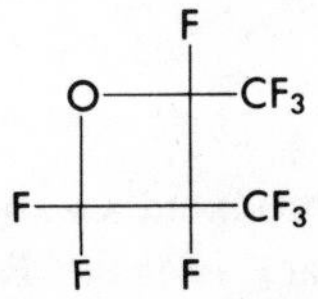 (oxetane ring) top: O—CF_3 with F above; bottom: F—CF_3; ring carbon: F, F	170
trifluoroacet-aldehyde	$CF_2{=}CF(CF_2)_2H$	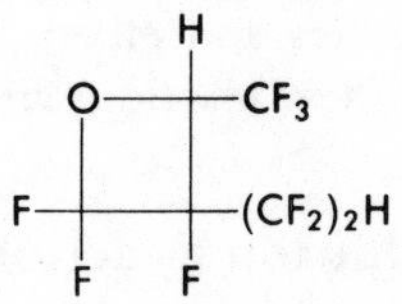 (oxetane ring) top: O—CF_3 with H above; bottom: F—$(CF_2)_2H$; ring carbon: F, F	170
4-acetobutene-1	none	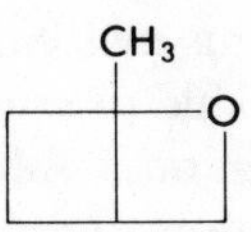 (bicyclic ring) CH_3 at top, O at right	171

the carbon-sulfur bond. Kaiser and Wulfers[174] propose initial addition of olefins to thioketones; however, the expected products, thiooxetanes, are not observed. The cyclic products appear to be labile to either photochemical or thermal activation with resultant decomposition and sulfur exchange. For example, irradiation of 2-butene and thiobenzophenone in an inert atmosphere produces 1,1-diphenyl-1-propene, whereas 1-hexene and thiobenzophenone give a mixture of 1,1-diphenyl-1-hexene and 1,1-diphenylethylene, the former being predominant. Kaiser proposes the reaction mechanism shown in eqs. (75) and (76).

(75) $(C_6H_5)_2C{=}S$ + $RCH{=}CHR'$ $\xrightarrow[N_2]{h\nu}$

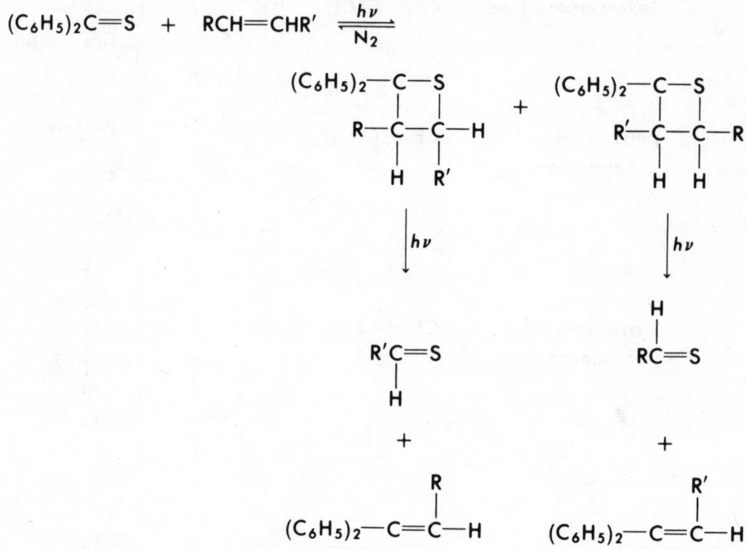

Photolysis of thiooxetanes should cause cleavage in the manner proposed if their intermediacy is real. Results by Gritter and Sabitino[175] indicate that carbon-sulfur and carbon-oxygen bonds are photochemically cleaved in cyclic thioethers and ethers, albeit in extremely low quantum yield. The products of these reactions are those expected of simple cleavage to radicals.

Addition Reactions Between Unlike Olefins

Photochemical addition reactions of olefins to other olefins take place readily providing that either suitable chromophores are present in the unsaturated molecule to cause excitation or sufficiently short wavelengths are used for excitation. Addition reactions of olefins to olefins are elegant synthetic entrances to cyclobutane systems and as such have received much attention. Illustrative of the synthetic importance of olefin to olefin photo-cycloaddition reactions are the additions of maleimides to ethylenes. Scharf and Korte report[176] that halogenated maleic acid imides as well as maleic anhydride add to ethylene to give *cis* adducts in very high yields. The reaction occurs stereospecifically and can be sensitized by benzophenone; therefore, triplet state excitation of a π complex between olefin and maleic acid derivatives is a mechanistic pathway worthy of consideration.[196]

The mechanism of the photochemical addition of olefins to olefins is, like that of dimerization processes, not known for certain. Several interesting features of these photoaddition reactions have been observed by Corey and co-workers[177] and by Robson, Grubb, and Barltrop.[178,179] First, these reactions appear to be somewhat stereospecific in that *trans* ring systems are frequently formed. Second, good π electron donors react both more rapidly and with more orientational stereospecificity. Third, electron donors on the unexcited olefinic moiety increase the relative rate of addition, whereas electron withdrawers decrease the relative rate of addition of the same excited olefin. Finally, charge transfer complexes between π systems have been observed spectroscopically for some systems. Irradiation at wavelengths sufficient only for absorption by the charge transfer complex produces specifically oriented products, whereas excitation of either of the olefinic components of the reaction mixture using shorter wavelengths produces nonstereospecific addition.

These observations point to a general mechanism like either eq. (77) or (78).

$$(77) \quad \text{olefin X} + \text{olefin Y} \xrightleftharpoons{h\nu} \text{oriented } \pi \text{ complex} \rightleftharpoons \text{diradical}$$
$$\text{cycloadduct} \longleftarrow$$

$$(78) \quad \text{olefin X} + \text{olefin Y} \rightleftharpoons \text{oriented } \pi \text{ complex} \xrightleftharpoons{h\nu} \text{excited } \pi \text{ complex (may be diradical)}$$
$$\text{cycloadduct} \longleftarrow$$

Cookson presents evidence to substantiate the claim[194] that even in strained bicyclic systems charge transfer phenomena are important so that either mechanism, eq. (77) or (78), can be valid. Extensive reviews on the nature of charge transfer complexes have appeared, and the interested reader is referred to these for more detailed explanations of the valence theory of charge transfer complexes and its importance in photochemical processes.[180-182]

Aldehydes and ketones have been observed to undergo cycloadditions to the carbon-carbon double bond of ketenimines.[183,184] As in the case of additions to carbon-carbon bonds of alkenes, two isomers are observed, and the isomer ratios vary substantially depending upon the triplet state energy of the carbonyl group undergoing the cycloaddition, eq. (79). Thermal or

$$
(79) \quad \underset{\text{RCR}'}{\overset{O}{\parallel}} \; + \; \underset{R}{\overset{R}{\underset{}{>}}} C{=}C{=}N \overset{R}{\diagup} \quad \xrightarrow{h\nu} \quad R{-}\overset{O{-}C{=}NR}{\underset{\underset{R}{|}}{\underset{|}{C}}}{-}\overset{}{\underset{\underset{R}{|}}{C}}{-}R \; + \; R{-}\overset{O{-}\overset{R}{\underset{|}{C}}{-}R}{\underset{\underset{R}{|}}{C}}{-}C{=}NR
$$

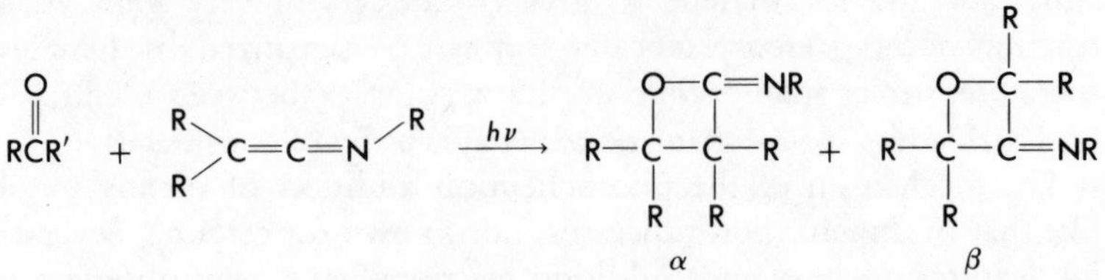

$$
\qquad\qquad\qquad\qquad\qquad\qquad\qquad\qquad \alpha \qquad\qquad\qquad\qquad \beta
$$

photochemical decomposition of the α isomer from 2-fluorenone and di-methyl-N-(2-cyano-2-propyl)-ketenimine gives 9-isopropylidinefluorene and 2-cyano-2-propyl isocyanate, eq. (80). The α isomers are generally not

$$(80)$$

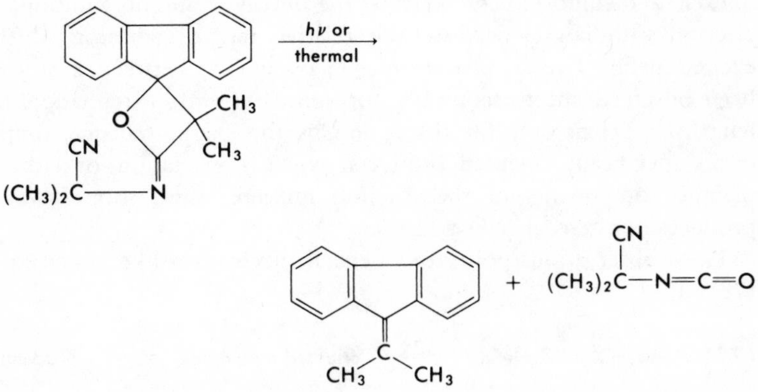

isolable because of rapid hydrolysis to the corresponding amide. As in the case of photoaddition of carbonyl groups to olefins, the photoaddition to ketenimines probably involves triplet state intermediates because those carbonyl compounds that undergo no photoreduction with isopropyl alcohol also undergo no photocycloaddition reaction—except for fluorenone. Fluorenone's case is unclear at the moment; perhaps a second, higher lying triplet state is being trapped by the strong excited state trap, the ketenimine. The degree of α versus β addition appears to be some function of triplet state energy, but more probably is a function of the degree of polar character of the triplet state.

A more pronounced stereospecific photochemical addition reaction takes place when 4,6-diene-3-ketosteroids[185,186] and 3,5-diene-7-ketosteroids are irradiated in alcohol solution.[187] In both cases, only one of a variety of possible dimers is isolated, eqs. (81) and (82). Irradiation of 4,6-diene-3-ones

(81) 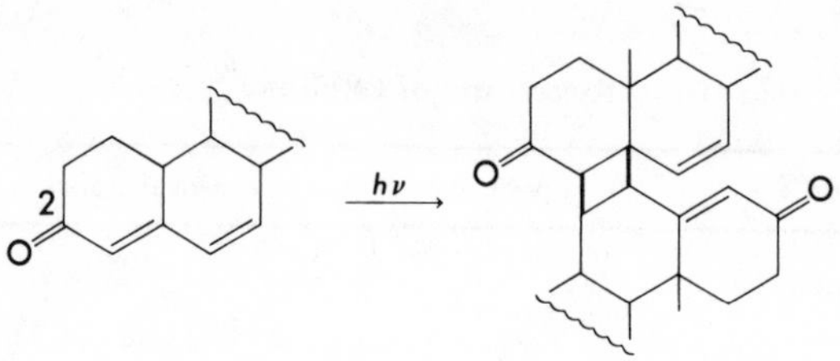 $\xrightarrow{h\nu}$

(82) 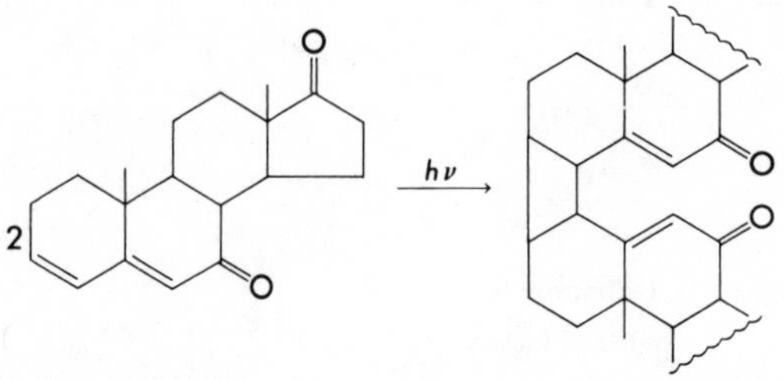 $\xrightarrow{h\nu}$

in cyclopentene affords cross dimers, indicating that the α-, β-unsaturated bond of the excited dienone molecule adds to the ground state of the olefin. It appears that the less hindered γ, δ position of the dienone is more readily attacked by the excited state of the dienone. De Mayo and Takeshita[188,189] report the photochemical additions of olefins to the carbon-carbon double bond of enols, eq. (83).

(83) 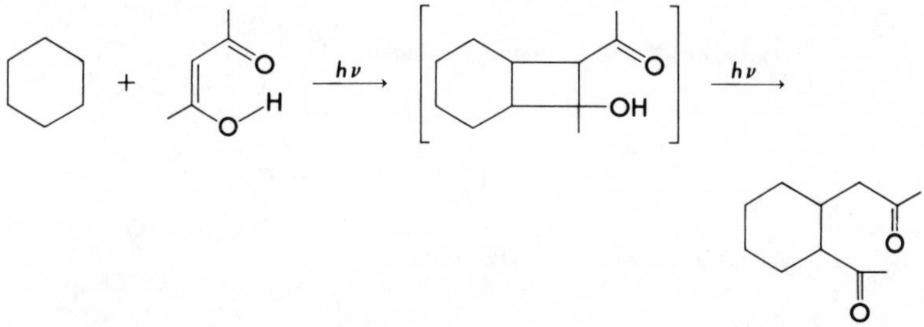 $\xrightarrow{h\nu}$ $\xrightarrow{h\nu}$

Table 6-11 lists some examples of photochemical olefin-olefin cycloaddition reactions recently observed.

Additions to Aromatic Molecules

Additions of olefinic and acetylenic compounds also occur, but with some difficulty, to aromatic systems. Those olefins that have been successfully added to aromatic systems are generally strong Diels-Alder dienophiles such as maleic anhydride or acetylene dicarboxylate, and isolation of 1:1 adducts

Table 6-11

Photocycloaddition Reactions of Olefins

Olefin X	Olefin Y	Major Product	Reference
cyclohexene-3-one	isobutylene	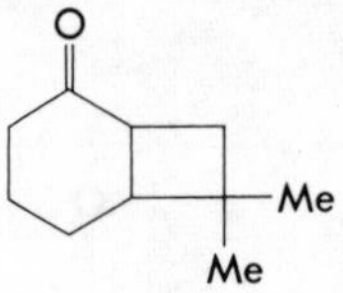	177, 190, 191, 192
cyclohexene-3-one	1,1-dimethoxy-ethylene	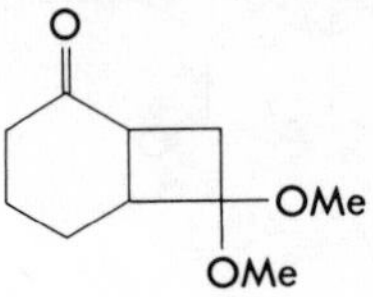	177
cyclohexene-3-one	benzyl vinyl ether	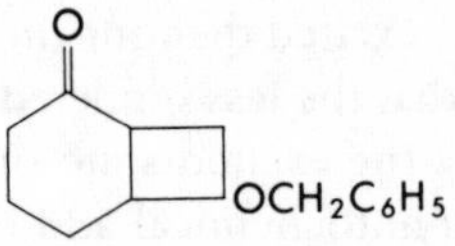	177
cyclohexene-3-one	methyl vinyl ether	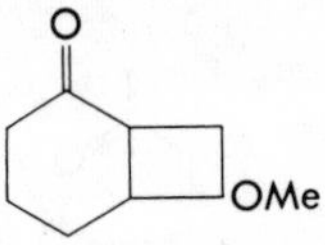	177
cyclohexene-3-one	vinyl acetate	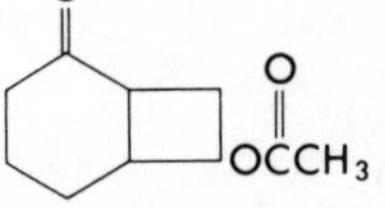	177
cyclohexene-3-one	allene	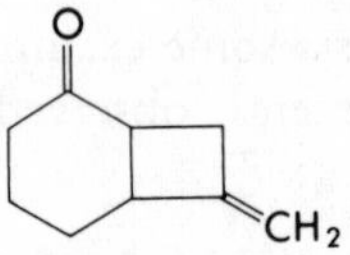	177
cyclohexene-3-one	2-butene (cis or trans)	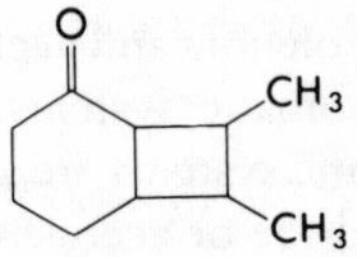	177

Table 6-11 (*cont.*)

Olefin X	Olefin Y	Major Product	Reference
cyclohexene-3-one	cyclopentene	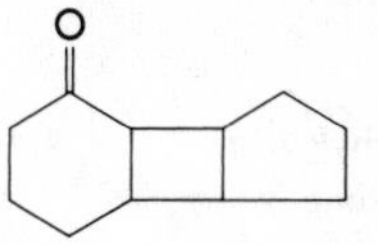	177
cyclohexene-3-one	acrylonitrile	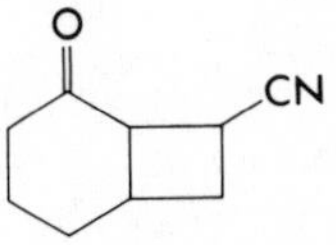	177
cyclopentenone	1,1-dimethoxy-ethylene	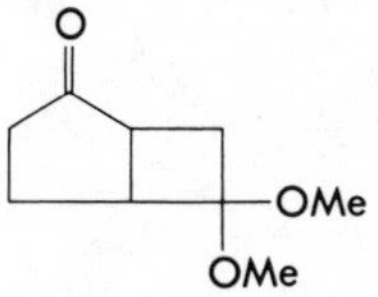	177
cycloheptene-3-one	1,1-dimethoxy-ethylene	No product	177
cyclooctene-3-one	1,1-dimethoxy-ethylene	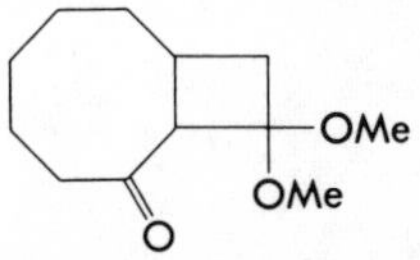	177
2-methylcyclo-hexene-3-one	isobutylene	Products not isolable	177
3-methylcyclo-hexene-3-one	isobutylene	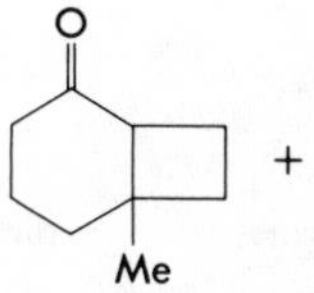 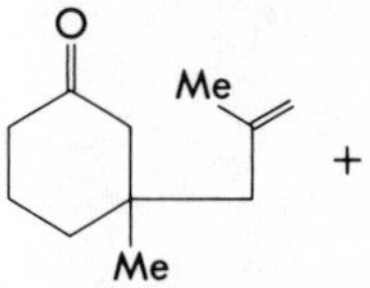 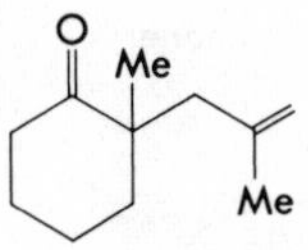	177

Table 6-11 (cont.)

Olefin X	Olefin Y	Major Product	Reference
3-methylcyclo-hexene-3-one	4,4-dimethyl-cyclopentene	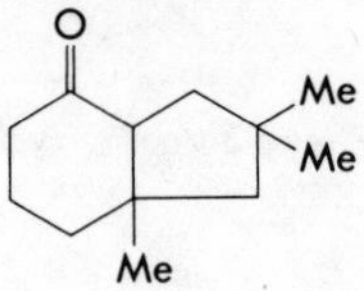	193
cyclohexene	maleic anhydride
Major	179
cyclohexene	maleonitrile
Major	179
cyclohexene	fumaronitrile	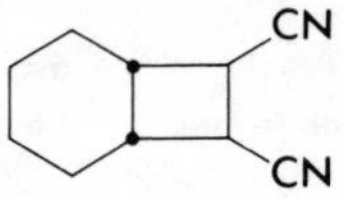	179
cyclohexene	dimethyl maleate
Mixture	179, 193, 195
quinone	cyclopentadiene	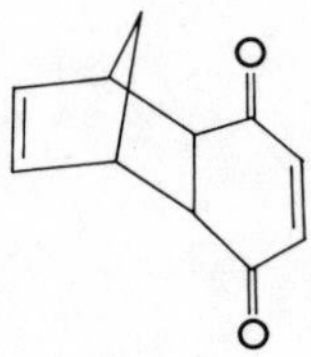	194

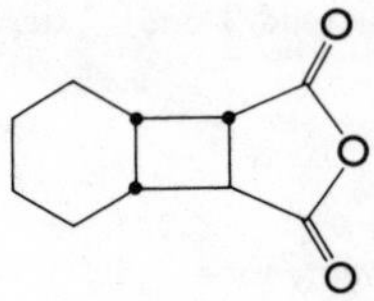

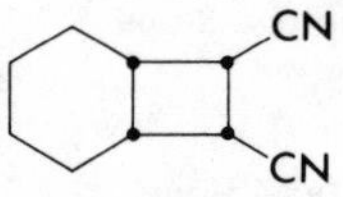

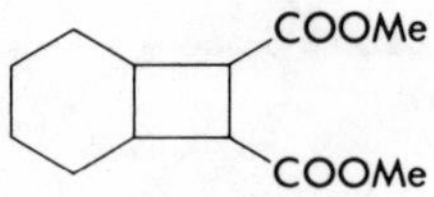

Table 6-11 (cont.)

Olefin X	Olefin Y	Major Product	Reference
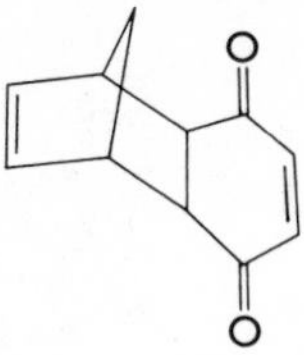	cyclopentadiene	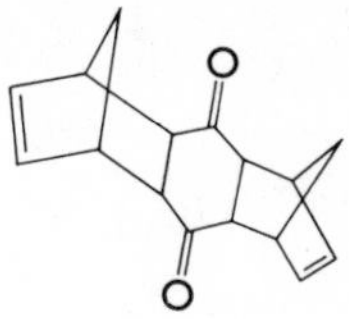 (exo)	194
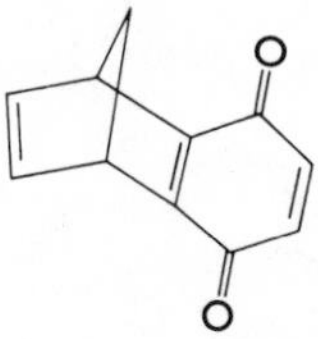	cyclopentadiene	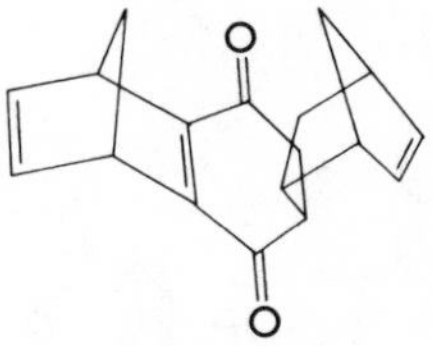 (endo)	194

is often complicated by the product's further reaction as a Diels-Alder diene.

An unusual photochemical addition reaction to an aromatic nucleus has been reported by Srinivasan and Hill.[197] These workers find that benzene and cyclobutene react photochemically to give the interesting cyclobutene shown in eq. (84). They propose that the actual addition takes place to Dewar benzene.

(84)

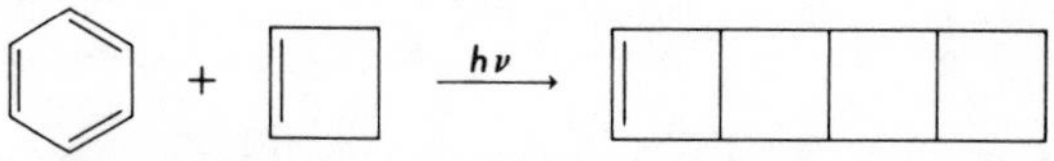

Angus and Bryce-Smith[198] and Grovenstein, Rao, and Taylor[199] have examined the photochemical reaction of benzene with maleic anhydride and observe two products, eq. (85). Dichloromaleic anhydride also reacts with benzene.[200]   When certain substituted aromatic compounds and maleic anhydride are photolyzed, maleic anhydride polymers containing aromatic nuclei result.[201] Phenanthrene, on the contrary, leads to a simple 1:1 adduct, eq. (86).

Two groups have observed that the addition of benzene and substituted benzenes to maleic anhydride can be sensitized by triplet state sensitizers such as benzophenone.[202,203]

(85)

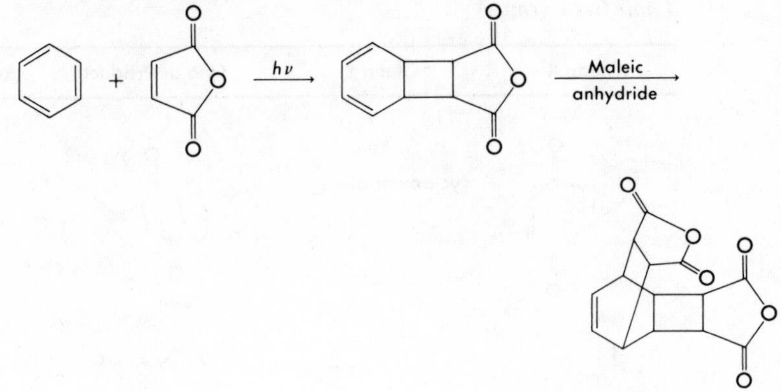

(86)

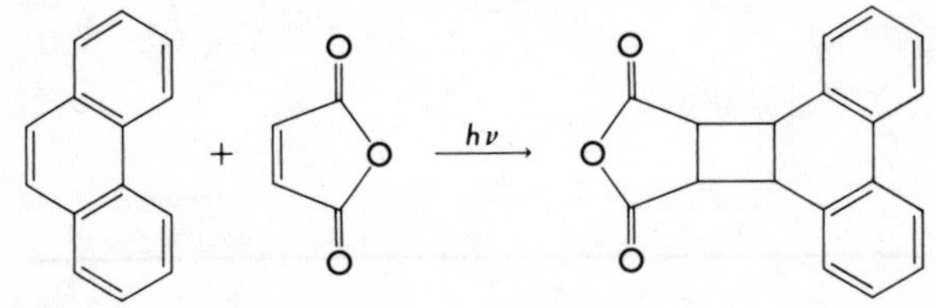

With acetylenes, aromatic compounds yield cycloöctatetraene deriva-tives.[205-206] Presumably, bicycloöctatriene intermediates that decay to cyclo-öctatetraene products are involved, eq. (87).

(87) 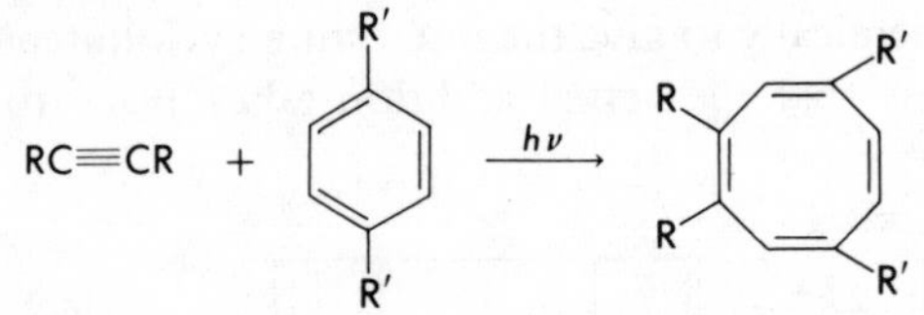 $RC\equiv CR$ +

White and Stern[207] have reported that the photoaddition of acetylenes to benzene is reversible. Photolysis of cycloöctatetraene derivatives in dilute oxygen free solutions of inert solvents produces benzene or benzene deriva-tives and the appropriate substituted acetylenes, eq. (88). Examples of these addition reactions are given in Table 6-12.

(88)

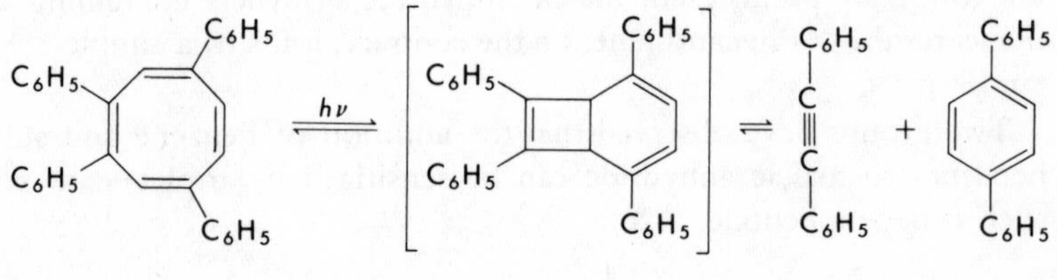

Table 6-12

Photocycloaddition Reactions of Aromatic Compounds with Acetylenes

Aromatic	Acetylene	Product
benzene [205,206]	methyl acetylenecarboxylate	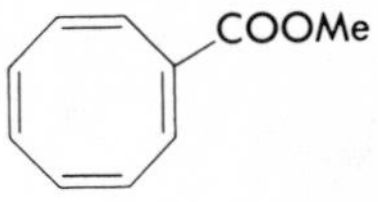
benzene [204,205,206]	dimethyl acetylenedicarboxylate	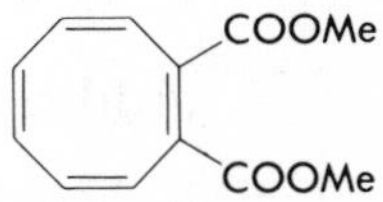
benzene [204,205]	phenylacetylene	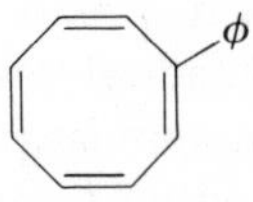
phenylacetylene [204]	phenylacetylene	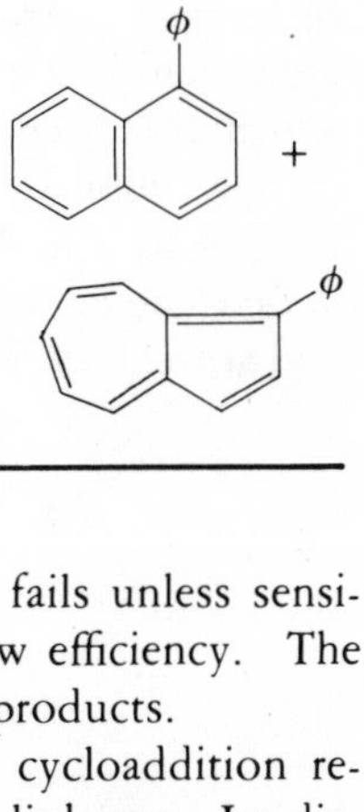

The simple addition reaction of benzene and acetylene fails unless sensitized by acetone, and even then the reaction is of very low efficiency. The dimerization of phenylacetylene also produces anomalous products.

Taylor and co-workers[208] have reported intramolecular cycloaddition reactions of nitro compounds to suitably positioned olefinic linkages. Irradiation of the *p*-chlorophenyl anil of *o*-nitro-*o'*-formylbiphenyl in ethanol gives *p*-chloronitrosobenzene and 5(6H)-phenanthridone, eq. (89).

(89)

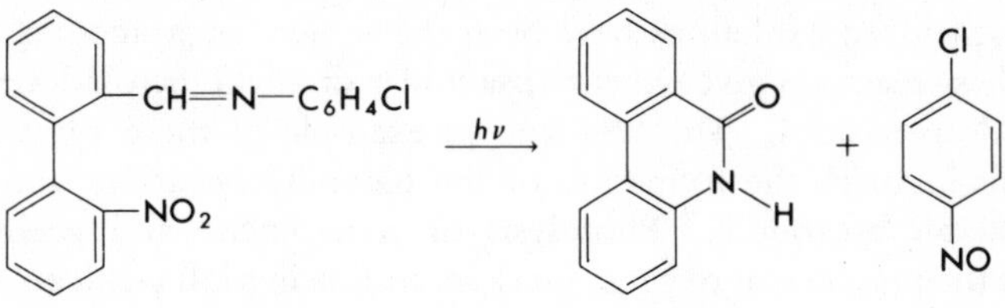

Taylor proposes that the initial reaction step is that of an addition of both oxygens of the nitro group to the carbon-nitrogen double bond, eq. (90).

(90)

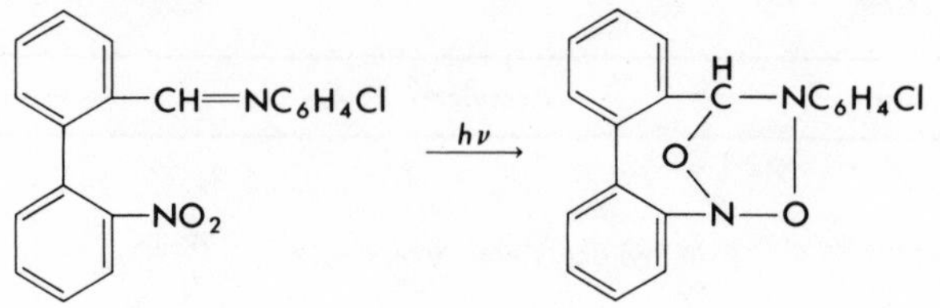

Additions of Oxygen to Olefins

Certain photochemical reactions lead to addition products, the formation of which appears to involve the trapping of an intermediate excited state by a strong radical trapping agent such as oxygen or by sulfur dioxide. Formation of transannular peroxides, of allylic hydroperoxides, and of some epoxides often results from photolysis of olefinic materials in the presence of excesses of oxygen. Aromatic materials that are known to photooxidize include anthracene and its derivatives, naphthacene, and pentacene. These reactions, which have been studied extensively by Bowen and co-workers,[209-212] may go through moloxide intermediates resulting from addition of a molecule of oxygen to a molecule of lowest triplet state anthracene, although singlet anthracene derivatives can also be trapped by oxygen if proper substituent and solvent are chosen, eq. (91).[213] The majority of peroxidations of aro-

(91)

moloxide

matic hydrocarbon derivatives involve similar mechanistic sequences.

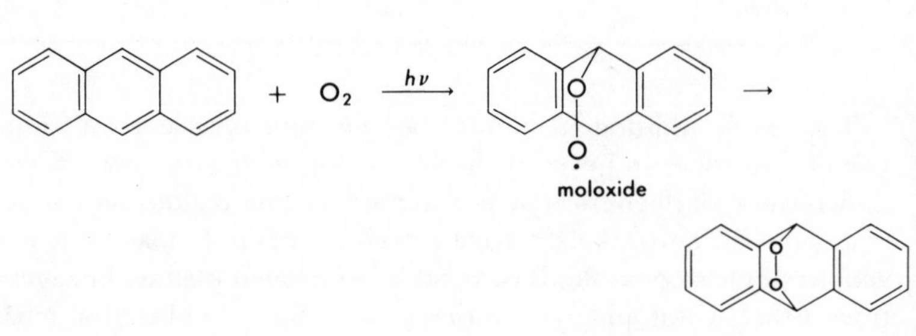

Photosensitized oxidations have been the subject of numerous investigations. These reactives give either transannular or allylic peroxides and sometimes hydroperoxides. The best known example of these photosensitized oxidations involves the formation of the naturally occurring and commercially valuable ascaridole. Photolysis of α-terpinene and green spinach leaves, in the presence of oxygen, gives ascaridole in high yield, eq. (92).[214]

(92)

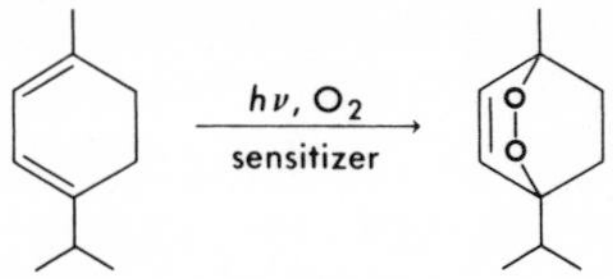

$$\xrightarrow[\text{sensitizer}]{h\nu,\ O_2}$$

Steroidal systems, particularly those with a homoannular diene system, undergo a fairly general reaction with oxygen leading to the formation of a transannular peroxide. Much of the early pertinent information concerning steroidal systems has been reviewed.[213] The reaction is equally as facile with simple dienes and cyclopentadiene; 1,3-cyclohexadiene, α-phellandrene, and α and γ pyrones have all been oxidized to transannular peroxides with photosensitization techniques.

Certain hydrocarbons tend to produce allylic hydroperoxides rather than transannular peroxides, eq. (93).

(93) $RCH{=}CHCHR_2 \xrightarrow[\text{sensitizer}]{h\nu,\ O_2} RHC{-}CH{=}CR_2$
$$\underset{OOH}{|}$$

Schenck suggests that the mechanism for photosensitization involves a new "excito" dimer, formed between the excited state of the donor and the ground state of the acceptor. Schenck's mechanism is shown in eqs. (94–96).

(94) $D \xrightarrow{h\nu} \underset{\text{(singlet)}}{D^*} \rightarrow \underset{\text{(triplet)}}{D^*}$

(95) $\underset{\text{(triplet)}}{D^*} + A \longrightarrow \cdot A{-}D\cdot$

(96) $\cdot A{-}D\cdot + Y \longrightarrow AY + D$

Schenck maintains that for the sensitizer to become involved in the chemical reaction, it must be bonded chemically to the donor. Schenck's evidence for involving "excito" dimer formation as an important step in photosensitized reactions is simply that the products obtained from photosensitized reactions are frequently different from the products of unsensitized photochemical reactions.

Typical examples of allylic hydroperoxide formation in a photosensitized oxidation are illustrated with α and β pinene in eqs. (97, 98).

(97) 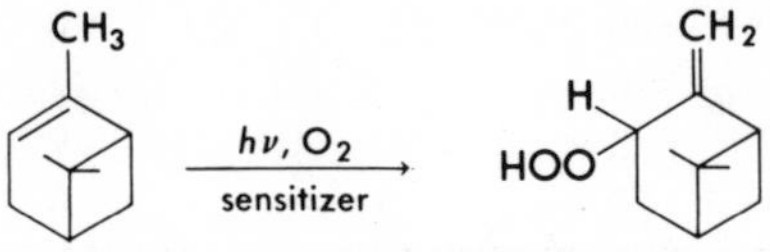   CH$_3$ $\xrightarrow[\text{sensitizer}]{h\nu,\ O_2}$ CH$_2$ ... H, HOO

(98)

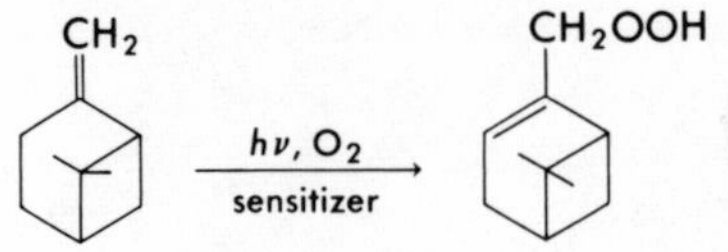

Sensitized photooxidations of (+) limonene and (+) carvomenthene have recently been reported, and the products are optically active.[215] The alcohols obtained from (+) limonene after lithium aluminum hydride reduction of the hydroperoxides are shown in eq. (99).

(99)

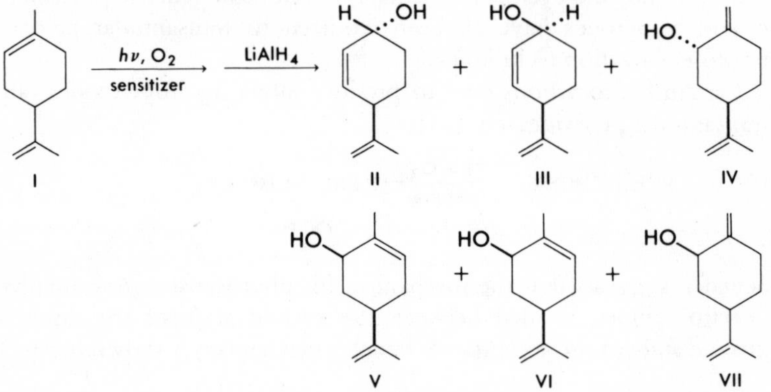

In all of the products molecular asymmetry is retained. In support of the proposed mechanism for photochemical allylic hydroperoxide formation, Schenck finds that the product ratios differ in the sensitized photooxidation of (+) limonene from those obtained by normal autoxidation procedures.[216] These product ratios are shown in Table 6-13. In addition, product alcohols V and VI obtained from the free radical chain autoxidation of (+) limonene

Table 6-13

Products from the Sensitized Oxidation of (+) Limonene

Allylalcohol	Photo Product, %	Peroxide Product, %
II	10	12
III	34	11
IV	20	0
V	10	22
VI	5	19
VII	21	0

are optically inactive. Schenck concludes that since the formation of hydroperoxides by allylic abstraction, eqs. (100–103), of a hydrogen atom, followed by oxidation of the formed radical, produces both a different product

$$(100) \quad CH_2{=}CHCHR_1R_2 \xrightarrow{\ R\cdot\ } CH_2{=}CH\overset{\cdot}{C}R_1R_2 \ \longleftrightarrow \ \cdot CH_2CH{=}CR_1R_2$$
$$\downarrow O_2 \qquad M\cdot \qquad \downarrow O_2$$

$$(101) \qquad\qquad\qquad\qquad \overset{\displaystyle O_2\cdot}{\underset{A\cdot}{\overset{|}{CH_2{=}CHCR_1R_2}}} \ + \ \underset{B\cdot}{\cdot O_2CH_2CH{=}CR_1R_2}$$

$$(102) \quad A\cdot \ or \ B\cdot \ \xrightarrow{\ CH_2{=}CHCHR_1R_2\ } \ \overset{\displaystyle O_2H}{\overset{|}{CH_2{=}CHCR_1R_2}} \ or \ HO_2CH_2CH{=}CR_1R_2 + M\cdot$$

$$(103) \qquad 2\,R\cdot \ \xrightarrow{\qquad\qquad\qquad} \ dimeric \ products$$

mixture and products having different stereochemistry than photosensitized oxidations, these oxidations do not involve free radical chains. He again proposes the mechanism of photosensitization, eqs. (94–95), that requires the formation of an "excito" dimer. The very large volume of literature on photooxidations tends to support the claim that, in general, free radical chain mechanisms are probably not involved. Table 6-14 lists a number of photosensitized oxidation reactions. The interested reader can find many other examples in some early reviews.[217-218]

Although the number of examples of photochemical oxidation is voluminous, the mechanism is still open to question. Recent work by Foote and Wexler[228-229] and by Corey[230] tends to substantiate an earlier belief set forth originally by Kautsky and co-workers[231-233] that singlet oxygen is the reactive species in oxidation reactions of olefins and dienes.

Oxygen is a ground state triplet. Its most stable configuration involves two unpaired electrons, one on each of the atoms of the molecule: $\cdot\overline{O}{-}\overline{O}\cdot$. Photosensitization of the oxygen has been proposed, by Kautsky, to reverse one of the electron spins and produce an excited oxygen molecule with paired rather than unpaired electron spins. The complete mechanism for photosensitized oxidation reactions, therefore, would involve sensitized conversion of triplet oxygen to singlet oxygen followed by reaction of the singlet oxygen with the ground state of the diene molecule. Generally, the triplet state sensitizer is responsible for the spin reversal.

Foote and Wexler[228] and Corey and Taylor[230] have succeeded in generating what are, presumably, singlet oxygen molecules in solution. Several workers have shown that the reaction of sodium hypochlorite and hydrogen peroxide produces *in situ* an excited oxygen molecule.[234-235] Its properties have been diagnosed and described by chemiluminescence studies. Foote and Wexler

Table 6-14

Photosensitized Oxidation Reactions

Compound	Sensitizer	Product	Reference
citronellal	rose bengal	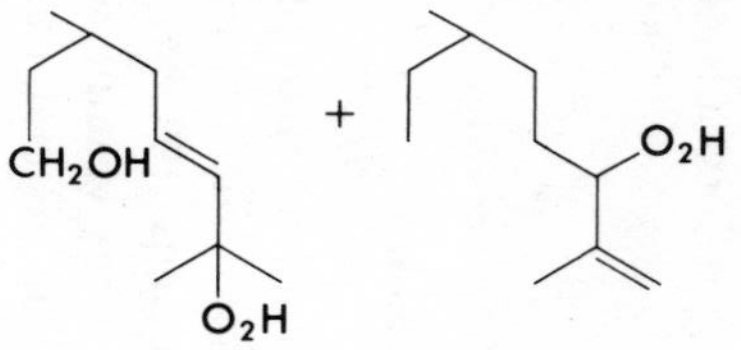	219
$(C_6H_5)_3SnCH_2CH{=}C(CH_3)_2$	rose bengal		220
furfural	eosin + ethanol	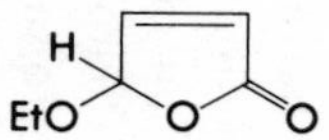	220
menthene	rose bengal	6 isomeric hydroperoxides	215, 222
$\Delta^{1,9}$-octalin	rose bengal	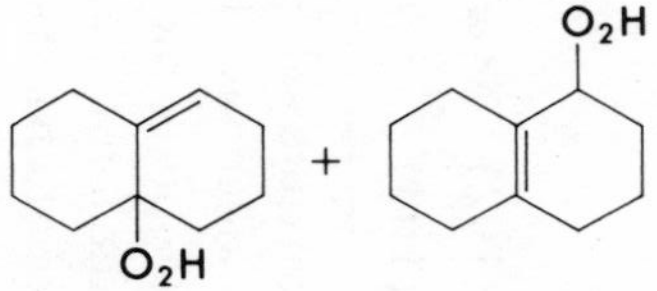	221

cyclohexylidinecyclohexane	rose bengal	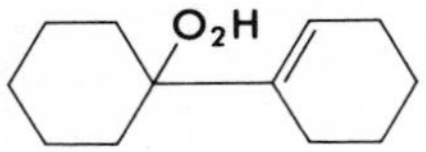	222
tetramethylethylene	rose bengal	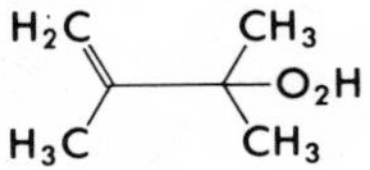	221
2,5-dimethylfuran	rose bengal, methanol	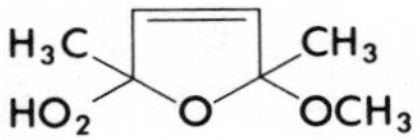	223
isopropyl alcohol	benzophenone	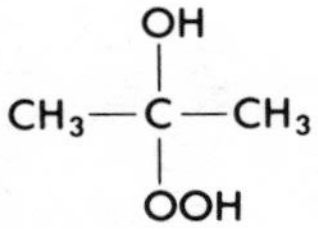	224
2-butanol	variety	hydroperoxides	225
3-pentanol	variety	hydroperoxides	225
dimethylsulfoxide	variety	dimethylsulfone	226
tetraphenylcyclopentadienone	variety	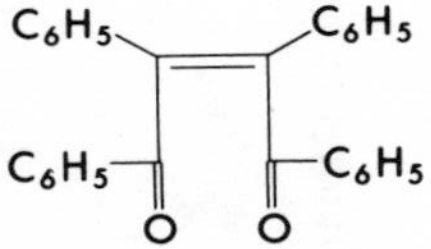	227

observe that the same product ratios are obtained when dienes and olefins are treated with oxygen generated by the reaction of hydrogen peroxide and sodium hypochlorite as are obtained from the photosensitized reaction of these unsaturated hydrocarbons with oxygen.   Thus α-terpinene yields ascaridole, eq. (104); 2,5-dimethylfuran yields I in methanol, eq. (105);

(104)

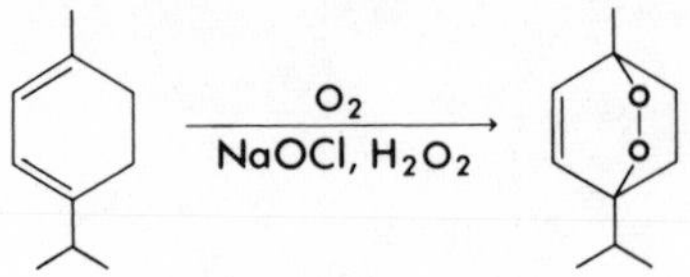

$$\xrightarrow[\text{NaOCl, H}_2\text{O}_2]{\text{O}_2}$$

(105)

$$\xrightarrow[\text{MeOH, H}_2\text{O}_2]{\text{NaOCl}}$$

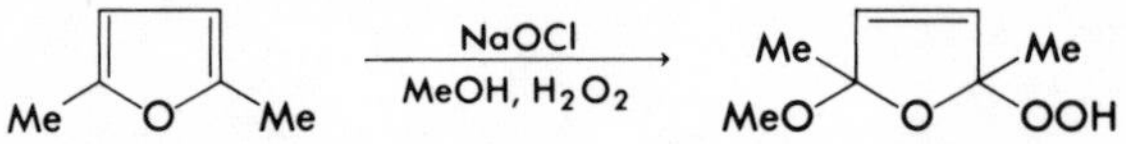

tetramethylethylene yields 2,3-dimethyl-3-hydroperoxybutene-1, eq. (106);

(106)

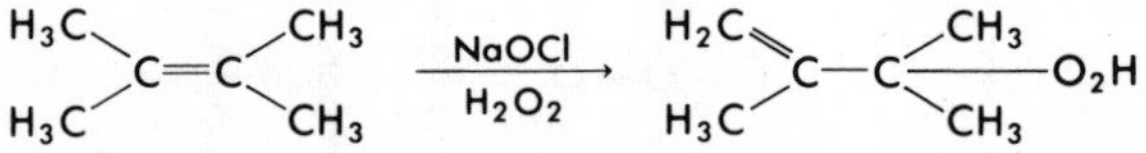

$$\underset{\text{H}_3\text{C}}{\overset{\text{H}_3\text{C}}{}}\text{C}=\text{C}\underset{\text{CH}_3}{\overset{\text{CH}_3}{}} \xrightarrow[\text{H}_2\text{O}_2]{\text{NaOCl}} \underset{\text{H}_3\text{C}}{\overset{\text{H}_2\text{C}}{}}\text{C}-\text{C}\underset{\text{CH}_3}{\overset{\text{CH}_3}{}}-\text{O}_2\text{H}$$

tetraphenylcyclopentadienone leads to II, eq. (107); and 1,3-cyclohexadiene

(107)

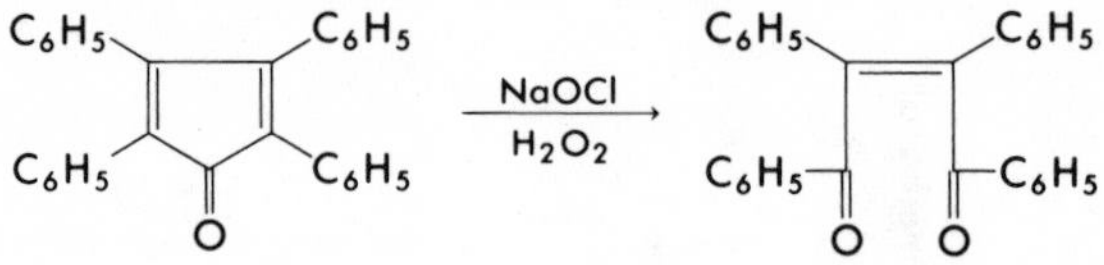

$$\xrightarrow[\text{H}_2\text{O}_2]{\text{NaOCl}}$$

II

(108)

$$\xrightarrow[\text{H}_2\text{O}_2]{\text{NaOCl}}$$

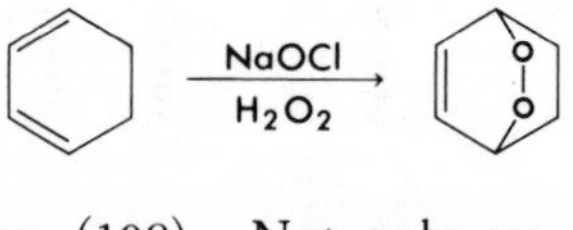

gives norascaridole, eq. (108).   Not only are all the products precisely the same as those obtained in the photosensitized reactions, but the yields of products obtained in this manner are also similar.

Corey and Taylor[230] have also proposed singlet oxygen as an intermediate in sensitized oxidation reactions.   They generated singlet oxygen by the method of Foner and Hudson,[236,237] which entailed excitation of ground state oxygen to a more energetic species by means of a radio-frequency discharge. Oxygen was passed through the discharge tube and into a stirred reaction mixture containing an active diene in an inert solvent.   By this method anthracene and substituted anthracenes were converted in high yields to *endo* peroxides identical in every respect to those prepared by a photooxidation

(109)

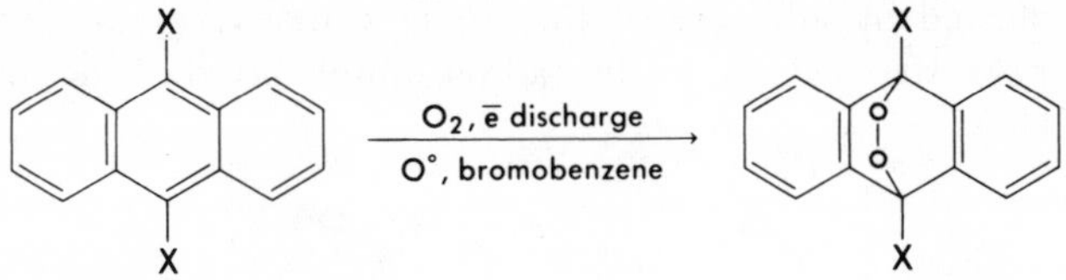

X = H, C$_6$H$_5$, or Me

pathway, eq. (109). No other products were isolated. Furthermore, reactive 1,3-dienes such as α-terpinene and 2,5-diphenyl-3,4-isobenzofuran were converted to peroxidic products and derivatives therefrom in analogous fashion to the photochemical reaction process. Attempts to isolate allylic hydroperoxides from suitable olefins and apparent singlet oxygen have been unsuccessful.

Owing to the tremendous practical importance of oxidation reactions, they have been studied in detail; however, the operative mechanisms are still not well understood. The interested reader is referred to one of the several extensive reviews on the subject.[238-242]

Addition Reactions Involving other Small Molecules

Addition of other small molecules (such as nitrosyl chloride, sulfur dioxide, the halogens, or the hydrogen halides) to olefins involves chain processes and will be discussed later. The only reported addition of any of these materials to unsaturated linkages proceeding through nonchain photosequences is the addition of sulfur dioxide to orthoquinones reported by Schenck, eq. (110).[218] Cyclic aryl sulfates are the reported products.

(110)

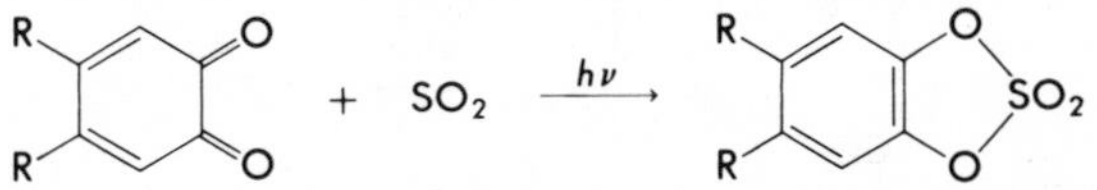

Addition reactions to orthoquinones and α-diketones also have been reported by Schönberg, Mustafa, and co-workers.[243] In general terms, the reaction involves the addition of an olefin to a 4π electron system in a manner somewhat analogous to the normal Diels-Alder thermal reaction sequence, eq. (111). The products are substituted 1,4 dioxanes. Although

(111)

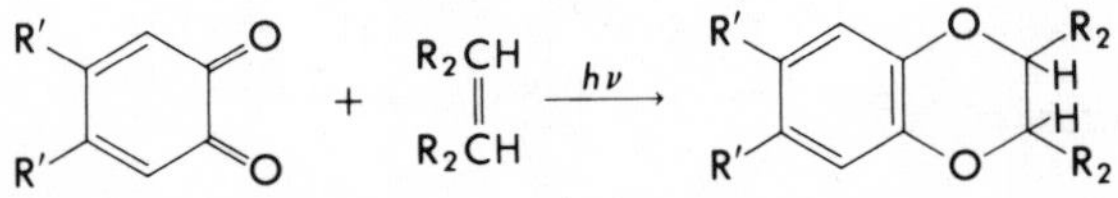

no mechanistic studies of this interesting reaction have been reported, a feasible reaction sequence would involve triplet state excitation of the quinone, followed by addition of the triplet carbonyl group, either in a concerted or two step fashion, to the carbon double bond of the olefin, eqs. (112) and (113).

(112)

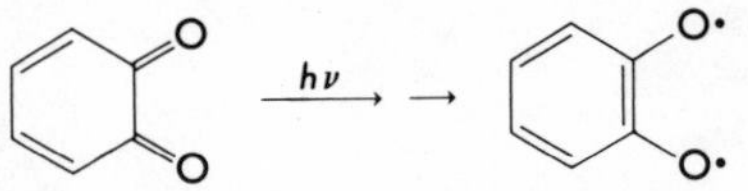

(113)

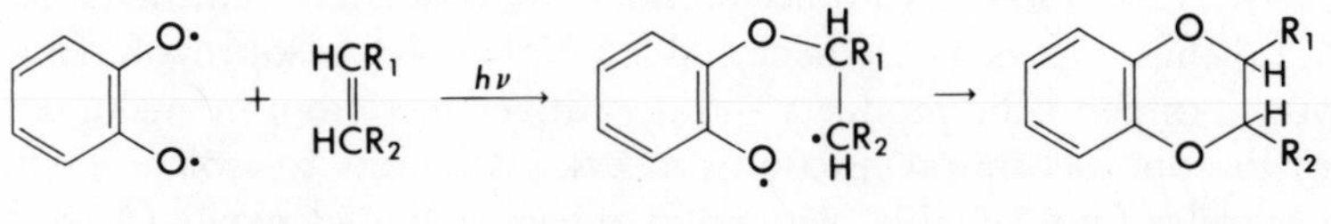

Since orthoquinones can also function as Diels-Alder dienes,[244] it is apparent that the photochemical addition to the carbon-oxygen double bond system competes favorably with this Diels-Alder reaction because of the greater spectroscopic availability of the carbonyl chromophore and the greater reactivity of the excited state of the carbonyl over the thermally excited state of the quinoid diene. Quinone-olefin couples for which facile Diels-Alder reactions occur in the dark lead to photoadducts exclusively at similar temperatures in sunlight, eqs. (114) and (115).[244] Schenck and

(114)

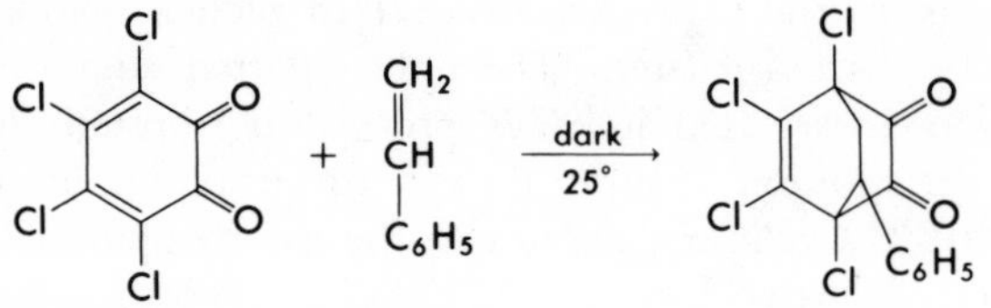

(115)

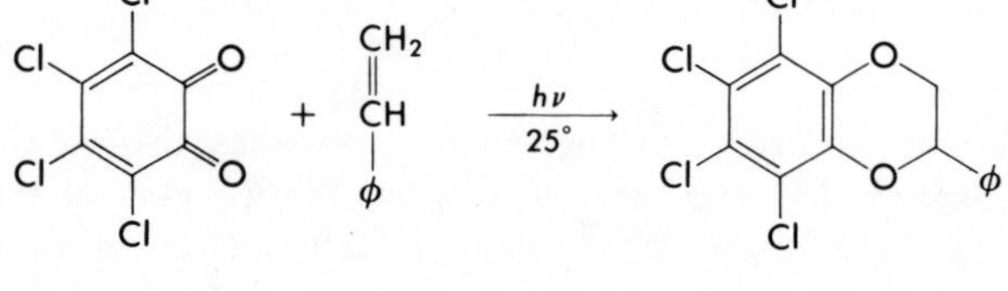

co-workers have reported similar addition reactions with unsaturated ethers.[168]

References

1. Fritzsche, J., *J. prakt. Chem.*, **101**, (1) 337 (1867).
2. Elbs, K., *J. prakt. Chem.*, (2) **44**, 467 (1891).
3. Orndorff, W. R., and F. K. Cameron, *Am. Chem., J.*, **17**, 658 (1895).

4. Fischer, O., and H. J. Ziegler, *J. prakt. Chem.*, (2) **86**, 289 (1912).
5. Orndorff, W. R., and H. A. Megraw, *Am. Chem. J.*, **22**, 152 (1899).
6. Applequist, D. E., R. L. Litle, E. C. Friedrich, and R. E. Wall, *J. Am. Chem. Soc.*, **81**, 452 (1959).
7. Weigert, F., and L. Kummerer, *Chem. Ber.*, **47**, 898 (1914).
8. Willemart, A., *Compt. rend.*, **205**, 993 (1937).
9. Greene, F. D., S. Misrock, and J. R. Wolfe, Jr., *J. Am. Chem. Soc.*, **77**, 3852 (1955).
10. Bartlett, P. D., and F. D. Greene, *J. Am. Chem. Soc.*, **76**, 1088 (1954).
11. Calas, R., R. Lalande, J. G. Faugere and F. Moulines, *Bull. Soc. Chim. France*, 119 (1965).
12. Etienne, A., *Ann. chim.*, **12**, 1, 5 (1946).
13. Etienne, A., *Compt. rend.*, **219**, 622 (1944).
14. Mustafa, A., *Advances in Photochemistry*, Vol. II, p. 91, New York, Wiley, 1964.
15. For a general reference to photochemical dimerization reactions, the reader is referred to A. Mustafa, *Chem. Rev.*, **51**, 1 (1952).
16. Applequist, D. E., E. C. Friedrich, and M. T. Rogers, *J. Am. Chem. Soc.*, **81**, 457 (1959).
17. Suzuki, M., *Bull. Chem. Soc. Japan*, **18**, 146 (1943).
18. Suzuki, M., *ibid.*, **22**, 172 (1949).
19. Suzuki, M., *ibid.*, **23**, 120 (1950).
20. Cherkasov, A. S., *Optika i Spektroskopiya*, **7**, 326 (1959).
21. Cherkasov, A. S., and T. M. Vember, *ibid.*, **7**, 321 (1959).
22. Vember, T. M., and A. S. Cherkasov, *ibid.*, **6**, 232 (1959).
23. Schönberg, A., *Trans. Faraday Soc.*, **32**, 514 (1936).
24. Clar, E., *Chem. Ber.*, **65**, 503 (1932).
25. See, for example, E. J. Bowen and D. W. Tanner, *Trans. Faraday Soc.*, **51**, 475 (1955).
26. Vember, T. M., L. A. Kiyanskaya, and A. Cherkasov, *Zh. Obshch. Khim.*, **33**, (4), 2342 (1963).
27. Cherkasov, A. S., and T. M. Vember, *Optika i Spektroskopiya*, **6**, 503 (1959).
28. Wan, J. K. S., R. N. McCormick, E. J. Baum, and J. N. Pitts, Jr., *J. Am. Chem. Soc.*, **87**, 4409 (1965).
29. Bradshaw, J. S., and G. S. Hammond, *J. Am. Chem. Soc.*, **85**, 3953 (1963).
30. Doeller, E., and T. Foerster, *Z. Phyzik. Chem.*, **34**, 132 (1962).
31. Doeller, E., *ibid.*, **34**, 151 (1962).
32. Taylor, E. C., W. W. Paudler, and I. Kuntz, Jr., *J. Am. Chem. Soc.*, **83**, 2967 (1961).
33. Taylor, E. C., and W. W. Paudler, *Tetrahedron Letters*, **25**, 1 (1960).
34. Taylor, E. C., R. O. Kan, and W. W. Paudler, *J. Am. Chem. Soc.*, **83**, 4484 (1961).
35. Taylor, E. C., and R. O. Kan, *J. Am. Chem. Soc.*, **85**, 776 (1963).
36. Slomp, G., F. A. MacKellar, and L. A. Paquette, *J. Am. Chem. Soc.*, **83**, 4472 (1961).
37. Paquette, L. A., and G. Slomp, *J. Am. Chem. Soc.*, **85**, 765 (1963).
38. Ayer, W. A., R. Hayatsu, P. de Mayo, S. T. Reid, and J. B. Strothers, *Tetrahedron Letters*, 648 (1961).
39. de Mayo, P., and R. W. Yip, *Proc. Chem. Soc.*, 84 (1964).
40. Corey, E. J., and J. Streith, *J. Am. Chem. Soc.*, **86**, 950 (1964).
41. Pirkle, W. H., *J. Am. Chem. Soc.*, **87**, 3022 (1965).
42. Padwa, A., and R. Hartman, *J. Am. Chem. Soc.*, **86**, 4212 (1964).
43. Stobbe, H., and A. Lehfeldt, *Chem. Ber.*, **58**, 2415 (1925).
44. de Jong, A. W. K., *Chem. Weekblad*, **26**, 270 (1929).
45. Stobbe, H., *Chem. Ber.*, **45**, 3396 (1912).
46. Stobbe, H., and F. Kuhrmann, *Chem. Ber.*, **58**, 85 (1925).
47. Lohaus, H., *Ann. Chem.*, **514**, 137 (1934).
48. Stobbe, H., A. Hensel, and W. Simon, *J. prakt. Chem.*, **110**, 129 (1925).

49. Stobbe, H., and C. Rücker, *Chem. Ber.*, **44**, 869 (1911).
50. Ruheman, S., *J. Chem. Soc.*, **85**, 1451 (1904).
51. Stobbe, H., *Chem. Ber.*, **58**, 2859 (1925).
52. Filler, R., and E. J. Piasek, *J. Org. Chem.*, **28**, 221 (1963).
53. Schmidt, G. M. J., *Acta Cryst.*, **10**, 793 (1957).
54. Griffin, G. W., A. F. Vellturo, and K. Furukawa, *J. Am. Chem. Soc.*, **83**, 2725 (1961).
55. Griffin, G. W., J. E. Basinski, and L. I. Peterson, *J. Am. Chem. Soc.*, **84**, 1012 (1962).
56. Griffin, G. W., and D. F. Veber, *J. Am. Chem. Soc.*, **82**, 6417 (1960).
57. Griffin, G. W., private communication.
58. Cohen, M. D., and G. M. J. Schmidt, *J. Chem. Soc.*, 1996 (1964).
59. Cohen, M. D., G. M. J. Schmidt, and F. I. Sonntag, *J. Chem. Soc.*, 2000 (1964).
60. Schmidt, G. M. J., *ibid.*, 2014 (1964).
61. Bregman, J., K. Osaki, G. M. J. Schmidt, and F. I. Sonntag, *ibid.*, 2021 (1964).
62. Rabinovich, D., and G. M. J. Schmidt, *ibid.*, 2030 (1964).
63. Cohen, M. D., G. M. J. Schmidt, and S. Flavian, *ibid.*, 2041 (1964).
64. Cohen, M. D., Y. Hirshberg, and G. M. J. Schmidt, *ibid.*, 2051 (1964).
65. Cohen, M. D., Y. Hirshberg, and G. M. J. Schmidt, *ibid.*, 2060 (1964).
66. Hertel, E., Z. *Electrochem.*, **37**, 536 (1931).
67. Norment, H. G., Jr., *Dissertation Abstr.*, **16**, 2323 (1956).
68. Hammond, G. S., N. J. Turro, and R. S. H. Liu, *J. Org. Chem.*, **28**, 3297 (1963).
69. Liu, R. S. H., N. J. Turro, and G. S. Hammond, *J. Am. Chem. Soc.*, **87**, 3406 (1965).
70. Dziewonski, K., and C. Paschalski, *Chem. Ber.*, **46**, 1986 (1913).
71. Adams, R., and M. H. Gold, *J. Am. Chem. Soc.*, **62**, 2038 (1940).
72. Schönberg, A., et al., *J. Chem. Soc.*, 374 (1950).
73. Ciamician, G., and P. Silber, *Chem. Ber.*, **35**, 4129 (1902).
74. Williams, J. L. R., *J. Org. Chem.*, **25**, 1839 (1960).
75. Jorgenson, M. J., *J. Org. Chem.*, **28**, 2929 (1963).
76. Koller, G., *Chem. Ber.*, **60b**, 1920 (1927).
77. Henze, M., *Chem. Ber.*, **70b**, 1273 (1937).
78. Williams, J. L. R., S. K. Webster, and J. A. Van Allan, *J. Org. Chem.*, **26**, 4893 (1961).
79. Ueberreiter, K., and K. Jander, *Macromol. Chem.*, **40**, 95 (1960).
80. Uhler, R. O., H. Schechter, and G. V. D. Tiers, *J. Am. Chem. Soc.*, **84**, 3397 (1962).
81. Eaton, P. E., *J. Am. Chem. Soc.*, **84**, 2344 (1962).
82. Eaton, P. E., *J. Am. Chem. Soc.*, **84**, 2454 (1962).
83. Schönberg, A., *Praparative Organische Photochemie*, Berlin, Springer, 1958.
84. de Mayo, P. in *Advances in Organic Chemistry*, Vol. II, p. 387, New York, Interscience, 1960.
85. House, H. O., *J. Org. Chem.*, **24**, 1374 (1959).
86. Yates, P., and M. J. Jorgenson, *J. Am. Chem. Soc.*, **80**, 6150 (1958).
87. Yates, P., and M. J. Jorgenson, *J. Am. Chem. Soc.*, **85**, 2956 (1963).
88. Corse, J., B. J. Finkle, and R. E. Lundin, *Tetrahedron Letters*, 1 (1961).
89. Recktenwald, G. W., J. N. Pitts, Jr., and R. L. Letsinger, *J. Am. Chem. Soc.*, **75**, 3028 (1953).
90. Bradsher, C. K., L. E. Beavers, and J. H. Jones, *J. Org. Chem.*, **22**, 1740 (1957).
91. Chapman, O. L., H. G. Smith, and R. W. King, *J. Am. Chem. Soc.*, **85**, 806 (1963).
92. Laing, M., *Proc. Chem. Soc.*, 343 (1964).
93. Chapman, O. L., H. G. Smith, R. W. King, D. J. Pasto, and M. R. Stoner, *J. Am. Chem. Soc.*, **85**, 2031 (1963).
94. Anet, R., *Chem. Ind.*, 897 (1960).
95. Anet, F. A. L., *Can. J. Chem.*, **40**, 1249 (1962).

96. Hammond, G. S., C. A. Stout, and A. A. Lamola, *J. Am. Chem. Soc.*, **86**, 3103 (1964).
97. Wang, S. Y., *Nature*, **190**, 690 (1961).
98. Lamola, A. A., *J. Am. Chem. Soc.*, **88**, 813 (1966).
99. Miller, D. B., and H. Schechter, Div. of Org. Chem., A. C. S. Meeting, San Francisco, 1958.
100. Parham, W. E., P. L. Stright, and W. R. Hasek, *J. Org. Chem.*, **24**, 262 (1959).
101. Bryce-Smith, D., and A. Gilbert, *J. Chem. Soc.*, 2428 (1964).
102. Zavarin, E., *J. Org. Chem.*, **23**, 47 (1958).
103. Flaig, W., J. C. Salfeld, and A. Llanox, *Angew. Chem.*, **72**, 110 (1960).
104. Cookson, R. C., D. A. Cox, and J. Hudec, *J. Chem. Soc.*, 4499 (1961).
105. Cookson, R. C., and J. Hudec, *Proc. Chem. Soc.*, 11 (1959).
106. de Mayo, P., and R. W. Yip, *Proc. Chem. Soc.*, 84 (1964).
107. Blackburn, G. M., and R. J. H. Davies, *Chem. Comm.*, 215 (1965).
108. Cookson, R. C., J. J. Frankel, and J. Hudec, *Chem. Comm.*, 16 (1965).
109. Kornis, G., and P. de Mayo, *Can. J. Chem.*, **42**, 2822 (1964).
110. Eaton, P. E., and T. W. Cole, Jr., *J. Am. Chem. Soc.*, **86**, 962 (1964).
111. Eaton, P. E., and T. W. Cole, Jr., *J. Am. Chem. Soc.*, **86**, 3157 (1964).
112. Dauben, W. G., and R. L. Cargill, *Tetrahedron Letters*, **15**, 197 (1961).
113. Hammond, G. S., N. J. Turro, and A. Fischer, *J. Am. Chem. Soc.*, **83**, 4674 (1961).
114. Cristol, S. J., and R. L. Snell, *J. Am. Chem. Soc.*, **80**, 1950 (1958).
115. Cristol, S. J., and R. L. Snell, *J. Am. Chem. Soc.*, **76**, 5600 (1954).
116. Büchi, G., and I. M. Goldman, *J. Am. Chem. Soc.*, **79**, 4741 (1957).
117. Cookson, R. C., E. Crundwell, and J. Hudec, *Chem. Ind.*, 1003 (1958).
118. White, E. H., and J. P. Anhalt, *Tetrahedron Letters*, 3937 (1965).
119. Crowley, K. J., *J. Am. Chem. Soc.*, **86**, 5692 (1964).
120. Meinwald, J., A. Eckell, and K. L. Erickson, *J. Am. Chem. Soc.*, **87**, 3532 (1965).
121. Paquette, L. A., J. H. Barrett, R. P. Spitz, and R. Pitcher, *J. Am. Chem. Soc.*, **87**, 3417 (1965).
122. Chapman, O. L., and D. J. Pasto, *Chem. Ind.*, 53 (1961).
123. Brown, M., *Chem. Comm.*, 340 (1965).
124. Srinivasan, R., *J. Phys. Chem.*, **67**, 1367 (1963).
125. Srinivasan, R., *J. Am. Chem. Soc.*, **85**, 819 (1963).
126. Crowley, K. J., *Proc. Chem. Soc.*, 17 (1964).
127. de Kock, R. J., N. G. Minaard, and E. Havinga, *Rev. trav. chim.*, **79**, 922 (1960).
128. Cookson, R. C., and E. Crundwell, *Chem. Ind.*, 1004 (1958).
129. Cookson, R. C., and J. Hudec, *Proc. Chem. Soc.*, 11 (1959).
130. Woodward, R. B., and R. Hoffman, *J. Am. Chem. Soc.*, **87**, 395 (1965).
131. Havinga, E., R. J. de Kock, and M. P. Rappoldt, *Tetrahedron Letters*, **11**, 276 (1960).
132. Fonken, G. J., *Tetrahedron Letters*, 549 (1962).
133. Srinivasan, R., and K. A. Hill, *J. Am. Chem. Soc.*, **87**, 4988 (1965).
134. Baldwin, J. E., and R. H. Greeley, *J. Am. Chem. Soc.*, **87**, 4514 (1965).
135. Zirner, J., and S. Winstein, *Proc. Chem. Soc.*, 235 (1964).
136. Roth, W. R., and C. B. Peltzer, *Angew. Chem. Intern. Ed.*, **3**, 440 (1964).
137. Dauben, W. G., and F. G. Willey, *Tetrahedron Letters*, 893 (1962).
138. Roquitte, B. C., *J. Am. Chem. Soc.*, **85**, 3700 (1963).
139. Crowley, K. J., *Tetrahedron*, **21**, 1001 (1965).
140. Chapman, O. L., *Advances in Photochemistry*, Vol. I, p. 359, New York, Wiley, 1964.
141. Meinwald, J., *Record Chem. Progr.*, **22**, 39 (1961).
142. Büchi, G., and E. M. Burgess, *J. Am. Chem. Soc.*, **82**, 4333 (1960).
143. Fonken, G. J., *Chem. Ind.*, 1327 (1962).

144. Evanega, G. R., W. Bergmann, and J. English, Jr., *J. Org. Chem.*, **27**, 13 (1962).
145. Cookson, R. C., J. Hudec, S. A. Knight, and B. Whitear, *Tetrahedron Letters*, 79 (1962).
146. Jorgenson, M. J., and N. C. Yang, *J. Am. Chem. Soc.*, **85**, 1698 (1963).
147. Büchi, G., and E. M. Burgess, *J. Am. Chem. Soc.*, **84**, 3104 (1962).
148. van Tamelen, E. E., and S. P. Pappas, *J. Am. Chem. Soc.*, **84**, 3789 (1962).
149. van Tamelen, E. E., and S. P. Pappas, *J. Am. Chem. Soc.*, **85**, 3297 (1963).
150. Wilzbach, K. E., and L. Kaplan, *J. Am. Chem. Soc.*, **86**, 2307 (1964).
151. Burgstahler, A. W., P. L. Chien, and M. O. Abdel-Rahman, *J. Am. Chem. Soc.*, **86**, 5281 (1964).
152. Burgstahler, A. W., and P. L. Chien, *J. Am. Chem. Soc.*, **86**, 2940 (1964).
153. Kaplan, L., K. E. Wilzbach, W. G. Brown, and S. S. Yang, *J. Am. Chem. Soc.*, **87**, 675 (1965).
154. Wilzbach, K. E., and L. Kaplan, *J. Am. Chem. Soc.*, **87**, 4004 (1965).
155. Wynberg, H., and H. van Driel, *J. Am. Chem. Soc.*, **87**, 3998 (1965).
156. Wynberg, H., and H. van Driel, *Chem. Comm.*, 203 (1966).
157. de Mayo, P., in *Advances in Organic Chemistry: Methods and Results*, Vol. II, p. 372, New York, Interscience, 1960.
158. Masson, C. R., W. A. Noyes, Jr., and V. Boekelheide, in *Technique in Organic Chemistry*, Vol. II, p. 310 ff, New York, Interscience, 1956.
159. Paterno, E., and G. Chieffi, *Gazz. chim. ital.*, **39b**, 341 (1909).
160. Büchi, G., C. G. Inman, and E. S. Lipinsky, *J. Am. Chem. Soc.*, **76**, 4327 (1954).
161. Büchi, G., J. T. Kofron, E. Koller, and D. Rosenthal, *J. Am. Chem. Soc.*, **78**, 876 (1956).
162. Büchi, G., and N. C. Yang, *J. Am. Chem. Soc.*, **79**, 2318 (1957).
163. Arnold, D. R., R. C. Hinman, and A. H. Glick, *Tetrahedron Letters*, 1425 (1964).
164. Yang, N. C., *Pure Appl. Chem.*, **9**, 591 (1964).
165. Barltrop, J. A., and B. Hesp, *Proc. Chem. Soc.*, 195 (1964).
166. Barltrop, J. A., and B. Hesp, *J. Chem. Soc.*, 5182 (1965).
167. Bryce-Smith, D., and A. Gilbert, *Proc. Chem. Soc.*, 87 (1964).
168. Krauch, C. H., S. Farid, and G. O. Schenck, *Chem. Ber.*, **98**, 3102 (1965).
169. Kharasch, M. S., W. H. Urry, and B. M. Kuderna, *J. Org. Chem.*, **14**, 248 (1949).
170. Harris, J. F., Jr., and D. D. Coffman, *J. Am. Chem. Soc.*, **84**, 1553 (1962).
171. Srinivasan, R., *J. Am. Chem. Soc.*, **82**, 775 (1960).
172. de Mayo, P., and W. Templeton, reported in ref. 157, p. 397.
173. Bradshaw, J. S., *J. Org. Chem.*, **31**, 237 (1966).
174. Kaiser, E. T., and T. F. Wulfers, *J. Am. Chem. Soc.*, **86**, 1897 (1964).
175. Gritter, R. J., and E. C. Sabatino, *J. Org. Chem.*, **29**, 1965 (1964).
176. Scharf, H. D., and F. Korte, *Chem. Ber.*, **98**, 764 (1965).
177. Corey, E. J., J. D. Bass, R. LeMahieu, and R. B. Mitra, *J. Am. Chem. Soc.*, **86**, 5570 (1964).
178. Barltrop, J. A., and R. Robson, *Tetrahedron Letters*, 597 (1963).
179. Robson, R., P. W. Grubb, and J. A. Barltrop, *J. Chem. Soc.*, 2153 (1964).
180. Andrews, L. J., *Chem. Rev.*, **54**, 713 (1954).
181. McGlynn, S. P., *Chem. Rev.*, **58**, 1113 (1958).
182. Murrell, J. N., *Quart. Rev.*, **15**, 191 (1961).
183. Singer, L. A., and P. D. Bartlett, *Tetrahedron Letters*, 1887 (1964).
184. Singer, L. A., and P. D. Bartlett, unpublished observations.
185. Throndsen, H. C., G. Cainelli, D. Arigoni, and O. Jeger, *Helv. Chim. Acta*, **45**, 2342 (1962).
186. Rubin, M. B., G. E. Hipps, and D. Glover, *J. Org. Chem.*, **29**, 68 (1964).

187. Rubin, M. B., D. Glover, and R. G. Parker, *Tetrahedron Letters*, 1075 (1964).
188. de Mayo, P., and H. Takeshita, *Can. J. Chem.*, **41**, 440 (1963).
189. de Mayo, P., H. Takeshita, and A. B. M. A. Sattar, *Proc. Chem. Soc.*, 119 (1962).
190. Corey, E. J., R. B. Mitra, and H. Uda, *J. Am. Chem. Soc.*, **85**, 362 (1963).
191. Corey, E. J., R. B. Mitra, and H. Uda, *J. Am. Chem. Soc.*, **86**, 485 (1964).
192. Corey, E. J., and S. Nozoe, *J. Am. Chem. Soc.*, **86**, 1652 (1964).
193. de Mayo, P., R. W. Yip, and S. T. Reid, *Proc. Chem. Soc.*, 54 (1963).
194. Cookson, R. C., R. R. Hill, and J. Hudec, *J. Chem. Soc.*, 3043 (1964).
195. de Mayo, P., S. T. Reid, and R. W. Yip, *Can. J. Chem.*, **42**, 2828 (1964).
196. Scharf, H. D., and F. Korte, *Chem. Ber.*, **98**, 3672 (1965).
197. Srinivasan, R., and K. A. Hill, *J. Am. Chem. Soc.*, **87**, 4653 (1965).
198. Angus, H. J. F., and D. Bryce-Smith, *J. Chem. Soc.*, 4791 (1960).
199. Grovenstein, E., Jr., D. V. Rao, and J. W. Taylor, *J. Am. Chem. Soc.*, **83**, 1705 (1961).
200. Vermont, G. B., P. X. Riccobono, and J. Blake, *J. Am. Chem. Soc.*, **87**, 4024 (1965).
201. Bryce-Smith, D., A. Gilbert, and B. Vickery, *Chem. Ind.*, 2060 (1962).
202. Bryce-Smith, D., and J. E. Lodge, *J. Chem. Soc.*, 2675 (1962).
203. Schenck, G. O., and R. Steinmetz, *Tetrahedron Letters*, **21**, 1 (1960).
204. Bryce-Smith, D., and J. E. Lodge, *J. Chem. Soc.*, 695 (1963).
205. Bryce-Smith, D., and J. E. Lodge, *Proc. Chem. Soc.*, 333 (1961).
206. Grovenstein, E., Jr., and D. V. Rao, *Tetrahedron Letters*, 148 (1961).
207. White, E. H., and R. L. Stern, *Tetrahedron Letters*, 193 (1964).
208. Taylor, E. C., B. Furth, and M. Pfau, *J. Am. Chem. Soc.*, **87**, 1400 (1965).
209. Bowen, E. J., and D. W. Tanner, *Trans. Faraday Soc.*, **51**, 475 (1955).
210. Bowen, E. J., *Trans. Faraday Soc.*, **50**, 97 (1954).
211. Bowen, E. J., *Disc. Faraday Soc.*, **14**, 143 (1953).
212. For a review see E. J. Bowen in *Advances in Photochemistry*, Vol. I, pp. 37–39, New York, Wiley, 1963.
213. Bergmann, W., and M. J. McLean, *Chem. Rev.*, **28**, 367 (1941).
214. Schenck, G. O., and K. Ziegler, *Naturwissenschaften*, **32**, 157 (1945).
215. Schenck, G. O., K. Gollnick, G. Buchwald, S. Schroeter, and G. Ohloff, *Ann. Chem.*, **674**, 93 (1964).
216. Schenck, G. O., unpublished results quoted in reference 215.
217. Schönberg, A., *Präparative Organische Photochemie*, Springer, Berlin, 1958.
218. Schenck, G. O., *Angew. Chim.*, **64**, 12 (1952).
219. Ohloff, G., E. Klein, and G. O. Schenck, *Angew. Chem.*, **73**, 578 (1961).
220. Schenck, G. O., *Ind. Eng. Chem.*, **55** (6), 40 (1963).
221. Schenck, G. O., and H. K. Schulte-Elte, *Ann. Chem.*, **618**, 185 (1958).
222. Schenck, G. O., S. Schroeter, and G. Ohloff, *Chem. Ind.*, 459 (1962).
223. Schenck, G. O., and C. S. Foote, *Angew. Chem.*, **70**, 505 (1958).
224. Schenck, G. O., and H. D. Becker, *Angew. Chem.*, **70**, 504 (1958).
225. Schenck, G. O., H. D. Becker, K. H. Schulte-Elte, and C. H. Krauch, *Chem. Ber.*, **96**, 509 (1963).
226. Schenck, G. O., and C. H. Krauch, *Chem. Ber.*, **96**, 517 (1963).
227. Schenck, G. O., *Z. Electrochem.*, **56**, 855 (1952).
228. Foote, C. S., and S. Wexler, *J. Am. Chem. Soc.*, **86**, 3879 (1964).
229. Foote, C. S., and S. Wexler, *J. Am. Chem. Soc.*, **86**, 3880 (1964).
230. Corey, E. J., and W. C. Taylor, *J. Am. Chem. Soc.*, **86**, 3881 (1964).
231. Kautsky, H., and H. de Bruijn, *Naturwiss*, **19**, 1043 (1931).
232. Kautsky, H., H. de Bruijn, R. Neuwirth, and W. Baumeister, *Chem. Ber.*, **66**, 1588 (1933).

233. Kautsky, H., *Biochem. Z.*, **291**, 271 (1937).
234. See, for example, A. U. Khan and M. Kasha, *J. Chem. Phys.*, **39**, 2105 (1963).
235. Arnold, S. J., E. A. Ogryzlo, and H. Witzke, *J. Chem. Phys.*, **40**, 1769 (1964).
236. Foner, S. N., and R. L. Hudson, *J. Chem. Phys.*, **25**, 601 (1956).
237. Foner, S. N., and R. L. Hudson, *J. Chem. Phys.*, **23**, 1974 (1955).
238. Waters, W. A., *Ann. Rept. Chem. Soc.*, **42**, 130 (1945).
239. Bolland, J. L., *Quart. Rev.*, **3**, 1 (1949).
240. Bateman, L., *Quart. Rev.*, **8**, 147 (1954).
241. Ingold, K. U., *Chem. Rev.*, **61**, 563 (1961).
242. Waters, W. A., *Mechanisms of Oxidation Reactions of Organic Compounds*, London, Methuen, 1964.
243. See Schönberg, A., and A. Mustafa, *Chem. Rev.*, **40**, 181 (1947).
244. Schönberg, A., and N. Latif, *J. Chem. Soc.*, 446 (1952).

CHAPTER
7

Photochemical Atom Abstractions

The photochemical atom abstraction reaction may be defined as that reaction of a photochemically excited state in which one of the atoms of an excited chromophore abstracts an atom from the solvent or another reactant to give two free radical products. The atom abstraction generally involves hydrogen atoms, and we may visualize the atom abstraction process as a reaction in which a photochemically excited state displaces a radical from a ground state molecule, eq. (1). Atom abstraction reactions have many paral-

(1) $AB^* + RH \rightarrow R\cdot + ABH\cdot$

lels in normal free radical sequences, and many analogies between the reactions and reactivity of photoexcited states and those of similar free radicals contribute to our understanding of both types of reactions.

Benzophenone

Ciamician and Silber[1] and Cohen[2] discovered the first atom abstraction reaction. These workers showed that irradiation of benzophenone in alcohol solvents leads to benzpinacol and the oxidized alcohol as the sole products, eq. (2). The reaction was found to be general for many sources of atomic

$$(2) \quad \underset{\substack{\| \\ O}}{C_6H_5-C-C_6H_5} + \underset{\substack{| \\ R}}{RCHOH} \xrightarrow{h\nu} \underset{\substack{| \quad | \\ \quad C_6H_5C_6H_5}}{C_6H_5-C-C-C_6H_5} + \underset{\substack{\| \\ O}}{RCR'}$$

R = ,H, alkyl or aryl

hydrogen[3,4] but to fail in solvents possessing no labile hydrogen.[5] The alcohols were found to be the best source of hydrogen atoms with only those alcohols possessing independent chromophores, for example, cinnamyl alcohol, failing to produce pinacol. The yield of pinacol was higher for aliphatic than for aryl carbinols.

The reaction appears to be general for a variety of aryl ketones, and Weismann, Bergmann, and Hirschberg[6] have proposed the mechanism shown in eqs. (3–6) for the photoreduction of aryl and diaryl ketones.

$$(3) \quad \underset{\substack{\| \\ O}}{ArCAr'} \xrightarrow{h\nu} \underset{\substack{\| \\ O^*}}{ArCAr'}$$

$$(4) \quad \underset{\substack{\| \\ O^*}}{ArCAr'} + \underset{\substack{| \\ R'}}{RCHOH} \longrightarrow \underset{\substack{| \\ OH}}{Ar\overset{\bullet}{C}Ar'} + \underset{\substack{| \\ R'}}{R\overset{\bullet}{C}OH}$$

$$(5) \quad \underset{\substack{| \\ OH}}{2Ar\overset{\bullet}{C}Ar'} \longrightarrow \underset{\substack{| \quad | \\ Ar' \quad Ar'}}{Ar-C-C-Ar}$$

$$(6) \quad \underset{\substack{| \\ OH}}{2R\overset{\bullet}{C}R'} \longrightarrow \underset{\substack{\| \\ O}}{RCR'} + \underset{\substack{| \\ R'}}{RCH}$$

Weismann proposed that after the diaryl ketone absorbs the light, the excited state of the ketone then abstracts the α hydrogen from the alcohol, and free radical coupling and disproportionation reactions give the observed pinacolic and ketonic products.

Recent modifications of the mechanism of photoreduction of aromatic ketones have been proposed by Pitts and co-workers[7] and Hammond and co-workers.[8-10] Their results have been further substantiated by the results of Huyser and Neckers.[11,12] Pitts and co-workers found that optically active alcohols are recoverable without loss of optical activity when alcohol solutions of benzophenone are irradiated. Huyser and Neckers observed[12] that irradiation of either cis or trans 4-t-butylcyclohexanol solutions of benzophenone at somewhat higher temperatures leaves only the original alcohol after reaction. No production of the epimeric alcohol was observed. These results, presuming that free radicals lose their identity upon formation, disallow any radical disproportionation processes for the production of ketone. Pitts[7] suggested that ketone is formed by a hydrogen atom transfer from the alcohol radical to ground state diaryl ketone. This mechanism is shown in eqs. (7-9). Further evidence for the proposed atom transfer ketone forma-

$$(7) \quad C_6H_5\overset{O}{\overset{\|}{C}}C_6H_5 \;+\; R\overset{OH}{\underset{H}{\overset{|}{\underset{|}{C}}}}R' \;\xrightarrow{h\nu}\; R\overset{OH}{\underset{\cdot}{\overset{|}{C}}}R' \;+\; C_6H_5\overset{OH}{\underset{\cdot}{\overset{|}{C}}}C_6H_5$$

$$(8) \quad R\overset{OH}{\underset{\cdot}{\overset{|}{C}}}R' \;+\; C_6H_5\overset{O}{\overset{\|}{C}}C_6H_5 \;\longrightarrow\; R\overset{O}{\underset{\cdot}{\overset{\|}{C}}}R' \;+\; C_6H_5\overset{OH}{\underset{\cdot}{\overset{|}{C}}}C_6H_5$$

$$(9) \quad 2C_6H_5\overset{OH}{\underset{\cdot}{\overset{|}{C}}}C_6H_5 \;\longrightarrow\; \text{pinacol}$$

tion, eqs. (7-9), was provided by Huyser and Neckers[11,12] who showed that alcohol radicals generated in solution by other methods do transfer a hydrogen atom to diaryl and aryl ketones. Certain alkyl ketones are also reactive.[13,14]

Weizmann's mechanism, eqs. (3-6), in addition to requiring that optically active alcohol be racemized, also requires that each reacting benzophenone molecule absorb 1 light quantum. If this mechanism were operative, the limiting quantum yield for the disappearance of benzophenone would be 1, and if excited benzophenone moieties were distinguishable from nonexcited benzophenone moieties, the product benzpinacol would contain only excited benzophenone moieties. On the other hand, Pitts' modification would require that two benzophenone molecules be consumed per quantum of absorbed radiation, and that the product benzpinacol contain one excited and one unexcited benzophenone moiety. Since the quantum yield for benzophenone disappearance approaches two under ideal experimental conditions, Weismann's mechanism cannot be operative. Using C^{14}-tracer experiments, Franzen[15] has been able to distinguish between the excited and the nonexcited benzophenone portions of the product benzpinacol. In addition, Franzen[15] has observed that an exchange occurs between benzhydryl radicals and ground state benzophenone, eq. (10), so that when photolyzed in the

$$(10) \quad C_6H_5\overset{O}{\overset{\|}{C}}C_6H_5 \;+\; C_6H_5\overset{OH}{\overset{|}{C}}{}^*C_6H_5 \;\rightarrow\; C_6H_5\overset{OH}{\overset{|}{C}}C_6H_5 \;+\; C_6H_5\overset{O}{\overset{\|}{C}}{}^*C_6H_5$$

presence of α-C^{14} benzhydrol, benzophenone undergoes a reaction that gives benzpinacols containing two and zero C^{14} atoms, as well as benzpinacols containing only one C^{14} atom per molecule. Benzophenone marked with C^{14} is also produced.

The unique hydrogen atom transfer reaction proposed by Pitts[7] amounts to but the addition of a hydrogen atom to a π-bonded carbonyl system. The driving force for such a reaction is provided by the increase in resonance stabilization of the radical having two α-phenyl groups when aliphatic carbinols are used as hydrogen donors. However, as Franzen's work illustrates, the reaction also takes place when benzophenone is photolyzed in excess benzhydrol. No resonance stability is attained in the identity reaction between benzophenone and a benzhydryl radical. Since the rate of hydrogen atom exchange is affected by the polarity of the media, Franzen proposes an intermediate radical ion complex, eq. (11). (See, however, reference 13.)

(11)

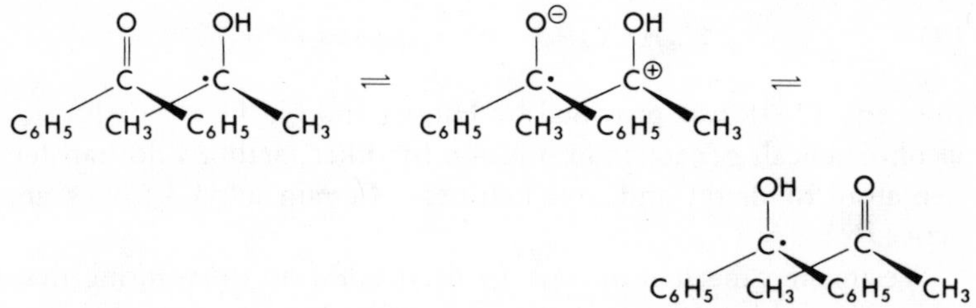

Huyser and Neckers[11] provide evidence suggesting that polar contributions are important in the forming of the intermediate in the hydrogen transfer reaction. These workers show that the reaction of alcohol radicals with aryl ketones can be caused by using other radical initiators and solutions of aryl ketones in alcohols. Thus, decomposition of di-t-butyl peroxide in 2-butanol-acetophenone solutions produces high yields of acetophenone pinacol, eq. (12), while decomposition of di-t-butyl peroxide in 2-butanol

(12)

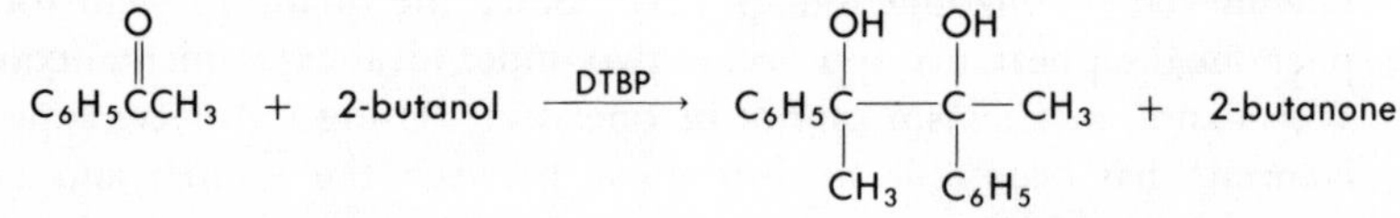

benzophenone produces benzhydrol* and 2-butanone, eq. (13). A chain

(13)

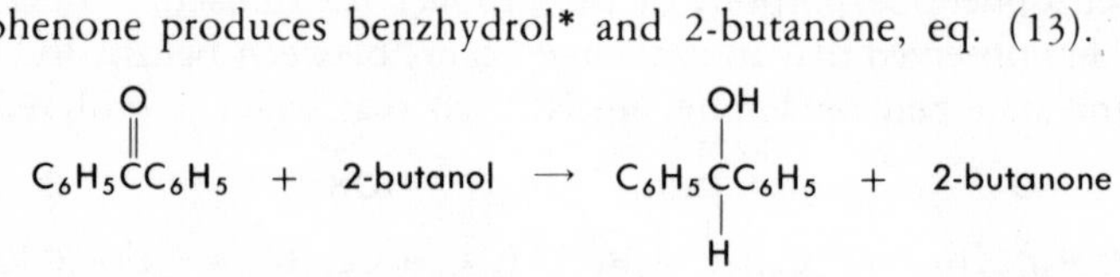

*Benzhydrol is the photoreduction product obtained when benzophenone is photolyzed in alcohol solutions at elevated temperatures. This observation (unpublished results of D. C. Neckers and E. S. Huyser) will be discussed shortly.

sequence is proposed in which the hydrogen atom transfer reaction is an important step, eqs. (14–17).

(14) $DTBP \longrightarrow 2tBuO\cdot$

(15) $tBuO\cdot \; + \; CH_3\overset{\overset{OH}{|}}{\underset{\underset{H}{|}}{C}}C_2H_5 \; \longrightarrow \; tBuOH \; + \; CH_3\overset{\overset{OH}{|}}{\underset{\cdot}{C}}C_2H_5$

(16) $CH_3\overset{\overset{OH}{|}}{\underset{\cdot}{C}}C_2H_5 \; + \; C_6H_5\overset{\overset{O}{||}}{C}C_6H_5 \; \longrightarrow \; CH_3\overset{\overset{O}{||}}{C}C_2H_5 \; + \; C_6H_5\overset{\overset{OH}{|}}{\underset{\cdot}{C}}C_6H_5$

(17) $2C_6H_5\overset{\overset{OH}{|}}{\underset{\cdot}{C}}C_6H_5 \; \longrightarrow \; C_6H_5\overset{\overset{O}{||}}{C}C_6H_5 \; + \; C_6H_5\overset{\overset{OH}{|}}{\underset{\underset{H}{|}}{C}}C_6H_5$

When acetophenone and substituted acetophenones are used as acceptor molecules in the hydrogen atom transfer sequence, it is observed that electron-withdrawing substituents accelerate the reaction rate. For a series of substituted acetophenones the rho value obtained via Hammett equation analysis equals $+1.59$. Large accumulation of negative character in the transition state is indicated.

The products obtained in the photoreduction of benzophenone depend markedly on temperature.[12] At ambient temperatures benzpinacol is the only observed product; however, as the temperature of the reaction mixture is raised in successive increments, more and more benzhydrol is isolated. At 100°, benzhydrol is formed in $3M$ excess to benzpinacol. In all probability the variation in products results because of the thermal instability of benzpinacol.[14]

Benzophenone versus Alkoxy Radicals

The nature of the excited state of benzophenone responsible for photohydrogen atom abstraction has recently been investigated by Hammond and co-workers,[9,10] by Walling and Gibian,[16,17] and by Padwa.[18] Walling has shown that, at least in terms of its reactivity as a hydrogen atom abstractor, excited benzophenone is very similar to an alkoxy radical. Table 7-1 lists the relative reactivities of several types of hydrogen atoms toward abstraction by t-butoxy radicals generated from t-butyl hypochlorite and by triplet state benzophenone generated photochemically.

Although a quantitative evaluation of the data indicates that there is some difference between excited benzophenone and ordinary t-butoxy radicals, the

Table 7-1

Relative Reactivities of Hydrogen Atoms Toward *t*-Butoxy Radicals and Triplet State Benzophenone

Solvent	Relative Reactivity		
	$(C_6H_5)_2C{=}O^{*a}$	$(C_6H_5)_2C{=}O^{*b}$	*t*BuOCl
toluene	1.0	1.0	1.0
cyclohexane	2.1		6.0
cumene	3.4	3.5	2.8
2-propanol	9.3		—
2-octanol	9.9		—
mesitylene	5.5		4.1
m-xylene	3.0		2.34
p-fluorotoluene	1.15		0.71
p-chlorotoluene	0.97		—
anisole	0.50		—
benzhydrol	—	250	—

[a]Data from Walling and Gibian, *J. Am. Chem. Soc.*, **86**, 3902 (1964).
[b]Data from Hammond et al., *J. Am. Chem. Soc.*, **83**, 2795 (1961).

relative rates of hydrogen donor ability are at least qualitatively similar. In addition, in every known case it appears that the solvent-derived products obtained from benzophenone hydrogen atom abstractions and from *t*-butoxy radical hydrogen abstractions are comparable. Several other examples pointing to this fact have been obtained by Huyser and Neckers.[12]

Cohen and Aktipis[19] report recent mechanistic studies on the photoreduction of benzophenone in ether solvents. The reaction of benzophenone with methyl-1-octyl ether proceeds about as rapidly as the reaction of benzophenone with 2-propanol. When optically active 2-octyl methyl ether is used, the ether recovered after partial reaction shows some racemization. Cohen also reports photoreductions using amines as hydrogen donors.[20]

The Excited State

Bäckström and Sandros[21-23] and Hammond and co-workers[24,8-10] have obtained spectroscopic and chemical evidence indicative of the apparent biradical character of photochemically excited benzophenone. Several observations concerning photochemical reactions of benzophenone indicate the complexity of the system. First, the quantum yield for photoreduction of benzophenone by benzhydrol in benzene solution decreases with decreasing concentration of hydrogen donor. Second, the quantum yield for photoreduction is decreased markedly by added oxygen, a fact indicative of biradical or triplet state intermediates or that certain of the radical intermediates react with oxygen to regenerate benzophenone and lower the quantum yield of the reduction. Third, even with low concentration of hydrogen donor ($0.1 M$), the quantum yield for the photoreduction is appreciable ($\phi = 0.26$), indicating that the lifetime of the excited state is long. Fourth, using the observation that the quantum yield of benzophenone disappearance decreases with decreasing concentration of hydrogen donor to indicate that a significant amount of collisional deactivation, eq. (18), occurs

$$(18) \quad \underset{\text{O*}}{\overset{\text{O*}}{\underset{\|}{C_6H_5\overset{\|}{C}C_6H_5}}} + \text{solvent} \longrightarrow \underset{\|}{\overset{\text{O}}{C_6H_5\overset{\|}{C}C_6H_5}} + \text{solvent} + h\nu$$

between solvent and excited benzophenone and the observation that $k_H/k_D = 2.7$ for hydrogen abstraction for the α-carbon of benzophenone, one can determine that the reaction between excited benzophenone and benzhydrol is *not* diffusion controlled. Fifth, since fluorescence has never been observed for benzophenone solutions,[25] the lifetime of benzophenone singlets before they undergo intersystem crossing to benzophenone triplets is less than 2×10^{-10} sec. Since the rate of hydrogen atom abstraction is not diffusion controlled, and the rate constant of thermal diffusion for benzophenone in benzene solution is calculated to be no greater than 2×10^{10} liter/mole sec, the rate constant for deactivation of excited singlet state benzophenone can be calculated to be at least 5×10^9 sec^{-1}. This suggests that singlet state decay always will occur before hydrogen atom abstraction. Therefore, since hydrogen atom abstraction occurs in solution, the excited state responsible must be the triplet state of benzophenone. Use of strong triplet state quenchers, such as paramagnetic metal salts and high concentrations of oxygen, supports the proposal that the paramagnetic triplet state is responsible for photoreduction of benzophenone. The quantum yield for photoreduction of benzophenone by benzhydrol in benzene solution in the presence of concentrations of oxygen or ferric dipivaloyl methide, a benzene-soluble iron salt, is decreased markedly.

The following rate constants for benzophenone triplet states have been calculated by Hammond and by Bäckström.[26] The lifetime of the triplet state of benzophenone $\cong 1.9 \times 10^{-6}$ sec, while the rate constant for hydrogen atom abstraction $\cong 5 \times 10^6$ liter/mole sec. The rate constant for collisional deactivation with solvent is $\cong 2.6 \times 10^5$ sec^{-1}, while the rate constants for quenching are nearly diffusion controlled $\cong 2 \times 10^9$ liter/mole sec.

Microscopically, the photoactivation of benzophenone to its triplet state involves the absorption of a light quantum at its n-π^* maximum (approximately 3300 Å), a process requiring about 10^{-12} sec, followed by intersystem crossing, requiring at least 10^{-9} sec, and hydrogen abstraction, requiring (depending upon concentration) about 10^{-5} sec. Since the reactions of free radical intermediates generally require nearly 10^{-6} sec, the free radical reactions (hydrogen abstraction and others) are the slow steps in the photoreduction of benzophenone. The energetics of the hydrogen abstraction process have been calculated by Walling and, at least for benzophenone, the reaction is estimated to be exothermic by about 102 kcal/mole.

Bell and Linschitz[27] have measured directly the rate constants for hydrogen abstraction by benzophenone triplets and for energy degradation of the same triplet. Flash photolysis of benzophenone in benzene solution results in two new species; one is benzophenone triplet and the other is a species, the concentration of which goes up as greater concentrations of hydrogen-donating material, such as benzhydrol or ethanol, are added to the solution.

$$\underset{|}{OH}$$

This second species is presumed to be the benzhydryl radical, $C_6H_5\underset{|}{C}C_6H_5$, observed by earlier workers.[28,29] Its appearance in pure benzene is hard to understand. The only detectable product from the photolysis of benzophenone in benzene is a trace amount of biphenyl. Whether or not benzpinacol is formed is open to question. The absorption attributed to benzophenone triplet decays following first order kinetics, $k = 1 \times 10^5$ sec^{-1}, whereas the reaction rate constant for hydrogen abstraction from benzhydrol is $k = 2 \times 10^6$ moles^{-1} sec^{-1}, which agrees with Hammond's results.

Application of the principles of benzophenone photoreduction to other systems, even very similar ones, is very tenuous. In comparing benzophenone to other systems, one must be certain that the lowest lying triplet state involves direct excitation of the nonbonded carbonyl electrons (n-π^* excitation) rather than the π electrons of the system (π-π^* excitation) and that the hydrogen abstraction reactions involve triplet rather than singlet state intermediates. Simple hydrogen abstraction reactions involving such apparently similar aromatic carbonyl systems as quinones appear to involve the singlet state.[30,31]

A further unusual aspect of benzophenone photoreduction is the appearance of a yellow colored intermediate in photoreductions carried out under carefully degassed conditions in alcohol and ether solvents. Pitts[7] attributes this yellow color to a hemiacetal radical intermediate formed by addition of an α-hydroxyalkyl radical to the carbonyl oxygen of benzophenone,

Bäckström[32] suggests that the yellow color results from a diradical charge transfer complex.

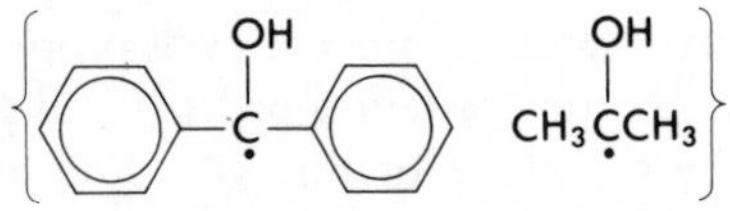

Still another suggestion is that the yellow color results from unsymmetrical coupling of an α-hydroxy-2-propyl radical and an α-hydroxydiphenylmethyl radical,

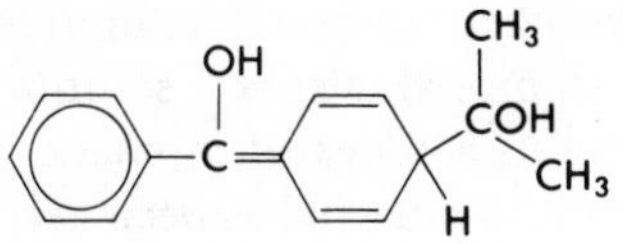

Other Aryl Ketones

Benzophenone is quite unique in its ability to serve as a hydrogen atom abstractor. The quantum yields for hydrogen abstraction by benzophenone are invariably much higher than those obtained with what appear to be very similar aryl and diaryl ketones. Table 7-2 illustrates this effect for photoreduction of benzophenone with toluene.

Table 7-2

Quantum Yields in Photochemical Reactions of Aryl Ketones with Toluene[a]

Aryl Ketone	Conversion, %	Quantum Yield
benzophenone	33	0.39
p,p'-dimethoxybenzophenone	49	0.20
p-cyanobenzophenone	37	0.30
acetophenone	29	0.15

[a]Hammond et al., *J. Am. Chem. Soc.*, **83**, 2795 (1961).

Benzophenone is more easily photoreduced than either *p*-cyanobenzophenone or *p,p'*-dimethoxybenzophenone so that there appears to be little or no polar contribution to the hydrogen abstraction transition state. However, this result may simply be indicative of the relative probability of n-π^* excitation with subsequent intersystem crossing to the triplet state, and the results may be completely unrelated to any polar effects on the transition state. Even when compared with aryl carbonyl compounds of similar triplet state energies such as phenyl cyclopropyl ketone, benzophenone appears to be the far superior hydrogen-abstracting agent. As a matter of fact, photo-reductions of phenyl cyclopropyl ketone are very inefficient.[33,14] Since the hydrogen addition to the carbonyl system of phenyl cyclopropyl ketone can be accomplished with some ease,[13,39] the excitation process and probably the intersystem crossing step may be the cause of this very low reactivity. Theoretical calculations suggest that there may be an excitation of cyclo-propane electrons to the antibonding π^* level which is responsible for this lack of photoreductivity.[34]

Photoreduction reactions of a great variety of aromatic carbonyl compounds have been reported. Those aromatic carbonyl compounds that reportedly undergo photoreduction in isopropyl alcohol solution do so through the n-π^* triplet state. Table 7-3 lists a series of aromatic carbonyl compounds whose photochemical reduction to pinacol has been examined.

Aryl Ketones that Cannot be Photoreduced

It has been proposed[40,41,42,43] that certain aromatic carbonyl compounds lack reactivity because the lowest lying triplet in these compounds has the π-π^* rather than n-π^* configuration. As a result, the excitation involves not the nonbonded electrons of the carbonyl group but the π electrons of the entire aryl system, and reactivity at the carbonyl group is unaltered by the absorption of a light quantum. However, the inefficient excitation can be utilized if more efficient hydrogen donors are present in solution. The tin hydrides like tri-n-butyl stannane provide excellent hydrogen sources[40] and, as such, readily react with 2-acetonaphthone and 1-naphthaldehyde to cause photoreduction.

Other aromatic carbonyl compounds that fail to react photochemically at the carbonyl group include the o-methyl-, o-hydroxybenzo-, and aceto-phenone derivatives as well as p-hydroxy- and p-aminobenzophenone.[44] p-Amino- and p-hydroxybenzophenone do not undergo photoreduction in alcohol solution because of the strong electron donation by the substituents to the carbonyl group. In effect, the electron donation is so strong that intra-molecular charge transfer occurs between the electron donor and the car-bonyl group in the excited state (19).[45] A chemical consequence of the

(19) $H_2N^{\oplus}$=⟨ ⟩=$C{<}^{R}_{O^{\ominus}}$

charge transfer state is that its tendency to form is increased in more polar media. In polar solvents, the normal n-π^* absorption of the carbonyl sys-

Table 7-3

Photoreduction Characteristics of Certain Diaryl Ketones

Diaryl Ketone (Aromatic Carbonyl Compound)	Pinacol Produced
o-chlorobenzophenone[2]	yes
m-chlorobenzophenone[2]	trace
p-chlorobenzophenone[2]	no
p-methoxybenzophenone[2]	yes
p-methylbenzophenone[2]	yes
p-p'-dimethylbenzophenone[2]	yes
p-bromobenzophenone[2]	yes
p-p'-dichlorobenzophenone[2]	trace
o,o',p,p'-tetrachlorobenzophenone[2]	yes
o-chloro-p-methylbenzophenone[2]	yes
p-chloro-p-methylbenzophenone[2]	yes
m-methylbenzophenone[2]	yes
o-methylbenzophenone[2]	no
p-phenylbenzophenone[2]	no
phenyl-1-naphthyl ketone[2]	no
fluorenone[2,35]	no
Michler's ketone[2]	no
anthrone[36]	no
xanthone[36]	no
2-acetonaphthone[37]	no
1-naphthaldehyde[37]	no
1-acetonaphthone[37]	no
di-α-naphthyl ketone[37]	no
o-phenylbenzophenone[37]	no
desoxybenzoin[37]	yes
benzylacetophenone[37]	no
1,4-diphenylbutanone[37]	trace
α-indanone[37]	no
benzalacetophenone[37]	no
benzalacetone[37]	no
p-acetoxypropiophenone[37]	no[a]
phenalen-1-one[38]	no
cyclopropyl phenyl ketone[39]	no
cyclobutyl phenyl ketone[14]	no

[a]Loss of the acetoxy group appears to be preferential.

tems is made more difficult by the increased energy required for the transition, while the π-π^* charge transfer excitation is more likely. This excitation energy difference in the two media is sufficient to cause a difference in the reductive dimerization ability of p-amino- and p-hydroxybenzophenone. In cyclohexane, pinacols are readily obtained from both ketones, while in isopropyl alcohol, no reaction is observed. Spectral observations support the thesis that a unique excited state exists for benzophenones having attached electron-donating substituents.* Of interest is the observation[45] that a strong electron-donating substituent, p-methoxy, has little effect on the photoreducibility of benzophenone and its derivatives. If p-methoxy is actually functioning as an electron-donating substituent in the same sense as p-hydroxy and p-amino, it should serve to form a charge transfer state with at least equal tenacity to the p-hydroxy and p-amino substituents, eq. (20).

(20)

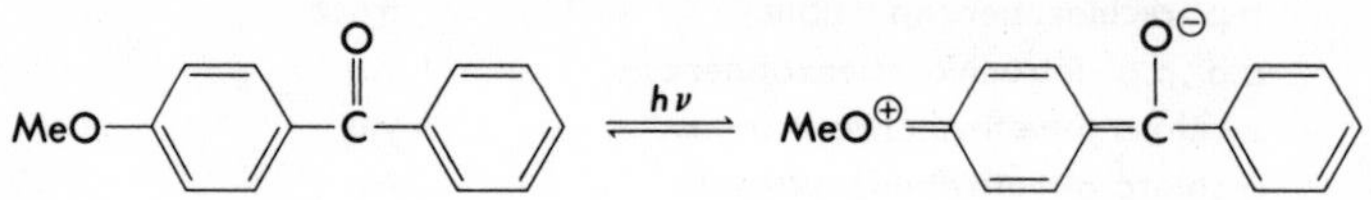

Cohen and Siddiqui[47] have reported that aminobenzophenones undergo rapid photoreduction in isopropyl alcohol when converted to their "onium" derivatives, eq. (21). For example, photoreduction of p-dimethylamino-benzophenone in isopropyl alcohol proceeds very slowly ($\phi = 0.003$) in

(21)

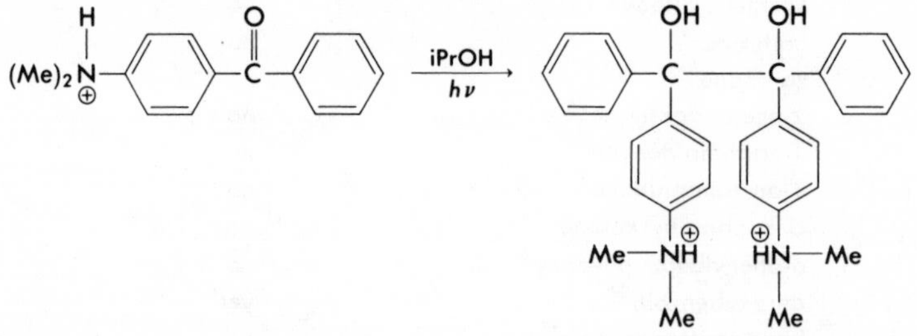

basic or neutral solution, but when hydrogen chloride is passed into the medium, the quantum yield is substantially increased ($\phi = 0.4$). These photoreductions, as well as similar photoreductions of o- and p-aminobenzophenone, also proceed smoothly in acidic aqueous solutions. Quarternary ammonium salts of benzophenone behave in a similar fashion. Conversion of the amino function to its ammonium salt prevents charge transfer state formation.

Ortho-substituted Benzophenones

Ortho-substituted benzophenones generally do not undergo photoreduction if the *ortho* substituent contains hydrogen atoms. Table 7-4 gives

* See, however, reference 17.

Table 7-4

Quantum Yields for Photoreduction of Certain Substituted Benzophenones in Isopropyl Alcohol

Compound	ϕ
benzophenone[46]	1.0^a
o-methylbenzophenone[46]	1×10^{-2}
o-ethylbenzophenone[46]	5.5×10^{-2}
o-butylbenzophenone (tertiary)[46]	0.50
p-methylbenzophenone[46]	0.50
p-hydroxybenzophenone[45]	0
p-aminobenzophenone[45]	0

^{a}Conditions of proper degassing assumed.

quantum yields of photoreduction in isopropyl alcohol for a series of benzophenone derivatives.

Ortho alkyl derivatives are capable of undergoing only an intramolecular hydrogen abstraction reaction. Since the methyl hydrogens are held in proximity to the carbonyl oxygen of *o*-methylbenzophenone, these hydrogens, rather than the hydrogen atoms of the solvent, are abstracted. Yang and Rivas[48] found that enolic products can be trapped by using active Diels-Alder dienophiles, such as acetylene dicarboxylate, when *o*-methyl- and *o*-benzylbenzophenone are photolyzed, eq. (22), in the presence of a

(22)

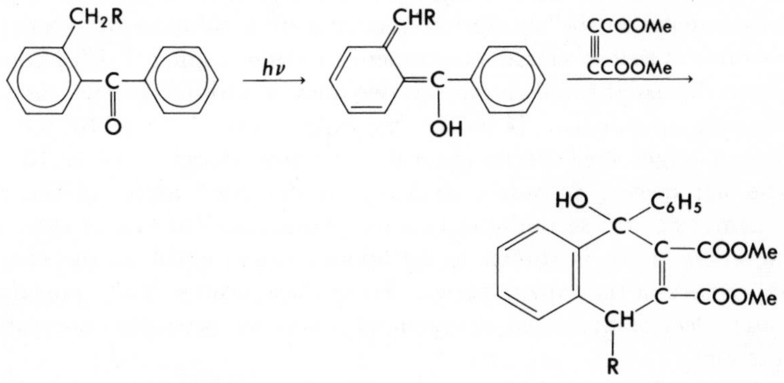

dienophile. A similar intramolecular hydrogen abstraction has been proposed for *o*-hydroxybenzophenone, eq. (23).[42]

(23)

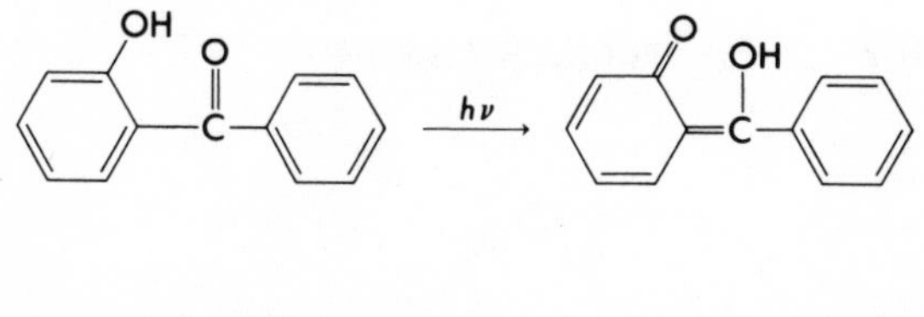

o-Hydroxybenzophenone, *o*-dihydroxybenzophenone, and other aromatic carbonyl compounds possessing α hydroxy substituents are widely used as photostabilizers. That is, when these materials are placed in a fiber, a suspension, or a solution, they tend to make the medium more light stable. This ability to impart photostability results from the rapid decay of these materials to ground states without a chemical reaction after they have absorbed a light quantum. The stabilization process may involve the described photoenolization followed by rapid tautomerization. Since most photostabilizers are incapable of triplet state energy transfer, they are dually unreactive photochemically. *o*-Hydroxybenzophenone and similar derivatives also have a phenolic hydrogen, a known inhibitor of free radical chain processes. Phenolic inhibitors are thought to inhibit free radical chain processes by donation of the phenolic hydrogen atom, eq. (24). The phenolic free radical

(24)   R· + ⟶ + RH

is presumed to be less reactive as a radical chain transfer agent than the radical from which it was formed although recent researchers have questioned the validity of this assumption. Thus, *o*-hydroxybenzophenone can function as a photostabilizer both by stopping chain processes and by light absorption and degradation.

Yang and co-workers, using flash techniques, have detected triplet state intermediates in the absorption spectrum of a solution of *o*-benzylbenzophenone as well as a rapidly tautomerizing enolic form.[49] Flash photolysis of *o*-benzylbenzophenone produces two new absorbing species, one rapidly decaying intermediate, (k for the first order decay = 1.9×10^3 sec^{-1}) and a second longer-lived species (k for the first order decay = 9.4×10^{-2} sec^{-1}). The first species, according to Yang, is the n-π^* triplet of the carbonyl system, while the second species is the photoenol. The rate of appearance of the enolic form is shown to be approximately equal to the rate of disappearance of the triplet species. From these results, Yang postulates that intramolecular hydrogen abstractions involving benzophenones are triplet reactions.

The reaction mechanism, after triplet state formation, involves abstraction of the 6-positioned hydrogen atoms by the excited oxygen atom, eqs. (25–27).

$$
(25) \quad \underset{\text{RCCH}_2\text{CH}_2\text{CH}_2\text{R}'}{\overset{O}{\overset{\|}{}}} \xrightarrow{\;h\nu\;} \underset{\text{RCCH}_2\text{CH}_2\text{CH}_2\text{R}'}{\overset{O^*}{\overset{\|}{}}}
$$

(26) $\overset{O^*}{\overset{\|}{R\text{C}}}CH_2CH_2CH_2R'$ $\longrightarrow$ $\overset{OH}{\overset{|}{R\dot{\text{C}}}}CH_2CH_2\dot{\text{C}}HR'$

(27)   products $\longleftarrow$

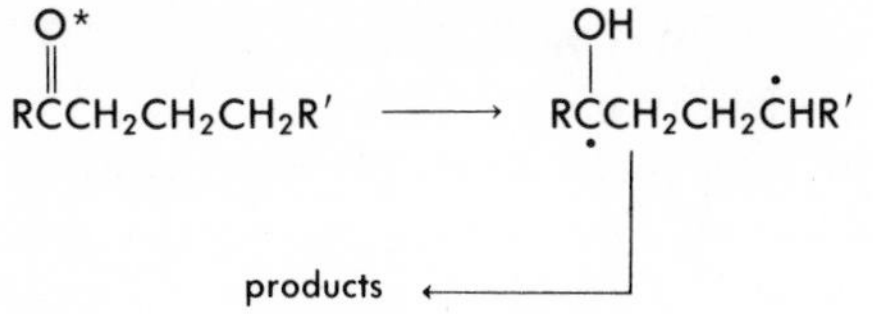

Intramolecular Hydrogen Abstraction

A variety of other intramolecular hydrogen abstraction reactions are well known to the photochemist. As mentioned, Yang and Rivas observed that photochemical enolization takes place when o-methyl- and o-benzylbenzophenone are photolyzed in cyclohexane. In addition, an intramolecular hydrogen abstraction process has been observed with aliphatic and alicyclic ketones. Yang and Yang[50] reported that long chain aliphatic ketones, when photolyzed in cyclohexane or without solvent, led to the formation of

(28) $CH_3\overset{O}{\overset{\|}{\text{C}}}CH_2CH_2CH_2R$ $\longrightarrow$ [cyclobutanol structure with CH_3C—OH and R]

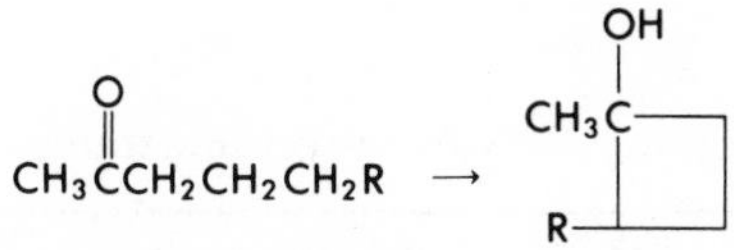

R = H, C$_3$H$_7$, C$_4$H$_9$

cyclobutanols, eq. (28), although the yields are very low. A stereospecific synthesis has been reported by Barnard and Yang, eq. (29).[51]

(29)

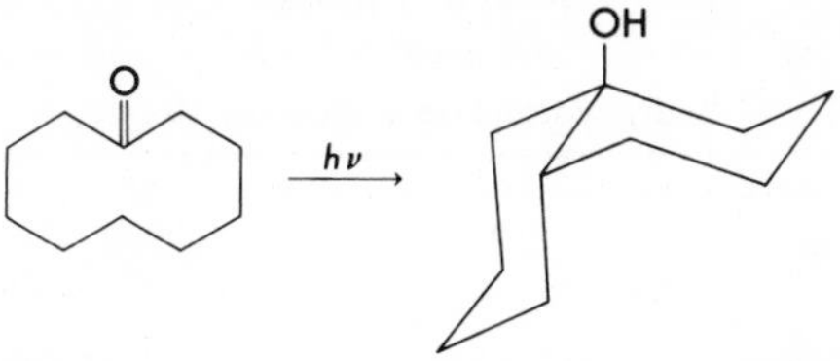

Recent evidence indicates that the intramolecular hydrogen abstraction may not be a stepwise process involving discrete radical intermediates. Using ketones possessing an optically active carbon atom in the γ position, Schulte-Elte and Ohloff[52] as well as Orban, Schaffner, and Jeger[53] observed that cyclobutanol products retaining some optical activity are produced. Since the wealth of evidence gathered on the stereochemistry of free radical intermediates tends to indicate that carbon atom asymmetry is lost upon free radical formation, free radical intermediates are discounted in cyclobutanol formation from long chain aliphatic ketones, eq. (30). Radical intermediates are not completely ruled out, however, since significant racemization is also observed.

(30)

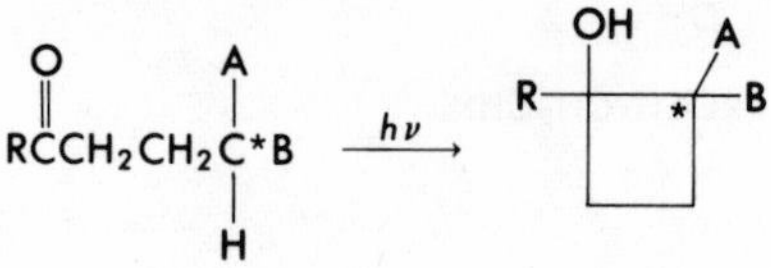

Wagner and Hammond[54] and Dougherty[55] recently observed that both the singlet excited state and triplet excited state of the ketone moiety are responsible for the γ hydrogen abstraction reaction.

Urry and co-workers[56,57] have observed cyclobutanol formation from photolysis of aliphatic α-diketones. Yields for cyclobutanol formation are much higher for α-diketones than for similar monoketones owing to the added stability imparted to the excited state by the α carbonyl group. Some α-diketones that yield cyclobutanol derivatives are listed in Table 7-5. Urry proposes that triplet state intermediates are important in the photocyclization of α-diketones.

Table 7-5

Aliphatic α-Diketones Yielding 2-Hydroxycyclobutanones[a]

Diketone[b]	-2-hydroxycyclobutanone	Yield, %
5,6-decanedione	2-butyl-3-ethyl-	89
2,7-dimethyl-4,5-octanedione	3,3-dimethyl-(2-methylpropyl)-	95
4,5-octanedione	3-methyl-2-propyl-	92
3,4-hexanedione	2-ethyl-	60
1,2-cyclodecanedione	1-hydroxybicyclo[6.2.0]decan-10-one	74

[a] W. H. Urry and D. J. Trecker, *J. Am. Chem. Soc.*, **84**, 118 (1962).
[b] The solvent is cyclohexane.

Intramolecular hydrogen atom transfer has also been observed with *ortho*-substituted quinones, eq. (31).[58]   Quinones behave as hydrogen atom ab-

(31)

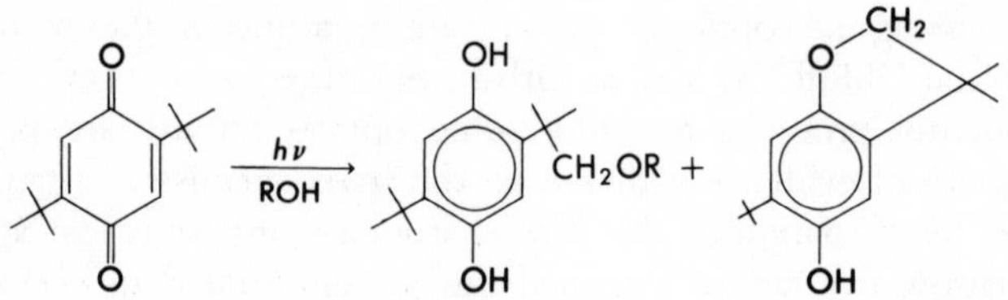

stracting agents in many photochemical reactions.   The addition of acetaldehyde to benzoquinone has recently been reported, eq. (32).[59]

(32)

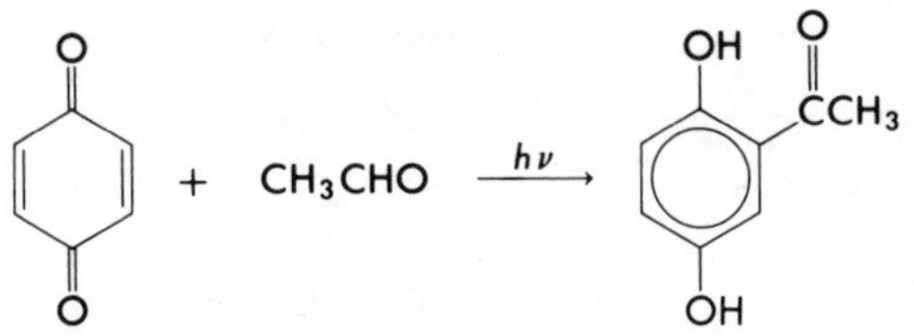

$$\text{[quinone structure]} + CH_3CHO \xrightarrow{h\nu} \text{[salicyl ketone product structure]}$$

Intramolecular hydrogen abstraction reactions by photochemically excited states also occur with α-keto esters and α-keto acids. Leermakers and co-workers[60-62] have examined the photochemical reactions of α-keto acids and have shown that pyruvic acid in aqueous media decomposes to acetoin, acetaldehyde, and carbon dioxide. The yield of carbon dioxide is nearly quantitative. Benzoylformic acid in aqueous media also evolves nearly quantitative amounts of carbon dioxide. Benzaldehyde and benzoin are the other products. In nonaqueous media containing good hydrogen donors, the α-carbonyl group of both pyruvic and benzoylformic acid is readily reduced and pinacolic products are observed.[63]

Leermakers and co-workers propose that, at least in aqueous media, methylene intermediates are important. Since both pyruvic acid and benzoyl-formic acid possess readily accessible triplet states, reactions of these molecules probably involve triplet state intermediates. Alkali metal salts of pyruvic acid do not undergo photodecarboxylation, indicating that the acid hydrogen may play some role in the reaction mechanism. An intramolecular abstraction reaction is proposed, eqs. (33–35).

Esters of benzoylformic acid behave somewhat analogously. Huyser and Neckers[64] have observed intramolecular hydrogen abstraction reactions for a

(33)

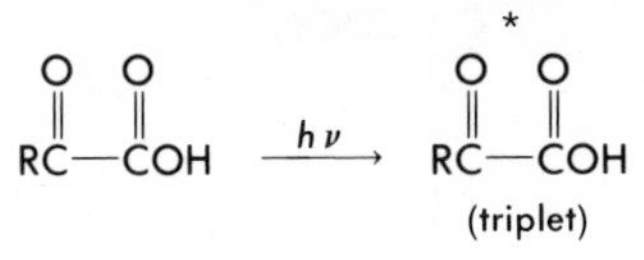

$$RC\text{—}COH \xrightarrow{h\nu} RC\text{—}COH \quad \text{(triplet)}$$

(34)

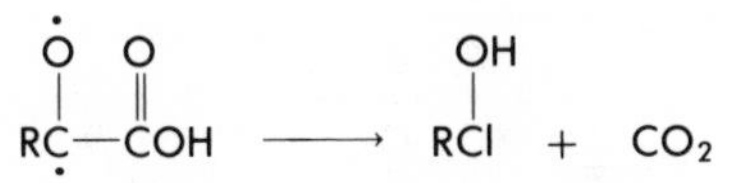

$$RC\text{—}COH \longrightarrow RCl + CO_2$$

(35)

$$2RCl \longrightarrow RC\text{—}CR$$

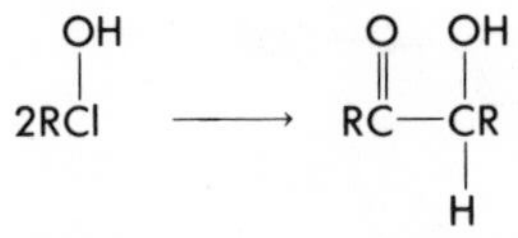

series of alkyl esters of benzoylformic acid in alcohol solution. The course of the reaction is observed to be temperature dependent with reductive dimeri-zation being the important pathway at lower temperatures and intramolecular hydrogen abstraction followed by decomposition at higher temperatures,

$$(36) \quad \text{Ph}-\overset{O}{\underset{}{C}}-\overset{O}{\underset{}{C}}-\overset{R}{\underset{}{O}}\text{CHR} \xrightarrow[\substack{R'OH \\ 25°}]{h\nu} \quad \text{Ph}-\overset{HO}{\underset{}{C}}-\overset{O}{\underset{}{C}}-\overset{R}{\underset{}{O}}\text{CHR}$$

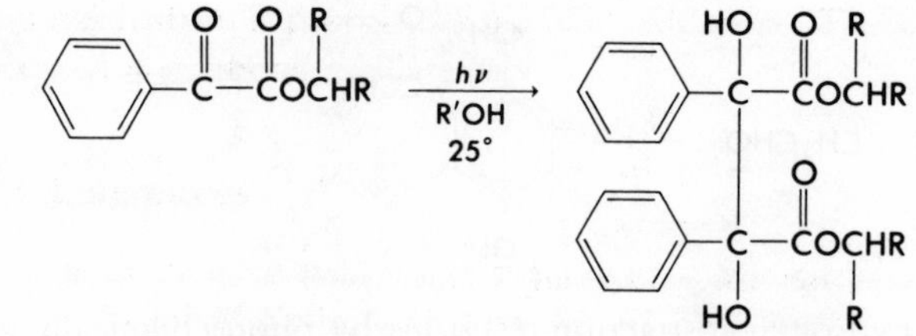

$$\text{Ph}-\overset{O}{\underset{HO}{C}}-\overset{O}{\underset{R}{C}}\text{OCHR}$$

$$(37) \quad \text{Ph}-\overset{O}{\underset{}{C}}-\overset{O}{\underset{}{C}}-\overset{R}{\underset{}{O}}\text{CHR} \xrightarrow[\substack{R'OH \\ 80°}]{} \quad \text{Ph}-\overset{HO}{\underset{H}{C}}-\overset{O}{\underset{}{C}}\text{OR}' \quad + \quad R_2C\!=\!O$$

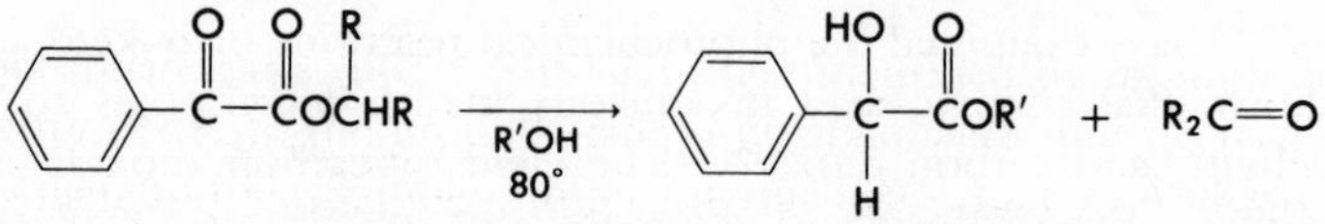

eqs. (36) and (37). The reaction is general for a series of benzoylformates in a variety of alcohols, and the decomposition occurs even in the absence of solvent. Huyser and Neckers propose a mechanism including a hydroxyketene intermediate, eqs. (38–41).

$$(38) \quad \text{Ph}-\overset{O}{\underset{}{C}}-\overset{O}{\underset{}{C}}-\text{OCHR} \xrightarrow{h\nu} \quad \text{Ph}-\overset{O^*}{\underset{}{C}}-\overset{O}{\underset{R}{C}}\text{OCHR}$$

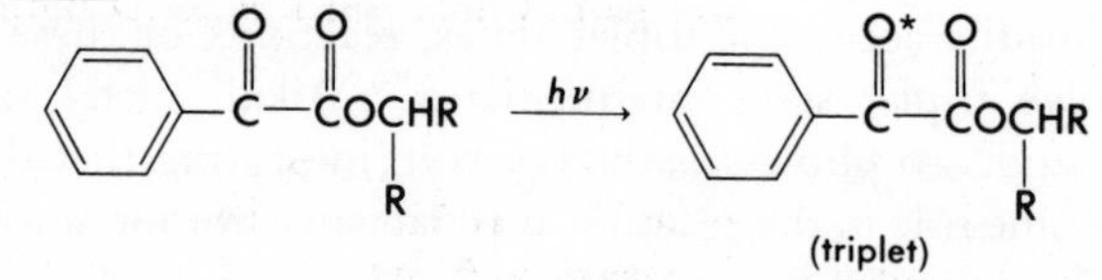

(triplet)

$$(39) \quad \text{Ph}-\overset{\overset{\cdot}{O}}{\underset{\cdot}{C}}-\overset{O}{\underset{}{C}}\text{OCHR}_2 \longrightarrow \quad \text{Ph}-\overset{HO}{\underset{\cdot}{C}}-\overset{O}{\underset{}{C}}\text{OĊR}_2$$

(triplet)

$$(40) \quad R_2C\!=\!O \quad + \quad \text{Ph}-\overset{OH}{\underset{}{C}}\!=\!C\!=\!O \longleftarrow$$

$$(41) \quad \xrightarrow{R'OH} \quad \text{Ph}-\overset{HO}{\underset{H}{C}}-\overset{O}{\underset{}{C}}\text{OR}'$$

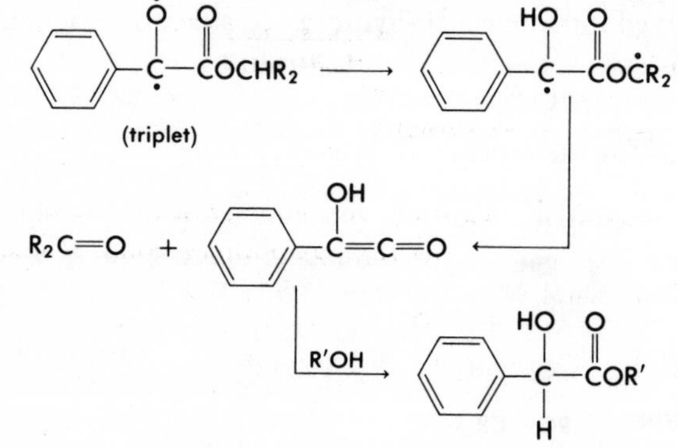

Table 7-6 lists a series of alkyl benzoylformates for which reductive ester exchange has been observed in ethanol. Yang and Morduchowitz[65] have observed that ethyl pyruvate shows no tendency to form hydroxyketene intermediates. They observe only pinacol type products at lower temperatures.

Table 7-6

Alkyl Benzoylformates Giving Ester-Exchanged Products Upon Attempted Photoreduction[a]

Benzoylformates	Solvent Alcohol	Products
ethyl benzoylformate	2-butanol	2-butyl mandelate
ethyl benzoylformate	cyclohexanol	cyclohexyl mandelate
ethyl benzoylformate	*l*-menthol	*l*-menthyl mandelate
2-propyl benzoylformate	ethanol	ethyl mandelate (0.003 mole) + acetone (0.003 mole)
2-hexyl benzoylformate	ethanol	ethyl mandelate + 2-hexanone
cyclohexyl benzoylformate	ethanol	ethyl mandelate (0.018 mole) + cyclohexanone (0.019 mole)
2-octyl benzoylformate	ethanol	ethyl mandelate + 2-octanone
2-octyl benzoylformate	2-butanol	2-butyl mandelate + 2-octanone

[a]Data from E. S. Huyser and D. C. Neckers, *J. Org. Chem.*, **29**, 276 (1964).

Leermakers and co-workers oppose the hydroxyketene postulate in favor of an initial decomposition of the pyruvate and benzoylformate esters to acyl and carboxylate radicals followed by cage recombination and disproportionation, eqs. (42–44). The major portion of Leermakers' evidence rests on

$$(42) \quad RC\overset{O}{\overset{\|}{C}}-\overset{O}{\overset{\|}{C}}OCHR'_2 \xrightarrow{h\nu} \left[RC\overset{O}{\overset{\|}{C}}-\overset{O}{\overset{\|}{C}}\cdot \;+\; R_2CHO\cdot \right]$$

$$(43) \quad \longrightarrow \left[R\overset{O}{\overset{\|}{C}}\cdot \;+\; R'_2CHO\cdot \;+\; CO \right]$$

$$(44) \quad RCHO \;+\; R'_2C{=}O \longleftarrow$$

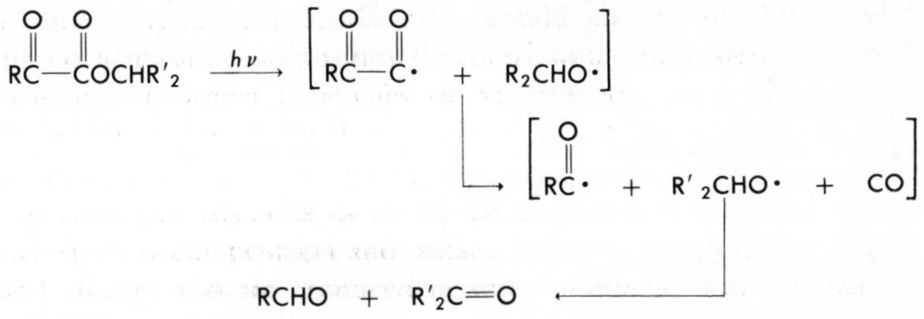

the fact that, at least during photolysis in benzene, the major products are carbon monoxide, the aldehyde and the ketone, and that the quantum yield for ester disappearance is no different for deuterated pyruvates than for protonated pyruvates, eqs. (45) and (46). Several other pieces of information, however, would tend to disallow such a decomposition mechanism.

$$(45) \quad CH_3\overset{O}{\overset{\|}{C}}-\overset{O}{\overset{\|}{C}}O\overset{H}{\overset{|}{C}}CH_3 \xrightarrow{h\nu} CO \;+\; CH_3\overset{O}{\overset{\|}{C}}H \;+\; CH_3\overset{O}{\overset{\|}{C}}CH_3$$
$$\underset{CH_3}{} \qquad\qquad \Phi \;=\; 0.18$$

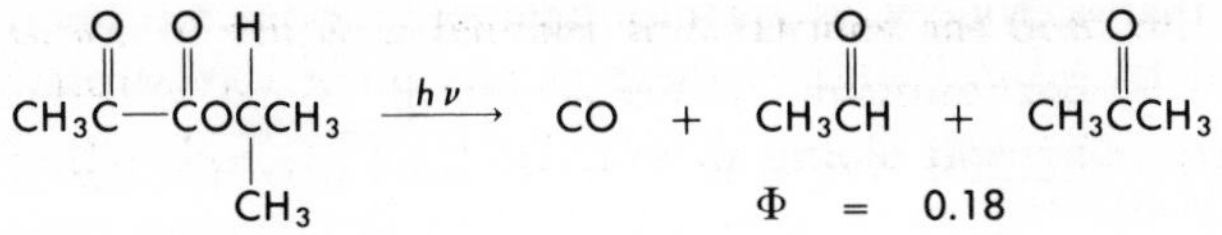

$$(46) \quad CH_3\overset{O}{\overset{\|}{C}}-\overset{O}{\overset{\|}{C}}\overset{D}{\underset{\underset{CH_3}{|}}{C}}CH_3 \xrightarrow{h\nu} CO + CH_3CD + CH_3\overset{O}{\overset{\|}{C}}CH_3$$

$$\Phi \quad = \quad 0.19$$

First, the quantum yield for α-naphthoylformate esters are extremely low, eq. (47). This result is reminiscent of the hydrogen abstraction results with

$$(47) \quad \alpha\text{-}C_{10}H_7\overset{O}{\overset{\|}{C}}-\overset{O}{\overset{\|}{C}}OCHRR' \xrightarrow{h\nu} \alpha\text{-}C_{10}H_7\overset{O}{\overset{\|}{C}}H + CO + R'\overset{O}{\overset{\|}{C}}R$$

$$\Phi \quad = \quad <0.01$$

1-naphthaldehyde and 2-acetonaphthone. The lowest lying triplet state could be a π-π^* triplet in the case of the naphthoylformates as in the case of other naphthalene carbonyl derivatives. Second, alkyl pyruvates decompose with a higher quantum yield than do alkyl benzoylformates. Resonance considerations would tend to argue that conjugate stability imparted to the acyl radical by the adjacent aromatic nucleus would favor a higher quantum yield for the aromatic benzoylformate esters. Third, the fact that all the alkyl pyruvates decompose with the same efficiency probably means that the abstraction reaction is very exothermic and rapid so that no isotope effect would be expected even if a hydrogen abstraction step did occur.

The possibility of γ hydrogen abstractions in gas phase photochemical decompositions of aliphatic ketones was recognized long ago.[66-72] The well-known Norrish Type II* process, eq. (48), is proposed to proceed via abstraction of the γ hydrogen atom followed by molecular decomposition.

$$(48) \quad R\overset{O}{\overset{\|}{C}}CH_2CH_2CH_2R' \xrightarrow{h\nu} R\overset{O}{\overset{\|}{C}}CH_3 + R'CH{=}CH_2$$

$$(49) \quad R\overset{O}{\overset{\|}{C}}CH_2CH_2CH_2R' \xrightarrow{h\nu} R\overset{OH}{\overset{|}{C}}CH_2CH_2\overset{\cdot}{C}HR'$$

$$(50) \quad R\overset{OH}{\overset{|}{C}}{=}CH_2 + RCH{=}CH_2 \longleftarrow$$

Pitts and co-workers recently obtained spectral evidence for the intermediacy of enolic acetone in the gas phase photolysis of 2-pentanone.[73] In addition, it has been reported that the acetone produced in the photolysis of 2-hexanone can exchange one hydrogen for deuterium at the walls of the vessel,[74] and that acetone d_6 is an important product in the photolysis of 2-pentanone-1,1,1,3,3-d_5.[75] All of these factors point very strongly to the

*See Chapter 5 of this book.

intermediacy of an enolic form of the ketone during the course of the reaction.

Yates and Szabo[76] have shown that photoirradiation of α-alkoxy ketones also produces 3-oxetanols, eq. (51), as well as a ketone and an aldehyde.

$$(51) \quad \underset{\displaystyle RCCH_2OCH_2R'}{\overset{\displaystyle O}{\|}} \quad \xrightarrow{h\nu} \quad \underset{\displaystyle O}{\overset{\displaystyle OH \quad R'}{\underset{\|}{RC-\boxed{}}}} \quad + \quad \underset{\displaystyle RCCH_3}{\overset{\displaystyle O}{\|}} \quad + \quad \underset{\displaystyle H}{\overset{\displaystyle O}{R'C}}$$

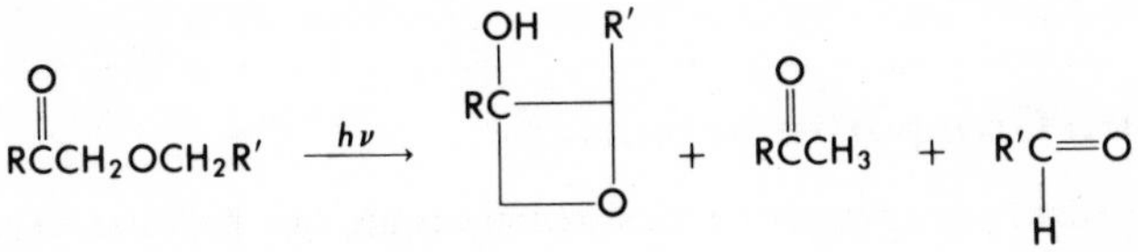

α-Methoxyacetophenone produces a mixture of products from which 3-phenyl-3-oxetanol may be isolated in addition to acetophenone and formaldehyde. α-Ethoxyacetophenone gives 2-methyl-3-phenyl-3-oxetanol, while 1-methoxy-3,3-dimethyl-2-butanone gives 3-t-butyl-3-oxetanol. Srinivasan has reported that in the vapor phase a similar reaction with methoxyacetone gives acetone and formaldehyde, eq. (52).[77]

$$(52) \quad \underset{\displaystyle CH_3CCH_2OCH_3}{\overset{\displaystyle O}{\|}} \quad \xrightarrow{h\nu} \quad \underset{\displaystyle CH_3CCH_3}{\overset{\displaystyle O}{\|}} \quad + \quad \underset{\displaystyle HCH}{\overset{\displaystyle O}{\|}}$$

An interesting example of an intramolecular γ hydrogen abstraction reaction may be observed after the photochemical addition of cyclohexene to certain diones, eq. (55). Good yields of cycloadducts are obtained from the photolysis of cyclopentane-1,3-enol acetate and cyclopentene, eq. (53), while

$$(53)$$

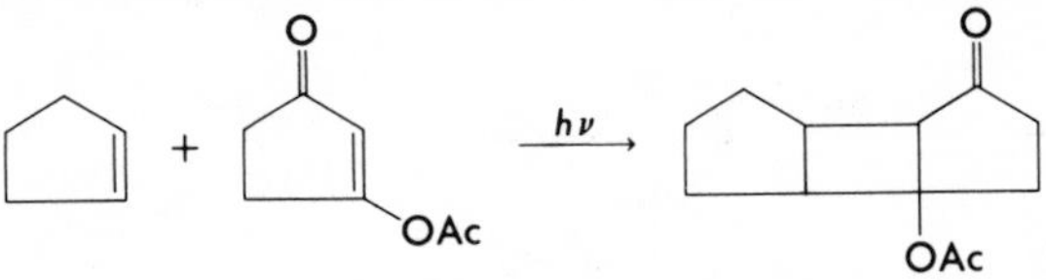

dimedone in cyclohexene gives the dione, eq. (54),[78] a result of cleavage of the cycloadduct. The dione, eq. (54), undergoes further hydrogen abstraction followed by cycloaddition in cyclohexene to yield a tricyclic intermediate, eq. (55).

$$(54)$$

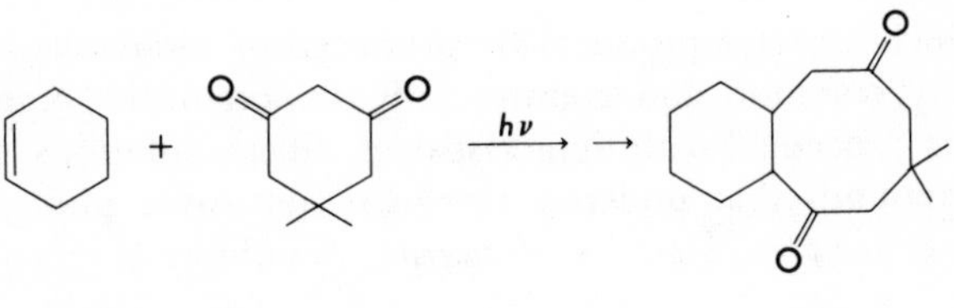

(55)

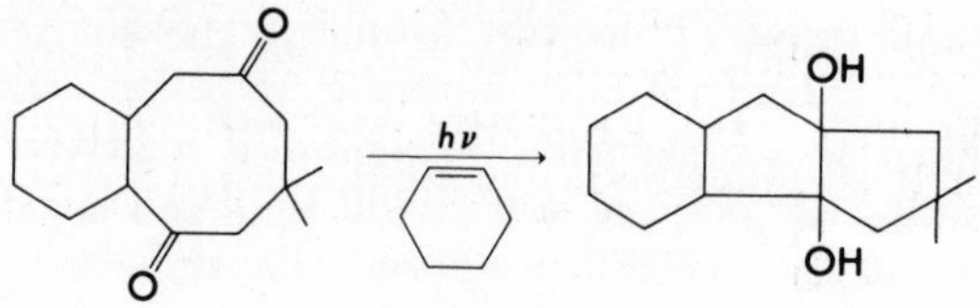

Nitro Group Abstractions

Intramolecular hydrogen abstraction reactions are not peculiar to carbonyl chromophores, but have also been observed with certain nitro compounds. Like the carbonyl group, the nitro group has a low intensity, longer wavelength spectral band attributable to an n-π^* electronic excitation. Wettermark[79-82] has observed, in studies of the flash photolysis of o-nitrotoluene and similar derivatives, spectral patterns characteristic of an *aci* nitro derivative, eq. (56). This *aci* nitro derivative is unstable and reverts rapidly to the

(56)

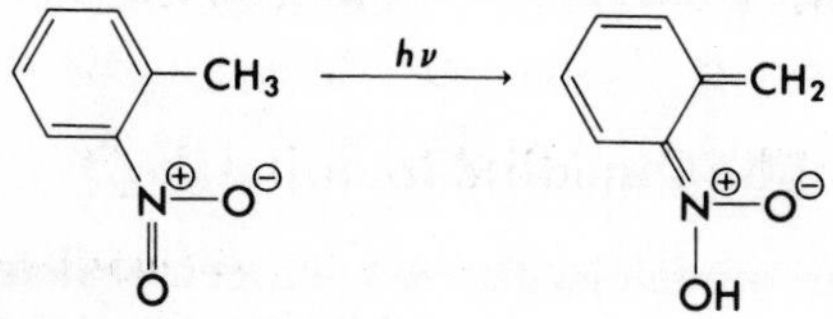

nitrotoluene under the conditions of the reaction. In basic solution a second derivative, thought to be the conjugate base of the *aci* nitro derivative, eq. (57), is formed. A number of nitro compounds are known to behave

(57)

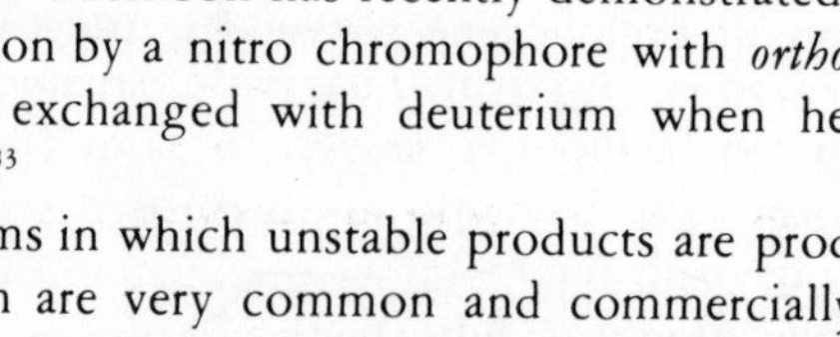

similarly. Morrison has recently demonstrated the intramolecular hydrogen abstraction by a nitro chromophore with *ortho* nitrotoluene. The *aci* nitro product exchanged with deuterium when heavy water was used as the solvent.[83]

Systems in which unstable products are produced by ultraviolet or visible radiation are very common and commercially important to organic and physical chemists concerned with light-fast dyes, fibers, solutions, and suspensions. Compounds that undergo thermally reversible photochemical color change are called *photochromic* or *phototropic*. A number of types of compounds are photochromic and lead to unstable products. Among the most important types that behave in this fashion are anils, certain hydrazones and osazones, stilbene derivatives, o-nitrobenzyl derivatives, and many thioindigos. In several cases, it has been shown that the color change results when an intramolecular hydrogen abstraction gives a molecule with isolated, as compared to conjugated, chromophores. Often the products are thermally unstable because a 1,3-cyclohexadiene system has resulted from disruption of a benzene system. Many phototropic systems involve the formation of unstable enols by intramolecular hydrogen abstraction. The early examples of Tschitschibabin and co-workers[84] as well as others[85-87] of phototropic rearrangement reactions of 2',4'-dinitrobenzylpyridine derivatives are examples of intramolecular enolizations and are quite typical, eq. (58). Similar photo-

(58)

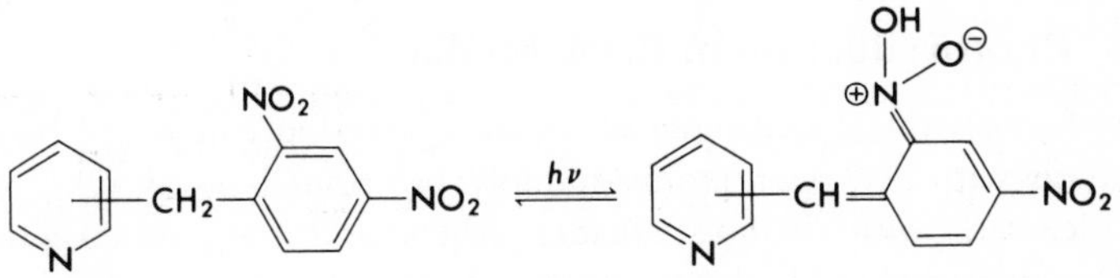

chromic enolizations have been reported for certain 1,4-diamino derivatives

(59)

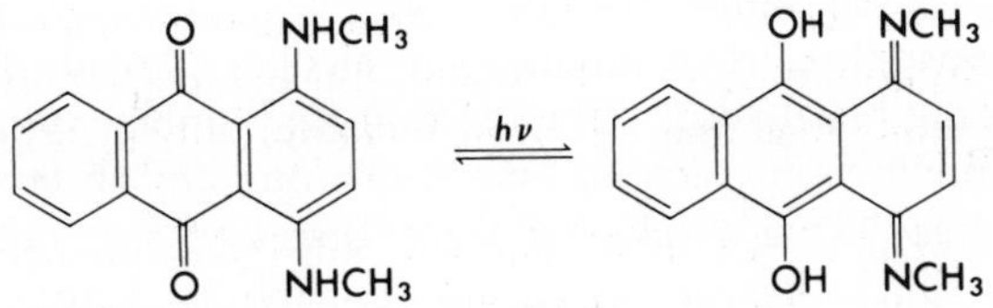

of anthraquinone, eq. (59).[88]

Phototropy of anils has been studied extensively by Schmidt and co-workers.[89-92] They have found that the anils of salicylaldehyde are phototropic, whereas anils possessing o-methoxy and p-hydroxy substituents fail to undergo a color change when photolyzed. These workers propose an intramolecular hydrogen transfer reaction to explain the phototropy. In the crystalline state, the reaction is controlled by the topochemistry (crystal lattice geometry) and substituents in the *ortho* and *para* positions of either ring of the anil have little or no effect on the reaction, eq. (60). Benzaldehyde anils have been found to be unreactive, whereas those of β-hydroxy-α-naphthaldehyde and α-hydroxy-β-naphthaldehyde are photochromic, eq. (61). Similar intramolecular hydrogen transfer reactions of phenolic hydrogens have been observed by other workers.[93]

(60)

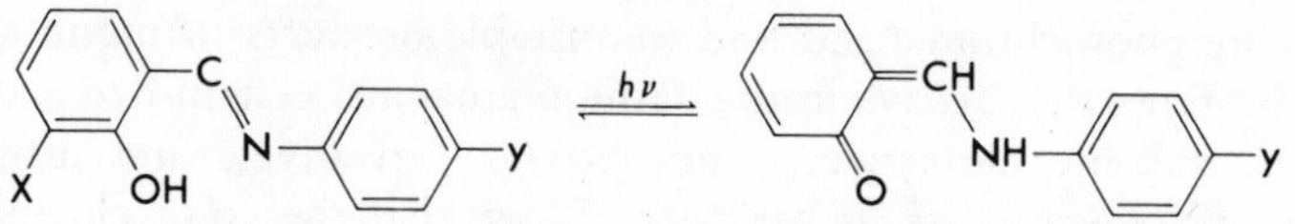

(61)

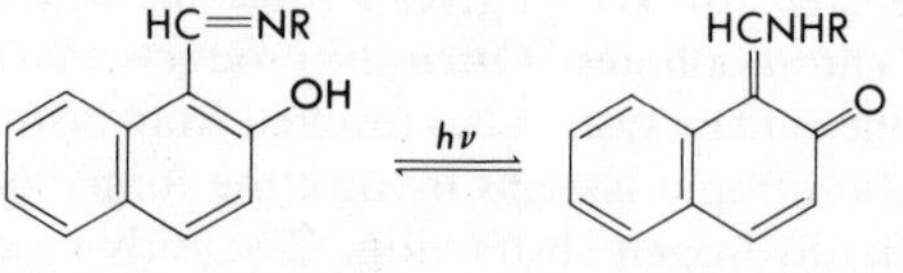

Many other interesting examples of phototropic reactions, a great number of which directly account for color changes of dyestuffs, are reviewed by better authorities in other sources.[94-96]

Photoreduction in Basic Media

The photochemical hydrogen abstraction reaction can occur both intramolecularly with hydrogen atoms suitably positioned on an alkyl chain or intermolecularly with alcohols, alkanes, ethers, and many other compounds providing the supply of hydrogen atoms. In the presence of added alkoxide, the reaction takes a completely different course. The products obtained from benzophenone and isopropyl alcohol in the presence of added isopropoxide are benzhydrol and acetone rather than benzpinacol.[97,98] Table 7-7 lists a variety of diaryl ketones that, when irradiated in alcohol-alkoxide solution, yield the corresponding benzhydrol. The reaction has synthetic utility. As in the case of photoreduction reactions, no reductions are observed with those aromatic ketones having the lowest triplet states of π-π^* character. Thus, fluorenone, Michler's ketone, and phenyl α-naphthyl ketone do not undergo photoreduction in the presence of an added base.

Table 7-7

Photoreductions of Diaryl Ketones in Basic Media[a]

Diaryl Ketone	Yield of Hydrol, %
benzophenone	98
p-methylbenzophenone	95
p,p'-dimethylbenzophenone	90
p-methoxybenzophenone	90
p-chloro-p'-methylbenzophenone	80
p-chlorobenzophenone	80

[a] Data from W. F. Bachmann, *J. Am. Chem. Soc.*, **85**, 355, 391 (1933).

The mechanism of the photoreduction of diaryl ketones in the presence of an added base has been studied by Bachmann[99] and by Cohen.[100]   Since sodium ethoxide is observed to cleave benzpinacol to equimolar mixtures of benzophenone and benzhydrol, Bachmann proposed that the photochemical reduction of benzophenone in the presence of added alkoxide proceeds first to the pinacol followed by reversal of the pinacol-forming reaction to yield the sodium ketyl radical.   The sodium ketyl radical exchanges with the alcohol present in solution, and disproportionation to benzophenone and benzhydrol follows, eqs. (62–66).   Bachmann observed that many benz-pinacols react with sodium alkoxide to yield quantitatively the corresponding benzhydrol and benzophenone.   The sodium ketyl of the pinacols can be prepared by treating the pinacols with sodium amalgam or other bases.[101, 102]

$$(62)\quad 2C_6H_5\overset{O}{\overset{\|}{C}}C_6H_5 \xrightarrow[R_2CHOH]{h\nu} 2C_6H_5\overset{OH}{\underset{C_6H_5}{C}}\cdot \longrightarrow C_6H_5\overset{OH}{\underset{C_6H_5}{C}}\text{---}\overset{OH}{\underset{C_6H_5}{C}}C_6H_5$$

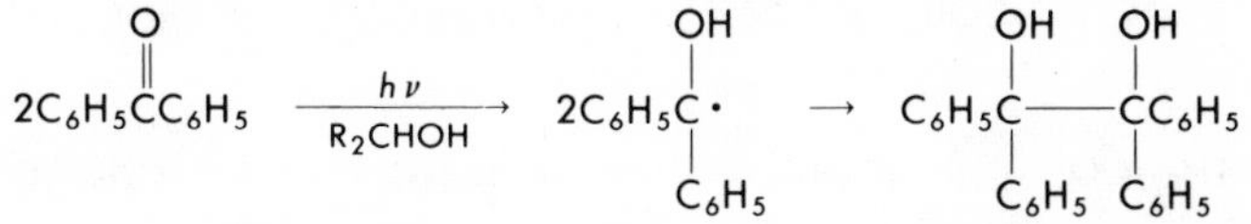

$$(63)\quad C_6H_5\overset{OH}{\underset{C_6H_5}{C}}\text{---}\overset{OH}{\underset{C_6H_5}{C}}C_6H_5 + 2NaOEt \longrightarrow C_6H_5\overset{ONa}{\underset{C_6H_5}{C}}\text{---}\overset{ONa}{\underset{C_6H_5}{C}}C_6H_5$$

$$(64)\quad 2C_6H_5\overset{ONa}{\underset{}{C}}C_6H_5 \longleftarrow$$

$$(65)\quad C_6H_5\overset{ONa}{\underset{\cdot}{C}}C_6H_5 + C_6H_5\overset{OH}{\underset{C_6H_5}{C}}\text{---}\overset{OH}{\underset{C_6H_5}{C}}C_6H_5 \longrightarrow 2C_6H_5\overset{OH}{\underset{\cdot}{C}}C_6H_5 +$$

$$C_6H_5\overset{ONa}{\underset{C_6H_5}{C}}\text{---}\overset{ONa}{\underset{C_6H_5}{C}}C_6H_5$$

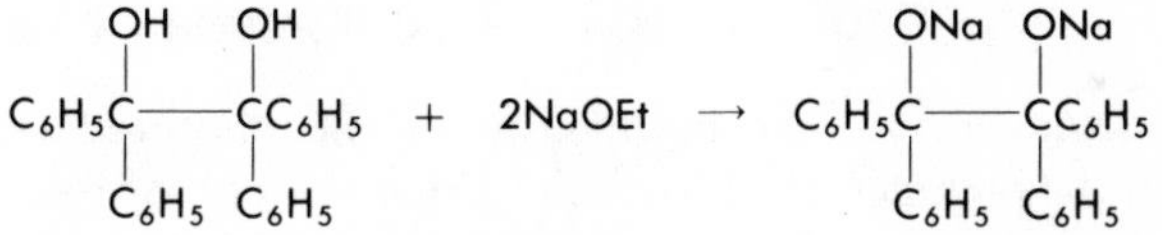

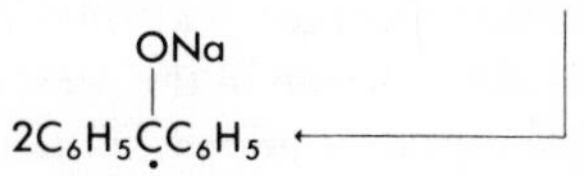

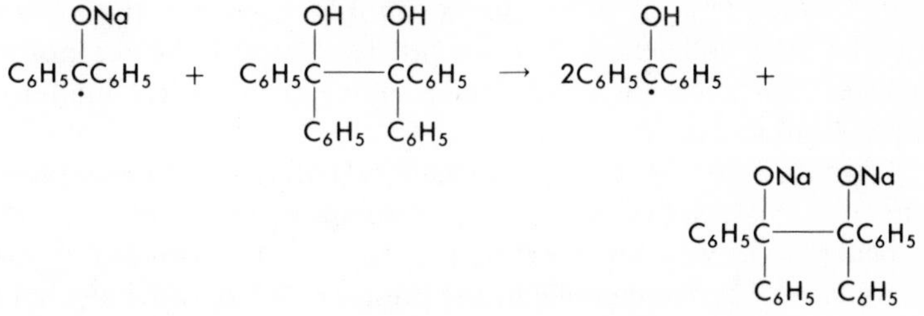

$$(66)\quad 2C_6H_5\overset{OH}{\underset{\cdot}{C}}C_6H_5 \longrightarrow C_6H_5\overset{O}{\overset{\|}{C}}C_6H_5 +$$

$$C_6H_5\overset{OH}{\underset{H}{C}}C_6H_5$$

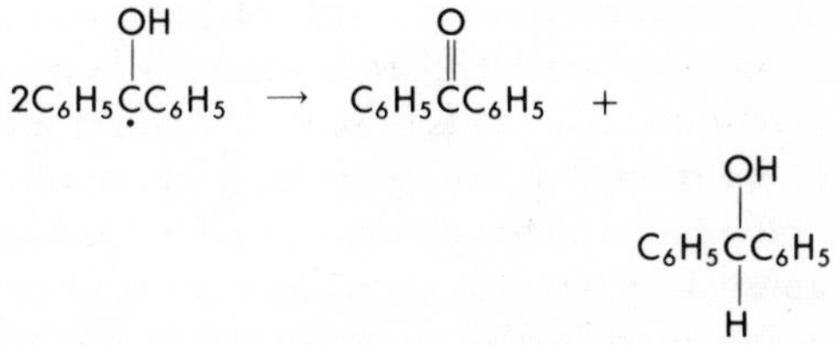

Cohen, on the other hand, concludes that carbanions as well as ion radicals (ketyls) are important in the photochemical reduction of benzophenone in the presence of added base to benzhydrol, but that benzpinacol is not initially formed and then cleaved as proposed by Bachmann. Cohen proposes the reaction sequence shown in eqs. (67–72).

$$(67) \quad C_6H_5\overset{\overset{O}{\parallel}}{C}C_6H_5 \quad \xrightarrow{\;h\nu\;} \quad \to \quad C_6H_5\overset{\overset{O^*}{\parallel}}{C}C_6H_5 \;\text{(triplet)}$$

$$(68) \quad C_6H_5\overset{\overset{O^*}{\parallel}}{C}C_6H_5 \;\text{(triplet)} \;+\; R_2CHO^{\ominus} \quad \to \quad C_6H_5\overset{\overset{OH}{|}}{\underset{\bullet}{C}}C_6H_5 \;+\; R_2\overset{\bullet}{C}O^{\ominus}$$

$$(69) \quad R_2\overset{\bullet}{C}OH \;+\; C_6H_5\overset{\overset{O}{\parallel}}{C}C_6H_5 \quad \to \quad C_6H_5\overset{\overset{OH}{|}}{\underset{\bullet}{C}}C_6H_5 \;+\; R_2C{=}O$$

$$(70) \quad (C_6H_5)_2\overset{\bullet}{C}OH \;+\; OR^{\ominus} \quad \to \quad (C_6H_5)_2\overset{\bullet}{C}O^{\ominus} \;+\; HOR$$

$$(71) \quad (C_6H_5)_2\overset{\bullet}{C}O^{\ominus} \;+\; (C_6H_5)_2\overset{\overset{OH}{|}}{C}{\cdot} \quad \to \quad (C_6H_5)_2C{=}O \;+\; (C_6H_5)_2C^{\ominus}OH$$

$$(72) \quad (C_6H_5)_2\overset{\ominus}{C}OH \;+\; ROH \quad \to \quad (C_6H_5)_2CHOH \;+\; RO^{\ominus}$$

Cohen's evidence for the mechanism of the photoreduction of benzophenone in the presence of added base is that the rate of formation of benzpinacol in benzophenone-isopropyl alcohol systems without added base and the rate of benzhydrol formation in the presence of added base are essentially the same. When mercaptan is added, its rate of disappearance is lower with added alkoxide than when just alcohol is used for the photoreduction. Excited state quenchers, like naphthalene, retard the reaction by energy transfer, but they are much less effective than radical inhibitors such as mercaptans and disulfides.

It would appear that the photochemical reduction of benzophenone in the presence of added base does not go through benzpinacol as an intermediate. If benzpinacol were an intermediate, the rate of benzhydrol formation from photolysis of benzophenone in the presence of isopropyl alcohol and added base would be twice the rate of benzpinacol formation when only alcohol and no base is added. In addition, a build up of benzpinacol would occur in solution. Neither is observed. Radical intermediates of the same type (or at least formed at the same rate) are involved in both reactions since rates of retardation in the presence of added radical inhibitors are the same. Since naphthalene serves as a quencher of the photoreduction of benzophenone by alcohol both in the presence and in the absence of added base, the same triplet state intermediates are presumed to be involved in both reactions. It appears that the radical ion pathway suggested by Cohen is at least consistent with all the data. Electron spin resonance studied to detect the intermediate ketyl from benzophenone, a known reaction intermediate prepared easily by the reaction of benzophenone with sodium or potassium, are in order. One might photolyze benzophenone in the presence of sodium isoproxide and benzhydrol to investigate the feasibility of electron transfer and dimerization. Since the rate constants and activation energies for electron transfer between benzophenone ketyl radicals and benzophenone are known,[103,104] it might be possible to compare the photoprocess with the ground state process. In any event, electron spin resonance investigation of the photochemical reactions of diaryl ketones would provide interesting comparisons of the photochemical process to other methods of radical generation.

Photoreduction in the Presence of Sulfur Compounds

Cohen's observation that the photochemical formation of benzpinacol from benzophenone in alcohol solution and of benzhydrol from benzophenone in alcohol solution in the presence of added base is inhibited by mercaptans and disulfides provides an example of another type of photochemical stabilization.[105] The mercaptans and disulfides serve to inhibit the free radical reaction, by either hydrogen atom or electron transfer. The inhibitor, whether mercaptan or disulfide, is converted to an equilibrium mixture of the two materials, eqs. (73–75). Cohen's evidence for the mechanism is kinetic. The rate of photoreduction is inhibited by the presence of

$$(73) \quad C_6H_5\overset{O}{\overset{\|}{C}}C_6H_5 \ + \ R\overset{R'}{\overset{|}{C}}HOH \ \xrightarrow{h\nu} \ C_6H_5\overset{OH}{\overset{|}{C}}C_6H_5 \ + \ R\overset{OH}{\overset{|}{\underset{\cdot}{C}}}R$$

$$(74) \quad C_6H_5\overset{OH}{\overset{|}{C}}C_6H_5 \ + \ RSSR \ \longrightarrow \ C_6H_5\overset{O}{\overset{\|}{C}}C_6H_5 \ + \ RSH \ + \ RS\cdot$$

$$(75) \quad RS\cdot \ + \ C_6H_5\overset{OH}{\overset{|}{C}}C_6H_5 \ \rightleftharpoons \ RSH \ + \ C_6H_5\overset{O}{\overset{\|}{C}}C_6H_5$$

mercaptans and disulfides, and none of the disulfide or mercaptan is consumed during the early stages of the reaction. Optically active 2-octanol is racemized during the course of the inhibited reaction, indicating that a radical process involving 2-octyl radicals as hydrogen abstractors is also

$$(76) \quad \underset{\text{radical}}{\text{2-octyl}} \ + \ RSH \ \longrightarrow \ \underset{\text{racemic}}{\text{2-octanol}} \ + \ RS\cdot$$

important, eq. (76). Additional evidence is provided by the observation that the same free radical reaction sequence,[106] initiated by cobalt 60 radiation, is also inhibited by mercaptans and disulfides. Energy quenchers like naphthalene, which quench the photochemical reaction, fail to quench the γ radiation process.   Since triplet state intermediates are not important in radiation processes[107] while free radical intermediates are, it can be concluded that the disulfides and mercaptans are functioning as inhibitors of radical chain sequences.*

Benzophenone-Sensitized Photodecarbonylations

Disulfides and mercaptans do not inhibit all photoprocesses. For example, decarbonylation of aliphatic aldehydes in the presence of benzophenone is accelerated by low concentrations of mercaptans.[108]   Cohen proposes that since aliphatic aldehydes appear to quench the photoreduction of benzophenone to benzpinacol by isopropyl alcohol, an energy transfer mechanism is operative in the photodecarbonylation of aliphatic aldehydes when benzophenone catalysis is used.   Borrell proposes that the energy transferred is triplet energy.[109]   In addition, it is inferred that since no Norrish Type II reaction products are obtained in the sensitized sequence, the Type II process must proceed through an excited singlet state.   This observation has been disputed by Ausloos and Rebbert[110] who observe that triplet state intermediates are important in the photocyclization and photodecomposition of 2-pentanone by triplet state quencher experiments.**   The validity of the Borrell experiment is questionable on other grounds.   Cohen's evidence that energy transfer rather than hydrogen atom abstraction is the important ititiation step in the photosensitized decarbonylation of aldehydes rests only on quantum yield measurements.   Thus, photolysis of benzophenone-isopropyl alcohol solutions in the presence of increasing concentrations of an aliphatic aldehyde, 2-ethylhexanal, leads to benzpinacol, but the quantum yield decreases regularly as the concentration of aldehyde increases.

These results could indicate energy transfer to the aldehyde as an important quenching step of the benzophenone triplet as Cohen suggests, or they might also indicate that aldehydes fail to react as rapidly by hydrogen abstraction with triplet state benzophenone as do the alcohols.   In view of Walling's recent results[16] on the comparative relative reactivities of various hydrogen donors toward t-butoxy radicals and the benzophenone triplet state, such a rate decrease is not surprizing when the aldehydic hydrogen is compared with the α-carbon of alcohols.   In addition, the wealth of existing evidence indicating that t-butoxy radicals are capable of abstracting hydrogen atoms from aldehydes makes the inability of benzophenone to accomplish this same end surprising.   Huyser and Neckers[12] have isolated an α-

* See, however, R. A. Caldwell et al., *J. Am. Chem. Soc.*, **86**, 2659 (1966).
** See, however, references 54 and 55.

diketone and benzpinacol from the short term photolysis of benzophenone in isobutyraldehyde at low temperatures. The intermediacy of the acyl radical is indicated, eq. (77).

$$
\underset{\text{(77)}}{
\text{C}_6\text{H}_5\overset{\text{O}}{\overset{\|}{\text{C}}}\text{C}_6\text{H}_5 \;+\; \text{RCHO} \;\xrightarrow{h\nu}\;
}
$$

$$
\begin{array}{c}
\text{OH} \\
|\\
\text{C}_6\text{H}_5\text{C}\text{C}_6\text{H}_5 \\
|\\
\text{C}_6\text{H}_5\text{C}\text{C}_6\text{H}_5 \\
|\\
\text{OH}
\end{array}
\;+\;
\text{RC}\overset{\text{O}\ \ \text{O}}{\overset{\|\ \ \ \|}{—}}\text{CR}
\;+\; \text{other products}
$$

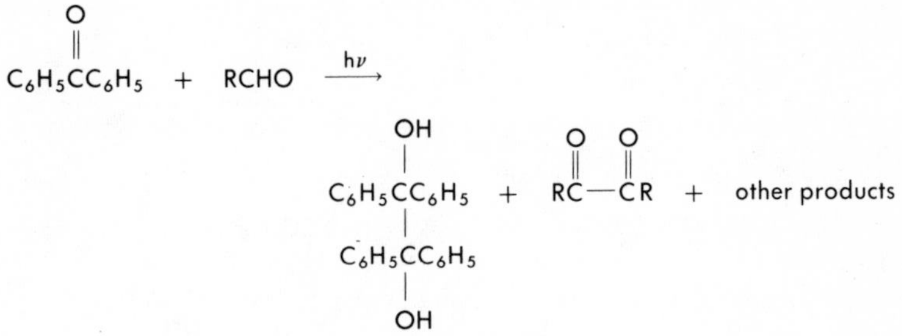

Conjugate Hydrogen Abstractions

Griffin and co-workers have observed the conjugate addition of hydrogen atoms to an α, β-unsaturated carbonyl system.[111, 112] Photolysis of 1,2-dibenzoylethylene in the presence of benzophenone and isopropyl alcohol leads to reduction of the double bond with 1,2-dibenzoylethane as the major product. A mechanism involving hydrogen atom addition to the carbonyl group followed by enolization and chain transfer can account for the observed products, eqs. (78) and (79). The product 1,2-dibenzoylethane, is formally the result of an olefinic carbon-hydrogen abstraction reaction.

(78)

(79)

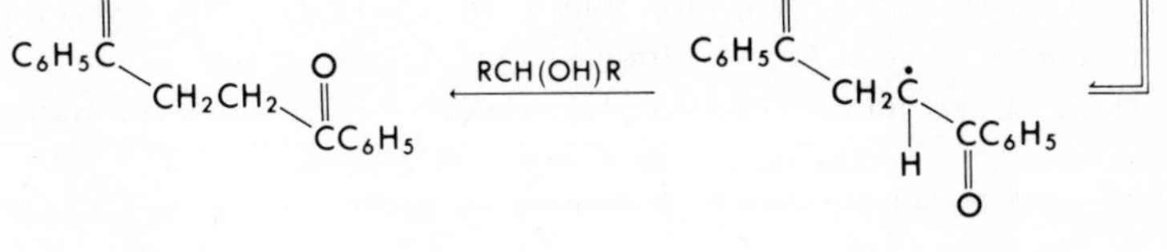

Dibenzoylcyclopropane undergoes a hydrogen atom addition in the presence of benzophenone and 2-propanol. The major reaction product is 1,3-dibenzoylpropane, eqs. (80) and (81). In the absence of photosensitizers

(80)

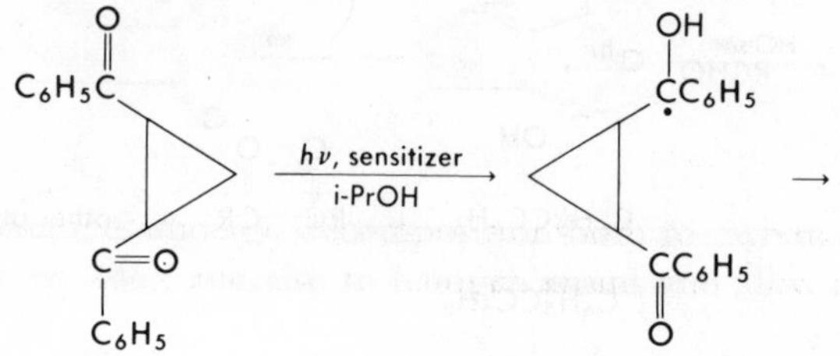

(81)

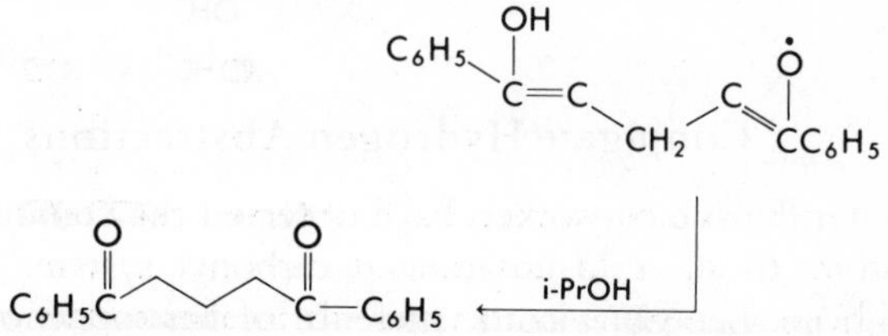

such as benzophenone, dibenzoylcyclopropane and dibenzoylethylene undergo preferred photochemical rearrangements rather than hydrogen abstractions even in the presence of strong hydrogen donors. 1,2-Dibenzoylethylene undergoes a carbon to oxygen-phenyl rearrangement[113] analogous to the anomolous Hunsdiecker reaction discovered by Wilt and coworkers.[114,115] 1,2-Dibenzoylcyclopropane, like many cyclopropyl compounds, undergoes *cis-trans* isomerization in the absence of photosensitizer.[113] This result might be rationalized if triplet state intermediates were necessary for hydrogen abstraction while singlet state intermediates were prerequisite for the rearrangement reactions.* In general, photochemical hydrogen transfer takes place from carbon to oxygen. Carbon-carbon-hydrogen transfers also take place.

Abstraction by Olefins

Crowley has reported that certain dienes equilibrate stereochemically when photolyzed and undergo a photochemically irreversible electrocyclic addition reaction to give cyclobutenes, eq. (82).[116] Thus, *trans*-2-methylpentadiene is converted to 1,3-dimethylcyclobutene as well as the *cis* isomer. Similarly, 1-cyclohexylbutadiene-1,3 gives 3-cyclohexylcyclobutene and

---

*See, however, references 13 and 14 for an alternative explanation.

(82)

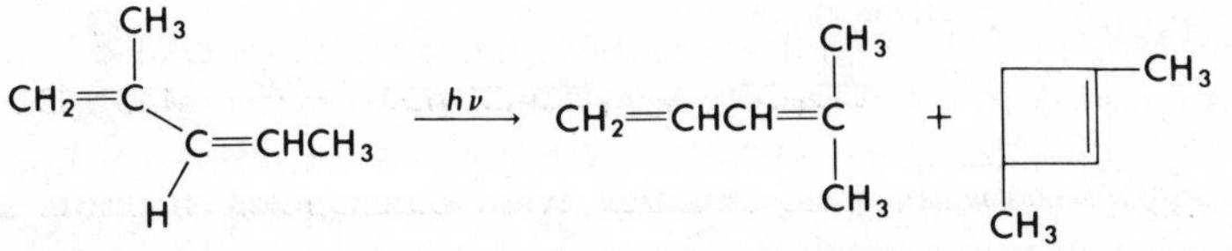

$$CH_2{=}C\underset{\underset{H}{|}}{\overset{\overset{CH_3}{|}}{}}\text{—}C{=}CHCH_3 \quad \xrightarrow{h\nu} \quad CH_2{=}CHCH{=}C\underset{\overset{|}{CH_3}}{\overset{\overset{CH_3}{|}}{}} \quad + \quad \text{[cyclobutene with CH}_3\text{ substituents]}$$

cyclohexylidenebutene-2, eq. (83). Allo-ocimene gives an allene upon photolysis, eq. (84).[117]

(83) 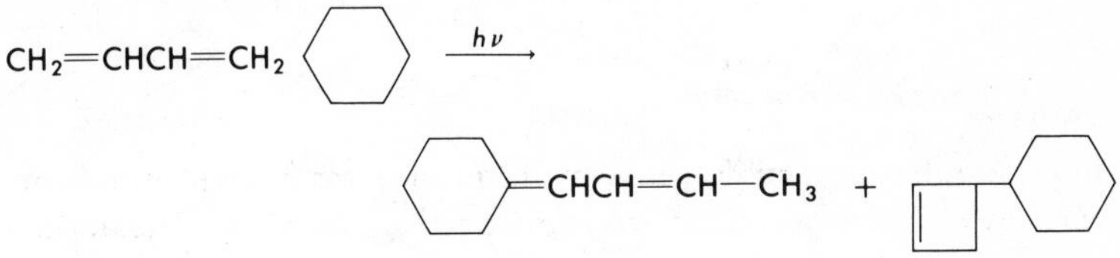 $CH_2{=}CHCH{=}CH_2$ [cyclohexane ring] $\xrightarrow{h\nu}$

[cyclohexylidene]$={=}CHCH{=}CH{-}CH_3$ + [bicyclic cyclobutane-cyclohexane]

(84)

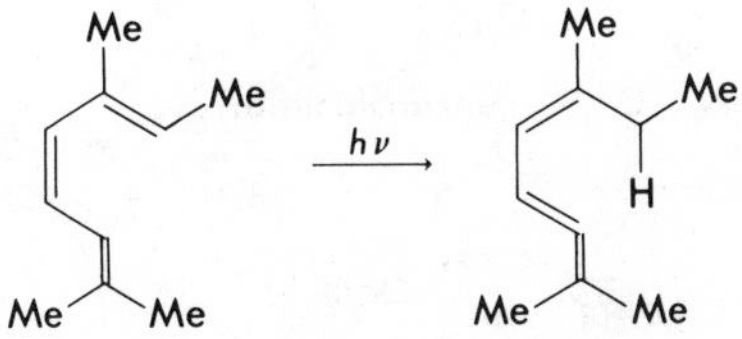

In all probability, these rearrangements are examples of hydrogen abstraction by excited carbon in a photochemical sequence, eq. (85).

(85)

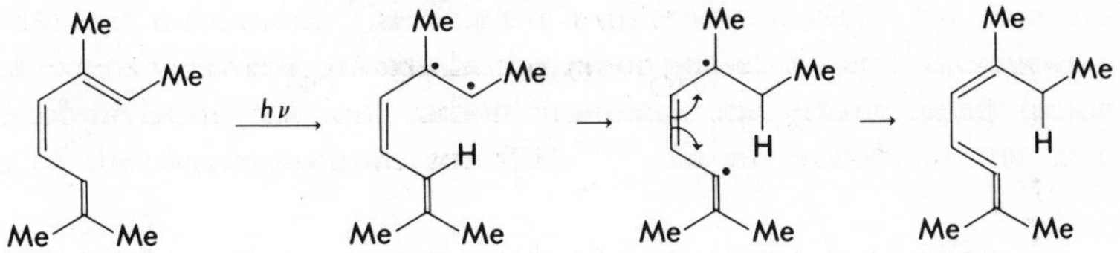

Crowley[118] observes intramolecular hydrogen addition to diene systems when dienoic acids are photolyzed in dry ether. The products are allenes,

(86) $RCH{=}CHCH{=}CHCOOH \quad \xrightarrow{h\nu} \quad RCH{=}C{=}CHCH_2COOH$

eq. (86). No allenic products are observed when potassium salts of the dienoic acids are photolyzed.

Williams and Bladon[119] have observed formal hydrogen abstraction reactions with steroidal systems containing α-, β-unsaturated carbonyl systems. 3β-Acetoxypregna-6,16-diene-20-one gives 3-acetoxypregna-5-ene-20-one when photolyzed in alcohol solution, eq. (87). Mechanistically, the reaction can be explained by a hydrogen atom abstraction reaction of the α-, β-unsaturated carbonyl group followed by enolization and either hydrogen abstraction or free radical coupling, eq. (88).

(87)

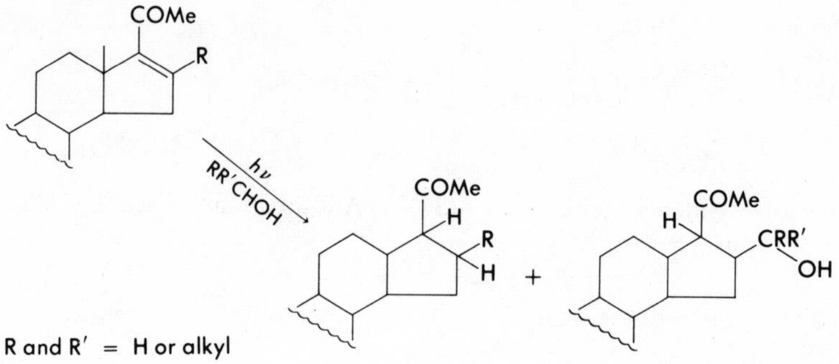

R and R' = H or alkyl

(88)

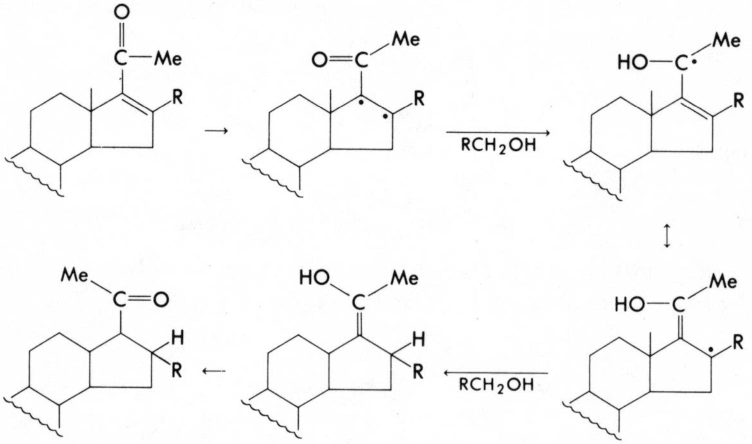

Photoreduction of Carbon Nitrogen Double Bonds

Carbon nitrogen doubly bonded systems are formally similar to carbonyl groups. Few photoreductions of these systems are known, however. Linschitz and co-workers have observed photoreduction reactions of N,N diphenyl-*p*-phenylenediimine,[120] but the reduction is markedly affected by the solvent so that in strongly hydrogen bonding media, little or no reaction takes place[121], eq. (89).

(89) $\xrightarrow[\text{RH}]{h\nu}$ semiquinoneimine

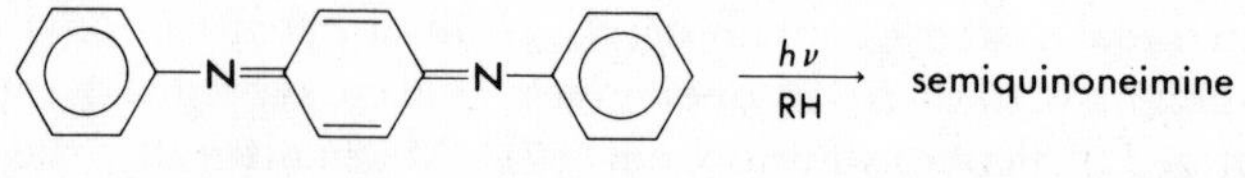

Photochemical atom abstraction reactions of atoms other than hydrogen are quite uncommon. As mentioned, benzophenone will not remove chlorine atoms from carbon tetrachloride photochemically.[5]   A thermodynamic analysis of the reactions proposed indicates that even though the carbon-chlorine bond in carbon tetrachloride probably requires less energy to dissociate than does the same carbon-hydrogen bond on the α-carbon of an alcohol, no stable product would be formed from the benzophenone abstraction of chlorine so that only products of chlorine atom chains would be detected.

In photochemical reactions involving most of the halogens, halocarbons and hydrogen halides chain sequences resulting from photochemical cleavage of the carbon-halogen, halogen-halogen, or hydrogen-halogen bond are observed. These reactions are discussed in a subsequent chapter. Similarly, photochemical reactions involving atomic carbon, atomic sulfur, and atomic oxygen have been discussed in detail elsewhere[122,123] and have been mentioned earlier in this book.

References

1. Ciamician, G., and P. Silber, *Chem. Ber.*, **33**, 2911 (1900).
2. Cohen, W. D., *Rec. trav. chim.*, **39**, 243 (1920).
3. Paterno, E., and G. Chieffi, *Gazz. chim. ital.*, **39b**, 415 (1909).
4. Paterno, E., and G. Chieffi, *Gazz. chim. ital.*, **40b**, 321 (1910).
5. Bowen, E. J., and E. L. de la Praudiere, *J. Chem. Soc.*, 1503 (1934).
6. Weismann, C., E. Bergmann, and Y. Hirshberg, *J. Am. Chem. Soc.*, **60**, 1530 (1938).
7. Pitts, J. N., Jr., R. Letsinger, R. Taylor, S. Patterson, G. Recktenwald, and R. Martin, *J. Am. Chem. Soc.*, **81**, 1068 (1959).
8. Hammond, G. S., and W. M. Moore, *J. Am. Chem. Soc.*, **81**, 6334 (1959).
9. Moore, W. M., G. S. Hammond, and R. P. Foss, *J. Am. Chem. Soc.*, **83**, 2789 (1961).
10. Hammond, G. S., W. P. Baker, and W. M. Moore, *J. Am. Chem. Soc.*, **83**, 2795 (1961).
11. Huyser, E. S., and D. C. Neckers, *J. Am. Chem. Soc.*, **85**, 3641 (1963).
12. Neckers, D. C., Ph. D. thesis, University of Kansas, 1963.
13. Neckers, D. C., A. P. Schaap, and J. Hardy, *J. Am. Chem. Soc.*, **88**, 1265 (1966).
14. Neckers, D. C., and A. P. Schaap, in press.
15. Franzen, V., *Ann. Chem.*, **633**, 1 (1960).
16. Walling, C., and M. J. Gibian, *J. Am. Chem. Soc.*, **86**, 3902 (1964).
17. Walling, C., and M. J. Gibian, *J. Am. Chem. Soc.*, **87**, 3361 (1965).
18. Padwa, A., *Tetrahedron Letters*, 3465 (1964).
19. Cohen, S. G., and S. Aktipis, *Tetrahedron Letters*, 579 (1965).
20. Cohen, S. G., and R. J. Baumgarten, *J. Am. Chem. Soc.*, **87**, 2996 (1965).
21. Bäckström, H. L. J., and K. Sandros, *Acta Chem. Scand.*, **14**, 48 (1960).
22. Bäckström, H. L. J., *Z. physik. Chem.*, **B25**, 99 (1934).
23. Bäckström, H. L. J., and K. Sandros, *J. Chem. Phys.*, **23**, 2197 (1955).
24. Moore, W. M., G. S. Hammond, and R. P. Foss, *J. Chem. Phys.*, **32**, 1594 (1960).
25. Kasha, M., *Disc. Faraday Soc.*, **9**, 14 (1950).
26. Bäckström, H. J. L., A. Steneryr, and P. Perlmann, *Acta Chem. Scand.*, **12**, 8 (1958).
27. Bell, J. H., and H. Linschitz, *J. Am. Chem. Soc.*, **85**, 528 (1963).
28. Porter, G., and F. Wilkinson, *Trans. Faraday Soc.*, **57**, 1686 (1961).
29. McClure, D., and P. Hanst, *J. Chem. Phys.*, **23**, 1772 (1955).

30. Bridge, N. K., and G. Porter, *Proc. Roy. Soc.*, (London) **A244**, 259 (1958).
31. Bridge, N. K., and G. Porter, *Proc. Roy. Soc.*, (London) **A244**, 276 (1958).
32. Bäckström, H. L. J., K. L. Appelgren, and R. J. V. Niklasson, *Acta Chem. Scand.*, 1555 (1965).
33. Brown, W. G., and D. G. Coyle, *Chem. Absts.*, **57**, 4219e (1962).
34. Hoffman, R., *Tetrahedron Letters*, 3819 (1965).
35. Bachman, W. E., *J. Am. Chem. Soc.*, **55**, 391 (1933).
36. Schönberg, A., and A. Mustafa, *J. Chem. Soc.*, 67 (1944).
37. Bergmann, F., and Y. Hirshberg, *J. Am. Chem. Soc.*, **65**, 1429 (1943).
38. Köller, H., G. P. Rabold, K. Weiss, and T. K. Mukherjee, *Proc. Chem. Soc.*, 332 (1964).
39. Neckers, D. C., *Tetrahedron Letters*, 1889 (1965).
40. Hammond, G. S., and P. A. Leermakers, *J. Am. Chem. Soc.*, **84**, 207 (1962).
41. Hammond, G. S., N. J. Turro, and P. A. Leermakers, *J. Phys. Chem.*, **66**, 1144 (1962).
42. Hammond, G. S., and P. A. Leermakers, *J. Phys. Chem.*, **66**, 1148 (1962).
43. Beckett, A., and G. Porter, *Trans. Faraday Soc.*, **59**, 2051 (1963).
44. Porter, G., and P. Suppan, *Proc. Chem. Soc.*, 191 (1964).
45. Porter, G., and P. Suppan, *Pure Appl. Chem.*, **9**, 499 (1964).
46. Pitts, J. N., H. W. Johnson, and T. Kuwana, *J. Phys. Chem.*, **66**, 2456 (1962).
47. Cohen, S. G., and M. N. Siddiqui, *J. Am. Chem. Soc.*, **86**, 5047 (1964).
48. Yang, N. C., and C. Rivas, *J. Am. Chem. Soc.*, **83**, 2213 (1961).
49. Zwicker, E. F., L. I. Grossweiner, and N. C. Yang, *J. Am. Chem. Soc.*, **85**, 2671 (1963).
50. Yang, N. C., and D. H. Yang, *J. Am. Chem. Soc.*, **80**, 2913 (1958).
51. Barnard, M., and N. C. Yang, *Proc. Chem. Soc.*, 302 (1958).
52. K. H. Schulte-Elte, and G. Ohloff, *Tetrahedron Letters*, 1143 (1964).
53. Orban, I., K. Schaffner, and O. Jeger, *J. Am. Chem. Soc.*, **85**, 3033 (1963).
54. Wagner, P. J., and G. S. Hammond, *J. Am. Chem. Soc.*, **87**, 4009 (1965).
55. Dougherty, T. J., *J. Am. Chem. Soc.*, **87**, 4011 (1965).
56. Urry, W. H., and D. J. Trecker, *J. Am. Chem. Soc.*, **84**, 118 (1962).
57. Urry, W. H., D. J. Trecker, and D. A. Winey, *Tetrahedron Letters*, 609 (1962).
58. Schulgin, A. T., and H. O. Kerlinger, *Tetrahedron Letters*, 3355 (1965).
59. Bruce, J. M., and E. Cutts, *Chem. Comm.*, 2 (1965).
60. Leermakers, P. A., and G. F. Vesley, *J. Am. Chem. Soc.*, **85**, 3776 (1963).
61. Leermakers, P. A., P. C. Warren, and G. F. Vesley, *J. Am. Chem. Soc.*, **86**, 1768 (1964).
62. Leermakers, P. A., and G. F. Vesley, *J. Org. Chem.*, **28**, 1160 (1963).
63. Schönberg, A., N. Latif, R. Moubasher, and A. Sina, *J. Chem. Soc.*, 1364 (1951).
64. Huyser, E. S., and D. C. Neckers, *J. Org. Chem.*, **29**, 276 (1964).
65. Yang, N. C., and A. Morduchowitz, *J. Org. Chem.*, **29**, 1654 (1964).
66. Norrish, R. G. W., and M. E. S. Appleyard, *J. Chem. Soc.*, 874 (1934).
67. Davis, W., Jr., and W. A. Noyes, Jr., *J. Am. Chem. Soc.*, **69**, 2153 (1947).
68. Masson, C. R., *J. Am. Chem. Soc.*, **74**, 4731 (1952).
69. Nicholson, A. J. C., *Trans. Faraday Soc.*, **50**, 1067 (1954).
70. Martin, T. W., and J. N. Pitts, Jr., *J. Am. Chem. Soc.*, **77**, 5465 (1955).
71. For a review see W. Davis, Jr., *Chem. Rev.*, **40**, 201 (1947).
72. Srinivasan, R., *Advances in Photochemistry*, Vol. I, p. 83, New York, Wiley, 1963.
73. McMillan, G. R., J. G. Calvert, and J. N. Pitts, Jr., *J. Am. Chem. Soc.*, **86**, 3602 (1964).
74. Srinivasan, R., *J. Am. Chem. Soc.*, **81**, 5061 (1959).
75. McNesby, J. R., and A. S. Gordon, *J. Am. Chem. Soc.*, **80**, 261 (1958).
76. Yates, P., and A. G. Szabo, *Tetrahedron Letters*, 485 (1965).
77. Srinivasan, R., *J. Am. Chem. Soc.*, **84**, 2475 (1962).
78. Hikino, H., and P. de Mayo, *J. Am. Chem. Soc.*, **86**, 3582 (1964).
79. Wettermark, G., *J. Am. Chem. Soc.*, **84**, 3658 (1962).

80. Wettermark, G., *J. Phys. Chem.*, **66**, 2560 (1962).
81. Wettermark, G., *Nature*, **194**, 677 (1962).
82. Wettermark, G., E. Black, and L. Dogliotti, *Photochem. Photobiol.*, **4**, 229 (1965).
83. Morrison, H., and B. H. Migdalof, *J. Org. Chem.*, **30**, 3996 (1965).
84. Tschitschibabin, A. E., B. M. Kuindshi, and S. W. Benewolenskaja, *Chem. Ber.*, **58**, 1580 (1925).
85. Kortum, G., M. Kortum-Seiler, and S. D. Bailey, *J. Phys. Chem.*, **66**, 2439 (1962).
86. Margerum, J. D., L. J. Miller, E. Saito, M. S. Brown, H. S. Mosher, and R. Hardwick, *J. Phys. Chem.*, **66**, 2434 (1962).
87. Margerum, J. D., *J. Am. Chem. Soc.*, **87**, 3772 (1965).
88. Schwab, O., and F. Dorr, *Z. Electrochem. Ber. Bunsenges. phyzik Chem.*, **66**, 870 (1962).
89. Cohen, M. D., and G. M. J. Schmidt, *J. Phys. Chem.*, **66**, 2442 (1962).
90. Cohen, M. D., G. M. J. Schmidt, and S. Flavian, *J. Chem. Soc.*, 2041 (1964).
91. Cohen, M. D., Y. Hirshberg, and G. M. J. Schmidt, *J. Chem. Soc.*, 2051 (1964).
92. Cohen, M. D., Y. Hirshberg, and G. M. J. Schmidt, *J. Chem. Soc.*, 2060 (1964).
93. Weller, A., *Z. Electrochem.*, **60**, 1144 (1956).
94. Luck, W., and H. Sand, *Angew. Chem., Intern. Ed.*, **3**, 570 (1964).
95. Dessauer, R., and J. P. Paris, *Advances in Photochemistry*, Vol. I, p. 275, New York, Wiley, 1963.
96. Exelby, R., and R. Grinter, *Chem. Rev.*, **65**, 247 (1965).
97. Bachmann, W. E., *J. Am. Chem. Soc.*, **55**, 391 (1933).
98. Bachmann, W. E., *Org. Syn.*, Coll. Vol. II, p. 71, New York, Wiley, 1943.
99. Bachmann, W. E., *J. Am. Chem. Soc.*, **55**, 355 (1933).
100. Cohen, S. G., and W. V. Sherman, *J. Am. Chem. Soc.*, **85**, 1642 (1963).
101. Russell, G. A., E. T. Strom, E. R. Talaty, and S. A. Weiner, *J. Am. Chem. Soc.*, **88**, 1998 (1966).
102. Strom, E. T., G. A. Russell, and J. H. Schoeb, *J. Am. Chem. Soc.*, **88**, 2004 (1966).
103. Hirota, N., and S. I. Weissman, *J. Am. Chem. Soc.*, **86**, 2537 (1964).
104. Hirota, N., and S. I. Weissman, *J. Am. Chem. Soc.*, **86**, 2538 (1964).
105. Cohen, S. G., S. Orman, and D. A. Laufer, *J. Am. Chem. Soc.*, **84**, 3905 (1962).
106. Cohen, S. G., D. A. Laufer, and W. V. Sherman, *J. Am. Chem. Soc.*, **86**, 3060 (1964).
107. Sherman, W. V., and S. G. Cohen, *J. Am. Chem. Soc.*, **86**, 2390 (1964).
108. Berman, J. D., J. H. Stanley, W. V. Sherman, and S. G. Cohen, *J. Am. Chem. Soc.*, **85**, 4010 (1963).
109. Borrell, P., *J. Am. Chem. Soc.*, **86**, 3156 (1964).
110. Ausloos, P., and R. E. Rebbert, *J. Am. Chem. Soc.*, **86**, 4512 (1964).
111. Griffin, G. W., and E. J. O'Connell, *J. Am. Chem. Soc.*, **84**, 4148 (1962).
112. Griffin, G. W., private communication.
113. Griffin, G. W., E. J. O'Connell, and H. A. Hammond, *J. Am. Chem. Soc.*, **85**, 1001 (1963).
114. Wilt, J. W., and J. L. Finnerty, *J. Org. Chem.*, **26**, 2173 (1961).
115. Wilt, J. W., and D. D. Oathoudt, *J. Org. Chem.*, **23**, 218 (1958).
116. Crowley, K. J., *Proc. Chem. Soc.*, 17 (1964).
117. Crowley, K. J., *Tetrahedron Letters*, 2863 (1965).
118. Crowley, K. J., *J. Am. Chem. Soc.*, **85**, 1210 (1963).
119. Williams, I. A., and P. Bladon, *Tetrahedron Letters*, 257 (1964).
120. Linschitz, H., J. Rennert, and T. M. Korn, *J. Am. Chem. Soc.*, **76**, 5839 (1954).
121. Rennert, J., and J. Wiesenfeld, *Photochem. Photobio.*, **5**, 337 (1966).
122. Noyes, W. A., G. S. Hammond, and J. N. Pitts, *Advances in Photochemistry*, Vol. I, p. 43, New York, Wiley, 1963.
123. *Ibid.*, p. 25.

CHAPTER

8

Rearrangement Reactions

A photochemical rearrangement reaction is any photochemical process in which a product similar in composition but altered in structure results. Many photochemical rearrangements are known. Rearrangement reactions of olefins, dienones, esters, unsaturated ketones, nitrogen compounds, and epoxides have been studied.

cis-trans Isomerization

The simplest type of photochemical rearrangement involves *cis-trans* isomerization about a carbon-carbon double bond. Both direct irradiation processes and energy transfer methods yield useful information about the mechanisms of photochemical *cis-trans* isomerization processes. Studies of stilbene and its derivatives are particularly convenient.

When either *cis* or *trans* stilbene is directly irradiated in hydrocarbon or aromatic hydrocarbon solvents, a photostationary state is attained that favors the *cis* isomer, eq. (1).[1-7] The actual value of the *cis-trans* ratio varies with

(1)

$$
\begin{array}{ccc}
\underset{H}{\overset{C_6H_5}{>}}C-C\underset{C_6H_5}{\overset{H}{<}} & \xrightarrow{h\nu} & \underset{H}{\overset{C_6H_5}{>}}C=C\underset{H}{\overset{C_6H_5}{<}} \\
10\% & & 90\%
\end{array}
$$

solvent, concentration, temperature, and the purity of the sample; however, the photochemical equilibrium invariably favors the *cis* compound.

The mechanism for the direct photochemical irradiation isomerization of *cis* to *trans* stilbene was predicted initially to involve triplet state intermediates. Lewis and co-workers[2] proposed that if the isomerization involved singlet state intermediates, measurable fluorescence emission competitive with rearrangement to the stereoisomeric state would be observed. Since this is not true of *cis* to *trans* isomerization, a reaction involving stilbene triplets is postulated, eqs. (2) and (3).* According to Lewis, stilbene triplets are transformed into vibrationally activated ground state species that rearrange.

(2) $C_6H_5C\!\!=\!\!C\,C_6H_5$ $\xrightarrow{\;h\nu\;}$ singlet $\rightarrow$ $C_6H_5\,\overset{\bullet}{C}\!\!-\!\!\overset{\bullet}{C}\,C_6H_5$
           H H   H H
        cis or trans   *triplet*

(3)   *cis* + *trans* stilbene

The quantum yield for the rearrangement of *cis* or *trans* stilbene varies with temperature.[8-12] Several other theories may explain the variance of Φ with temperature. One theory proposes that two distinct intermediate excited states are important (Fig. 8-1a). One excited state is derived from the *cis* isomer, and the other is derived from the *trans* isomer, and an energy of activation for interconversion between *cis* and *trans* excited states exists. Another theory proposes that the same *meta*-stable intermediate excited state is formed from both *cis* and from *trans* stilbene, but that the temperature effect results from an energy barrier to intersystem crossing from the excited singlet state to the intermediate (Fig. 8-1b).

Stegemeyer has derived the kinetic expressions for the two model processes (Fig. 8-1a and 8-1b). From an evaluation of the quantum yields for

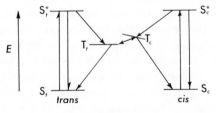

Figure 8-1a

*Stilbene isomerizations are complicated by a second photochemical rearrangement reaction, a formation of dihydrophenanthrene. This process is known to be quite dependent upon the concentration of added oxidizing agents and will be discussed in detail shortly.

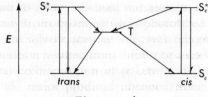

Figure 8-1b

rearrangement of both the *cis* and the *trans* isomers and an evaluation of the spectral emission rates, Stegemeyer has concluded that no common intermediate is involved in the rearrangement of *cis* to *trans* or *trans* to *cis* stilbene and that the actual rearrangement sequence is best represented by Figure 8-1a. Since the quantum yield of fluorescence is also temperature dependent for *trans* stilbene,[9] a competition between fluorescence and rearrangement occurs.

Hammond and co-workers,[1] as well as others,[13] have studied energy transfer and photochemical isomerization. Their observations with the sensitized isomerization of *cis* to *trans* stilbene and vice versa suggest that unusual non-Franck-Condon processes are important. The unique behavior of certain low energy sensitizers in causing the photoisomerization of stilbene and other conjugated olefins has caused Hammond and co-workers[1,14,15] to propose a triplet state intermediate that is intermediate in energy between the *cis* and the *trans* triplet state and directly reachable by triplet energy transfer. This intermediate differs from either the *cis* or the *trans* form in structure in that the methylene groups may be twisted with respect to one another. Hammond calls this triplet a "phantom triplet" because it can be reached directly from the ground state by energy transfer—an apparent violation of the Franck-Condon principle.

Schulte-Frohlinde and co-workers[5] have reported direct excitation isomerization reactions of a number of substituted stilbenes. They have found interesting variations in the quantum yield of the isomerizations depending on the substituent, the solvent, the temperature, and the concentration. Their findings indicate that, as a general rule, *cis* stilbene is the more favored form in the less polar solvents. As the polarity of the solvent is increased, the *trans* form of the stilbene becomes more predominant, reflecting an increased quantum yield in the *cis* → *trans* isomerization or a decreased quantum yield in the *trans* → *cis* isomerization. Some of Schulte-Frohlinde's data is recorded in Table 8-1.

Substituents appear to influence the quantum yield for *trans* → *cis* isomerization more significantly than the quantum yield for the reverse reaction. As the strength of the electron donor substituent increases, the quantum

Table 8-1

Quantum Yields for Stilbene Isomerizations

Stilbene	Solvent	$\phi\, c \rightarrow t$	$\phi\, t \rightarrow c$	cis-Stationary states, %
4,4'-dinitro	benzene	0.34	0.27	80.0
	DMF	0.33	0.31	82.0
4-nitro,	benzene	0.40	0.38	85.5
3'-methoxy	DMF	0.38	0.20	69.0
4-nitro,	benzene	0.43	0.40	73.0
4'-methoxy	DMF	0.42	0.035	17.0
4-nitro-4'-amino	benzene	0.44	0.10	34.0
	DMF	0.20	0.00	0.0
4-nitro-4'di-	benzene	0.40	0.016	6.5
methylamino	DMF	0.00	0.15	0.0

yield for isomerization decreases and the percentage of *cis* isomer in the photostationary state decreases. This fact is indicative of an increasing electron density at the ethylenic carbon atoms during the course of the rearrangement of *trans* to *cis* stilbene, eq. (4). The growing radical character

$$(4) \qquad \underset{X-C_6H_5}{\overset{H}{\diagdown}}C=C\underset{H}{\overset{C_6H_5-X}{\diagup}} \xrightarrow{h\nu} \underset{X-C_6H_5}{\overset{H}{\diagdown}}\dot{C}-\dot{C}\underset{C_6H_5-X}{\overset{H}{\diagup}}$$

of the vinylic carbons as they go to the transition state for rearrangement is facilitated by electron-donating substituents for the *cis* to *trans* rearrangement. The fact that polar solvents decrease the quantum yield for the rearrangement is indicative of noncharged transition state for the isomerization process. More polar solvents would facilitate the formation of charged intermediates.

Hammond and co-workers also report an energy transfer study of 1,2-diphenylpropene. As in the case of stilbene and its derivatives, two stereoisomeric triplet states and an intermediate twisted form are thought to be important intermediates leading to isomerization. The photochemical isomerization of α-, β-unsaturated acids and diacids and their derivatives have also been reported.[16-20] Frequently, the isomer of lesser ground state stability is formed in the higher yield because of the energy difference between the *cis* and *trans* triplet states in *cis-trans* isomerization reactions. Since *cis* isomers generally show absorption maxima at shorter wavelengths than their *trans*

Table 8-2

Olefins for Which *Cis-Trans* Isomerizations Have Been Observed

Olefin	Example	Reference
RCCOOR $\parallel$ RCCOOR	HCCOOH $\parallel$ HCCOOH	17
RCH $\parallel$ HCCOOR'	C_6H_5CH $\parallel$ HCCOOH	18, 19, 20
RCH $\parallel$ RCH	CHCl $\parallel$ CHCl	24, 25
RCH $\parallel$ RCH	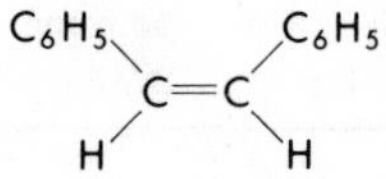 C_6H_5, H / C=C \ C_6H_5, H	1–15
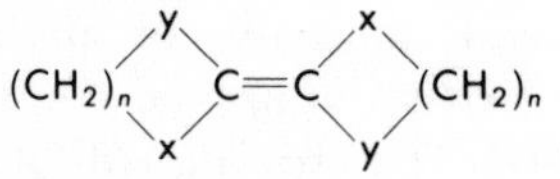 $(CH_2)_n$ $\begin{smallmatrix}y\\x\end{smallmatrix}$ C=C $\begin{smallmatrix}x\\y\end{smallmatrix}$ $(CH_2)_n$	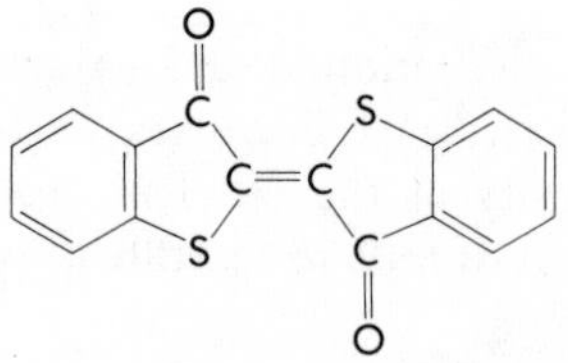 (thioindigo-type structure)	26
RC≡CCN	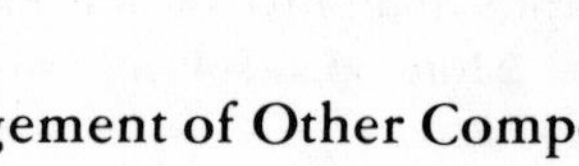 $(Me)_2N$⟨C₆H₄⟩CH=CHCN	27, 28, 29, 30

analogs, the isomerization process is useful synthetically. Table 8-2 lists some olefins for which *cis-trans* isomerization reactions have been observed.*

Stereoisomeric Rearrangement of Other Compounds

Griffin and co-workers[31] have reported that certain cyclopropane compounds behave like olefins and undergo photochemical *cis-trans* isomerizations. Irradiation of either *cis* or *trans* diphenylcyclopropane, *cis* or *trans* dibenzoylcyclopropane, or *cis* or *trans* 1-phenyl-2-benzoylcyclopropane gives photostationary states of the isomeric materials. Neither the *cis* nor the *trans* isomer generally predominates, unlike the olefins. Griffin proposes a diradical intermediate resulting from the π-π* excitation of the phenylcyclo-

*The earlier literature has been thoroughly reviewed by Wyman[22] and Rollefson and Burton.[23]

propane system. Ring closure of olefins to cyclopropanes can also be affected photochemically.[32,33]

The *cis-trans* isomerization of cyclopropanes can be photosensitized. Hammond and Cole have found that when an optically active sensitizer is used, optically active cyclopropanes result.[34]

Mislow and Gordon[21] report that biphenyl type hydrocarbons, which are optically active due to molecular asymmetry, can be racemized photolytically, eq. (5),[21] with wavelengths shorter than 3000 Å. Racemization and

(5)

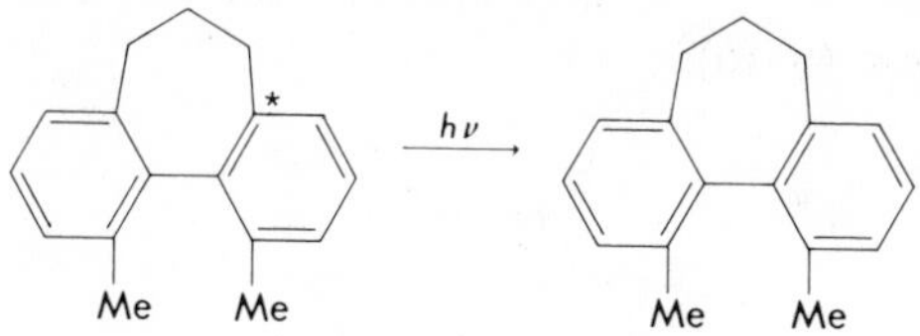

decarbonylation of the biphenyl-like ketone occurs with wavelengths longer than 3000 Å, eq. (6). Racemization of the hydrocarbon, eq. (5), is proposed

(6)

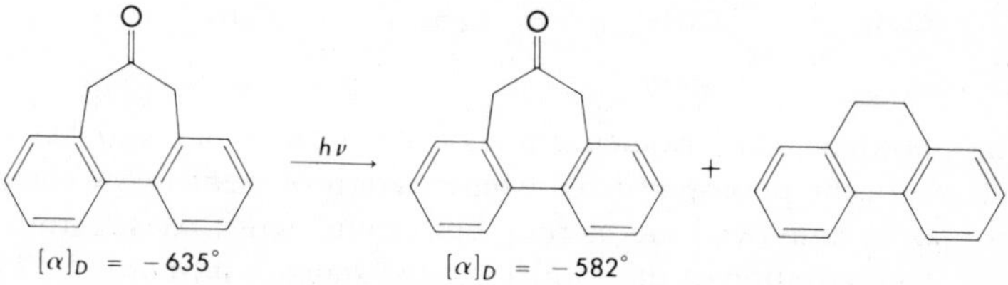

$[\alpha]_D = -635°$ $[\alpha]_D = -582°$

to occur via a π-π^* transition, whereas the similar racemization of the ketone is proposed to involve the n-π^* excitation. Both racemization reactions are suggested to require internal conversion to a vibrationally excited or "hot" ground state molecule from which the racemization occurs.

Racemization of optically active sulfoxides has also been reported.[35,36] An intramolecular sensitization mechanism has been suggested.

Azo Compounds

Photochemical *cis-trans* isomerisms are by no means confined to carbon systems. There are reports of photochemical isomerization of azo compounds and of oximes, and some workers propose that rearrangements may occur in imine and ketenimine systems as well.[37] With aromatic azo compounds, photochemical isomerization occurs in a manner quite analogous to isomerization of olefin derivatives, eq. (7).[38,39] The quantum yields of the forward and reverse isomerization are affected differently by temperature; the photo-

(7) 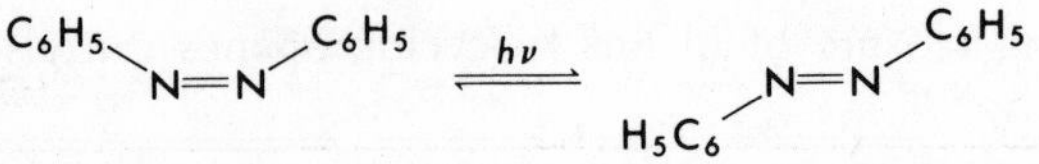 $\quad$

isomerization from *cis* to *trans* azobenzene is virtually the same at all temperatures, but low temperatures drive the quantum yield for the *trans* to *cis* photoisomerization to zero. Fischer's results indicate that the processes of photochemical isomerizations of azo compounds are analogous to processes involving olefins although some controversy exists as to the actual mechanism for the isomerization.[6,7,11,40-42] A mechanism for the direct irradiation isomerization is shown in eqs. (8–10).

(8) 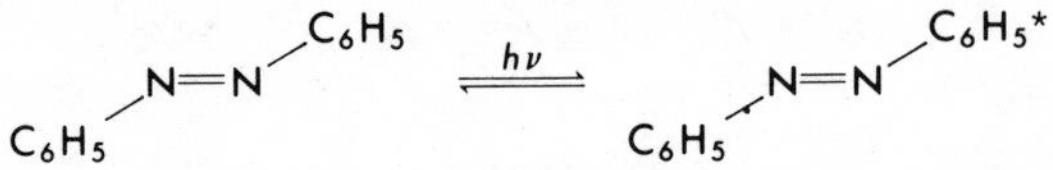 $\quad$

(9) 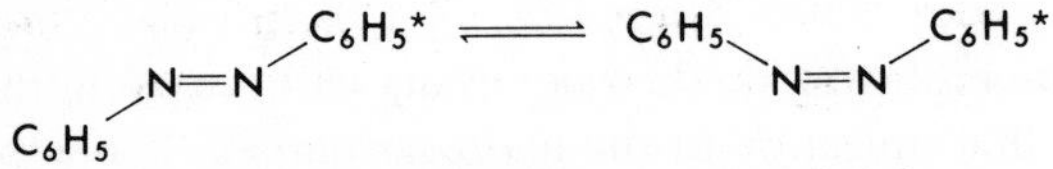 $\quad$

(10) 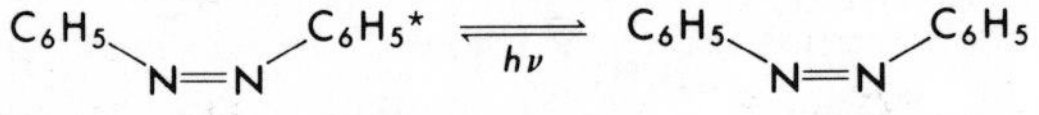 $\quad$

The photosensitized isomerization of azobenzene has also been investigated. As in the photosensitized isomerization of olefins, low energy sensitizers may be employed successfully but careful sensitizer selection is more crucial. Isomerization of the singlet excited states is proposed.[43] The transformation is not specific for azobenzene, but also occurs with azonaphthalene and 1-phenylazonaphthalene.[44] It has been suggested that with *ortho* hydroxyazo compounds hydrogen transfer precedes or accompanies the isomerization about the double bond, eq. (11).[45-47] Kearns predicts, from molecular orbital calculations, that population of the $n\text{-}\pi^*$ triplet state of azobenzene is the most efficient means of promoting *cis* $\rightarrow$ *trans* azobenzene isomerization. Experimentally, monochromatic excitation capable of pop-

(11) 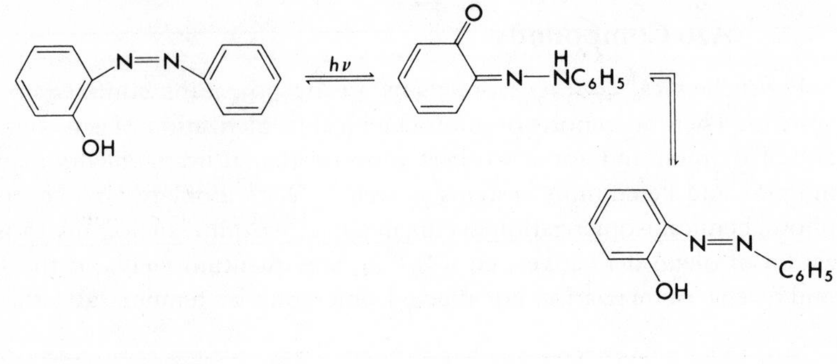 $\quad$

ulating the n-π^* triplet preferentially results in a higher quantum yield for the isomerization reaction.

Wettermark and co-workers[48,49,50] have investigated other systems in which the possibility of *cis-trans* isomerization and concomitant hydrogen transfer exists, eq. (11). The simple *trans* to *cis* isomerization of certain anils can be followed by converting the phenol to its phenolate anion. A different transient species is observed in basic media than in acidic media because in acidic media hydrogen transfer can accompany *cis-trans* isomerization. Wettermark finds that anils in which hydroxy groups are *ortho* to the imino linkage are capable of hydrogen transfer[51-55] with little, if any, activation energy required for the hydrogen transfer reaction. Wettermark and co-workers have successfully observed the intramolecular hydrogen transfer from an examination of the absorption spectrum of the photolysis mixture shortly after a high intensity flash, eq. (12).

(12)

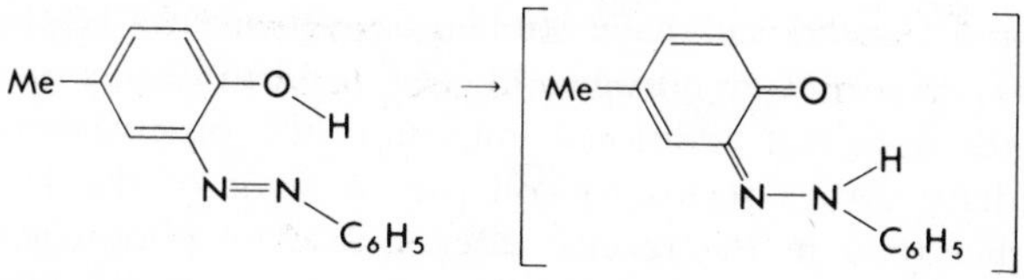

The photochemical behavior of a variety of azo compounds and azo dyes has been reported by Brode, Gould, and Wyman.[56,57] A similar photochemical isomerization between the *syn* and *anti* forms of various oximes has also been reported, eq. (13).[58-61]

(13)

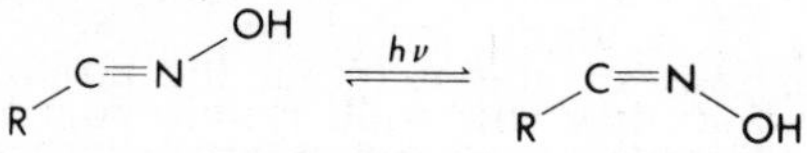

Oxygen Transfer Rearrangements

Rearrangement reactions of double-bonded nitrogen compounds do not always involve just geometrical isomerization reactions. Azoxy compounds, for example, tend to react by photocyclization and cleavage in what resembles an oxygen transfer type of reaction, eq. (14).[62] Badger and Buttery,[63]

(14)

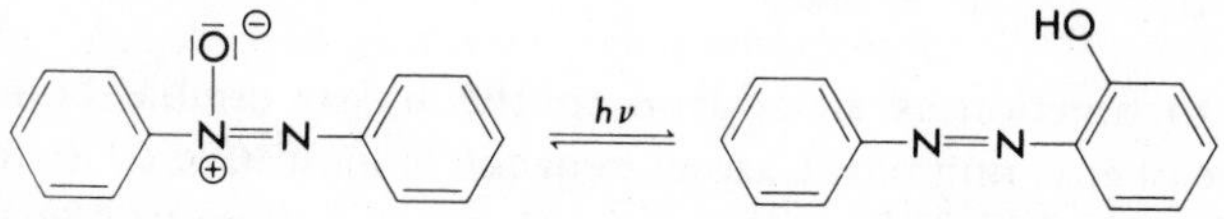

in conjunction with a study of the sulfuric-acid-catalyzed isomerization of azoxybenzenes to *ortho* and *para* hydroxyazobenzenes (the Wallach rearrangement), investigated the photochemical reactions of a series of substituted azoxybenzenes. Cyclic intermediates were indicated for the photochemical rearrangement of azoxybenzenes by the observation that substituents in the ring away from the azoxy group always were found in the ring of the hydroxy group and vice versa, eq. (15).

(15)

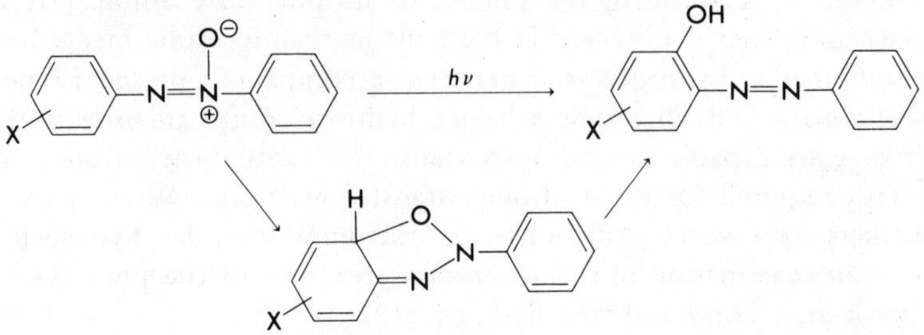

Shemyakin and co-workers[65] have studied azoxybenzenes labeled appropriately with oxygen-18 and nitrogen-15 and confirm the intramolecular nature of the reaction. Of additional interest is the observation that the cyclic intermediate always seems to collapse in favor of the hydroxyazo compound rather than in the reverse direction. The photochemical behavior of oximo and imino systems confined to rigid rings would also provide for an interesting investigation.

Jaffè and co-workers[64] report the isomerization of *trans* to *cis* azoxybenzenes upon low temperature photolysis in benzene solution. A 6% yield of the *cis* compound is obtained by isolation, although the photostationery state favors the *trans* isomer.

Nitrogen oxygen transfer reactions are important in the photochemical behavior of nitrones and their derivatives. Several groups have observed that nitrones undergo a photochemical oxygen transfer to yield oxazirine derivatives, eq. (16).[66-73] The ability of the excited oxygen atom of azoxy

(16)

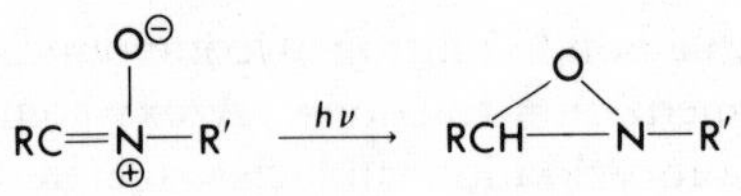

$$R = p\text{-}NO_2 \qquad R' = Et, t\text{-}Bu$$
$$R = \phi \qquad R' = t\text{-}Bu$$

compounds to function as an addend to the imino double bond of the nitrone or the phenyl ring of the azoxy benzene is indicative of its reactivity. These ring closures take place without concomitant *cis-trans* isomerism about the carbon nitrogen double bond.[71]

Jaffè and co-workers have studied the excited state pKa's of azo and azoxybenzene.[74,75,76] By measuring the difference in the absorption spectra (or fluorescence spectra[77]) of the azo or azoxy derivative in solutions of varying pH, one can determine the difference in the pKa of the excited state and the ground state. Jaffé's results indicate that the pKa's of the excited states of azo and azoxybenzenes are generally much higher than the pKa's for the ground states of the molecules.

A number of photochemical rearrangements take place by means of atom migration. The mechanisms of these rearrangements are not always straightforward, and the reactions are often accompanied by other transformations. The oxygen transfer reaction of azoxybenzenes and of nitrones is a simple example. So-called oxygen transfer reactions occur with a variety of other systems as well. Many oxygen transfer rearrangements take place with organic nitro compounds, and it is presumed that these oxygen transfer reactions occur by means of an n-π^* excitation of the nitro group. The oxygen atom of the n-π^* triplet presumably is somewhat like the oxygen of carbonyl group n-π^* triplets, and as such it is able to abstract hydrogen atoms or add to unsaturated systems.

Nitro Group Rearrangements

Photolysis of *ortho*-nitrobenzaldehyde in solution[78-80] or in a solid matrix[81] leads to *ortho*-nitrosobenzoic acid in high yield. The reaction is intramolecular since it is concentration-independent and does not occur with *meta*- and *para*-nitrobenzaldehydes.[82] Filter studies indicate that the nitro chromophore is excited and not the carbonyl chromophore. One possible mechanism for the rearrangement involves a hydrogen abstraction reaction by the nitro group followed by ring closure and collapse, eqs. (17–19).

(17)

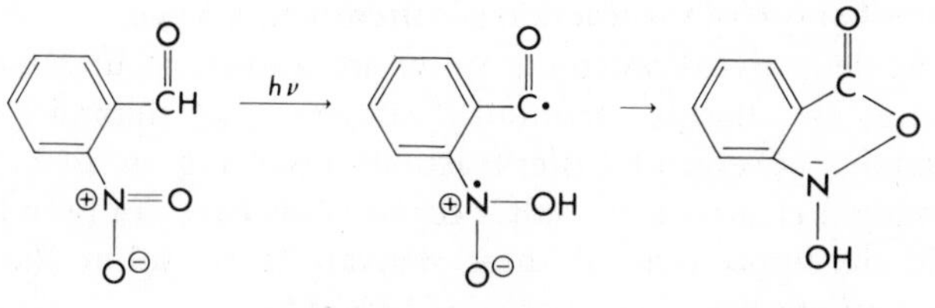

(18)

(19)

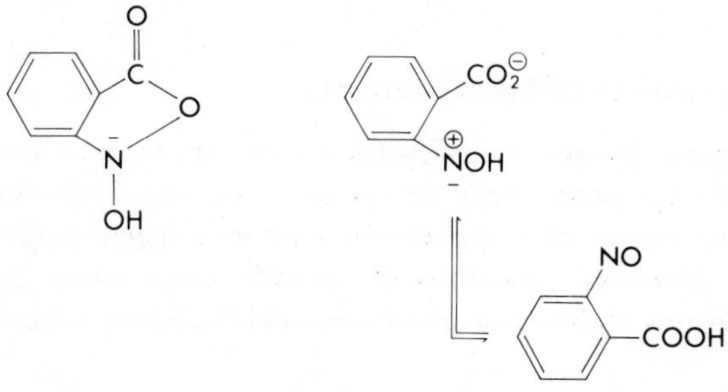

Other rearrangements of organic nitro compounds are known, and the nature of the products of these rearrangements points to cyclic intermediates in many instances. 2,4-Dinitrotolane undergoes a ring closure rearrangement, eq. (20).[83]

$$(20) \quad O_2N-\underset{NO_2}{\bigcirc}-C{\equiv}CC_6H_5 \quad \xrightarrow{h\nu} \quad O_2N-\underset{\underset{\ominus O}{\overset{\oplus}{N}}}{\bigcirc}-C_6H_5$$

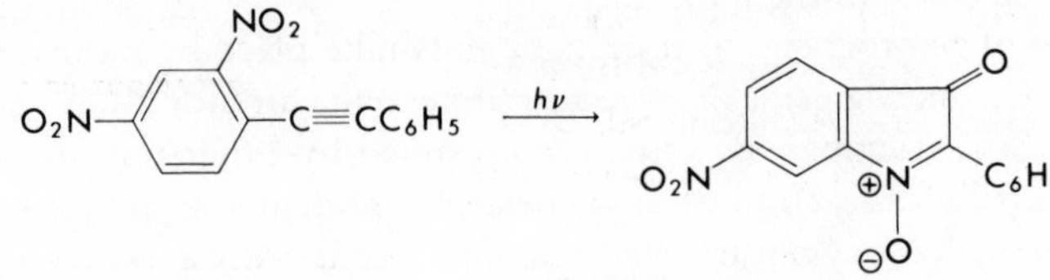

Table 8-3 lists organic nitrogen compounds that undergo photochemical oxygen transfer rearrangement.

Miscellaneous Rearrangements

Schmid and co-workers have reported an interesting atom migration in heterocyclic derivatives.[93]   They found that imidazole rearranges photochemically to give benzamidazole, eq. (21).   The rearrangement is reported

$$(21) \quad \xrightarrow{h\nu}$$

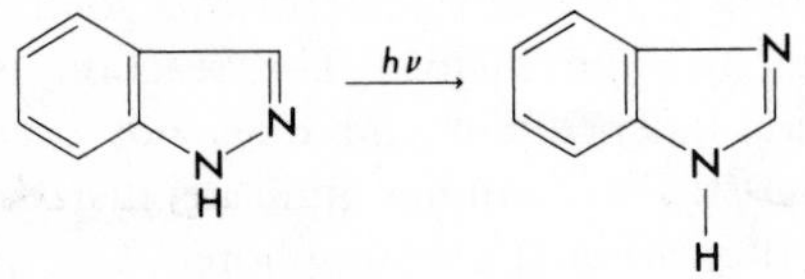

to occur in a variety of solvents under a variety of conditions, and substituents in the benzene portion of the imidazole ring are generally without effect. The mechanism of the reaction is currently unknown.

Heterocyclic derivatives containing sulfur are known to undergo *cis-trans* isomerization as the already mentioned isomerism of thioindigo and its derivatives implies. Oxygen transfer reactions involving sulfur heterocyclic sulfones or straight chain organic sulfur compounds have not been observed; however, the decomposition of these derivatives to sulfur dioxide and dimeric hydrocarbons has been reported (Chapter 5).

Rearrangements of Epoxyketones

The simplest organic oxygen heterocycles are the epoxides. Rearrangement reactions involving epoxides and compounds containing epoxide rings appear generally to involve cleavage of the carbon oxygen bond of the epoxide; however, photolysis reactions of epoxide rings alone generally result in transformations of very low quantum yield.[94] When adjacent to a

Table 8-3

Oxygen Transfer Rearrangements of Organic Nitro Compounds

Compound	Product	Reference
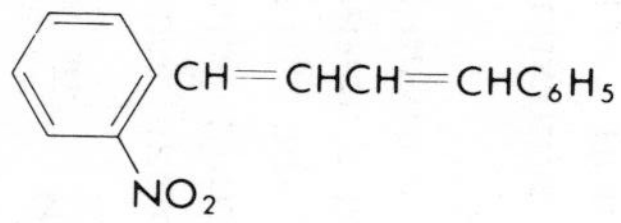	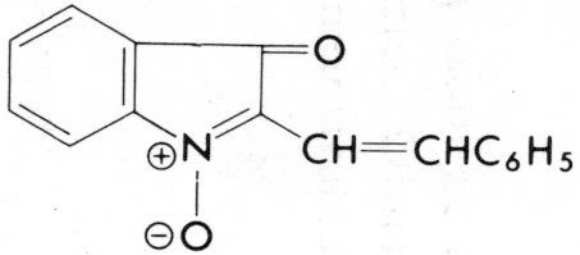	84
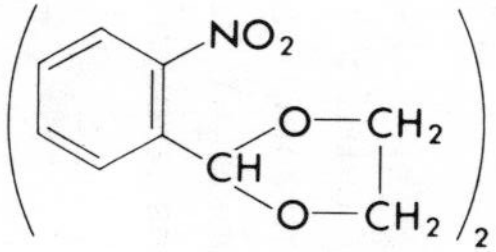	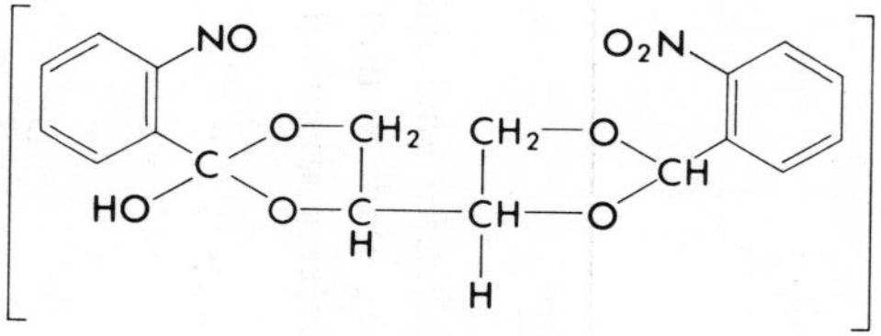	85
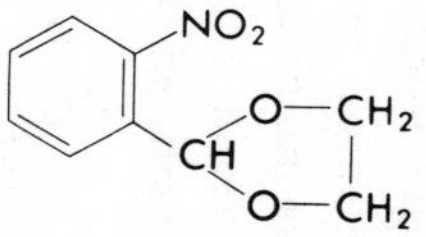	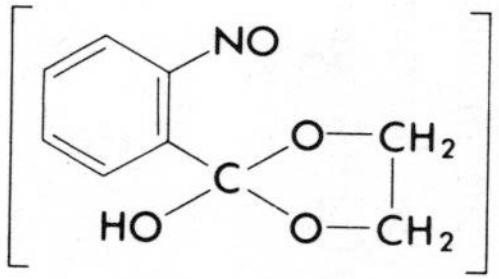	85
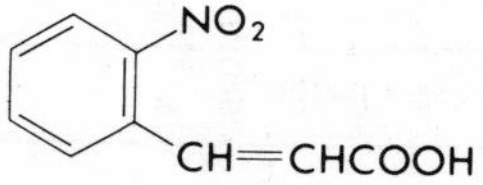	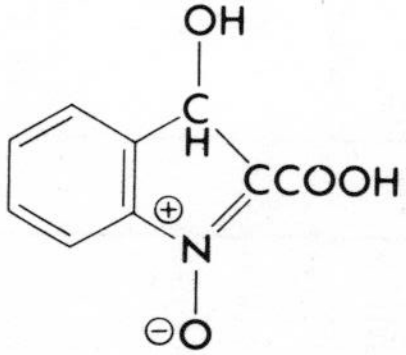	86

Table 8-3

Compound	Product	Reference
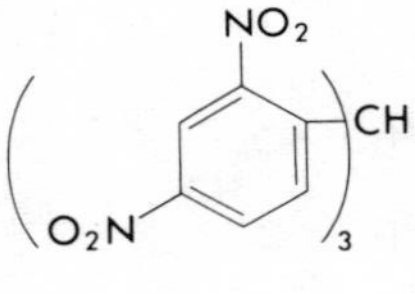 (structure: $(C_6H_3(NO_2)_2$–O_2N ... $CH)_3$)	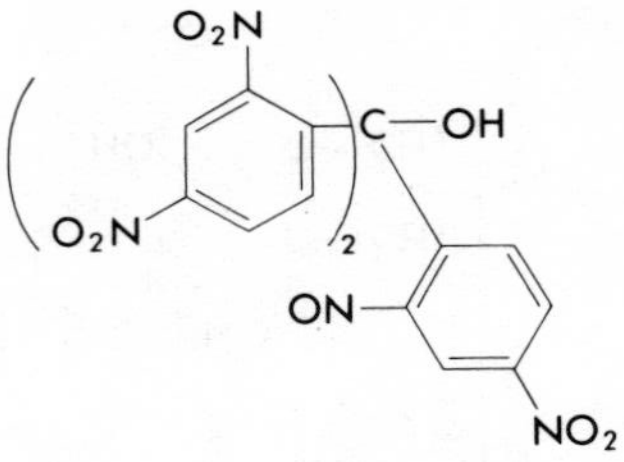 (structure with O_2N, O_2N, C–OH, NO_2, NO_2)	87
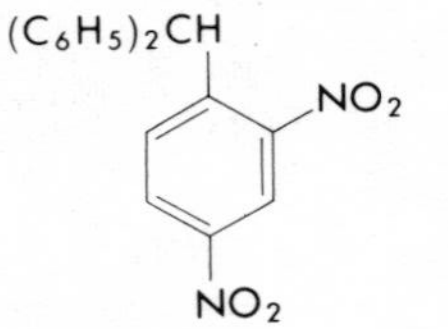 $(C_6H_5)_2CH$ with NO_2, NO_2	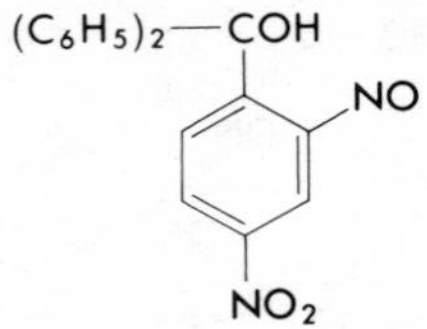 $(C_6H_5)_2$–COH with NO, NO_2	87
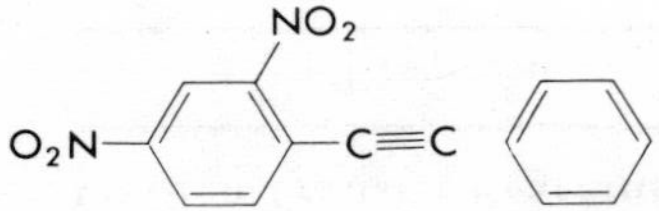 O_2N ... $C\equiv C$–C_6H_5, O_2N	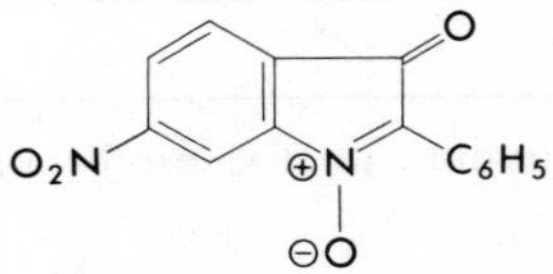 (structure with O, C_6H_5, $N^{\oplus}$–$O^{\ominus}$, O_2N)	83

89, 90

91

92

carbonyl group or ethylenic chromophore, quantum yields for the ring opening and rearrangements of epoxides depend on the excited state behavior of the ethylenic chromophore or the carbonyl chromophore rather than on the epoxide itself. Like other systems, epoxides adjacent to chromophoric groups undergo rapid photochemical reaction. The rearrangement reactions of α-epoxyketones involve the carbonyl chromophore and as such are quite rapid. Zimmerman has reported the photochemical rearrangement of trans-dypnone oxide to give an α-hydroxyketone, eq. (22).[95]

(22)

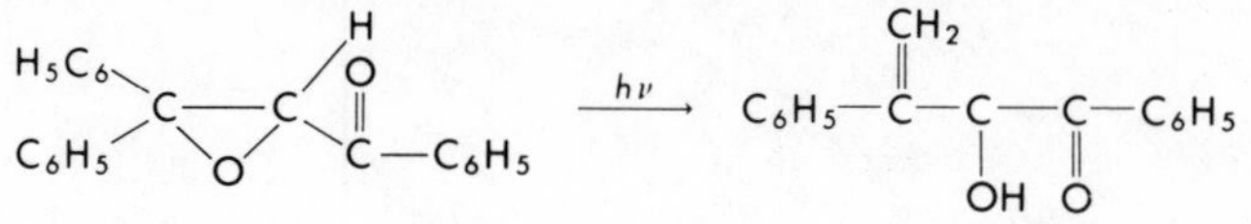

The rearrangement of epoxy ketones to α-ketoalcohols has been described as an intramolecular hydrogen abstraction reaction followed by cleavage of an ether oxygen carbon bond, eqs. (23–26). An n-π^* triplet excited state intermediate is presumed to be the hydrogen abstracting agent.

(23)

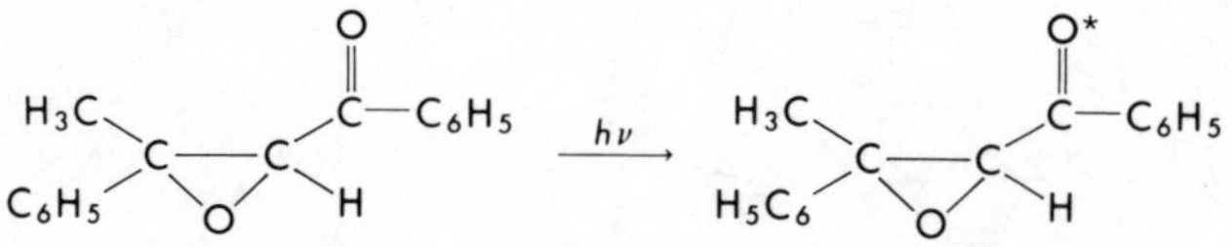

(24)

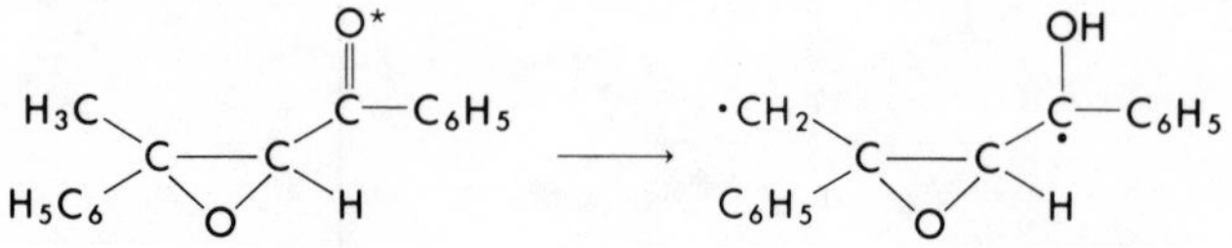

(25)

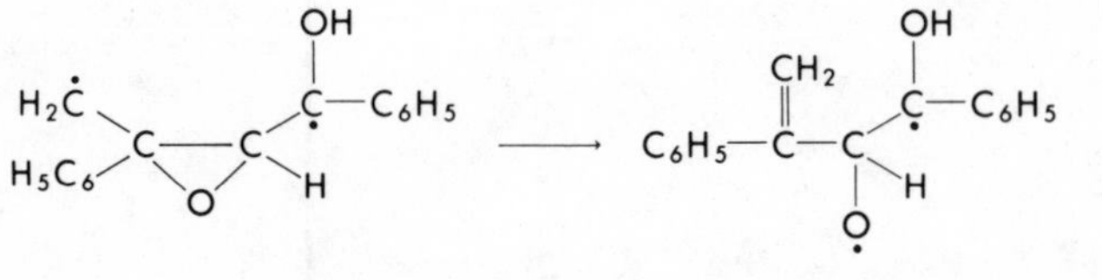

(26)

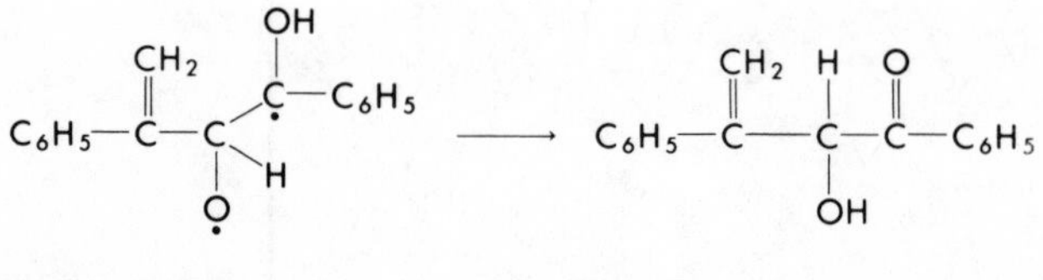

When the phenyl of the ketone is replaced by methyl, a novel alkyl free radical migration takes place, eqs. (27–29).

(27)

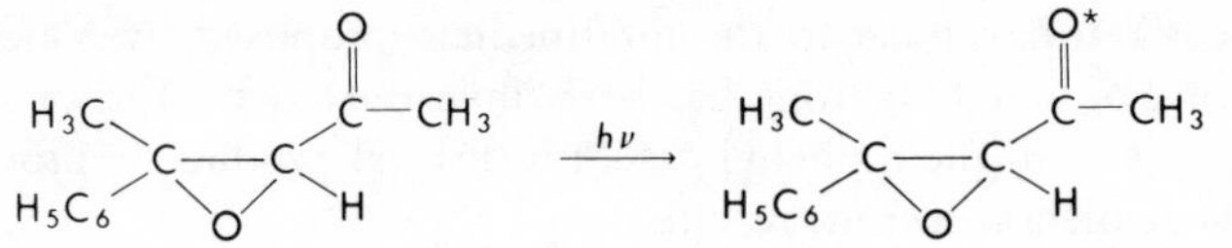

(28)

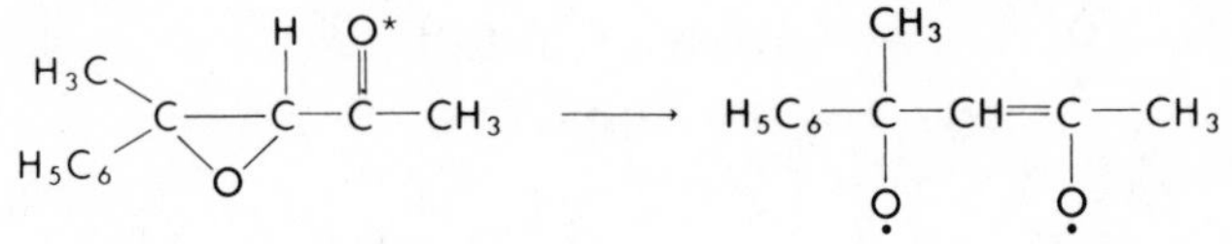

(29)

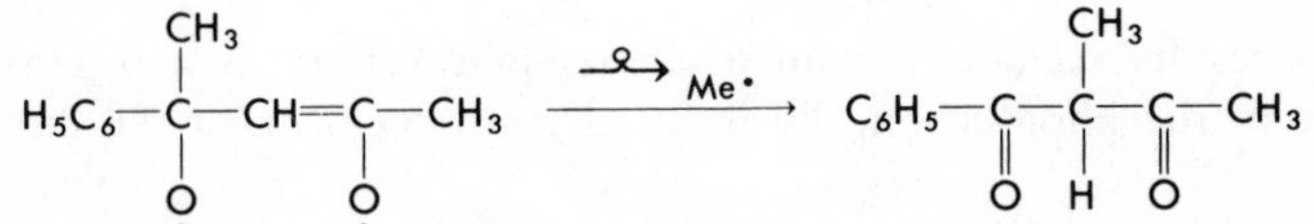

Although the proposed migration of methyl is not without precedent in free radical reactions,[96] it is highly unusual.[97] In most free radical rearrangement reactions, the migrating group is aryl or, in some cases, halogen.[98] These results again point to the great similarity, but yet the significant difference between photochemical reactions in which the intermediate states are in some excited state and reactions involving ordinary free radical intermediates, which possess that energy concomitant with a nonpaired electron. Padwa has reported rearrangement of a β-γ epoxyketone. Thus, trans-1,4-diphenyl-3,4-epoxybutan-1-one affords dibenzoylethane and a cyclobutene oxide (X) when photolyzed in benzene, eq. (30).[99]

(30)

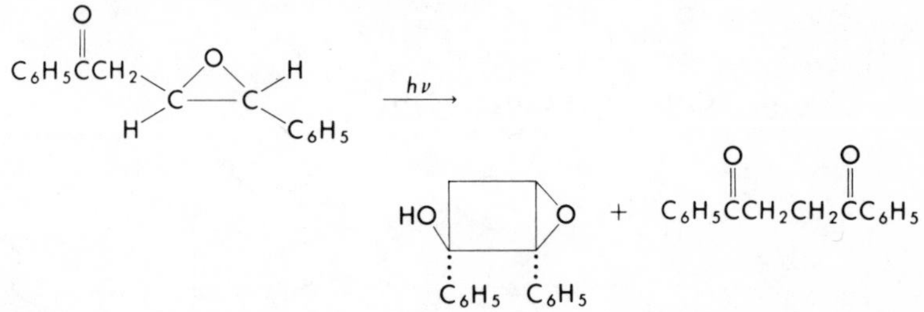

Yates and Stille have reported that the solution phase photolysis of 2,6-dimethyl-4-pyrone leads to 4,5-dimethylfurfural[100] and have proposed an α-epoxyketone intermediate for the reaction, eq. (31). Photolytic behavior

(31)

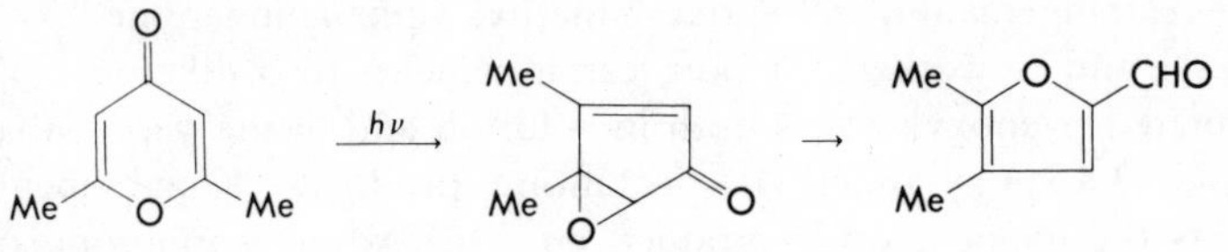

of an α-epoxyketone similar to the intermediate proposed by Yates in the photolysis of 2,6-dimethylpyrone has been investigated by Padwa with the result that, at least in the diphenyl case, no furfural product is produced.[101] Instead a cyclic dienoic lactone resulted, eq. (32).

(32)

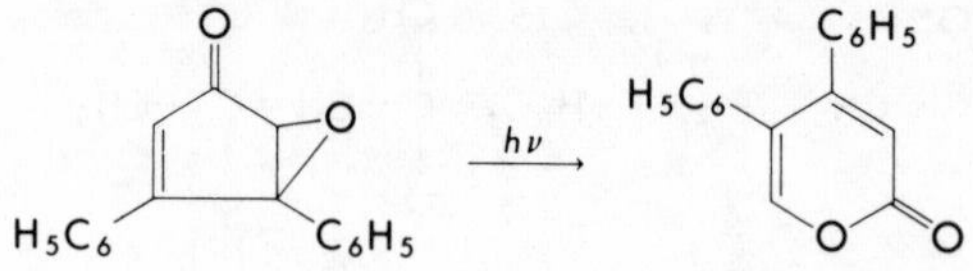

Padwa's results seem to eliminate an α-epoxyketone as a reaction intermediate in the photochemically induced rearrangement of 2,6-dimethyl-4-pyrone.

Rearrangement of the α-epoxyketone to the lactone, eq. (32), presents, in itself, an interesting photochemical rearrangement reaction. Padwa suggests the mechanism shown in eqs. (33–35) for the rearrangement. Similar results

(33)

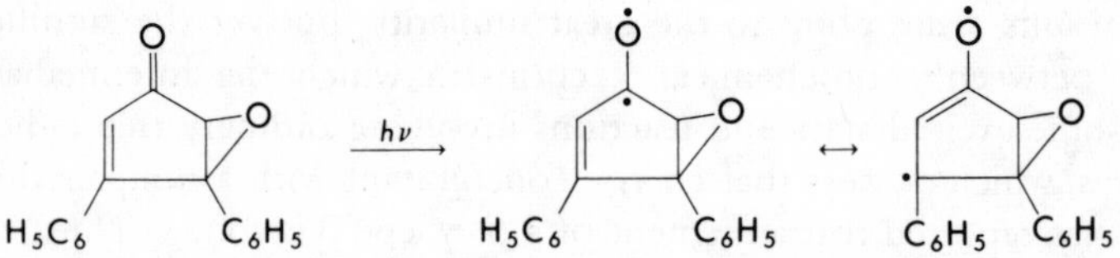

(34)

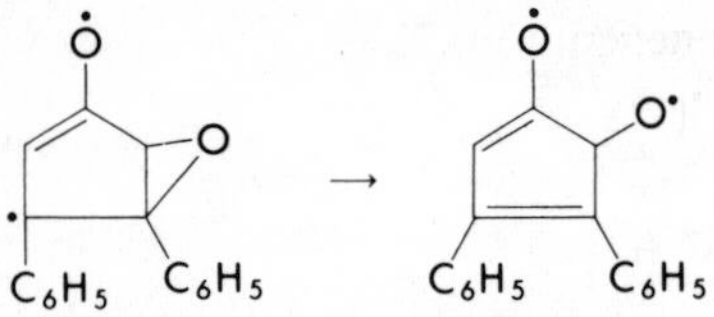

(35)

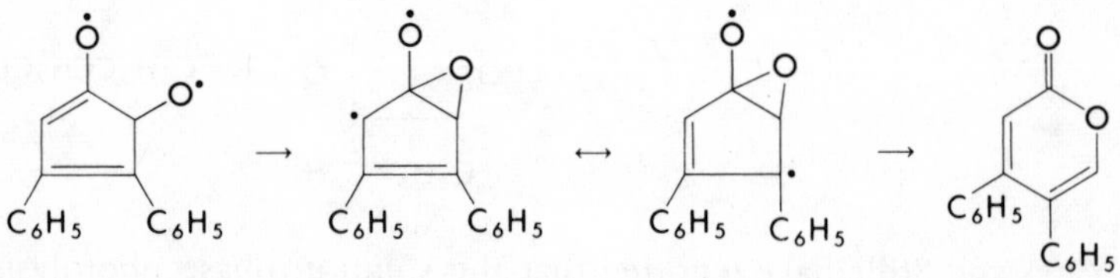

have been reported by Dunston and Yates[102] for the rearrangement of 4,5-epoxy-2,3,4,5-tetraphenylcyclopent-2-enone and by Zimmerman and Simkin for the rearrangement of 2,3-epoxy-2-methyl-3-phenylindanone.[103]

Reusch and co-workers[104] report rearrangements to β-diketones of a series of saturated α-epoxyketones both in solution and in the vapor phase. For example, 3,4-epoxy-4-methyl-2-pentanone produces 3-methylpentane-2,4-dione as the major isolable product, eq. (36), while isophorone oxide re-

(36)

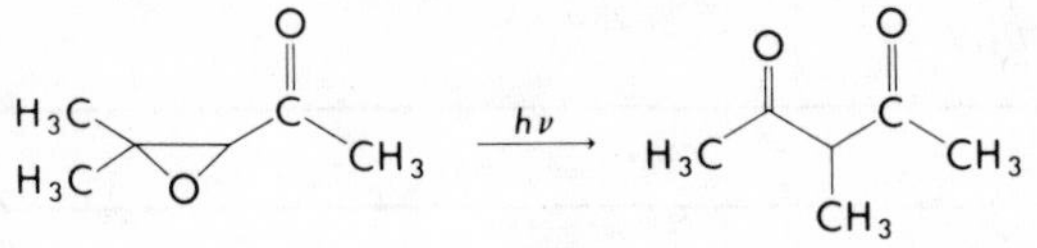

arranges photochemically to 2-acetyl-4,4-dimethylcyclopentanone and 2,5,5-trimethylcyclohexanedione-1,3, eq. (37).

(37)

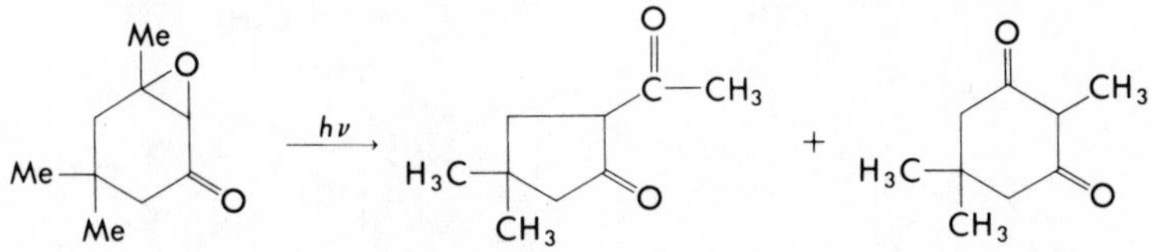

Alkyl group migration is again proposed. Since the thermal rearrangement of certain epoxyketones is known to give products analogous to the photochemical rearrangement, Reusch and other workers[105] propose that vibrationally excited species rather than electronically excited intermediates are important in the rearrangement reaction. Other epoxyketones for which rearrangement reactions have been observed are listed in Table 8-4.

The transformations involving the cyclopentadienone oxides and indenone oxides are thermally reversible.

Table 8-4

Rearrangements of Epoxyketones

Ketone	Major Product	Reference
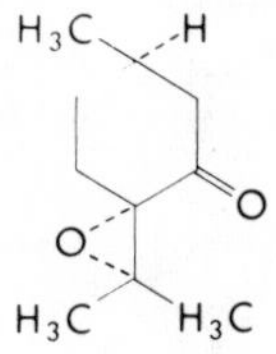	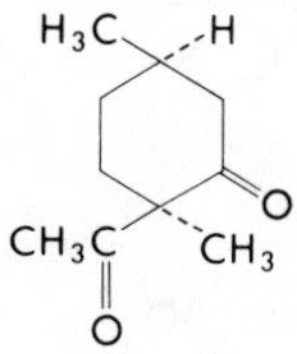	104
		104

Table 8-4 (cont.)

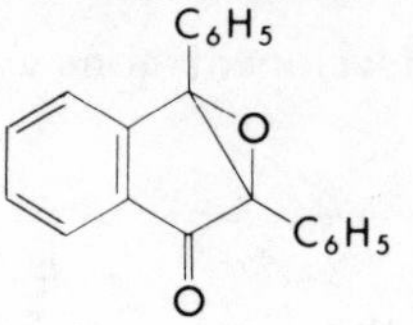

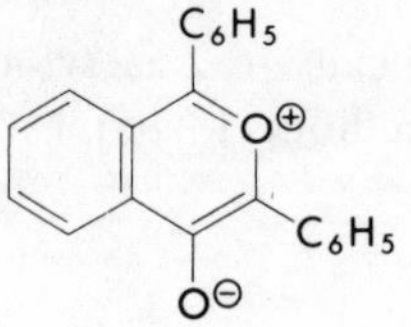

105, 106, 107

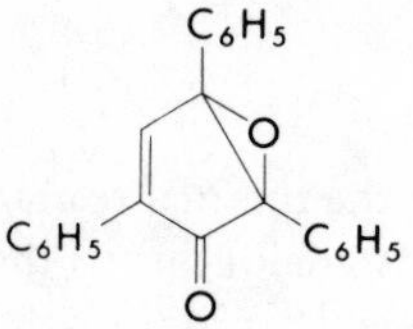

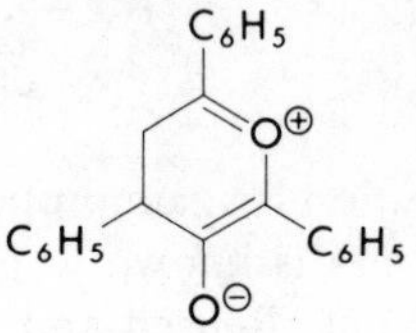

108

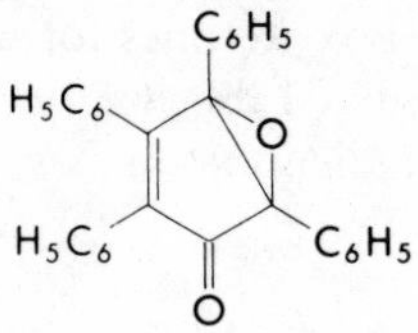

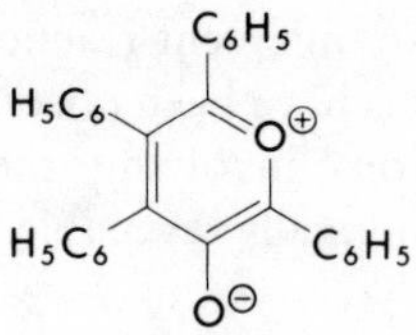

102

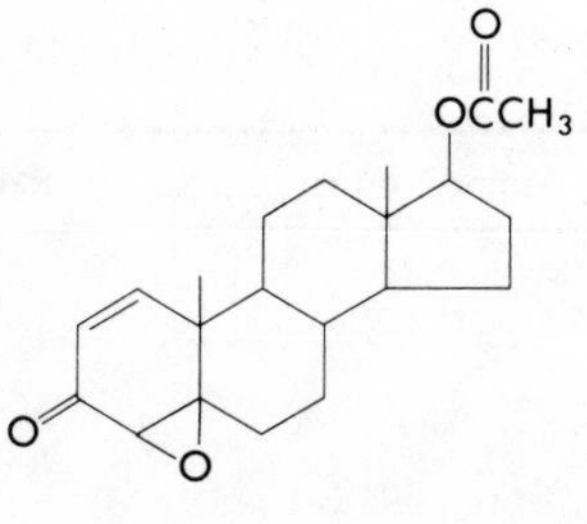

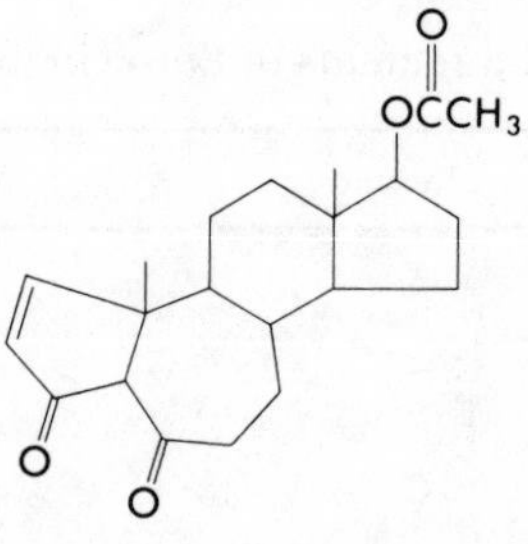

109

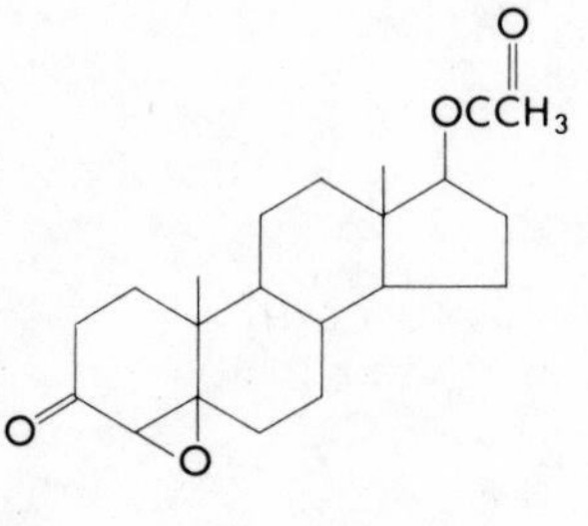

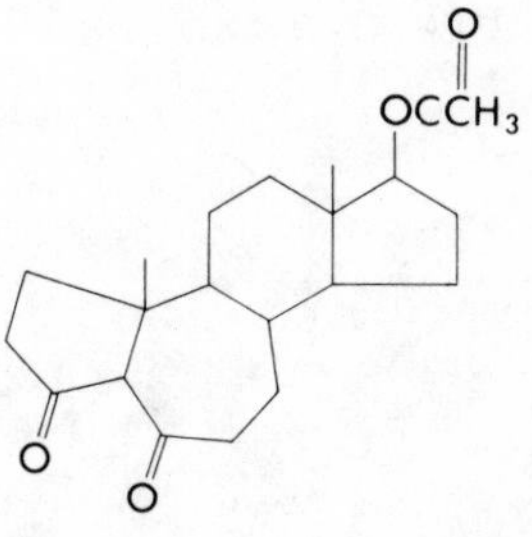

109

Rearrangements of Dienones

Rearrangement reactions involving dienones probably constitute the most extensively studied type of rearrangement reaction. The rearrangement of santonin, a naturally occurring dienone, provided the first example of the interesting transformations that dienone systems undergo. Since the photochemical behavior of santonin has been reviewed elsewhere,[110-113] the phototransformations of santonin are only summarized in Figure 8-2.

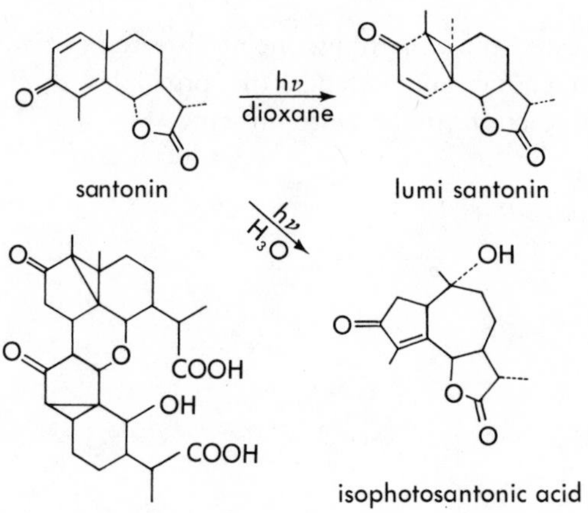

santonin

lumi santonin

isophotosantonic acid

Figure 8-2

The mechanism for the photochemical rearrangement of santonin involves a photochemical dienone-phenol rearrangement. Its mechanistic diversity can be more simply illustrated with the less complex dienone 6,6-diphenyl-cyclohexa-2,5-dienone. Photolysis of this dienone leads to 2,3-diphenyl-phenol and 6,6-diphenyl-3,5-hexadienonic acid as the major reaction products, eq. (38).[113-115]

(38)

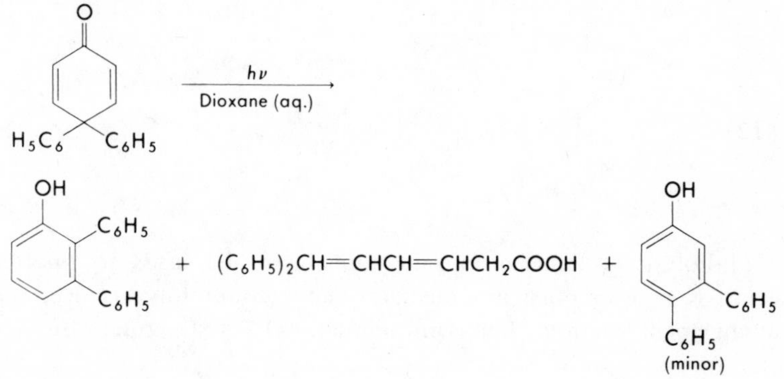

$$+ \quad (C_6H_5)_2CH{=}CHCH{=}CHCH_2COOH \quad +$$

(minor)

An intermediate for the reaction is a bicyclic ketone, 6,6-diphenylbicyclo-[3.1.0]hex-3-ene-2-one, as was proven by isolation and photolysis under the conditions of the reaction, eq. (39). Zimmerman postulates the mechanism

(39)

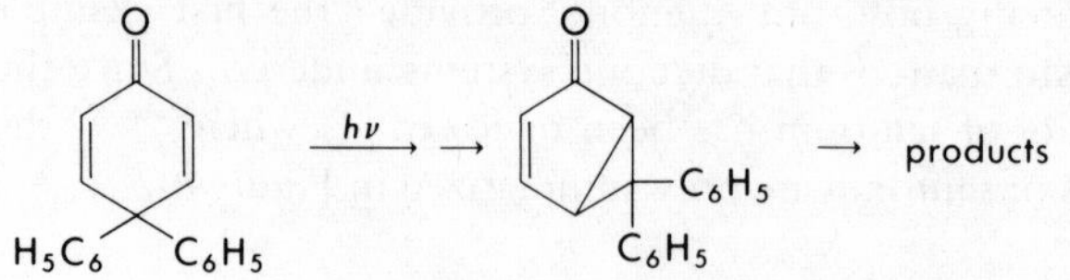

shown in eqs. (40–42) for the photochemical rearrangement of 6,6-diphenyl-cyclohexa-2,5-dienone, and extends the principles discovered to explain photochemical reactions in the santonin series.

(40)

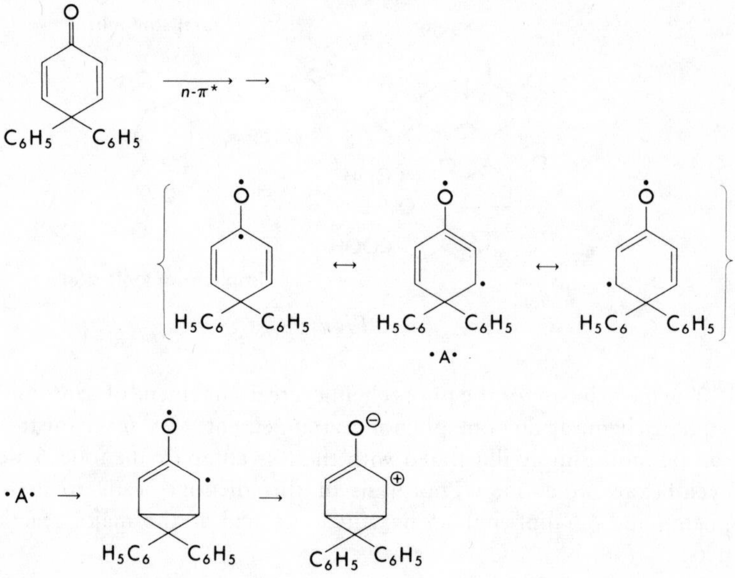

(41)

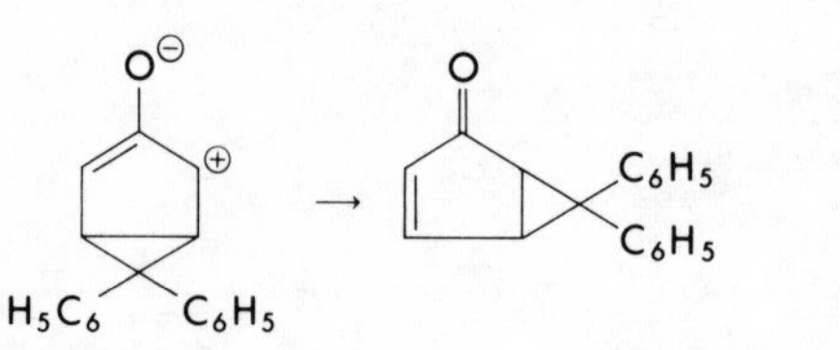

(42)

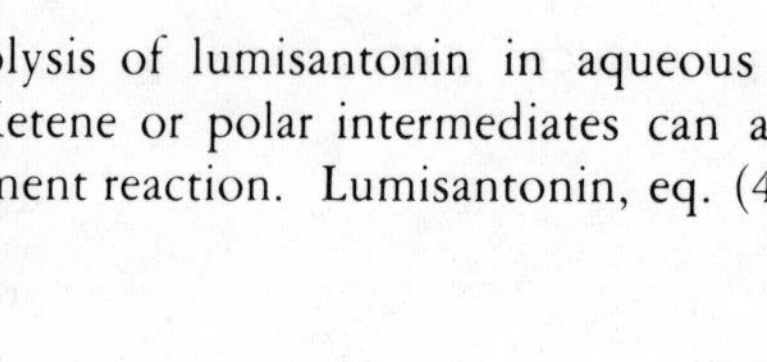

Photolysis of lumisantonin in aqueous media leads to photosantonic acid. Ketene or polar intermediates can account for this deep-seated rearrangement reaction. Lumisantonin, eq. (43), is structurally similar to the

(43)

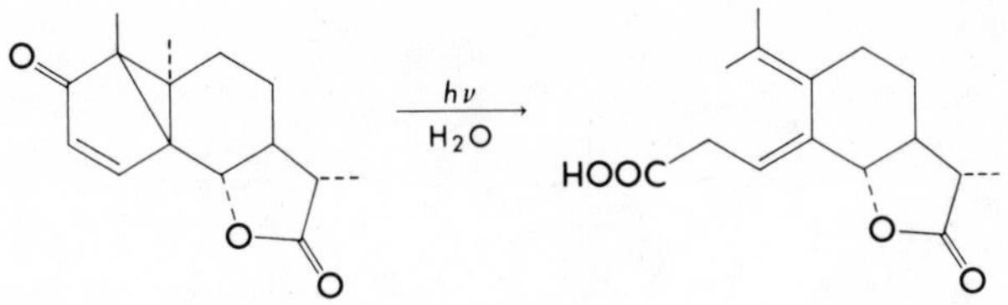

intermediate bicyclic ketone shown in eq. (39). Careful photolysis of lumisantonin in nonaqueous media allows the separation of a dienone lactone, eq. (44), a proposed precursor to the acid product.

(44) 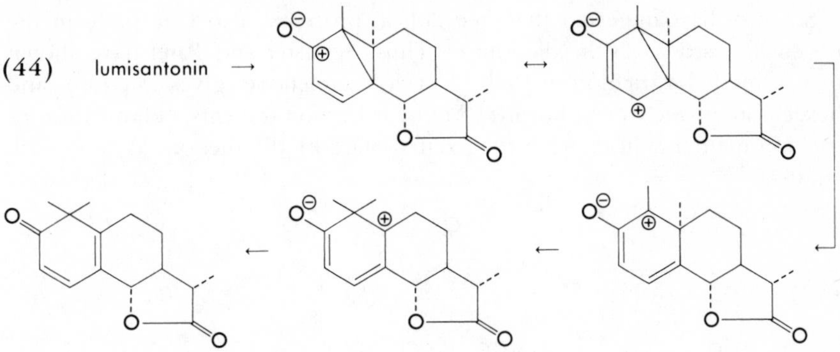   lumisantonin $\longrightarrow$

Various authors have questioned the necessity of the first bonding step in photochemical dienone rearrangements.[116-118] Chapman has suggested that since simple unsaturated ketones undergo similar rearrangement reactions, eq. (45),[118] the second double bond is unimportant to the rearrangement reaction, and the first rebonding step, eq. (41), suggested by Zimmerman is

(45)

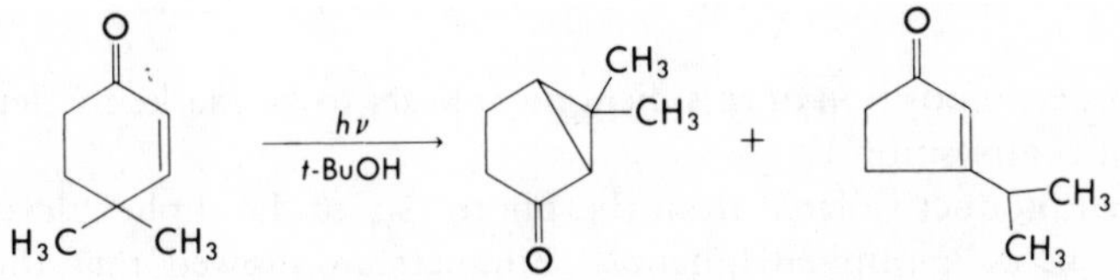

unnecessary. Recent evidence[119] suggests that, at least in the case of the diphenyl derivative, the double bond is necessary to the rearrangement. Photolysis of 4,4-diphenylcyclohexenone in 95% ethanol leads to two ketonic products, neither of which is the bicyclohexanone derivative that would be expected if the double bond should be unnecessary to migration, eq. (46).

The question then remains, why is there a difference between the alkyl examples of Chapman and Gardner[117,118] and the aryl dienone of Zimmer-

(46)

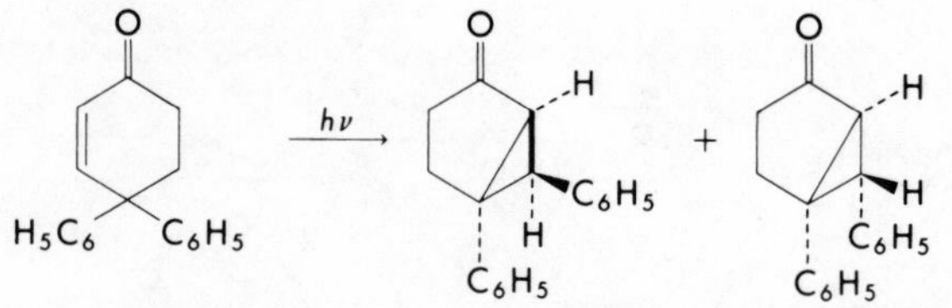

man? Perhaps the answer lies in the difference in the migratory ability of a methyl group and a phenyl group. With 4,4-diphenylcyclohexenone, phenyl migration becomes the preferred reaction in the absence of the second double bond.

Schuster has suggested that free radical processes also take place in the photochemistry of cyclic dienones. Thus, Schuster and Patel have shown that 4-methyl-4-trichloromethyl-2,5-cyclohexadienone gives *p*-cresol and hexachloroethane when photolyzed in hydrocarbon solvents. Elimination of trichloromethyl radicals from the excited state of the dienone is proposed, eq. (47).[120]

(47)

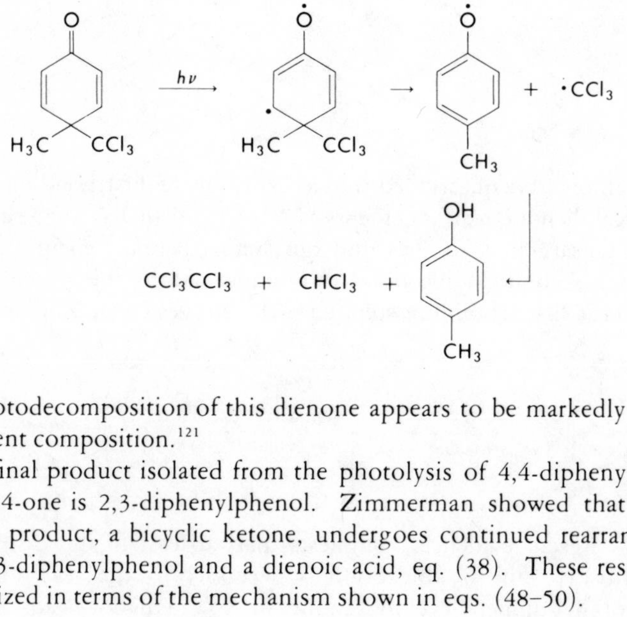

$$CCl_3CCl_3 \;+\; CHCl_3 \;+$$

The photodecomposition of this dienone appears to be markedly dependent on solvent composition.[121]

The final product isolated from the photolysis of 4,4-diphenylcyclohexa-diene-2,4-one is 2,3-diphenylphenol. Zimmerman showed that the initial reaction product, a bicyclic ketone, undergoes continued rearrangement to yield 2,3-diphenylphenol and a dienoic acid, eq. (38). These results can be rationalized in terms of the mechanism shown in eqs. (48–50).

(48)

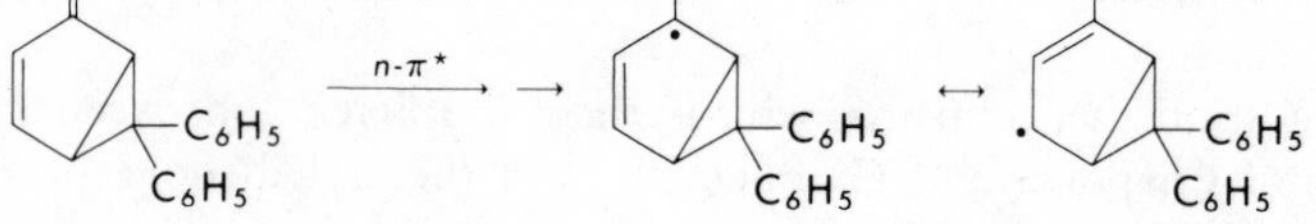

(49)

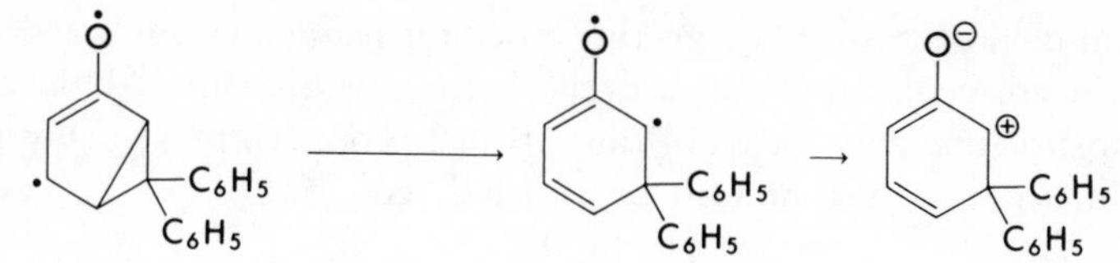

(50)

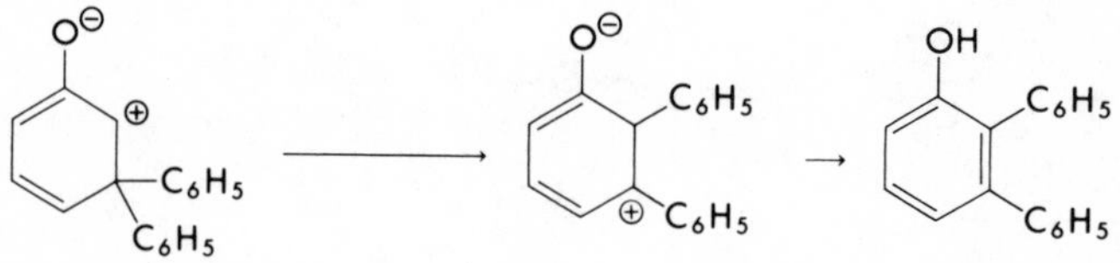

Cleavage of the cyclopropane ring is, for the most part, in the direction shown and not so as to give 3,4-diphenylphenol in equivalent quantities. Zimmerman proposes that this is because the intermediate phenonium ion species produced by the rearrangement toward the 2,3-phenol is more stable, due to conjugation, than that leading to the 3,4-phenol, eqs. (51–52).

(51)

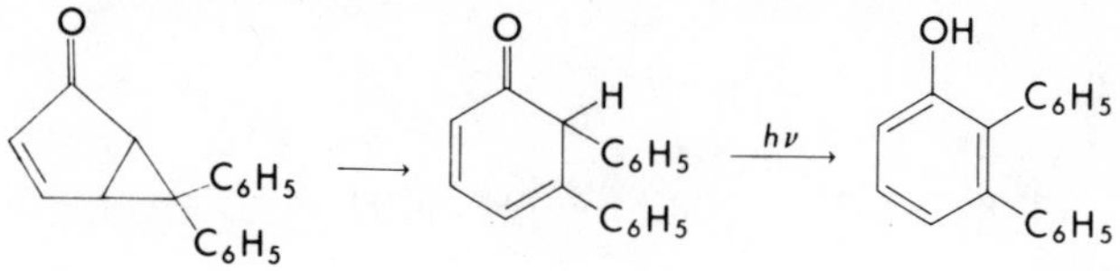

(52)

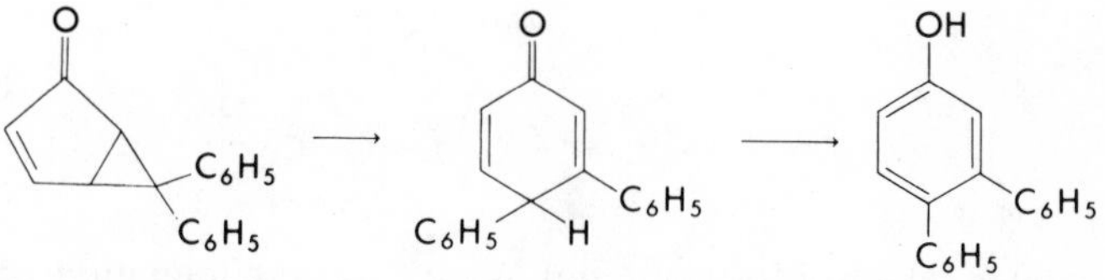

Photochemical rearrangements of cyclic α-, β-unsaturated ketones are also known.[122-124] Recent evidence from the laboratories of Chapman and Zimmerman suggests the mechanism shown in eq. (53) for the rearrangement of cyclic enones.

(53)

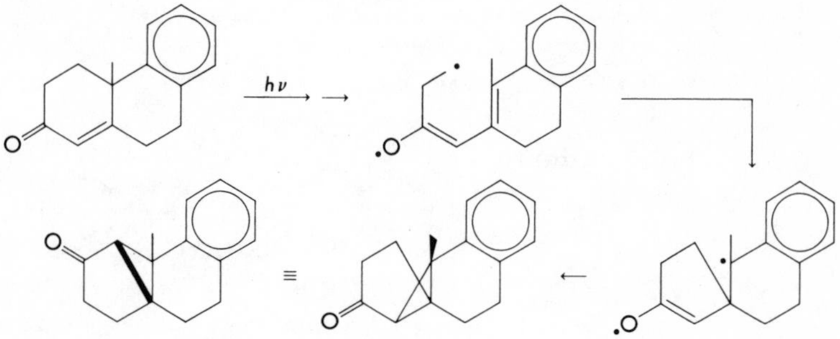

Certain dienones also undergo ring opening rearrangement reactions. If one of the adjacent carbons of a cyclic ketone or dienone is blocked with alkyl substituents, high yields of ring-opened products, presumably formed via an intermediate ketone, can be isolated, eq. (54).[125-127] For example,

(54)

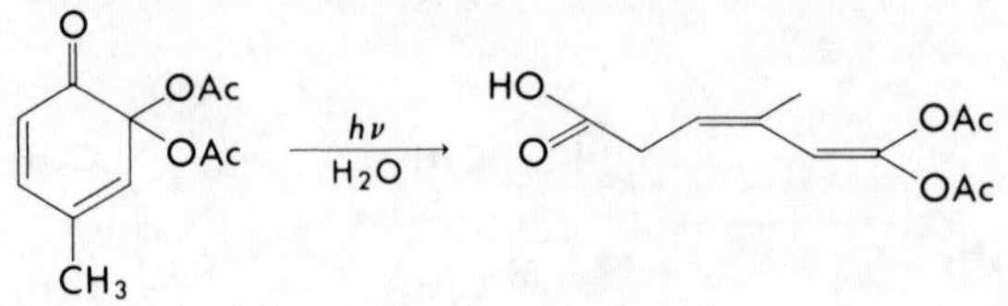

photolysis of 6,6-diacetoxy-4-methylcyclohexa-2,4-dienone gives 6,6-diacetoxy-4-methylhexa-3,5-dienoic acid when photolyzed in wet ether. In the presence of amines, amides are obtained. Quinkert has reviewed all the extensions and ramifications of photochemical reactions in which ring opening products are obtained.[127] The mechanism for the photochemical ring opening of cyclic ketones conceivably involves the steps shown in eqs. (55–56).

(55)

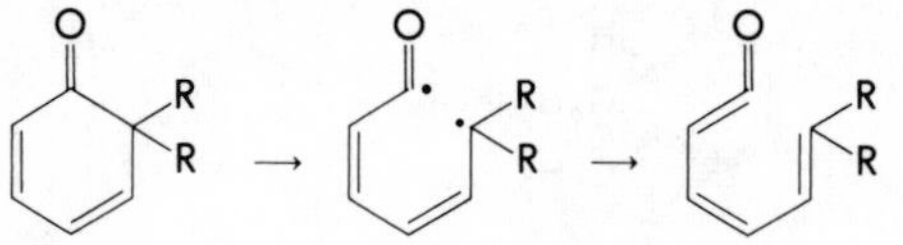

(56)

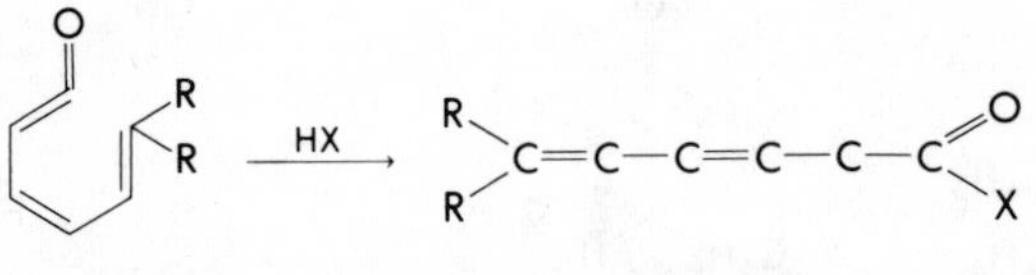

Zimmerman, Hahn, Morrison, and Wani[128] report migration of a γ aryl group to the β position of an α-, β-unsaturated ketone. They have shown that aryl groups with electron-withdrawing substituents migrate preferentially and that triplet state intermediates are involved, eq. (57). Their results favor intermediates possessing noncharged or electron rich γ carbon atoms.

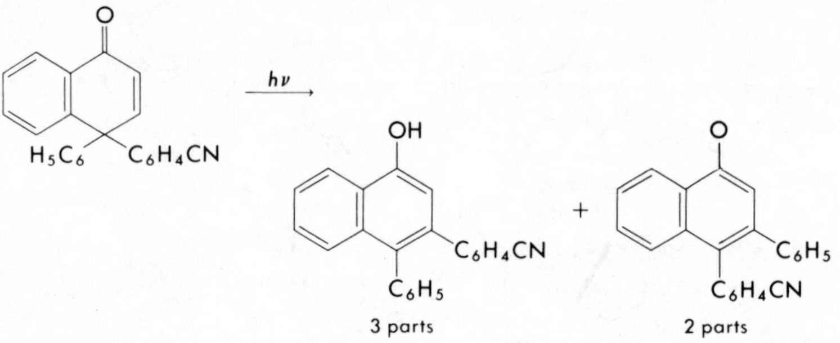

3 parts   +   2 parts

Kropp has investigated photochemical rearrangements of a variety of cross-conjugated dienones and observed some remarkable examples of steric control over the products.[129-132] Kropp also finds dienone-phenol rearrangements. Solvent composition causes marked variation in the direction and course of the reaction, and substituents on the dienone nucleus have a great deal of influence on the behavior of the dienones in a variety of solvents. For example, photolysis of a 4-methyl-1,4-diene-3-one gives, in neutral solvents, a bicyclic ketone, a lumi product like that proposed by Zimmerman as an intermediate in the photolysis of 4,4-diphenylcyclohexadiene-2,4-one, eq. (58). Removal of the methyl group vastly increases the number of

(58)

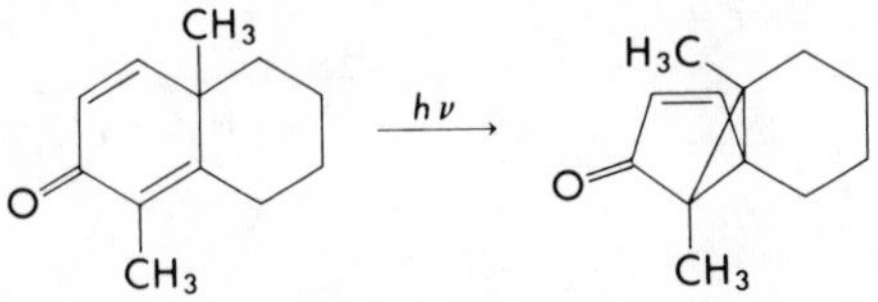

products resulting after photolysis.[13X] Photolysis of 2-methyldienones of the same type as shown in eq. (58) also produce spiroketones as the initial reaction product, but decomposition of the spiroketones gives a variety of other products, the first isolable product being a 2,4-dienone, eq. (59). In acid media, Kropp finds a new product, eq. (60). Kropp explains

(59)

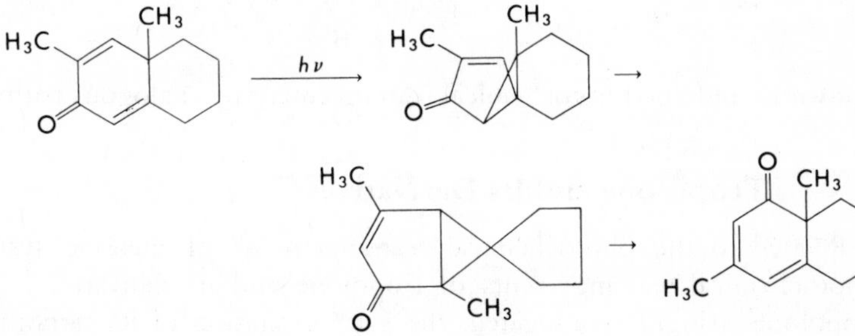

(60)

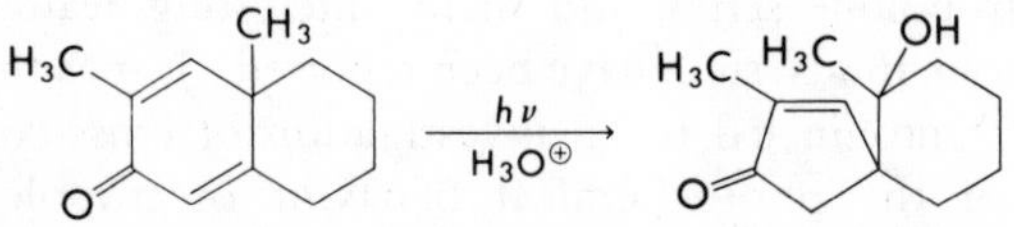

these results by assuming the intermediacy of the bicycloketone, which is labile to acid attack and nonphotochemical rearrangement, eqs. (61–62). Kropp proposes that the intermediate, eq. (62), is responsible for the

(61)

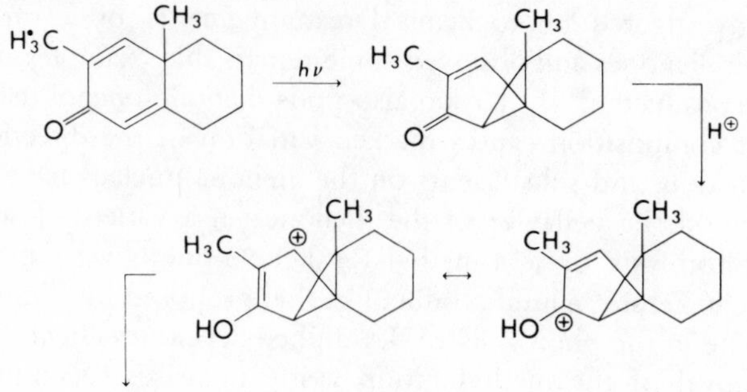

(62)

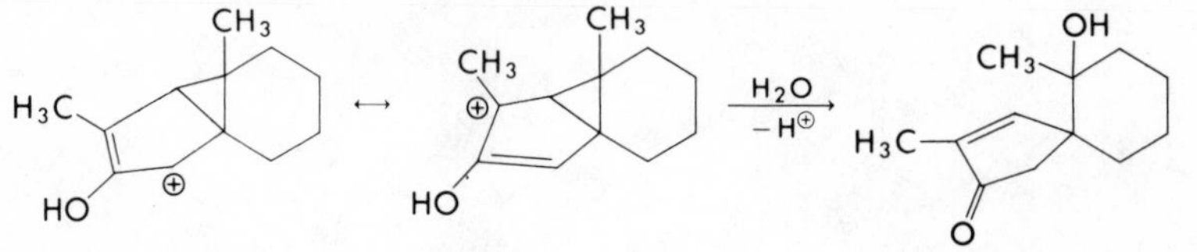

conversion of other dienones (e.g., santonin) to the cycloheptanol (iso-photosantonic acid), eq. (63). Table 8-5 lists some additional dienones

(63)

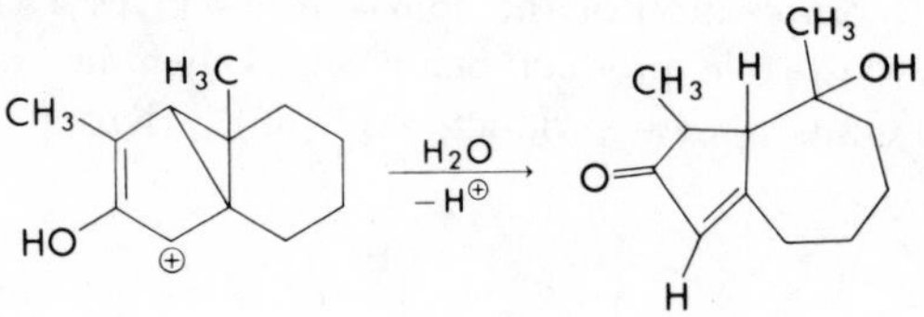

known to undergo photochemical rearrangement by analogous pathways.*

Tropolone and Its Derivatives

Related to the photochemical rearrangements of dienone systems are photochemical rearrangements of tropolone and its derivatives. Because tropolone is highly conjugated, the n-π^* excitation of its carbonyl group occurs at a moderately long wavelength. Photochemical transformations occur readily in the tropolone series, and many interesting rearrangement reactions of the tropolone ring system have been reported. Just as the photochemical reactions of santonin led to an investigation of cross-conjugated dienones, discovery of the photochemical behavior of tropolones and tropolone derivatives resulted from early experimental observations on the

*References 110–113 contain sections of some magnitude on the photochemical behavior of dienones. Examples illustrating the various modes of rearrangement of dienones are chosen for Table 8-5. Where possible, recent literature references (1962 to present) are used.

Table 8-5

Photochemical Rearrangements of Conjugated Dienones

Dienone	Products	Solvent	Reference
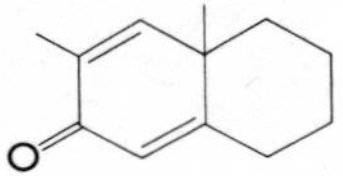	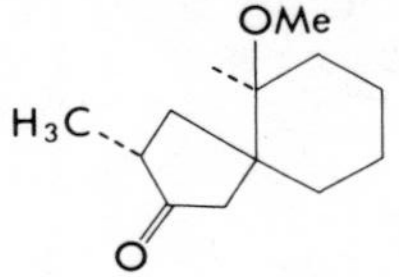 + other products	MeOH	132
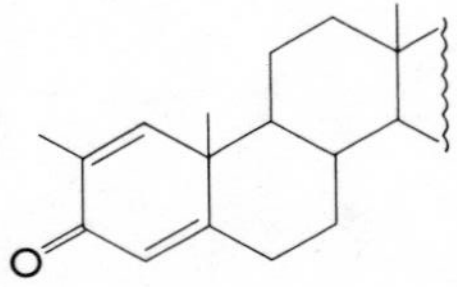	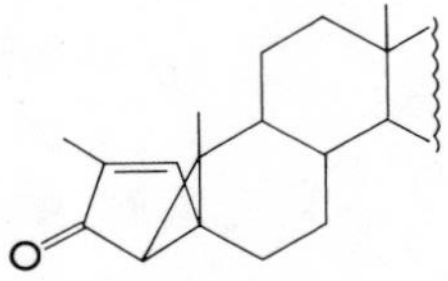	—	133
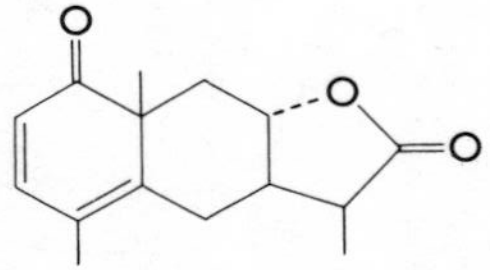	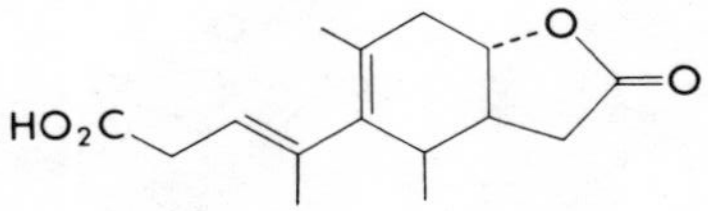	moist ether	142
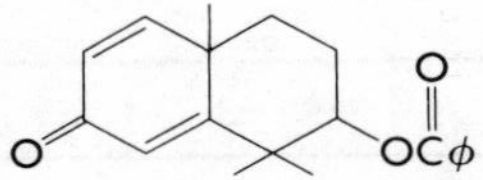	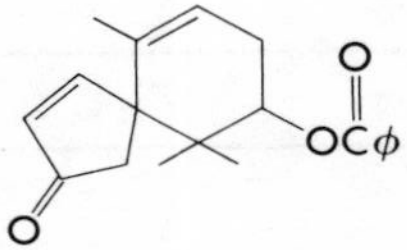 + 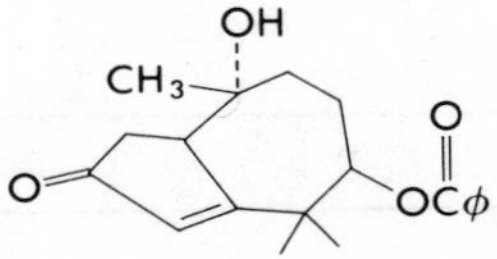	HOAc or HCOOH	131

Table 8-5 (cont.)

Dienone	Products	Solvent	Reference
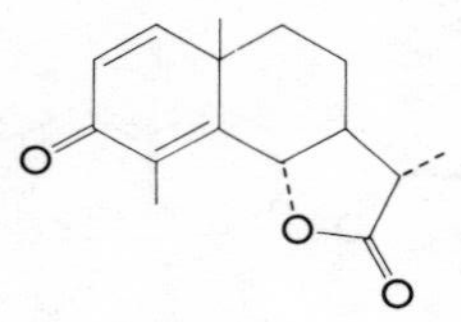	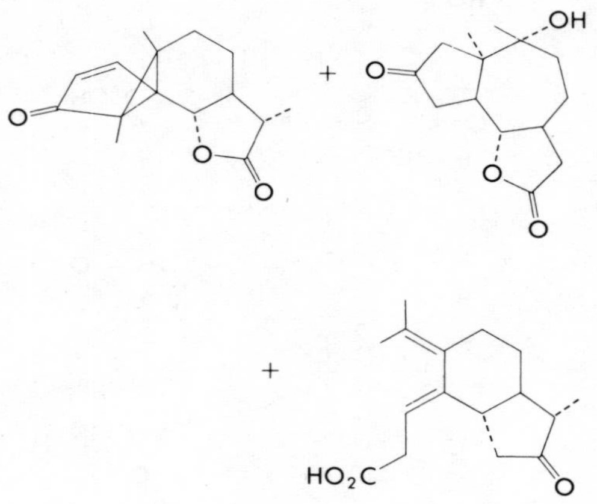	—	113, 114, 125, 134–138, 139–141
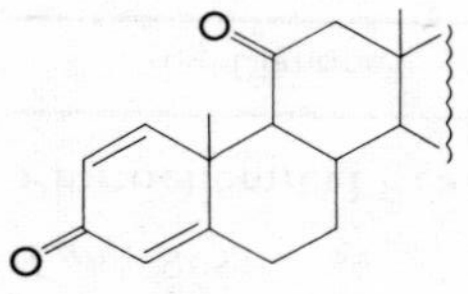	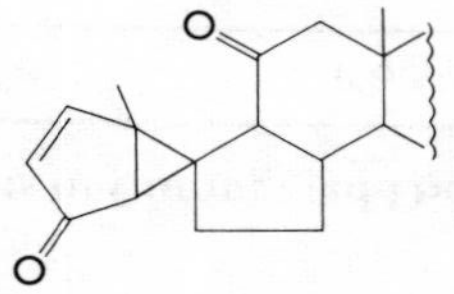	EtOH	144, 145

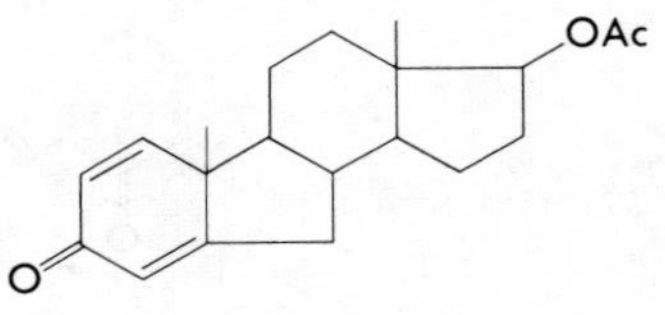	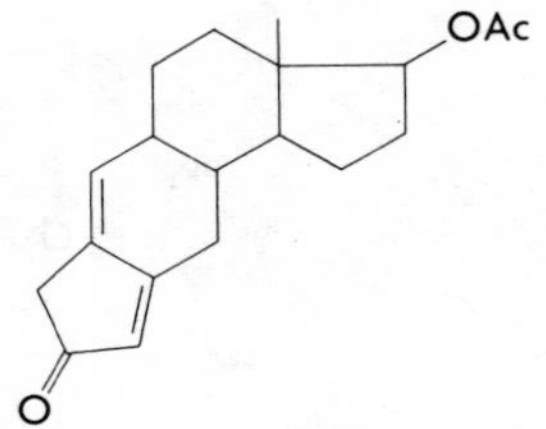	dioxane	143, 146
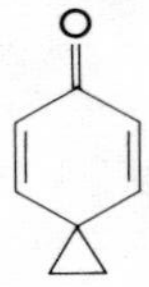	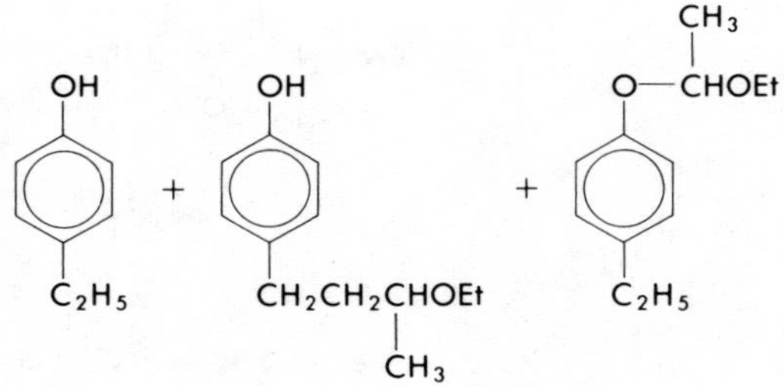	ether	148
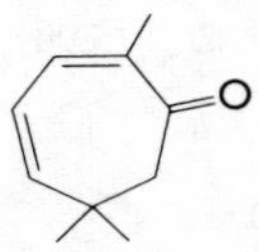	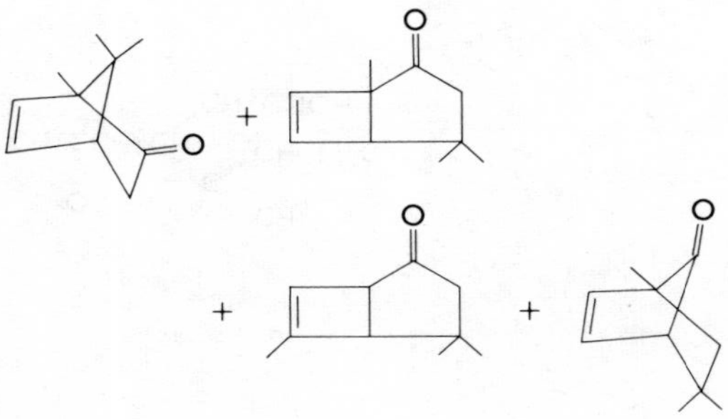	HOAc	147

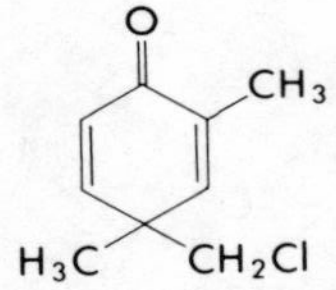

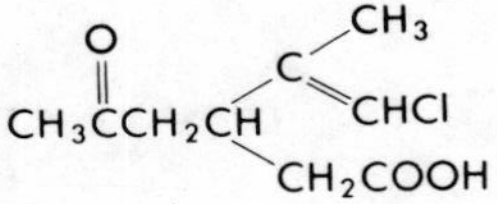

149

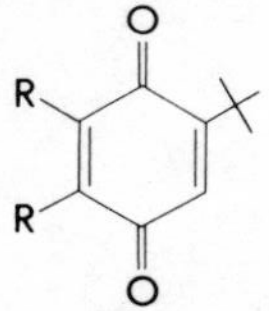

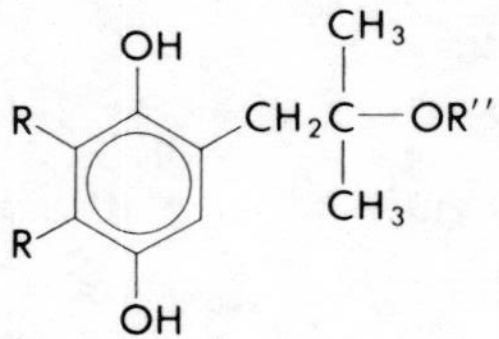

150

R''OH

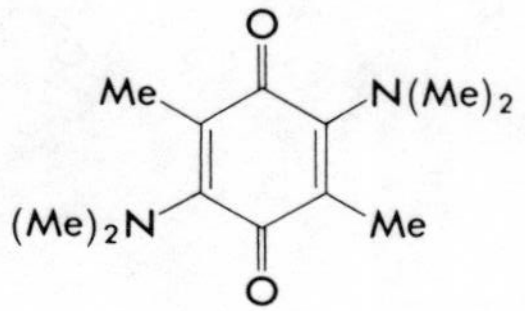

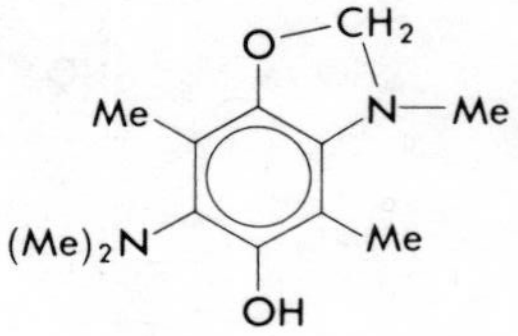

151

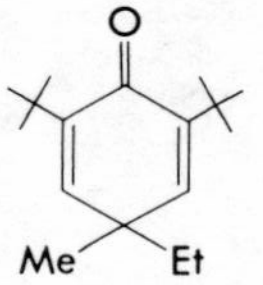

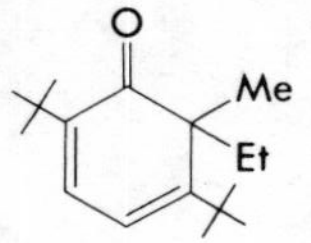

152

photochemical behavior of the natural product colchicine. Recent structural degradation has indicated that colchicine indeed possesses a tropolone ring.

Three products result from the photolysis of colchicine in solution.[155,157-159] These three products have been called, for want of something more original, α, β, and γ colochicine. The structure of each of these products has been elucidated, and Figure 8-3 illustrates the photochemical transformations[153-156] of this interesting natural product. Tropolones undergo photo-

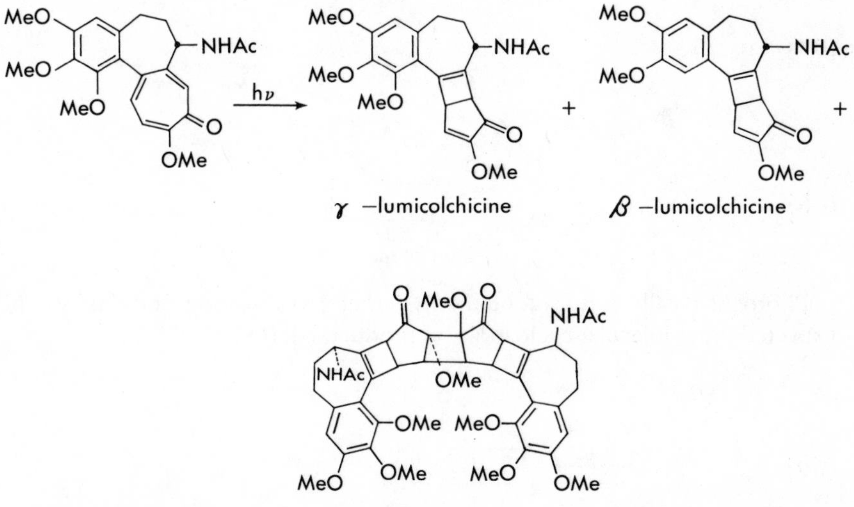

γ –lumicolchicine β –lumicolchicine

Figure 8-3

chemical rearrangements that amount initially to intramolecular photochemical additions, eqs. (64–65).[160,161]

(64)

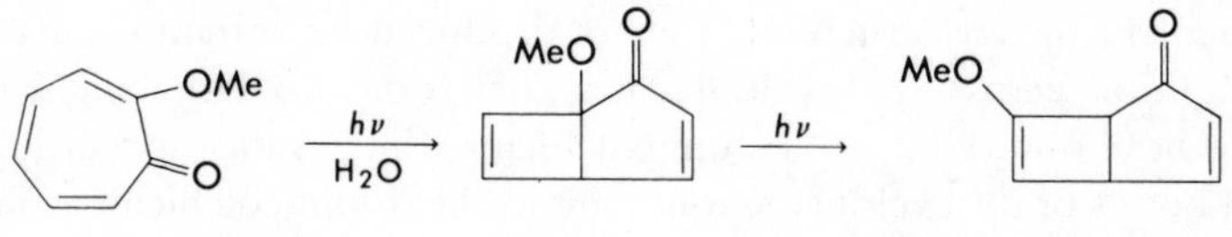

(65)

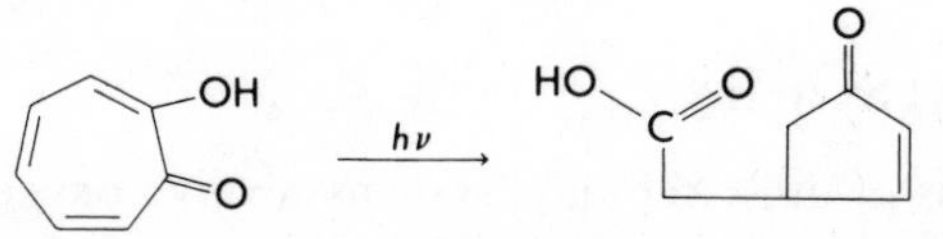

The mechanisms of tropolone rearrangement reactions are proposed by Chapman, Dauben, and co-workers to involve polar intermediates, eq. (66–68).[162]

(66)

(67)

(68)

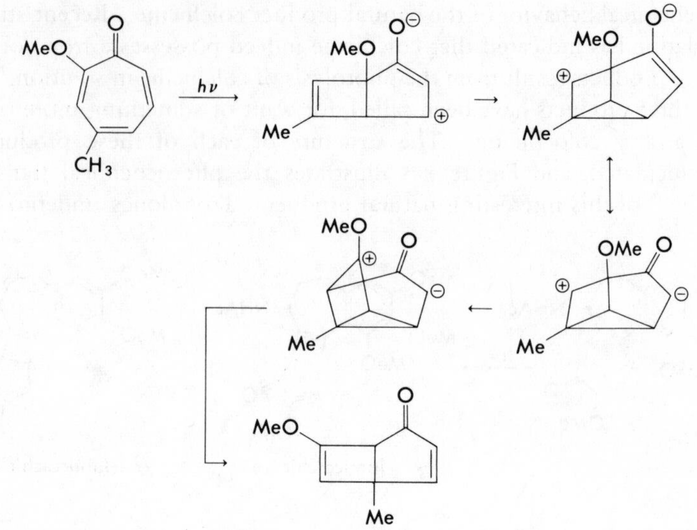

Photochemically γ tropolone methyl ether gives varying amounts of the expected intramolecular cycloaddition product, eq. (68).[163]

(69)

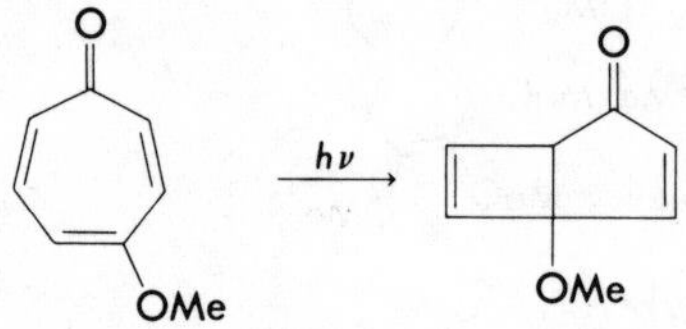

Application of all the obtained information to the photochemical reactions of colchicine and other naturally occurring tropolones becomes straight-forward in view of the photochemical behavior of simple tropolones. β- and γ-lumicolchicine are structural isomers produced by intramolecular photo-cycloaddition across the cycloheptatrienone ring. α-Lumicolchicine is a head-to-head photodimer of β-lumicolchicine, dimerization occurring across the 2,3 bonds of the cyclopentenone ring in the β-lumicolchicine isomer.

Other Carbonyl Systems

Rearrangement reactions of other carbonyl systems involve oxygen atom addition to carbon-carbon double bonds. The photo rearrangement of β-ionone, eqs. (70) and (71),[164,165] and cis 1,2-dibenzoylethylene[166,167] represent examples of such rearrangements, eqs. (72) and (73). Tetrabenzoyl-ethylene rearranges similarly, eq. (74).[168] The products are formed by

(70)

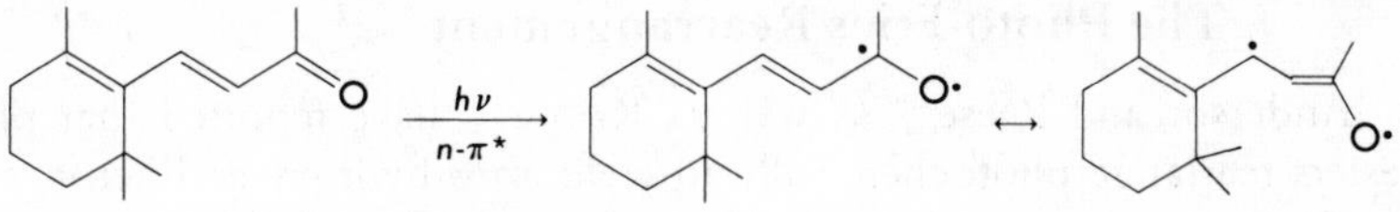

(71)

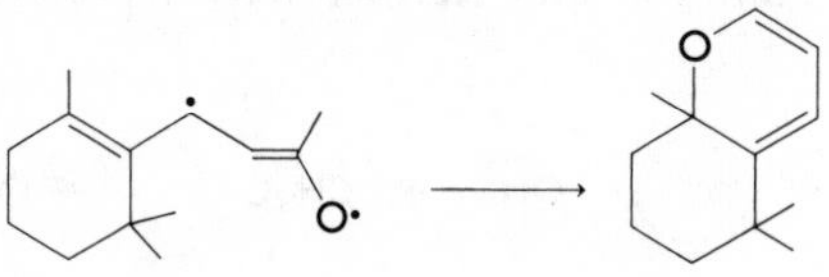

(72)

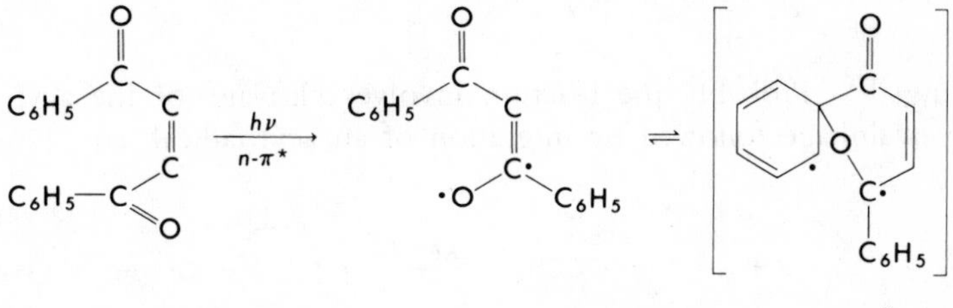

(73)

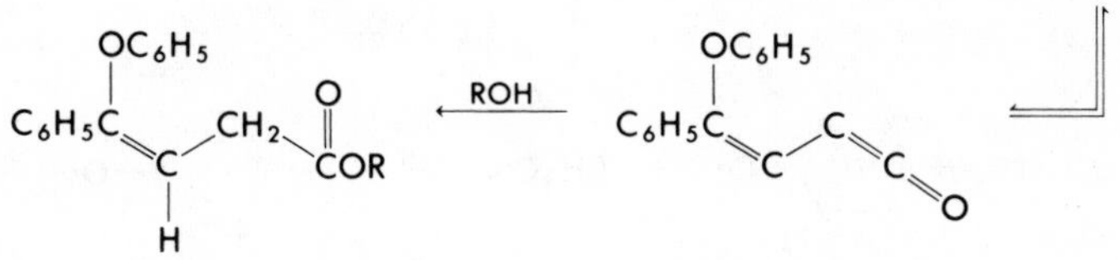

(74)

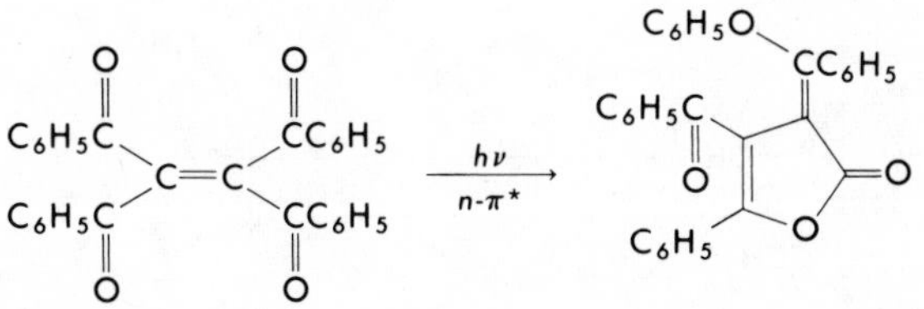

n-π^* excitation of the carbonyl system followed by addition of the carbonyl oxygen atom to the olefin.*

There are a variety of photochemical rearrangement reactions that parallel reactions catalyzed by other methods. Included in these known rearrangements are the photo-Fries rearrangement and the photo-Claisen rearrangement as well as the photo-Wallach rearrangement and the photo-dienone phenol reaction mentioned earlier.

---

*All of these photochemical addition reactions are examples of the well-known oxygen addition to olefinic linkages discovered by Wilt and co-workers. See for example, J. W. Wilt and D. A. Oathaudt, *J. Org. Chem.*, **23**, 218 (1958). Reactions of this type in normal free radical reactions are well documented.

The Photo-Fries Rearrangement

Anderson and Reese[169] as well as Kobsa[170] have reported that phenolate esters rearrange photochemically to yield *ortho*-hydroxy aryl ketones as well as the *para* isomers, eq. (75). Finnegan and Mattice have reported similar

(75)

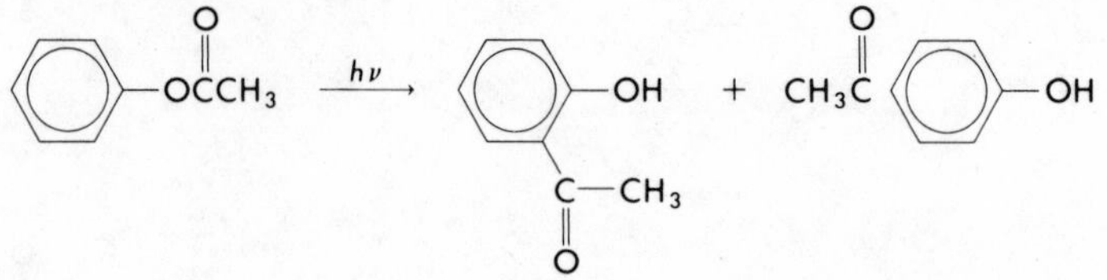

findings.[171] Probably the reaction involves cleavage of the acyl carbon-oxygen linkage followed by migration of an acyl radical, eqs. (76–78), in

(76)

(77)

(78)

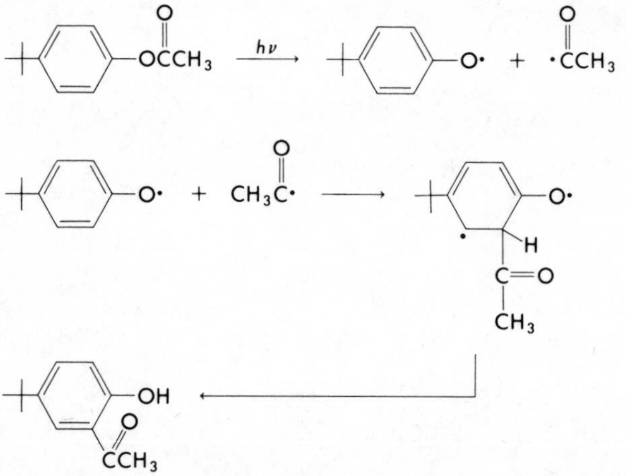

a manner analogous to the decomposition recombination mechanism proposed by Urry and co-workers (Chapter 5) to account for acylium exchange in certain triketones. Although the reaction is formally like the Fries rearrangement, the photoreaction leads to different products from and better yields than the acid-catalyzed rearrangement. For example, aromatic esters with both *ortho* positions occupied give intramolecular solvolysis reactions with the photo process and *para*-substitution with the Lewis acid-catalyzed process. Although little mechanistic work on the photo-Fries rearrangement has been reported, the absorption is probably of the π-π^* type, for it is well known that the n-π^* absorption of esters is weak and lies deep in the ultraviolet region even in conjugated molecules. It has been reported that enol and dienol acetates are photochemically reactive, and products of elimination and of rearrangement have been observed, eqs. (79) and (80).[172-174]

(79)

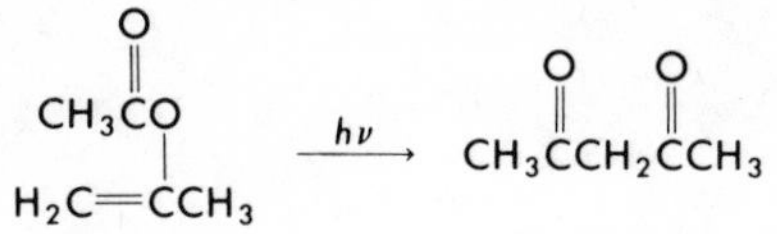

(80)

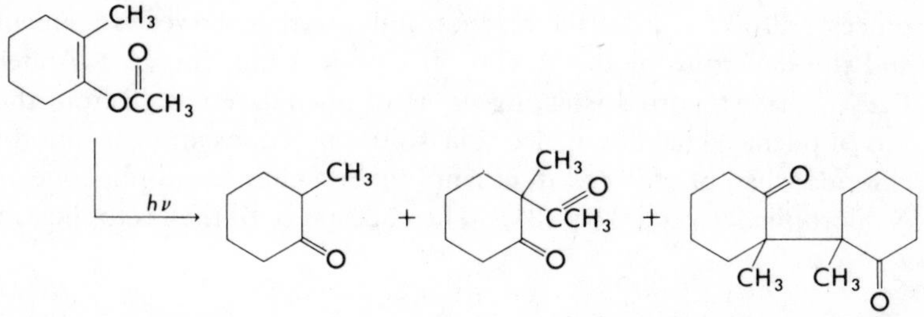

Rearrangements of cyclic enol ethers and enol lactones have also been reported.[173-178] Hill reports that aryl oxyacetones rearrange to 2-methyl-benzofurans via hydroxyketone intermediates. These reactions are analogous to both the Claisen and Fries rearrangements, eq. (81).[176]

(81)

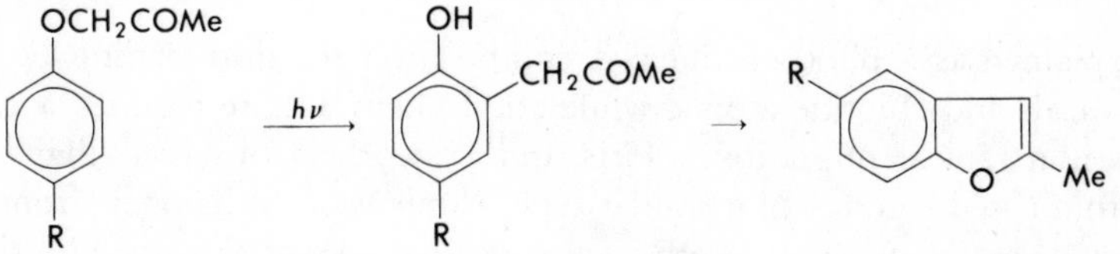

The Photo-Claisen Rearrangement

Kharasch and co-workers reported a photochemically induced Claisen rearrangement.[179] They observed the rearrangement of phenylallyl and phenylbenzyl ethers to the corresponding phenols after irradiation in hydrogen donor solvents, eqs. (82–84). These rearrangements are somewhat

(82) 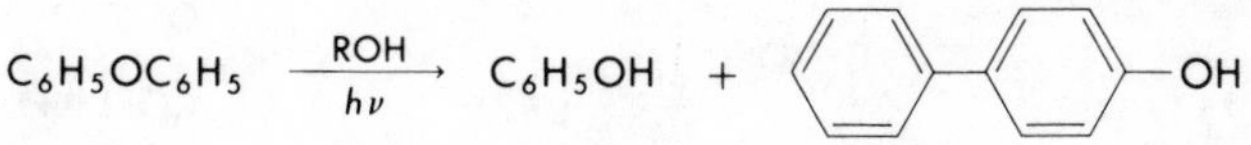 $C_6H_5OC_6H_5 \xrightarrow[h\nu]{ROH} C_6H_5OH +$

(83) 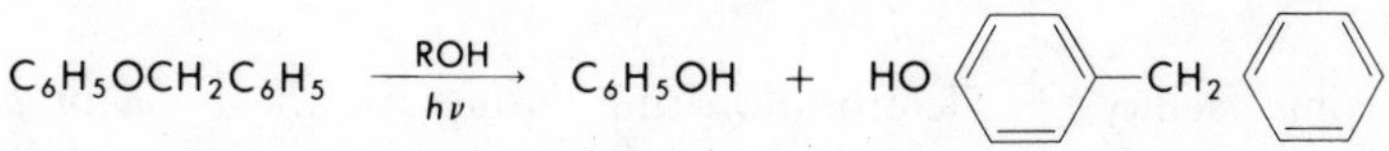 $C_6H_5OCH_2C_6H_5 \xrightarrow[h\nu]{ROH} C_6H_5OH + HO$

(84) $C_6H_5OCH_2CH{=}CH_2 \xrightarrow[h\nu]{ROH} C_6H_5OH + C_6H_5CH_2CH{=}CH_2$

different from either the reported thermal Claisen rearrangements or the reported Fries (and other) photochemical rearrangements because exclusive *para* isomer formation is noted. However, recent results suggest that the *ortho* isomer is also obtained.[180]

Phenacyl Halides

The rearrangement of phenacyl halides appears to occur by a concerted process. Products from the reaction indicate that the rearrangement process and the departure of the leaving group are simultaneous. Anderson and Reese[181] have reported isolating esters of phenylacetic acid from the photolysis of phenacyl halides in alcoholic solution. For example, *p*-chlorophenacyl chloride when photolyzed in ethanol gives *p*-chloroacetophenone and ethyl-*p*-chlorophenylacetate, eq. (85). The appearance of the acetophenone can be

(85)

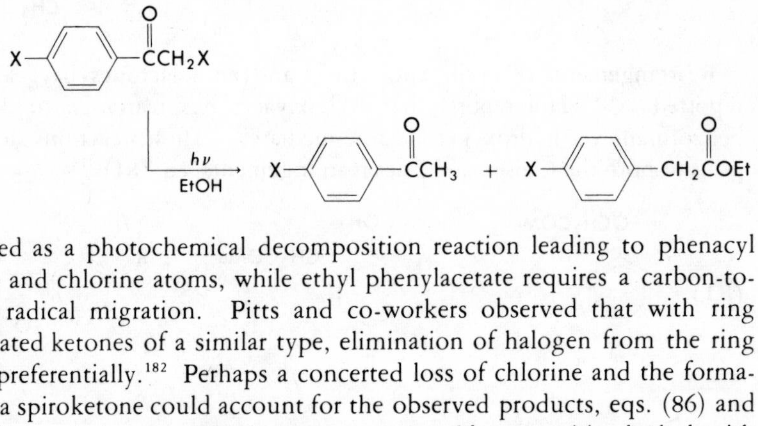

explained as a photochemical decomposition reaction leading to phenacyl radicals and chlorine atoms, while ethyl phenylacetate requires a carbon-to-carbon radical migration. Pitts and co-workers observed that with ring brominated ketones of a similar type, elimination of halogen from the ring occurs preferentially.[182] Perhaps a concerted loss of chlorine and the formation of a spiroketone could account for the observed products, eqs. (86) and (87). The spiroketone, a cyclopropanone, would react with alcohol with

(86)

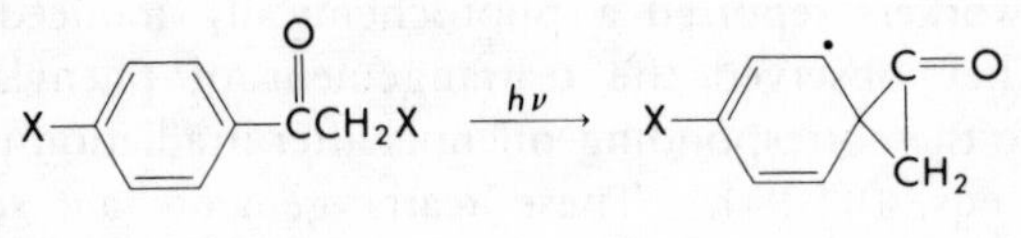

(87)

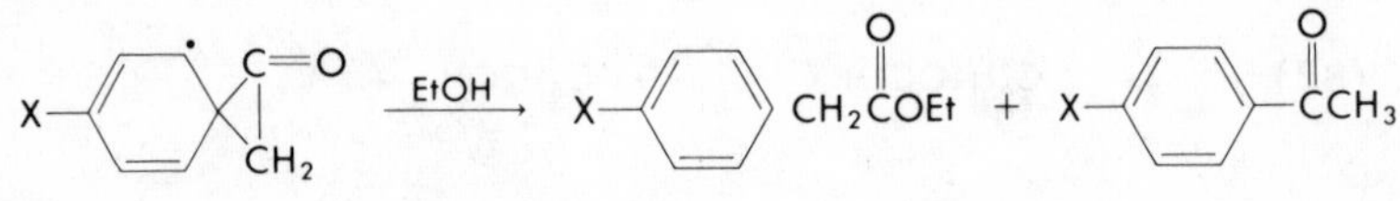

some facility.[183] Electron-donating groups in the *ortho* or *para* positions facilitate the rearrangement reaction. Photolysis of *para* hydroxy, *para* methoxy, or *ortho* methoxyphenacyl chloride in ethanol leads to rapid formation of the corresponding acetophenone as well as the appropriate ethyl phenylacetate and chlorobenzene, eq. (88).

$$(88) \quad D\!-\!\!\!\!\bigcirc\!\!\!\!-COCH_2Cl \xrightarrow[EtOH]{h\nu} D\!-\!\!\!\!\bigcirc\!\!\!\!-COCH_3$$

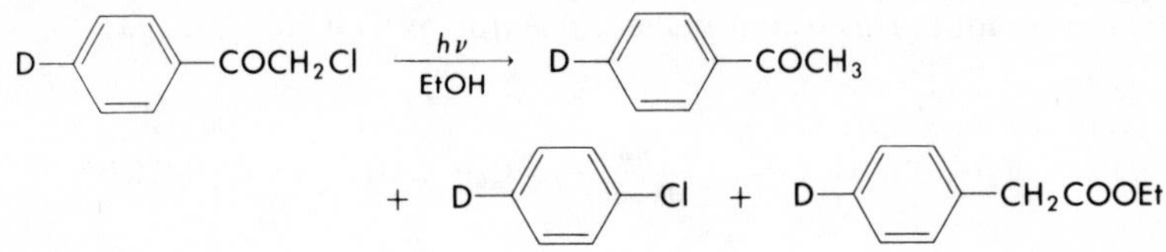

$$+ \quad D\!-\!\!\!\!\bigcirc\!\!\!\!-Cl \quad + \quad D\!-\!\!\!\!\bigcirc\!\!\!\!-CH_2COOEt$$

or

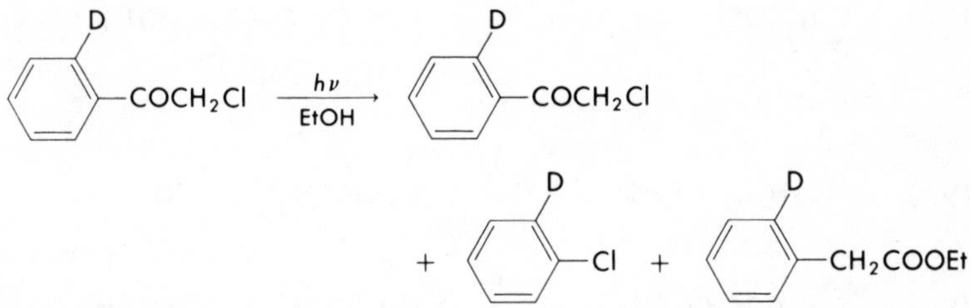

D = electron-donating group.

Ortho hydroxyphenacyl chloride does not produce an ester, and a coumarone is formed preferentially, eq. (89).[184]

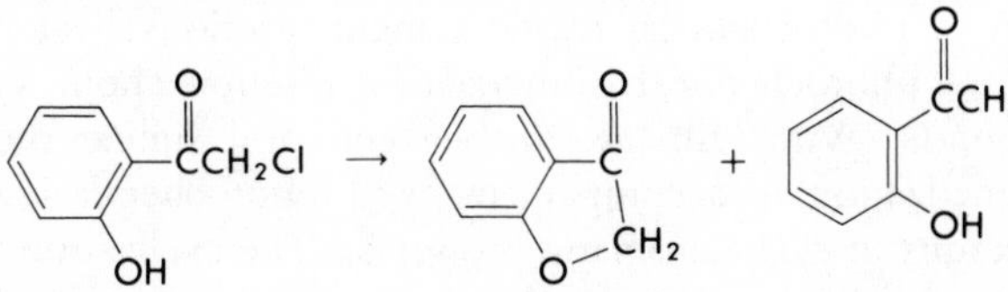

Anderson claims that since electron-donating substituents in the *para* position increase the yield of rearrangement products, aryl participation is important in the chlorine departing step.[184] However, in view of Zimmerman's observations (Chapter 9) concerning the increased yield of products from the solvolysis of *m*-methoxybenzyl acetates, the fact that *m*-methoxyphenacyl chloride gives no rearrangement product might be evidence opposing the aryl participation mechanism.

Attempted extensions of the reaction to aliphatic systems like 2-chlorocyclohexanone, a favorite of Favorskii reaction enthusiasts, do not lead to rearrangement products, a diethyl ketal being the major isolated product, eq. (90).[184] Similar cyclic intermediates can be envisioned for the 1,2-

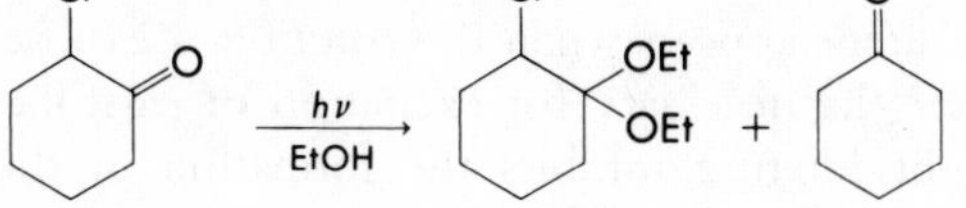

rearrangements of enol and dienolacetates. The rearrangement of vinyl benzoate to acetophenone and benzoic acid has been proposed to occur via acyl migration to a vinyl system, eq. (91),[185] but spiro intermediates could be important in this rearrangement reaction as well, eqs. (92–94).

$$(91) \quad C_6H_5\overset{O}{\overset{\|}{C}}OCH{=}CH_2 \xrightarrow[\text{dioxane}]{h\nu} C_6H_5\overset{O}{\overset{\|}{C}}CH_3 + C_6H_5\overset{O}{\overset{\|}{C}}OH$$

$$(92) \quad C_6H_5\overset{O}{\overset{\|}{C}}OCH{=}CH_2 \xrightarrow{h\nu} C_6H_5\underset{\underset{\overset{|}{C}H}{\overset{|}{H_2C}}}{\overset{\overset{\bullet}{O}}{\overset{|}{C}}}{-}O \xrightarrow{\,\,} C_6H_5\overset{O}{\overset{\|}{C}}CH_2CHO$$

$$(93) \quad C_6H_5\overset{O}{\overset{\|}{C}}CH_2CHO \xrightarrow{h\nu} C_6H_5\overset{O}{\overset{\|}{C}}CH_3 + CO$$

$$(94) \quad C_6H_5\overset{O}{\overset{\|}{C}}OCH{=}CH_2 \longrightarrow C_6H_5\overset{O}{\overset{\|}{C}}OH + CH{\equiv}CH$$

Cyclization of Stilbene and Its Derivatives

The discussion of photochemical rearrangement reactions began with a consideration of the photochemical isomerization reaction about a carbon-carbon double bond. With stilbene, azobenzene, and similar molecules, this *cis-trans* isomerization is accompanied by a photochemical addition reaction, which results in cyclic aromatic products. The cyclization reaction is of lower quantum yield than the simultaneous *cis-trans* isomerization and depends on the presence of suitable oxidizing agents, such as iodine or dissolved oxygen, in the solution. Mallory and co-workers[186–189] and others[190–202] propose that the cyclization reaction proceeds via a dihydrophenanthrene intermediate. Sargent and Timmons have isolated dihydrophenanthrene derivatives by photolyzing suitably substituted stilbene derivatives in reaction media from which oxygen is carefully excluded.[190–191] Moore[193] proposes the mechanism shown in eqs. (95–97) for the conversion of stilbene to phenanthrene.

Moore has observed that oxygen is necessary for the conversion, and that nearly 1 mole of oxygen is required per mole of phenanthrene produced. Hydrogen peroxide is observed as a reaction product. A yellow color appears in degassed samples, and this yellow color disappears at essentially the same rate that phenanthrene appears when the solution is exposed to the air. Exclusion of wavelengths necessary for excitation of *cis*-stilbene from the incident beam by light filtering inhibits the formation of the yellow

(95)

(96)

(97)

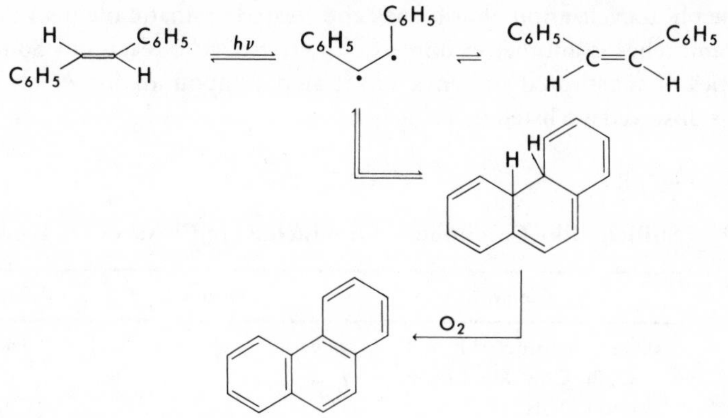

O_2

intermediate. An equilibrium between the intermediate and the stilbenes exists because the formation of the intermediate is temperature dependent. At lower temperatures the rate of intermediate formation is increased significantly.

Mallory and co-workers have observed that the reaction is quite general for substituted stilbenes and that the quantum yield for phenanthrene formation is independent of the oxygen concentration for each of the four substituted phenanthrenes investigated. In each case, reaction of the intermediate with oxygen depends only on the concentration of the intermediate, and formation of the intermediate is the rate-determining step in the sequence.

Mallory has measured the quantum yields for formation of the dihydrophenanthrene intermediate for substituted stilbenes and observed that the quantum yield varies with the substituent. Table 8-6 lists the quantum yields for intermediate formation as a function of the substituent on the stilbene.

Table 8-6

Quantum Yields for Dihydrophenanthrene Formation from Stilbenes

$C_6H_5CH\!=\!CHC_6H_4\text{-}X$	Φ = for intermediate formation
X = H	0.059
X = p-CH$_3$	0.071
X = p-OCH$_3$	0.046
X = p-Cl	0.023

The photocyclization of stilbenes and related aromatic olefins to dihydro-phenanthrenes is another example of an electrocyclic reaction. Some of the varieties of substituted stilbenes and related compounds for which the reaction is observed are listed in Table 8-7.

Table 8-7

Stilbene-like Compounds for which Ring Closures are Known

Olefin	Product	Reference
stilbene, substituted X = F, Cl, Br, OMe, Me, CF$_3$, ϕ, and COOH	phenanthrene	186
phenyl-α-naphthylethylene	1,2-benzphenanthrene	186
1,4-diphenylbutadiene	1-phenylnaphthalene	201
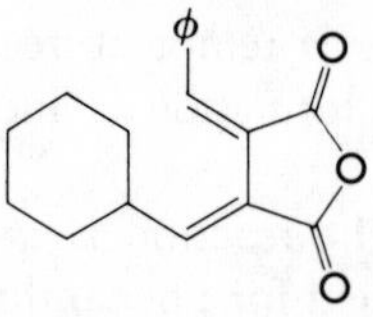	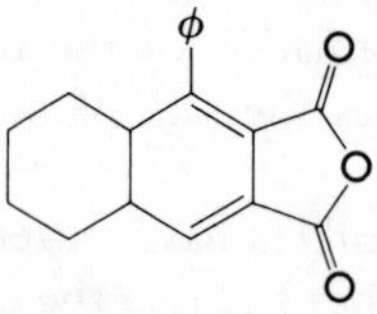	202, 203

Stilbenes possessing either strong electron-withdrawing groups like nitro and acetyl or strong electron donor groups like dimethylamino fail to undergo cyclization. Perhaps strong electron transfer contributions to the excited states can account for this observation, eq. (98). The single electron character on the ring possessing the withdrawing substituent is depleted to

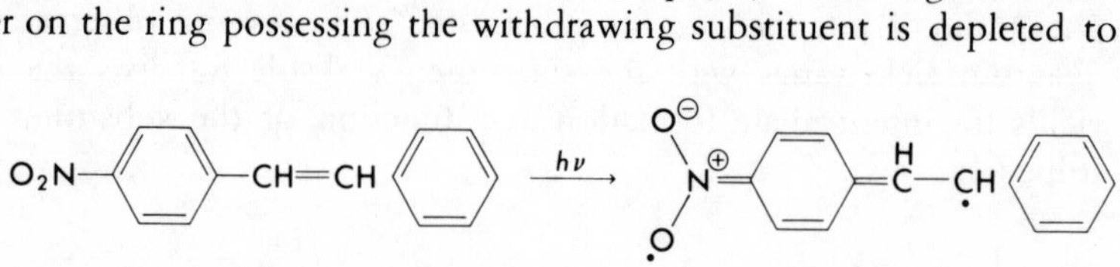

the point that the coupling reaction that would form the dihydrophenan-threne derivative cannot occur. In any event, cyclization reactions of stilbene derivatives deserve further mechanistic considerations.

Photochemical cyclization reactions also occur with azobenzene.[204,205]

Cyclization of Nitrogen Compounds

Unlike the cyclization of stilbene and related olefins, cyclization of azo-benzene is promoted in acid media, eq. (99). Lewis proposes that a cationic

(99)

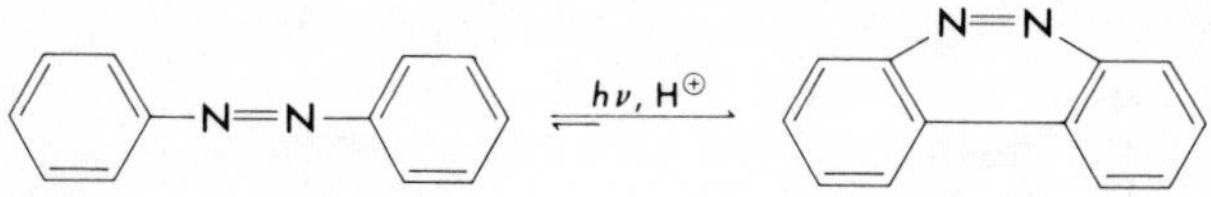

intermediate is responsible for the cyclization since only *cis-trans* isomerization is observed in neutral media. He proposes that the conjugate acid of azobenzene possesses the *cis* structure, eqs. (100–101), in accord with earlier observations.[206-208] Presumably, photocyclization reactions involving azo derivatives also require the presence of oxidizing agents such as oxygen.

(100)

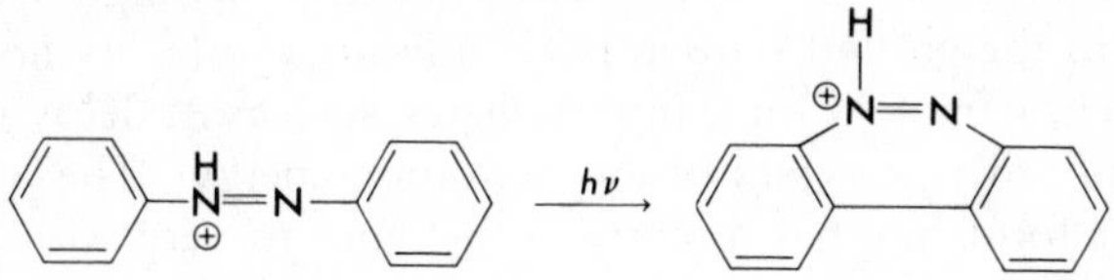

(101)

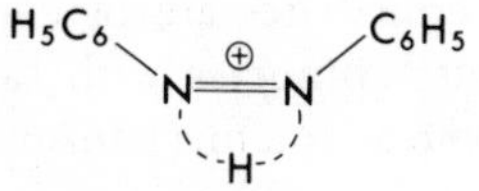

Cyclization of Amines

Finally, certain amine derivatives have been observed to undergo photochemical oxidative cyclization rearrangements. Linschitz and co-workers[209,210] have observed the flash photolytic cyclization of diphenylamine derivatives to carbazole, eq. (102).

(102)

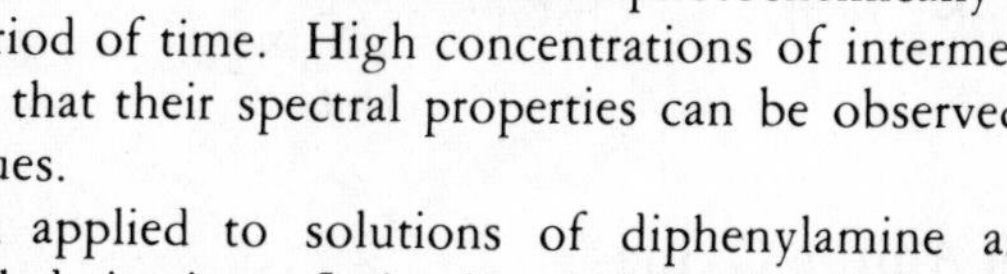

Flash photolysis, as mentioned earlier, is a technique whereby a non-equilibrium situation can be created photochemically in a system in a very brief period of time. High concentrations of intermediates are thereby derived so that their spectral properties can be observed by ordinary spectral techniques.

When applied to solutions of diphenylamine and its *n*-methyl and *n*-phenyl derivatives, flash photolysis techniques produce nonionic, nonradical intermediates presumed to be hydrocarbazoles, eq. (103). These hydrocarbazoles possess a characteristically visible absorption at 610 mμ, and Linschitz refers to B as "610." In the presence of O_2, the isolated product is

(103)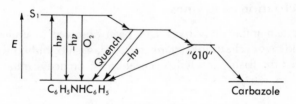

the appropriate carbazole. "610" is further identified by its high activation energy for decay to the ground state in polar solvents and by its first order decay kinetics (10 kcal/mole). Ionic intermediates, such as A, decay in polar solvents by second order processes of low activation energy. The quantum yield for carbazole formation has recently been found to vary with oxygen concentration.[210] High concentrations of oxygen quench the conversion to carbazole[211] presumably because triplet state intermediates are precursors to "610" formation. Quenching of the triplet state competes with carbazole formation under high oxygen pressure. The total reaction mechanism can be pictured schematically as in Figure 8-4.

Figure 8-4

Homolytic cleavage of the nitrogen hydrogen bonds occurs with aliphatic secondary amines, eq. (104).[212]

$$(104) \quad (Et)_2NH \longrightarrow (Et)_2N-N(Et)_2 \; + \; \underset{NHEt}{\overset{NHEt}{CH_3CH}} \underset{NHEt}{\overset{H}{CCH_3}}$$

Cyclization of Amine Oxides

Kaneko, Yamada, and Ishikawa report extensive studies of amine oxides cyclizations in aprotic solvents.[213-214] In general ring closure to the corresponding oxazirane derivative is observed, eq. (105).

(105)

R = Cl or H, R' = —CN or —C$_6$H$_5$

References

1. Hammond, G. S., J. Saltiel, A. A. Lamola, N. J. Turro, J. S. Bradshaw, D. O. Cowan, R. C. Counsell, V. Vogt, and C. Dalton, *J. Am. Chem. Soc.*, **86**, 3197 (1964).
2. Lewis, G. N., T. T. Magel, and D. Lipkin, *J. Am. Chem. Soc.*, **62**, 2973 (1940).
3. Smakula, A., *Z. phyzik Chem.*, **B25**, 90 (1934).
4. Stegemeyer, H., *J. Phys. Chem.*, **66**, 2555 (1962).
5. Schulte-Frohlinde, D., H. Blume, and H. Güsten, *J. Phys. Chem.*, **66**, 2486 (1962).
6. Zimmerman, G., L. Chow, and U. Paik, *J. Am. Chem. Soc.*, **80**, 3528 (1958).
7. Schulte-Frohlinde, D., *Ann. Chem.* **612**, 138 (1958).
8. Stegemeyer, H., *Z. Naturforsch.*, **16a**, 634 (1961).
9. Stegemeyer, H., *Z. Naturforsch.*, **17b**, 153 (1962).
10. Dyck, H., and D. S. McClure, *J. Chem. Phys.*, **36**, 2326 (1962).
11. Förster, T., *Z. Electrochem.*, **56**, 716 (1952).
12. Birnbaum, P. P., and D. W. G. Style, *J. Chem. Soc.*, 1192 (1955).
13. Berends, W., and J. Posthuma, *J. Phys. Chem.*, **66**, 2547 (1962).
14. Hammond, G. S., and J. Saltiel, *J. Am. Chem. Soc.*, **84**, 4983 (1962).
15. Saltiel, J., and G. S. Hammond, *J. Am. Chem. Soc.*, **85**, 2515 (1963).
16. Hoff, M. C., K. W. Greenlee, and C. E. Boord, *J. Am. Chem. Soc.*, **73**, 3329 (1951).
17. Olson, A. R., and F. L. Hudson, *J. Am. Chem. Soc.*, **55**, 1410 (1933).
18. Stoermer, R., *Chem. Ber.*, **42**, 4865 (1909).
19. Stoermer, R., *Chem. Ber.*, **44**, 637 (1911).
20. Pelletier, S. W., and W. L. McLeish, *J. Am. Chem. Soc.*, **74**, 6292 (1952).
21. Mislow, K., and A. J. Gordon, *J. Am. Chem. Soc.*, **85**, 3521 (1963).
22. Wyman, G. M., *Chem. Rev.*, **55**, 625 (1955).
23. Rollefson, G. K., and M. Burton, *Photochemistry and the Mechanisms of Chemical Reactions*, Englewood Cliffs, N.J., Prentice-Hall (1939).
24. Mahncke, H. E., and W. A. Noyes, Jr., *J. Am. Chem. Soc.*, **58**, 932 (1936).
25. Olson, A. R., and W. Maroney, *J. Am. Chem. Soc.*, **56**, 1320 (1934).
26. Wyman, G. M., and W. R. Brode, *J. Am. Chem. Soc.*, **73**, 1487 (1951).
27. Lippert, E., and W. Lüder, *J. Phys. Chem.*, **66**, 2430 (1962).
28. Lippert, E., and W. Lüder, *Z. phys. Chem.*, **33**, 60 (1962).
29. Coenen, M., and M. Pestemer, *Z. Electrochem.*, **57**, 785 (1953).
30. Lauerer, D., M. Coenen, M. Pestemer, and G. Scheibe, *Z. phys. Chem.*, **10**, 236 (1957).
31. Griffin, G. W., J. Covell, R. C. Petterson, R. M. Dodson, and G. Klose, *J. Am. Chem. Soc.*, **87**, 1410 (1965).
32. Jorgenson, M. J., *Chem. Comm.*, 137 (1965).
33. Griffin, G. W., A. F. Marcantonio, H. Kristinsson, R. C. Petterson, and C. S. Irving, *Tetrahedron Letters*, 2951 (1965).

34. Hammond, G. S. and R. S. Cole, *J. Am. Chem. Soc.*, **87**, 3256 (1965).
35. Mislow, K., M. Axelrod, D. R. Rayner, H. Gotthardt, L. M. Coyne, and G. S. Hammond, *J. Am. Chem. Soc.*, **87**, 4958 (1965).
36. Hammond, G. S., H. Gotthardt, L. M. Coyne, M. Axelrod, D. R. Rayner, and K. Mislow, *J. Am. Chem. Soc.*, **87**, 4959 (1965).
37. Singer, L. A., private communication.
38. Malkin, S., and E. Fischer, *J. Phys. Chem.*, **66**, 2482 (1962).
39. Fischer, E., *J. Am. Chem. Soc.*, **82**, 3249 (1960).
40. Birnbaum, P. P., and D. W. G. Style, *Trans. Faraday Soc.*, **50**, 1192 (1954).
41. Birnbaum, P. P., J. H. Linford, and D. W. G. Style, *Trans. Faraday Soc.*, **49**, 735 (1953).
42. Yamashita, S., *Bull. Chem. Soc., Japan*, **34**, 490 (1961).
43. Jones, L. B., and G. S. Hammond, *J. Am. Chem. Soc.*, **87**, 4219 (1965).
44. Gabor, G., and E. Fischer, *J. Phys. Chem.*, **66**, 2478 (1962).
45. Fischer, E., and Y. F. Frei, *J. Chem. Soc.*, 3159 (1959).
46. Fischer, E., and Y. F. Frei, *J. Chem. Phys.*, **27**, 328 (1957).
47. Kearns, D. R., *J. Phys. Chem.*, **69**, 1062 (1965).
48. Wettermark, G., M. E. Langmuir, and D. G. Anderson, *J. Am. Chem. Soc.*, **87**, 476 (1965).
49. Wettermark, G., and L. Dogliotti, *J. Chem. Phys.*, **40**, 1486 (1964).
50. Anderson, D. G., and G. Wettermark, *J. Am. Chem. Soc.*, **87**, 1433 (1965).
51. Kuhn, R., and F. Bär, *Ann. Chem.*, **516**, 143 (1935).
52. Ospenson, J. N., *Acta Chem. Scand.*, **4**, 1351 (1950).
53. Buroway, A., and J. T. Chamberlain, *J. Chem. Soc.*, 3734 (1952).
54. Buroway, A., and A. R. Thompson, *J. Chem. Soc.*, 1443 (1953).
55. Sawicki, E., *J. Org. Chem.*, **22**, 743 (1957).
56. Brode, W. R., J. H. Gould, and G. M. Wyman, *J. Am. Chem. Soc.*, **74**, 4641 (1952).
57. Brode, W. R., J. H. Gould, and G. M. Wyman, *J. Am. Chem. Soc.*, **75**, 1856 (1953).
58. Winkel, A., and H. Siebert, *Chem. Ber.*, **74B**, 670 (1941).
59. Hartley, G. S., *J. Chem. Soc.*, 633 (1938).
60. Cook, A. H., and D. G. Jones, *J. Chem. Soc.*, 1309 (1939).
61. Cook, A. H., D. G. Jones, and J. B. Polya, *J. Chem. Soc.*, 1315 (1939).
62. Badger, G. M., and R. G. Buttery, *J. Chem. Soc.*, 2243 (1954).
63. Badger, G. M., R. G. Buttery, and G. E. Lewis, *J. Chem. Soc.*, **1888** (1954).
64. Webb, D., and H. H. Jaffè, *Tetrahedron Letters*, 1875 (1964).
65. Shemyakin, M. M., V. I. Maimind, and B. K. Vaichunaite, *Izvest. Akad. Nauk. S.S.S.R. Otdel Khim. Nauk.*, 866 (1960); *Chem. Abstr.*, **54**, 24474g (1960).
66. Splitter, J. S., and M. Calvin, *J. Org. Chem.*, **23**, 651 (1958).
67. Kamlet, M. J., and L. A. Kaplan, *J. Org. Chem.*, **22**, 576 (1957).
68. Kröhnke, F., *Ann Chem.*, **604**, 203 (1957).
69. Bonnett, R., V. M. Clark, and A. Todd, *J. Chem. Soc.*, 2102 (1959).
70. Shinzawa, K., and I. Tanaka, *J. Phys. Chem.*, **68**, 1205 (1964).
71. Koyano, K., and I. Tanaka, *J. Phys. Chem.*, **69**, 2545 (1965).
72. Splitter, J. S., and M. Calvin, *J. Org. Chem.*, **30**, 3427 (1965).
73. Padwa, A., *J. Am. Chem. Soc.*, **87**, 4365 (1965).
74. Jaffè, H. H., D. L. Beveridge, and H. L. Jones, *J. Am. Chem. Soc.*, **86**, 2932 (1964).
75. Jaffè, H. H., H. L. Jones, and M. Isaks, *J. Am. Chem. Soc.*, **86**, 2934 (1964).
76. Jaffè, H. H., and H. L. Jones, *J. Org. Chem.*, **30**, 964 (1965).
77. Förster, T., *Z. Electrochem.*, **54**, 42 (1950).
78. Leighton, P. A., and F. A. Lucy, *J. Chem. Phys.*, **2**, 756 (1934).
79. Leighton, P. A., and F. A. Lucy, *J. Chem. Phys.*, **2**, 760 (1934).

80. Tanasescu, I., *Bull. soc. chim.*, **39**, 1443 (1926).
81. Pitts, J. N., J. K. S. Wan, and E. A. Schuck, *J. Am. Chem. Soc.*, **86**, 3606 (1964).
82. Tanasescu, I., and M. Ionescu, *Bull. soc. chim., France*, 84 (1940).
83. Pfeiffer, P., and E. Kramer, *Chem. Ber.*, **46**, 3655 (1913).
84. Kröhnke, F., G. Kröhnke, and I. Vogt, *Chem. Ber.*, **86**, 1500 (1953).
85. Tanasescu, I., and H. Tanasescu, *Bull. soc. Stiinte Cluj.*, **2**, 369 (1925); *Chem. Abst.*, **20**, 749 (1926).
86. Tanasescu, I., *Bull. soc. chim.*, **41**, 1074 (1927).
87. Tanasescu, I., *Bull. soc. chim.*, **39**, 1718 (1926).
88. Pfeiffer, P., S. Braude, R. Fritsch, W. Halberstadt, G. Kirchhoff, J. Kleber, and P. Wittkop, *Ann. Chem.*, **411**, 72 (1916).
89. Berson, J. A., and E. Brown, *J. Am. Chem. Soc.*, **77**, 447 (1955).
90. Berson, J. A., and E. Brown, *J. Am. Chem. Soc.*, **77**, 450 (1955).
91. Landquist, J. K., *J. Chem. Soc.*, 2830 (1953).
92. Chardonnens, L., and P. Heinrich, *Helv. Chim. Acta*, **32**, 656 (1949).
93. Tiefenthaler, H., W. Dörscheln, H. Göth, and H. Schmid, *Tetrahedron Letters*, 2999 (1964).
94. Gritter, R. J., and E. C. Sabatino, *J. Org. Chem.*, **29**, 1965 (1964).
95. Zimmerman, H. E., B. R. Cowley, C. Y. Tseng, and J. W. Wilson, *J. Am. Chem. Soc.*, **86**, 947 (1964).
96. Kharasch, M. S., A. Fono, and W. Nudenberg, *J. Org. Chem.*, **16**, 113 (1951).
97. Walling, C., in P. de Mayo (ed.), *Molecular Rearrangements*, p. 407, New York, Interscience, 1963.
98. Walling, C., *Free Radicals in Solution*, p. 267, New York, Wiley, 1957.
99. Padwa, A., *J. Am. Chem. Soc.*, **87**, 4205 (1965).
100. Yates, P., and I. W. J. Still, *J. Am. Chem. Soc.*, **85**, 1208 (1963).
101. Padwa, A., *Tetrahedron Letters*, 813 (1964).
102. Dunston, J. M., and P. Yates, *Tetrahedron Letters*, 505 (1964).
103. Zimmerman, H. E., and R. D. Simkin, *Tetrahedron Letters*, 1847 (1964).
104. Johnson, C. K., B. Dominy, and W. Reusch, *J. Am. Chem. Soc.*, **85**, 3894 (1963).
105. Ullman, E. F., and W. A. Henderson, Jr., *J. Am. Chem. Soc.*, **86**, 5050 (1964).
106. Ullman, E. F., and J. E. Milks, *J. Am. Chem. Soc.*, **84**, 1315 (1962).
107. Ullman, E. F., and J. E. Milks, *J. Am. Chem. Soc.*, **86**, 3814 (1964).
108. Ullman, E. F., *J. Am. Chem. Soc.*, **85**, 3529 (1963).
109. Lehmann, C., K. Schaffner, and O. Jeger, *Helv. Chim. Acta*, **45**, 1031 (1962).
110. de Mayo, P., and S. T. Reid, *Quart. Rev.*, **15**, 393 (1961).
111. de Mayo, P., in *Advances in Organic Chemistry, Methods and Results*, Vol. II, p. 367 ff., New York, Interscience, 1960.
112. Barton, D. H. R., *Helv. Chim. Acta*, **42**, 2604 (1959).
113. Zimmerman, H. E., in *Advances in Photochemistry*, Vol. I., p. 183, New York, Interscience, 1963.
114. Zimmerman, H. E., and D. I. Schuster, *J. Am. Chem. Soc.*, **84**, 4527 (1962).
115. Zimmerman, H. E., and D. I. Schuster, *J. Am. Chem. Soc.*, **83**, 4486 (1961).
116. Hammond, G. S., and N. J. Turro, *Science*, **142**, 1541 (1963).
117. Kwie, W. W., B. A. Shoulders, and P. D. Gardner, *J. Am. Chem. Soc.*, **84**, 2268, (1962).
118. Chapman, O. L., T. A. Rettig, A. A. Griswold, A. I. Dutton, and P. Fitton, *Tetrahedron Letters*, 2049 (1963).
119. Zimmerman, H. E., and J. W. Wilson, *J. Am. Chem. Soc.*, **86**, 4036 (1964).
120. Schuster, D. I., and D. J. Patel, *J. Am. Chem. Soc.*, **87**, 2515 (1965).
121. King, J., and D. Leaver, *Chem. Comm.*, 539 (1965).

122. Shoulders, B. A., W. W. Kwie, W. Klyne, and P. D. Gardner, *Tetrahedron*, **21**, 2973 (1965).

123. Zimmerman, H. E., R. G. Lewis, J. J. McCullough, A. Padwa, S. Staley, and M. Semmelhack, *J. Am. Chem. Soc.*, **88**, 159 (1966).

124. Chapman, O. L., J. B. Sieja, and W. L. Welstead, *J. Am. Chem. Soc.*, **88**, 161 (1966).

125. Barton, D. H. R., and G. Quinkert, *J. Chem. Soc.*, 1 (1960).

126. Barton, D. H. R., and G. Quinkert, *Proc. Chem. Soc.*, 197 (1958).

127. Quinkert, G., *Angew. Chem. Intern. Ed.*, **4**, 211 (1965).

128. Zimmerman, H. E., R. C. Hahn, H. Morrison, and M. C. Wani, *J. Am. Chem. Soc.*, **87**, 1138 (1965).

129. Kropp, P. J., and W. F. Erman, *Tetrahedron Letters*, 21 (1963).

130. Kropp, P. J., and W. F. Erman, *J. Am. Chem. Soc.*, **85**, 2456 (1963).

131. Kropp, P. J., *J. Am. Chem. Soc.*, **85**, 3779 (1963).

132. Kropp, P. J., *J. Am. Chem. Soc.*, **86**, 4053 (1964).

133. Dutler, H., C. Ganter, H. Ryf, E. C. Utzinger, K. Weinberg, K. Schaffner, D. Arigoni, and O. Jeger, *Helv. Chim. Acta*, **45**, 2346 (1962).

134. Chapman, O. L., in *Advances in Photochemistry*, Vol. I., p. 323 ff., New York, Wiley, 1963.

135. Quoted by E. Altenburger, H. Wehrli, and K. Schaffner, *Helv. Chim. Acta*, **46**, 2753 (1963). Work of J. Bollini, J. Frei, C. Ganter, D. Kagi, and H. Ryf.

136. Chapman, O. L., and L. F. Englert, *J. Am. Chem. Soc.*, **85**, 3028 (1963).

137. Barton, D. H. R., P. de Mayo, and M. Shafiq, *Proc. Chem. Soc.*, 345 (1957).

138. Barton, D. H. R., P. de Mayo, and M. Shafiq, *J. Chem. Soc.*, 3314 (1958).

139. van Tamelen, E. E., S. H. Levin, G. Brenner, J. Wolinsky, and P. E. Aldrich, *J. Am. Chem. Soc.*, **80**, 501 (1958).

140. van Tamelen, E. E., S. H. Levin, G. Brenner, J. Wolinsky, and P. E. Aldrich, *J. Am. Chem. Soc.*, **81**, 1666 (1959).

141. Fisch, M. H., and J. H. Richards, *J. Am. Chem. Soc.*, **85**, 3029 (1963).

142. Dauben, W. G., D. A. Lightner, and W. K. Hayes, *J. Org. Chem.*, **27**, 1897 (1962).

143. Wenger, R., H. Dutler, H. Wehrli, K. Schaffner, and O. Jeger, *Helv. Chim. Acta*, **45**, 2420 (1962).

144. Barton, D. H. R., and W. C. Taylor, *Proc. Chem. Soc.*, 96 (1957).

145. Barton, D. H. R., and W. C. Taylor, *J. Am. Chem. Soc.*, **80**, 244 (1958).

146. Bozzato, C., H. P. Throndsen, K. Schaffner, O. Jeger, *J. Am. Chem. Soc.*, **86**, 2073 (1964).

147. Schuster, D. I., M. J. Nash, and M. L. Kantor, *Tetrahedron Letters*, 1375 (1964).

148. Schuster, D. I., and C. J. Polowczyk, *J. Am. Chem. Soc.*, **86**, 4502 (1964).

149. van Tamelen, E. E., K. Kirk, and G. Brieger, *Tetrahedron Letters*, 939 (1962).

150. Orlando, C. M., and A. K. Bose, *J. Am. Chem. Soc.*, **87**, 3782 (1965).

151. Cameron, D. W., and R. G. F. Giles, *Chem. Comm.*, 573 (1965).

152. Miller, B., and H. Margulies, *Chem. Comm.*, 314 (1965).

153. Chapman, O. L., H. G. Smith, and R. W. King, *J. Am. Chem. Soc.*, **85**, 806 (1963).

154. Chapman, O. L., H. G. Smith, and R. W. King, *J. Am. Chem. Soc.*, **85**, 803 (1963).

155. Forbes, E. J., *J. Chem. Soc.*, 3864 (1955).

156. Gardner, P. D., R. L. Brandon, and G. R. Haynes, *J. Am. Chem. Soc.*, **79**, 6334 (1957).

157. Grewe, R., and W. Wulf, *Chem. Ber.*, **84**, 621 (1951).

158. Šantavý, F., *Biol. Listy*, **31**, 246 (1950).

159. Schönberg, A., *Präperative Organische Photochemie*, p. 6, Berlin, Springer, 1958.

160. Dauben, W. G., K. Koch, and W. E. Thiessen, *J. Am. Chem. Soc.*, **81**, 6087 (1959).

161. Forbes, E. J., and R. A. Ripley, *Chem. Ind.*, 589 (1960).

162. Dauben, W. G., K. Koch, O. L. Chapman, and S. L. Smith, *J. Am. Chem. Soc.*, **83**, 1768 (1961).
163. Chapman, O. L., and D. J. Pasto, *J. Am. Chem. Soc.*, **82**, 3642 (1960).
164. Büchi, G., and N. C. Yang, *Helv. Chim. Acta*, **38**, 1338 (1955).
165. Büchi, G., and N. C. Yang, *J. Am. Chem. Soc.*, **79**, 2318 (1957).
166. Griffin, G. W., and E. J. O'Connell, *J. Am. Chem. Soc.*, **84**, 4148 (1962).
167. Zimmerman, H. E., G. G. C. Dürr, R. G. Lewis, and S. Bram, *J. Am. Chem. Soc.*, **84**, 4149 (1962).
168. Schmid, H., M. Hochweber, and H. von Halban, *Helv. Chim. Acta*, **30**, 1135 (1947).
169. Anderson, J. D., and C. B. Reese, *Proc. Chem. Soc.*, 217 (1960).
170. Kobsa, H., *J. Org. Chem.*, **27**, 2293 (1962).
171. Finnegan, R. A., and J. J. Mattice, *Tetrahedron*, **21**, 1015 (1965).
172. Yogev, A., M. Gorodetsky, and Y. Mazur, *J. Am. Chem. Soc.*, **86**, 5208 (1964).
173. Gorodetsky, M., and Y. Mazur, *J. Am. Chem. Soc.*, **86**, 5213 (1964).
174. Gorodetsky, M., and Y. Mazur, *Tetrahedron Letters*, 369 (1963).
175. McGreer, D. E., M. G. Vinje, and R. S. McDaniel, *Can. J. Chem.*, **43**, 1417 (1965).
176. Hill, J., *Chem. Comm.*, 260 (1966).
177. Wieman, J., N. Thoai, and F. Weisbuch, *Tetrahedron Letters*, 2983 (1965).
178. Yogev, A., and Y. Mazur, *J. Am. Chem. Soc.*, **87**, 3520 (1965).
179. Kharasch, M. S., G. Stampa, and W. Nudenberg, *Science*, **116**, 309 (1952).
180. Bach, F. L., and J. C. Barclay, Absts. of Papers presented at the 150th Meeting, Am. Chem. Soc., Atlantic City, N. J., Sept., 1965, p. 95.
181. Anderson, J. D., and C. B. Reese, *Tetrahedron Letters*, 1 (1962).
182. Baum, E. J., and J. N. Pitts, *J. Phys. Chem.*, **70**, 2066 (1966).
183. Turro, N. J., G. W. Byers, and P. A. Leermakers, *J. Am. Chem. Soc.*, **86**, 955 (1964).
184. Anderson, J. D., unpublished work reported in M.I.T. Seminar Abstracts, 349, 1963.
185. Finnegan, R. A., and A. W. Hagan, *Tetrahedron Letters*, 365 (1963).
186. Mallory, F. B., J. T. Gordon, and C. S. Wood, *J. Am. Chem. Soc.*, **85**, 828 (1963).
187. Mallory, F. B., C. S. Wood, J. T. Gordon, L. C. Lindquist, and M. L. Savitz, *J. Am. Chem. Soc.*, **84**, 4361 (1962).
188. Mallory, F. B., C. S. Wood, and J. T. Gordon, *J. Am. Chem. Soc.*, **86**, 3094 (1964).
189. Mallory, F. B., and C. S. Wood, *Tetrahedron Letters*, 2643 (1965).
190. Sargent, M. V., and C. J. Timmons, *J. Am. Chem. Soc.*, **85**, 2186 (1963).
191. Sargent, M. V., and C. J. Timmons, *J. Chem. Soc.*, 5544 (1964).
192. Loader, C. E., M. V. Sargent, and C. J. Timmons, *Chem. Comm.*, 127 (1965).
193. Moore, W. M., D. D. Morgan, and F. R. Stermitz, *J. Am. Chem. Soc.*, **85**, 829 (1963).
194. Buckles, R. E., *J. Am. Chem. Soc.*, **77**, 1040 (1955).
195. Hugelshofer, P., J. Kalvoda, and K. Schaffner, *Helv. Chim. Acta*, **43**, 1322 (1960).
196. Parker, C. O., and P. E. Spoerri, *Nature*, **166**, 603 (1950).
197. Coe, D. G., E. W. Garnish, M. M. Gale, and C. J. Timmons, *Chem. Ind.*, 665 (1957).
198. Srinivasan, R., and J. C. Powers, Jr., *J. Am. Chem. Soc.*, **85**, 1355 (1963).
199. Srinivasan, R., and J. C. Powers, Jr., *J. Chem. Phys.*, **39**, 580 (1963).
200. Brockmann, H., and H. Eggers, *Angew. Chem.*, **67**, 706 (1955).
201. Fonken, G. J., *Chem. Ind.*, 1327 (1962).
202. Stobbe, H., *Chem. Ber.*, **40**, 3372 (1907).
203. Baddar, F. G., L. S. El-Assal, and M. Gindy, *J. Chem. Soc.*, 1270 (1948).
204. Lewis, G. E., *J. Org. Chem.*, **25**, 2193 (1960).
205. Lewis, G. E., *Tetrahedron Letters*, **9**, 12 (1960).
206. Jaffé, H. H., and R. W. Gardner, *J. Am. Chem. Soc.*, **80**, 319 (1958).

207. Jaffè, H. H., S. J. Yeh, and R. W. Gardner, *J. Molecular Spectroscopy*, **2**, 120 (1958).
208. Yeh, S. J., and H. H. Jaffè, *J. Am. Chem. Soc.*, **81**, 3279 (1959).
209. Grellmann, K. H., G. M. Sherman, and H. Linschitz, *J. Am. Chem. Soc.*, **85**, 1881 (1963).
210. Linschitz, H., and K. H. Grellmann, *J. Am. Chem. Soc.*, **86**, 303 (1964).
211. Bowen, E. J., and J. H. D. Eland, *Proc. Chem. Soc.*, 202 (1963).
212. Allan, L. T., and G. W. Swan, *J. Chem. Soc.*, 4822 (1965).
213. C. Kaneko, S. Yamada, and M. Ishikawa, *Tetrahedron Letters*, 2145 (1966).
214. M. Ishikawa, S. Yamada, and C. Kaneko, *Chem. Pharm. Bull.*, (Tokyo), **13**, 747 (1965).

CHAPTER

9

Photochemical Substitution Reactions

A photochemical substitution reaction is, as expected, a reaction initiated by light that leads to the displacement of one atom or group by another atom or group, eq. (1). There are several decided differences, however,

$$(1) \quad R—X \ + \ Y \ \xrightarrow{h\nu} \ RY \ + \ X$$

between ordinary ground state substitution reactions and their photochemical counterparts. For example, substituents seem to affect transition states involving excited molecules differently than transition states involving ground state molecules, and substitution reactions take different courses when excited states rather than ground states are involved. Most of the photolytic displacement reactions which are known involve aromatic nuclei, and they appear to resemble aromatic homolytic substitution reactions.

Halogen Substitutions

The halogen interchange reaction is the oldest known photochemical substitution reaction. This reaction involves the displacement of a heavier halogen atom by a lighter halogen atom, eq. (2), and was originally discovered by Eibner.[1]

A great number of workers have reported that the side chain chlorination

247

(2) 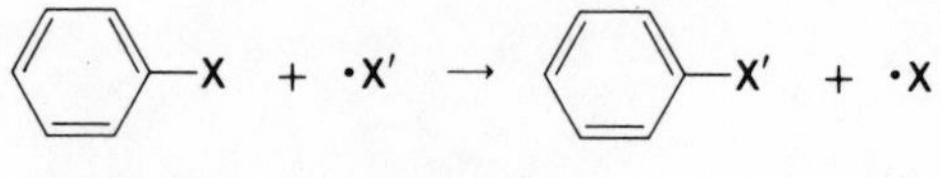   [benzene ring]—X + ·X′ → [benzene ring]—X′ + ·X

Atomic wt. X > atomic wt. X′

reaction of ring-brominated toluenes proceeds to give chlorine in the ring and bromine in the side chain.[1-7] The reaction is extremely complex, and attempts to interpret data from mechanistic studies of the reaction are frequently frustrated by the wealth of side reactions of the molecules involved.[8] However, it appears that a homolytic halogenation mechanism is reasonable, eqs. (3) and (4).

(3)   [benzene ring]—X + ·X′ → [cyclohexadiene ring]$\begin{array}{c}-X\\-X′\end{array}$

(4)   [cyclohexadiene ring with ·]$\begin{array}{c}-X\\-X′\end{array}$ → [benzene ring]—X′ + X·

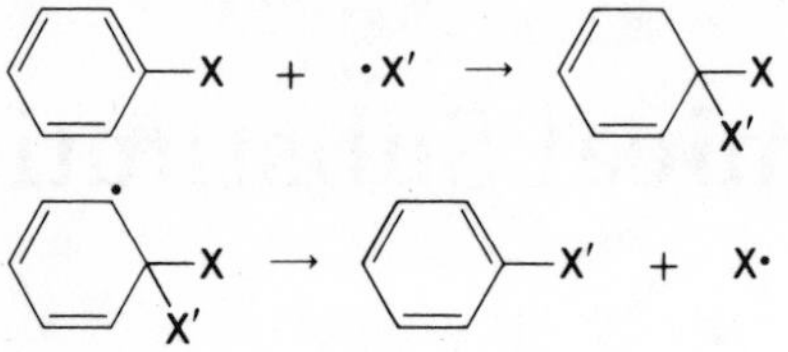

Walling presents the following evidence for the intermediacy of halogen atoms in the photochemical aromatic halogen substitution reaction.[9] First, the reaction is photochemical, not always a perfect diagnostic tool for a free radical mechanism but at least an indicator. Second, other sources of chlorine atoms (e.g., sulfuryl chloride and dibenzoyl peroxide) are equally effective in the displacement reaction. Third, typical inhibitors such as azobenzene, azoxybenzene, and nitrobenzene retard the reaction rate. Fourth, the reaction appears to be retarded by electron-withdrawing groups located on the benzene ring.

A mechanism that can account for the halogen exchange reaction is shown in eqs. (5-8). The reaction is formally the same as a photochemical chain reaction involving a halogen atom displacement on an aromatic nuclei.

(5) $X_2 \xrightarrow{h\nu} 2X·$

(6) 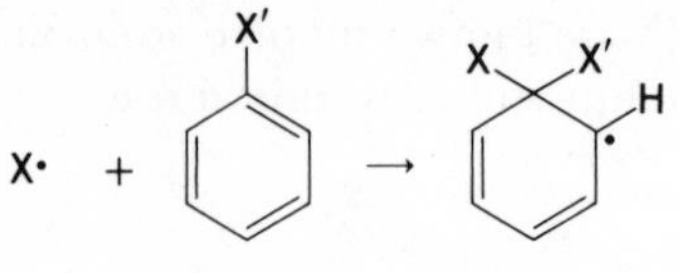   X· + [benzene ring with X′] → [cyclohexadiene ring with X, X′, H and ·]

(7) 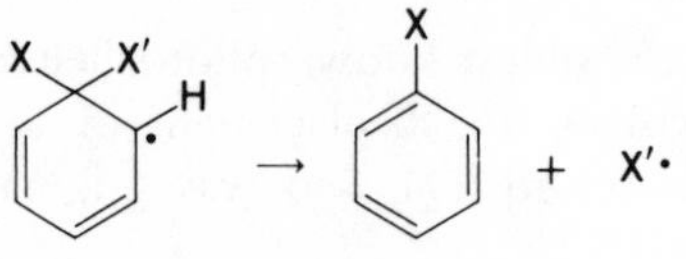   [cyclohexadiene ring with X, X′, H and ·] → [benzene ring with X] + X′·

(8)   2X′· → products

The reaction is general for chlorine and bromine; however, competing reactions cause the displacement of iodine from iodobenzene to be overshadowed. For example, the predominant product from the photolysis of chlorine in iodobenzene is iodobenzene dichloride, eqs. (9).[10,11] Displacement of iodine can be effected if bromine rather than chlorine is used,[12] while

$$(9) \quad C_6H_5{-}I \; + \; Cl_2 \; \xrightarrow{h\nu} \; C_6H_5{-}ICl_2$$

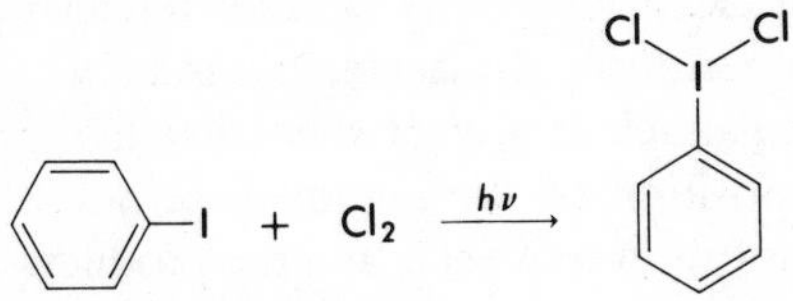

the displacement with chlorine can be effected if iodine monochloride or sulfuryl chloride and benzoyl peroxide are used as the chlorinating agents.[13,14]

Table 9-1 lists some specific examples of halogen interchange reactions of aromatic halides.

In typical competitive experiments Milligan and co-workers[12] found the following relative reactivity ratios for the displacement of bromine by chlorine from substituted bromobenzenes: p-phenyl > o-methoxy > p-chloro > unsubstituted > p-carbomethoxy > p-cyano. Walling and Miller[9] reported that p-nitro groups retard the reaction.

Table 9-1

Photochemical Halogen Interchange Reactions

Aromatic compound	Halogen	Product
bromobenzene[1]	Cl_2	chlorobenzene
p-bromotoluene[2]	Cl_2	p-chlorotoluene
p-bromotoluene[6]	$SO_2Cl_2 + Bz_2O_2$	p-chlorotoluene
bromochlorobenzene[7]	Cl_2	dichlorobenzene
p-fluorobromobenzene[7]	Cl_2	p-fluorochlorobenzene
iodobenzene[10,11]	Cl_2	iodobenzenedichloride
p-bromoiodobenzene[10,11]	Cl_2	p-bromoiodobenzene-dichloride
2,4,6-tribromoiodobenzene[10,11]	Cl_2	2,4,6-tribromoiodobenzene-dichloride
benzenesulfonyl chloride[9]	Cl_2	chlorobenzene
diphenylsulfone[15,16,9]	Cl_2	chlorobenzene
bromobenzene[9]	Br_2*	bromobenzene*
iodobenzene[12]	Br_2	bromobenzene
iodobenzene[17,18]	I_2*	iodobenzene*
iodobenzene[12,19]	ICl or SO_2Cl_2 + peroxide	chlorobenzene

Since electron withdrawers retard the rate of the displacement reaction, the halogen atom substitution reaction resembles an electrophilic rather than a nucleophilic aromatic substitution. If chlorine atoms resemble electrophilic agents in halogen interchange reactions, the question arises, why is the aromatic carbon atom to which the halogen atom is bonded attacked at all? Halogen, due to its high electronegativity, should render the intermediate radical necessary for halogen atom displacement less stable than that intermediate radical precursory to attack at any of the other five positions. It would appear that the decomposition of the intermediate radical is thus the slow step in the halogen substitution sequence, and the products are controlled by the ease of dissociation of the various carbon-halogen and carbon-hydrogen bonds in the molecule.

As expected, Milligan and co-workers found that iodine is displaced more easily than bromine in competitive experiments, reflecting the strength of the carbon-bromine bond as compared to the carbon-iodine bond in aromatic systems and substantiating the theory that the rate-determining step of the reaction is the decomposition of the intermediate radical complex. It would be interesting to see if other radicals like methyl radicals or t-butoxy radicals could also displace halogen from halobenzenes.

Bacon and Hill[19] have observed that cuprous halides are strikingly good sources of halogens in photolytic halogen exchange reactions, eq. (10).

(10) $ArX + CuX' \longrightarrow ArX' + CuX$

Although the reaction appears to be markedly influenced by solvent, the general observations characteristic of free-halogen-initiated interchange reactions are also characteristic of the cuprous-salt-induced reaction.

Diazonium Salt Reactions

Aromatic diazonium salts are also known to undergo a photochemical substitution reaction although the initial step of the reaction is a decomposition step. Formally one may think of the photochemical displacement of nitrogen from a diazonium salt as an analog of the well-known thermal decomposition reaction of diazonium salts. Thus, Kunitake and Price[20] found that by irradiating p-3,5-dimethylbenzenediazooxide in chlorobenzene or in chlorinated hydrocarbons, p-hydroxybiphenyls are obtained. They attribute these products to the reaction pathway given in eqs. (11–14).

(11)

(12)

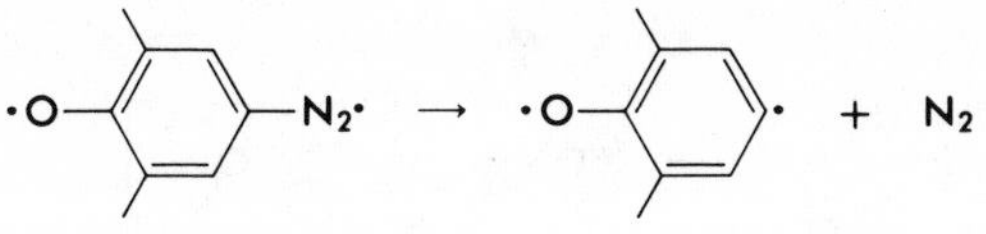

(13)

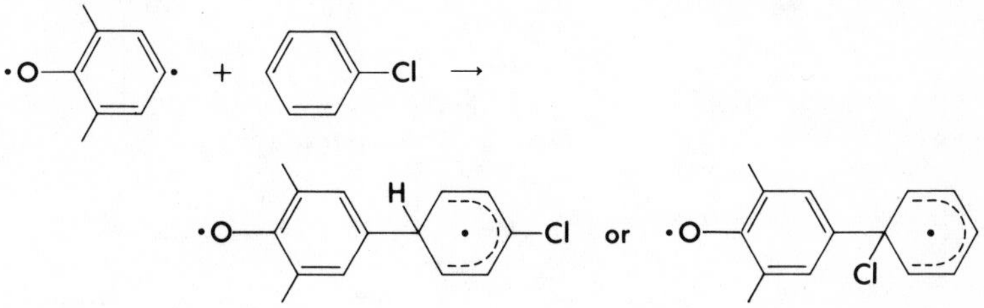

(14)

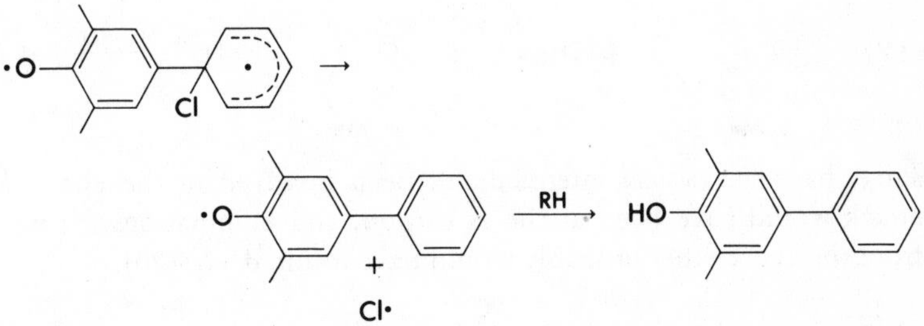

Similar observations were reported by Süs and co-workers[21] for the photochemical decomposition of benzenediazooxide in alcoholic solvents, eq. (15)

(15)

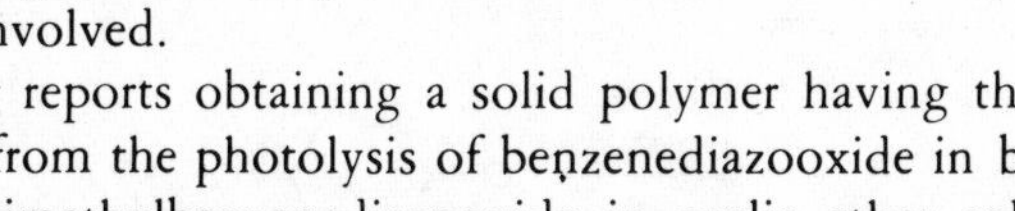

It is of interest that phenyl displaces chlorine from chlorobenzene in the reaction sequence (11–14); this mechanism is an exact analog of the halogen interchange reaction reported earlier in that a homolytic aromatic substitution is involved.

Wang reports obtaining a solid polymer having the characteristics of a phenol from the photolysis of benzenediazooxide in benzene.[22] Photolysis of 3,5-dimethylbenzenediazooxide in cyclic ether solvents gives products indicative of carbonium ion intermediates. Attack on the cyclic ether is, according to Kunitake and Price,[20] initially on the oxygen, eqs. (16–19),

(16)

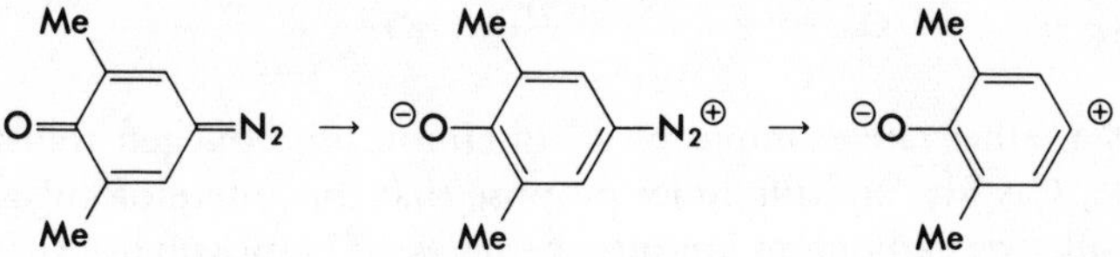

(17)

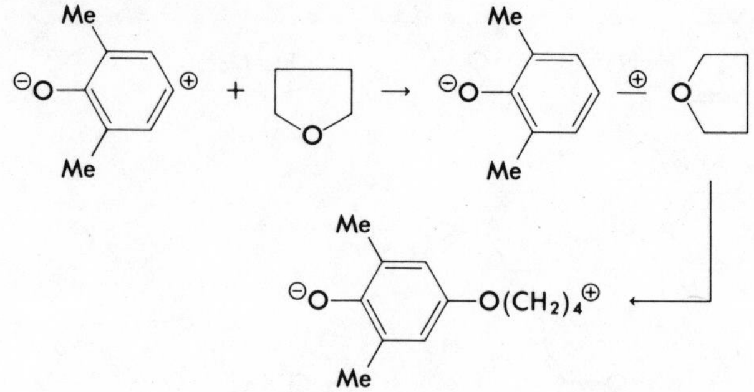

(18)

(19) 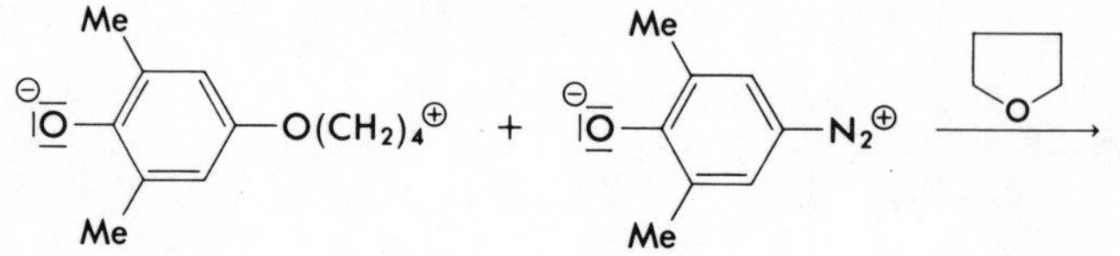   polymer

since, had free radical intermediates been involved in the chain sequence, attack would have been at the α carbon, and elimination or ring opening from the cyclic ether probably would have resulted, eq. (20).

(20)

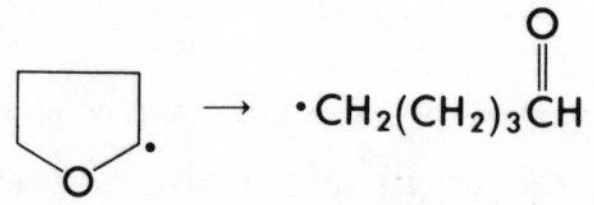

Stille, Cassidy, and Plummer report similar copolymerization reactions between the decomposition products of diazooxides and cyclic ethers.[23] They also propose a carbonium ion mechanism. They report that photolysis of benzene diazooxide in nitrobenzene gives nitrosobenzene and benzoquinone, eq. (21), while photolysis in benzene yields *p*-phenylphenol as the

(21)

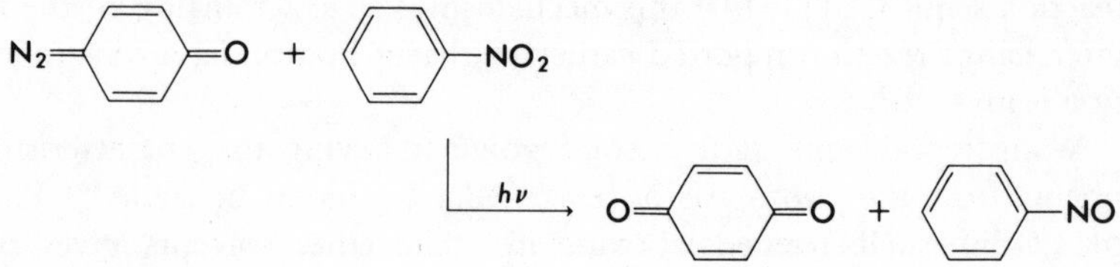

major product, eq. (22). The reaction of benzenediazooxide with nitro-

(22)

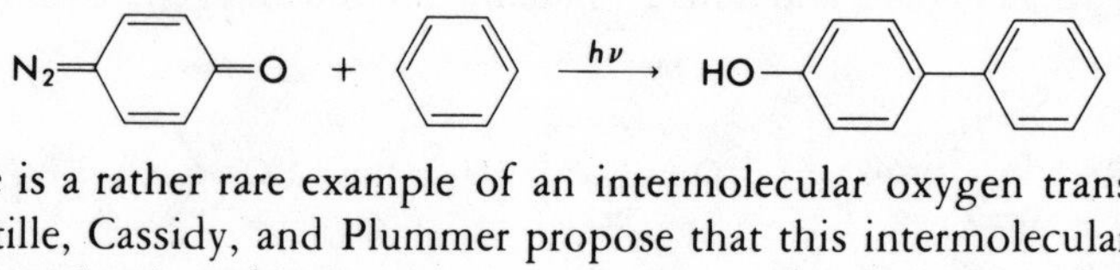

benzene is a rather rare example of an intermolecular oxygen transfer reaction. Stille, Cassidy, and Plummer propose that this intermolecular oxygen transfer results via carbonium ion intermediates. The possibility that photochemical reactions of benzenediazooxide may lead to carbenoid inter-mediates also exists, eq. (23).

(23) 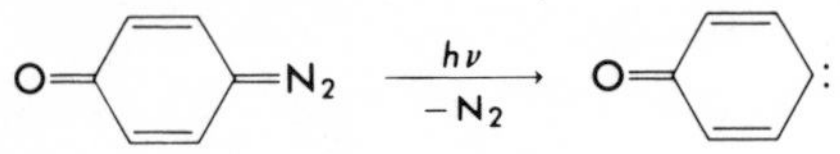 $\quad$ O=⟨ ⟩=N$_2$ $\xrightarrow[-N_2]{h\nu}$ O=⟨ ⟩:

Solvolysis Reactions

Photochemical solvolysis reactions resemble ordinary solvolysis reactions, except that they require photochemical initiation. An example, reported in Chapter 8, is the reaction of a phenacyl chloride with ethanol, eq. (24).[24]

(24)

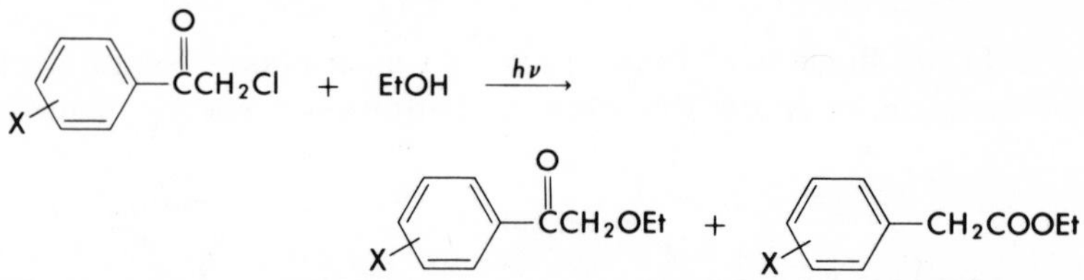

$$X-\text{⟨ ⟩}-\overset{\displaystyle O}{\overset{\|}{C}}CH_2Cl \; + \; EtOH \; \xrightarrow{h\nu}$$

$$X-\text{⟨ ⟩}-\overset{\displaystyle O}{\overset{\|}{C}}CH_2OEt \; + \; X-\text{⟨ ⟩}-CH_2COOEt$$

Havinga, de Jongh, and Dorst[25,26,34] have reported that the hydrolyses of certain phosphate and sulfate esters are accelerated by light. Similar results have been reported by Zimmerman and Somasekhara[27] and by Letsinger and Ramsey.[28] The latter workers have reported the reaction of pyridine with phosphate esters, eq. (25), and have observed the photochemical nucleo-

(25) 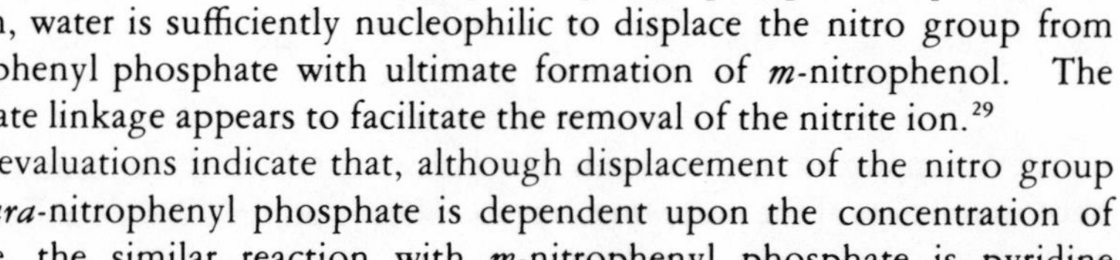 $\quad$ ⟨ ⟩N $\; + \;$ O$_2$N-⟨ ⟩-OPO$_3$Na$_2$ $\xrightarrow[H_2O]{h\nu}$

$$\text{⟨ ⟩}\overset{\oplus}{N}-\text{⟨ ⟩}-OPO_3^{-2}, Na^{\oplus} \; + \; NaNO_2$$

philic displacement of $NO_2^{\ominus}$ from p-nitrophenyl phosphate, eq. (25). In addition, water is sufficiently nucleophilic to displace the nitro group from m-nitrophenyl phosphate with ultimate formation of m-nitrophenol. The phosphate linkage appears to facilitate the removal of the nitrite ion.[29]

Rate evaluations indicate that, although displacement of the nitro group from $para$-nitrophenyl phosphate is dependent upon the concentration of pyridine, the similar reaction with m-nitrophenyl phosphate is pyridine independent. Letsinger and Ramsey interpret this observation to mean that the photolysis of the $para$-nitrophenyl phosphate requires the formation of an intermediate. This intermediate may either revert to the ground state or react with solvent to yield product, a concentration-dependent process. They propose the rate scheme shown in Figure 9-1. The nature of the intermediate is still open to question, for the intermediate could be nothing but the triplet excited state; however, a more exciting possibility is a cyclic phosphate intermediate, eq. (26).

(26)

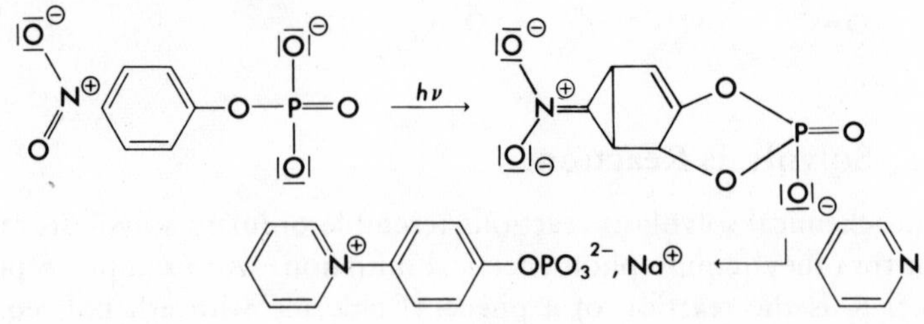

Gold and Rochester[30] have reported a similar photochemical nucleophilic displacement of nitrite ion from 1,3,5-trinitrobenzene by hydroxide ion.

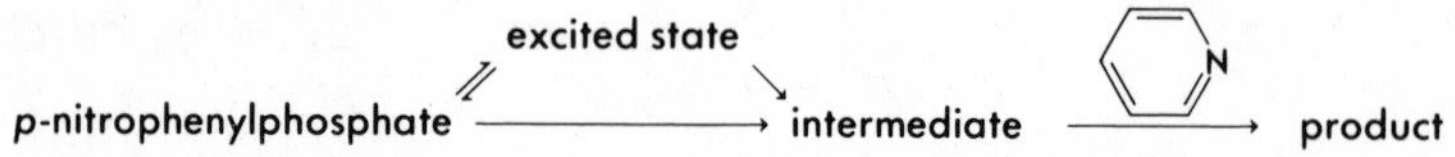

Figure 9-1

They propose formation of a 1:1 complex between 1,3,5-trinitrobenzene and hydroxide ion, followed by photo initiated dissociation.

An interesting extension of photochemical displacement reactions has been utilized by Bowie and Musgrave[31] to prepare boron-halide-substituted benzenes. Photolysis of benzene solutions of boron tribromide and boron triiodide gives good yields of phenyl boron dibromide and phenyl boron diiodide, respectively, eq. (27). Bowie and Musgrave propose that a charge

(27)

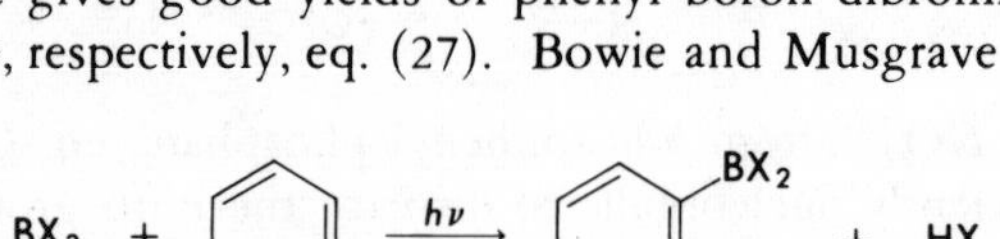

transfer complex forms between the boron halide and benzene and that photoactivation of the complex gives the phenyl boron dihalide and a hydrogen halide.

Johnson and Rees[32] have reported photochemical displacement reactions in heterocyclic systems. They found that photolysis of 4-nitropyridine-1-oxide with piperidine and ethanol gives 4-piperidinopyridine-1-oxide and piperidinium nitrate, eq. (28). Johnson and Rees propose that from the excited pyridine *n*-oxide, nitrite ion is displaced by piperidine.

(28)

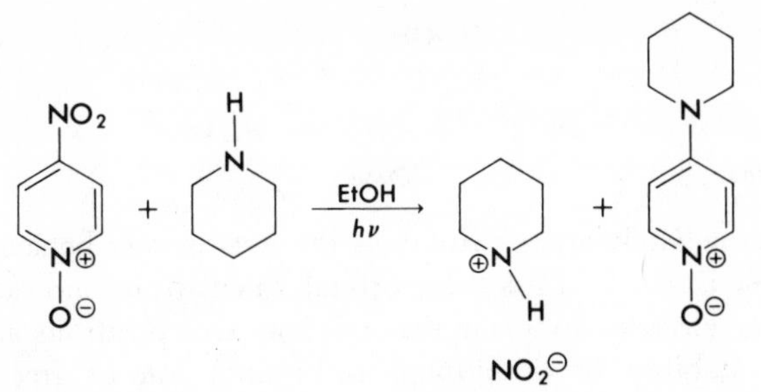

Zimmerman and co-workers[27,33] have observed that certain benzyl acetates and trityl ethers are readily solvolyzed in aqueous media. The products are the corresponding alcohols. For example, photolysis of p-methoxybenzyl acetate in aqueous dioxane gives, among other things, p,p' dimethoxy-bibenzyl and bidioxane, eqs. (29) and (30). The cleavage of p-methoxy-benzyl acetate to p-methoxybenzyl radicals and acetoxy radicals probably is the first chemical step of the reaction.

(29)

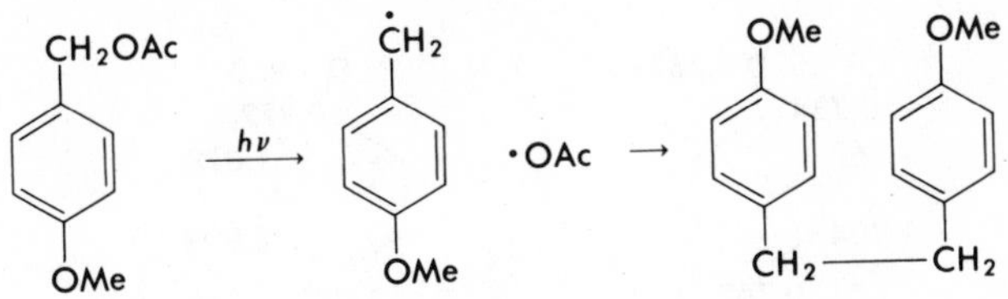

(30)

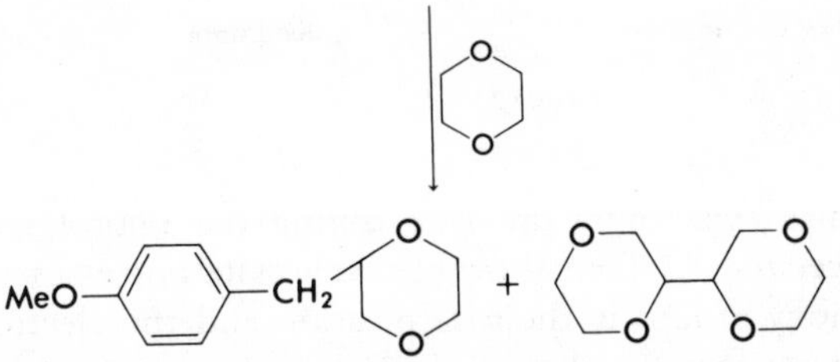

With 3-methoxybenzyl acetate, however, a significant quantity of 3-methoxybenzyl alcohol is found among the reaction products, the expected free radical coupling products being decreased in relative amounts. Zimmer-man and co-workers propose carbonium ion formation in the photolyses of the *meta* ester, eqs. (31) and (32).

(31)

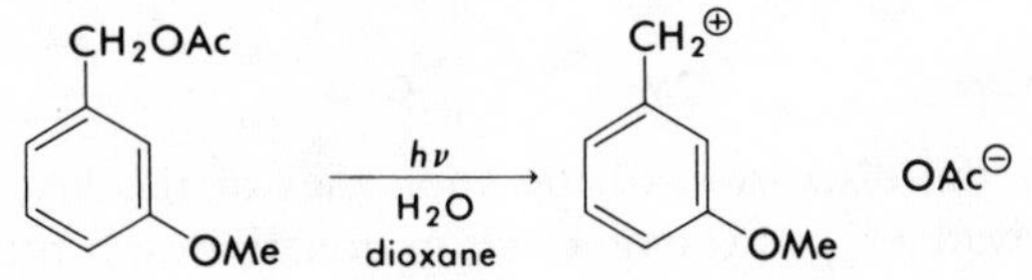

(32)

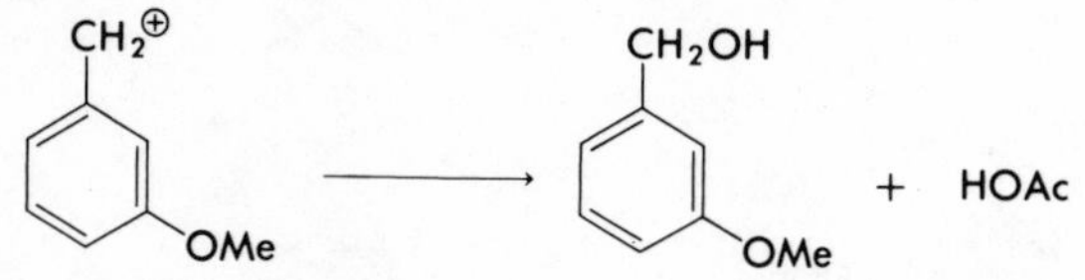

$$\underset{\text{OMe}}{\overset{\text{CH}_2^{\oplus}}{\bigcirc}} \longrightarrow \underset{\text{OMe}}{\overset{\text{CH}_2\text{OH}}{\bigcirc}} \quad + \quad \text{HOAc}$$

The question immediately arises, why does the *meta* isomer behave differently than the *para* isomer? Molecular orbital calculations indicate that, in the ground states, electron donors in the *ortho* and *para* positions are more important to the stability of developing carbonium ion or free radical benzylic carbons, whereas in the first excited π-π^* state, these same electron donors are most effective when located in the *ortho* and *meta* position. The electron-donating methoxy substituent seems most effectively to donate an electron pair from its oxygen atom when located in the *para* position for ordinary carbonium ion or free radical reactions, but its behavior is reversed in the first excited state. Figure 9-2 shows the calculated LCAO M.O. electron densities for cases where electron donors are on benzene for the ground state and the first excited state.

D 1.762
0.734
1.167
1.204
0.762
first excited state

D 1.953
0.972
1.028
0.999
1.021
ground state

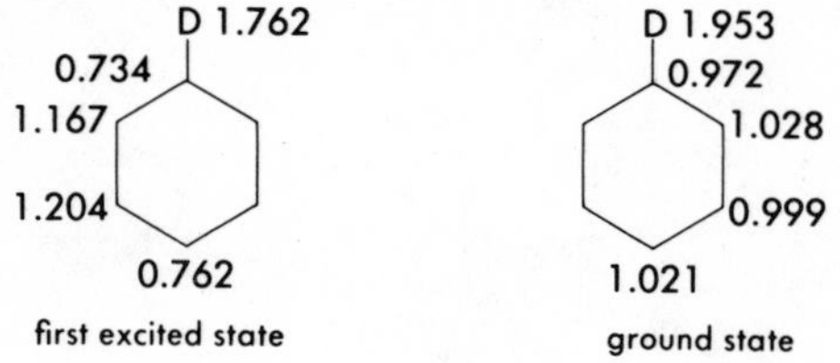

Figure 9-2

The point becomes even more dramatic during the photolysis of 3,5-dimethoxybenzyl acetate. 3,5-Dimethoxybenzyl acetate possesses two electron-donating methoxy groups in the *meta* position and the electron donation by these methoxy groups should reach the maximum attainable in benzene systems. The observation that the solvolysis product is the only reaction product indicates that this is indeed the case eq. (33).

(33)

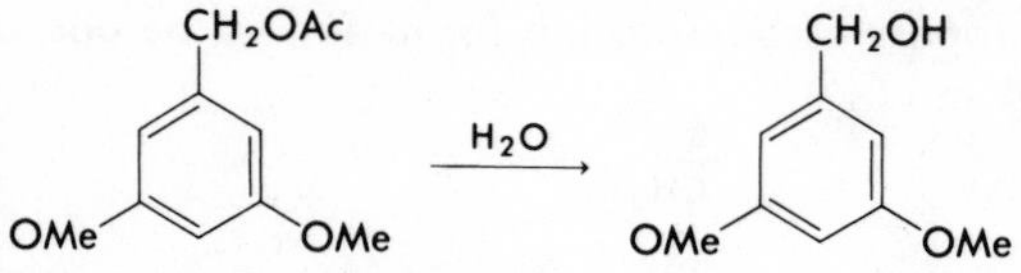

$$\underset{\text{OMe}\quad\quad\text{OMe}}{\overset{\text{CH}_2\text{OAc}}{\bigcirc}} \xrightarrow{\text{H}_2\text{O}} \underset{\text{OMe}\quad\quad\text{OMe}}{\overset{\text{CH}_2\text{OH}}{\bigcirc}}$$

A helpful model for the discussion of the anomalies of the first excited states of benzene derivatives possessing electron-donating substituents is shown for anisole in Figure 9-3. Facilitation of carbonium ion formation

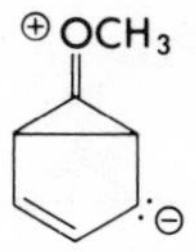

Figure 9-3

at the *meta* position results from the added electron pair at that position, eq. (34).

(34)

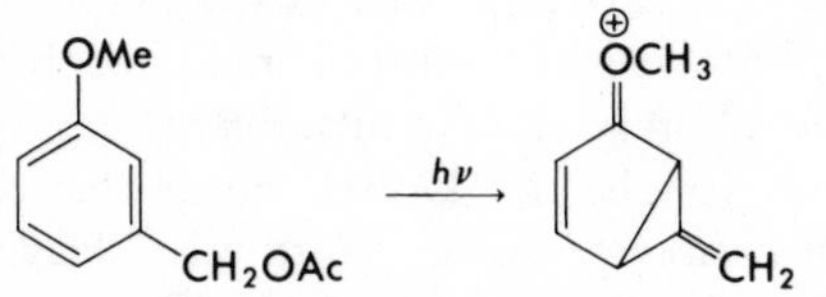

The substituted benzyl acetate with the substituent at the *para* position clearly does not have the proper charge distribution for expulsion of an acetate anion, eq. (35).

(35)

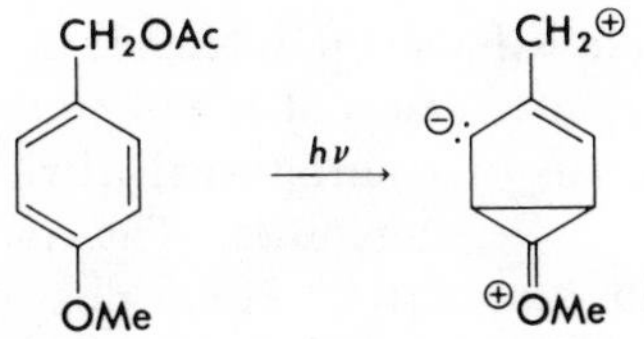

A correlative observation is that, relatively speaking, the yield of radical products goes down as the yield of ionic products goes up. Thus, as the solvolytic enhancement is increased by the methoxy groups, the stabilization of the benzylic radical is essentially unaffected.

Calculations for aromatic nuclei possessing electron-withdrawing substituents indicate that, relative to the ground state, the positions *ortho* and *meta* to the electron-withdrawing groups are electron depleted. The actual calculations for aromatic nuclei possessing electron-withdrawing groups are shown in Figure 9-4. A useful valence bond model can be illustrated by nitrobenzene, as shown in Figure 9-5.

Several observations support the postulate that the electron-withdrawing group in the *para* position selectively activates the number 1 carbon of

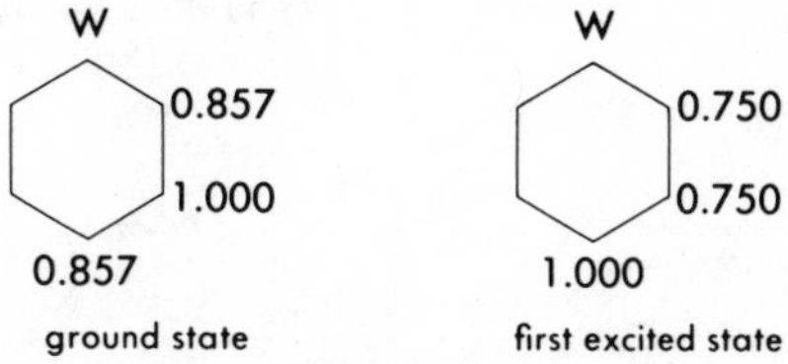

Figure 9-4

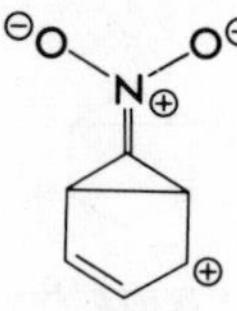

Figure 9-5

the benzene system in the first excited state. *meta* Nitrophenol is formed in isolable quantities from the photolysis of *m*-nitrophenyl phosphate, while no phenol is isolated from the photolysis of *p*-nitrophenyl phosphate in aqueous media.[25,28] Havinga, de Jongh, and Dorst[25] noted that the *ortho*-nitro phosphate ester undergoes an even slower hydrolysis. Havinga and co-workers[34,35] as well as Colpa, MacLean, and Mackor[36] have reported deuterium incorporation studies in photochemical reactions which also suggest that electron donators direct substitution to the *meta* position in excited state processes.

Zimmerman and Somasekhara[27] also noted a sharp difference in behavior between the ground state and the first excited states of *m* and *p*-nitrophenyl trityl ethers. Thus, in the dark, solvolysis of *p*-nitrophenyl trityl ether in aqueous dioxane is rapid; for example, $t_{1/2} = 30$ minutes. The corresponding *m*-nitrophenyl trityl ether is virtually unreactive. Upon photolysis, *m*-nitrophenyl trityl ether rapidly gives *m*-nitrophenol and triphenylmethyl carbinol, while the *para* isomer is virtually unreactive. These results are shown in eqs. (36–39).

(36) O_2N —⟨ ⟩— O—$\overset{\overset{C_6H_5}{|}}{\underset{\underset{C_6H_5}{|}}{C}}$—$C_6H_5$ $\xrightarrow[\text{H}_2\text{O-dioxane}]{h\nu}$ no reaction

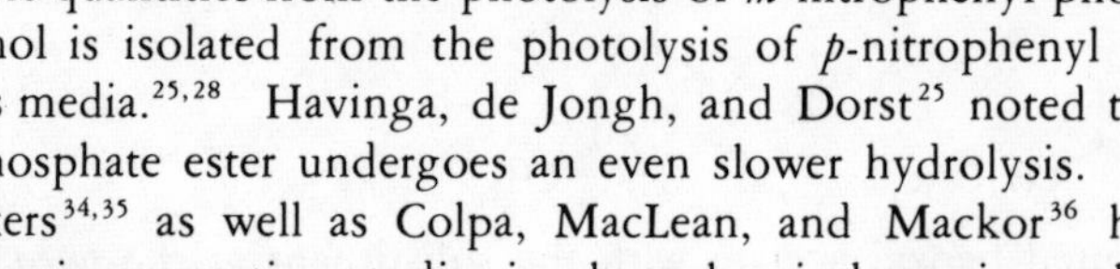

(37) O_2N —⟨ ⟩— O—$\overset{\overset{C_6H_5}{|}}{\underset{\underset{C_6H_5}{|}}{C}}$—$C_6H_5$ $\xrightarrow[\text{H}_2\text{O-dioxane}]{\text{dark}}$

O_2N —⟨ ⟩— OH + $(C_6H_5)_3COH$

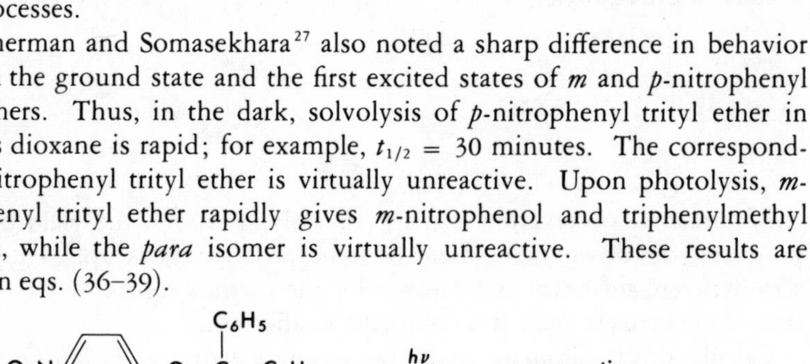

while

(38) $\overset{NO_2}{\underset{}{⟨\ ⟩}}$—$O$—$\overset{\overset{C_6H_5}{|}}{\underset{\underset{C_6H_5}{|}}{C}}$—$C_6H_5$ $\xrightarrow[\text{H}_2\text{O-dioxane}]{h\nu}$ $\overset{NO_2}{\underset{}{⟨\ ⟩}}$—$OH$ + $(C_6H_5)_3COH$

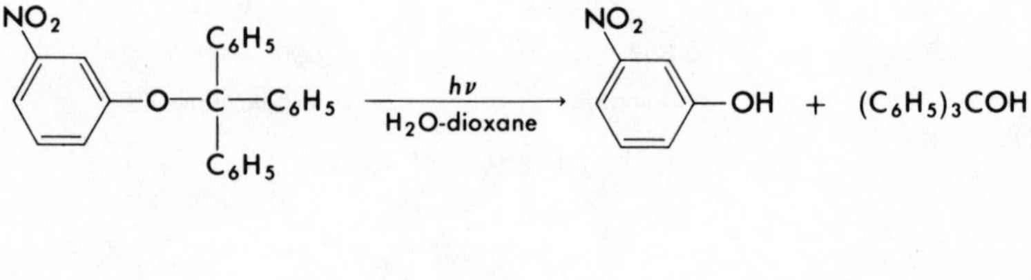

(39) 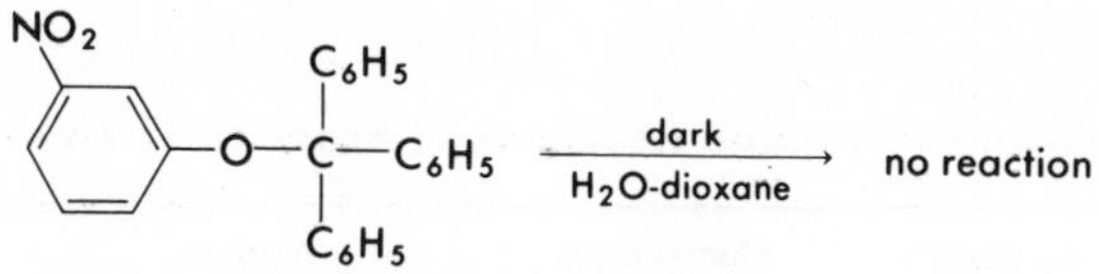
NO2
C6H5
O
C
C6H5
C6H5
dark
H2O-dioxane
no reaction

Mechanistically these results can be demonstrated by means of the valence bond pictures described earlier, as given in eqs. (40) and (41).

(40) 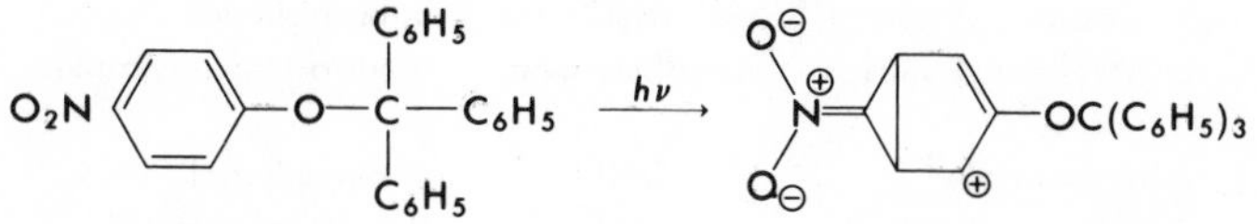
O2N
O
C
C6H5
C6H5
C6H5
hν
OC(C6H5)3

(41) 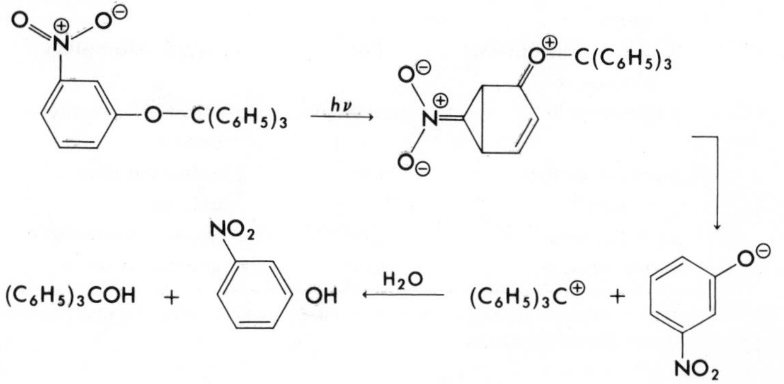
O—C(C6H5)3
hν
C(C6H5)3
(C6H5)3COH
+
NO2
OH
H2O
(C6H5)3C⊕
+
NO2

Photochemical substitution reactions of aromatic derivatives are remarkably clean reactions and appear to proceed with rather high quantum yield. A number of nucleophiles have been observed to participate in these light-accelerated processes. In Table 9-2 we list general examples of photochemical nucleophilic aromatic substitution reactions.

An interesting extension of photochemical solvolysis reactions could be made to allyl and vinyl systems containing appropriately positioned substituents. Molecular orbital approaches to excited state chemistry may provide an interesting and useful means for prediction of photochemical reaction sequences.

The postulate of carbonium ion intermediates in photochemical solvolysis reactions is at first glance rather unusual. However, bond heterolysis is probably not the primary dissociation step in these reactions. Substituted urethanes have also been observed to give carbonium ion products in photochemical processes.[40]

Table 9-2

Photochemical Substitution Reactions of Aromatic Derivatives

Aromatic Derivative	Nucleophile	Product	Φ
m-nitrophenyl phos- phate[a 25,35]	H_2O	m-nitrophenol	—
o-, or p-nitrophenyl phosphate[a 25,35]	H_2O	o-, or p-nitrophenol	—[a]
m-nitrophenyl sulfate[25]	H_2O	m-nitrophenol	—
m-nitrophenyl phos- phate[35]	methylamine	m-nitro-N-methylaniline	—
m-nitroanisole[35]	$OH^{\ominus}$	m-nitrophenol	0.225
3,5-dinitroanisole[35]	$OH^{\ominus}$	3,5-dinitrophenol	0.45
m-nitrophenyl phos- phate[35]	$OH^{\ominus}$	m-nitrophenol	0.065
3-nitro-5-chlorophenyl phosphate[35]	$OH^{\ominus}$	3-nitro-5-chlorophenol	0.175
p-nitroanisole[37]	dimethylamine	p-nitro-N,N-dimethyl- aniline	—
2-bromo-4-nitro- anisole[38]	$OH^{\ominus}$	2-hydroxy-4-nitro- anisole	—
p-nitroanisole[39]	$CN^{\ominus}$	2-cyano-4-nitroanisole	—
m-nitroanisole[39]	$CN^{\ominus}$	m-nitrobenzonitrile	—

[a]These reactions appear to be photoinduced hydrolyses of the phosphate esters rather than aromatic substitutions.

References

1. Eibner, A., *Chem. Ber.*, **36**, 1229 (1903).
2. Srpek, O., *Monatsh. Chem.*, **11**, 429 (1890).
3. Olivier, S. C., *Rec. trav. chim.*, **45**, 296 (1926).
4. Asinger, F., *Monatsh. Chem.*, **64**, 153 (1934).
5. Asinger, F., *J. prakt. Chem.*, **152**, 5 (1939).
6. Goerner, G. L., and R. C. Nametz, *J. Am. Chem. Soc.*, **73**, 2940 (1951).
7. Voegtli, W., H. Muhr, and P. Länger, *Helv. Chim. Acta*, **37**, 1627 (1954).
8. Milligan, B., private communication.
9. Miller, B., and C. Walling, *J. Am. Chem. Soc.*, **79**, 4187 (1957).
10. Willgerodt, C., *J. prakt. Chem.*, **2**, 33 (1886).
11. *Ibid.*, 154 (1886).
12. Milligan, B., R. L. Bradow, J. E. Rose, H. E. Hubbert, and A. Roe, *J. Am. Chem. Soc.*, **84**, 158 (1962).
13. Andrews, L. J., and R. M. Keefer, *J. Am. Chem. Soc.*, **80**, 1723 (1958).
14. Keefer, R. M., and L. J. Andrews, *J. Am. Chem. Soc.*, **80**, 5350 (1958).
15. Otto, R., *Ann. Chem.*, **141**, 93 (1867).
16. Otto, R., *J. prakt. Chem.*, (2), **30**, 179 (1884).

17. Noyes, R. M., *J. Am. Chem. Soc.*, **70**, 2614 (1948).
18. Noyes, R. M., and D. J. Sibbett, *J. Am. Chem. Soc.*, **75**, 767 (1953).
19. Bacon, R. C. R., and H. A. O. Hill, *J. Chem. Soc.*, 1097 (1964).
20. Kunitake, T., and C. Price, *J. Am. Chem. Soc.*, **85**, 761 (1963).
21. Süs, O., K. Möller, and H. Heiss, *Ann. Chem.*, **598**, 123 (1956).
22. Wang, C., *Proc. Chem. Soc.*, 309 (1961).
23. Stille, J. K., P. Cassidy, and L. Plummer, *J. Am. Chem. Soc.*, **85**, 1318 (1963).
24. Anderson, J. C., and C. B. Reese, *Tetrahedron Letters*, 1 (1962).
25. Havinga, E. O., R. O. de Jongh, and W. Dorst, *Rec. trav. chim.*, **75**, 378 (1956).
26. Havinga, E. O., *Chimia*, **16**, 145 (1962).
27. Zimmerman, H. E., and S. Somasekhara, *J. Am. Chem. Soc.*, **85**, 922 (1963).
28. Letsinger, R. L., and O. B. Ramsey, *J. Am. Chem. Soc.*, **86**, 1447 (1964).
29. Letsinger, R. L., O. B. Ramsey, and J. H. McCain, *J. Am. Chem. Soc.*, **87**, 2945 (1965).
30. Gold, V., and C. H. Rochester, *J. Chem. Soc.*, 1687 (1964).
31. Bowie, R. A., and O. C. Musgrave, *Proc. Chem. Soc.*, 15 (1964).
32. Johnson, R. M., and C. W. Rees, *Proc. Chem. Soc.*, 213 (1964).
33. Zimmerman, H. E., and V. E. Sandel, *J. Am. Chem. Soc.*, **85**, 915 (1963).
34. de Bie, D. A., and E. O. Havinga, *Tetrahedron*, **21**, 2359 (1965).
35. Havinga, E. O., and R. O. de Jongh, *Bull. Soc. Chim. Belg.*, **71**, 803 (1962).
36. Colpa, J. P., C. MacLean, and E. L. Mackor, *Tetrahedron*, **19**, Suppl. 2, 65 (1963).
37. Kronenberg, M. E., A. Van der Heyden, and E. O. Havinga, *Rec. trav. chim.*, **85**, 56 (1966).
38. Nijhoff, D. F., and E. O. Havinga, *Tetrahedron Letters*, 4199 (1965).
39. Letsinger, R. L., and J. H. McCain, *J. Am. Chem. Soc.*, **88**, 2884 (1966).
40. Barltrop, J. A., and P. Schofield, *J. Chem. Soc.*, 4758 (1965).

CHAPTER

10

Chain Reactions

Photochemical chain reactions can be defined as those chemical reactions initiated by photoillumination that lead to a change in more than one molecule per single quantum of absorbed radiation. Photochemical chain reactions must, for the great majority of cases, have quantum yields greater than unity.

Historically, photochemical chain reactions have been of great significance. Every neophyte organic chemist now recognizes that certain chemical reactions proceed differently in the light than in the dark and that commercial preparations of a variety of compounds, particularly those containing substituent halogen atoms, involve photo processes. Among the more important examples are the photo-initiated polymerization of styrene and other monomers and Kharasch, anti-Markownikoff addition reactions of hydrogen halides to olefins. Benzylic bromination and chlorination of aromatic hydrocarbon derivatives and photochemical decompositions of a variety of free radical initiators are also photochemical chain sequences. This chapter will be concerned with these as well as other photochemical chain reactions.

General Chain Reaction Theory

Free radical chain reactions involve, in the simplest sense, three sequential reaction steps. Initiation steps start the chain sequence by generating free radicals in the system. Propagation steps keep the sequence going by not removing free radicals from the system while at the same time yielding chemical products, and termination reactions remove free radicals from the system, generally producing reaction products.[1]

Many typical examples of photochemically initiated chain reactions can be found among the chemical reactions of the alkyl halides, the hydrogen halides, the halogens, and the interhalogens. In general, the reactions of the halogens and their derivatives involve a chain sequence like that shown in eqs. (1–8).

Initiation:

(1) $X—Y \xrightarrow{h\nu} X\cdot + Y\cdot$

     X = halogen, Y = halogen, hydrogen, or alkyl group

Propagation:

(2) $X + S{=}S \longrightarrow \cdot S_2X$

                       or

(3) $X\cdot + SH \longrightarrow S\cdot + HX$

(4) $S\cdot + XY \longrightarrow SX + Y\cdot$

(5) $\cdot S_2X + XY \longrightarrow XS_2X + Y\cdot$

Termination:

(6) $2X\cdot \longrightarrow$ product

(7) $2Y\cdot \longrightarrow$ product

(8) $S\cdot$ or $\cdot S_2X + X\cdot$ or $Y\cdot \longrightarrow$ product

In sequence (1–8), initiation of the chain results when the halogen derivative is photolytically decomposed. Propagation of the chain may result either from addition of the halogen atom to an olefin, eq. (2), or by abstraction of a hydrogen atom by the chain-carrying halogen atom, eq. (3). Products result when either the addition product or the abstraction product attacks the molecular halogen or the halogen derivative, eqs. (4–5). The chain is terminated by bimolecular radical coupling or disproportionation reactions, eqs. (6–8).

With the halogens and many halogen compounds, absorption of a light quantum results in an excitation of the nonbonded p electrons of the halogen to an antibonding σ^* excited energy level. As a general rule, the σ^* levels are unstable, and immediate decomposition of the molecule into free radicals results. We can visualize this absorption as in Figure 10-1.

It is well known that the molecular halogens are highly colored molecules. Chlorine and fluorine are greenish-yellow, bromine is red, and iodine

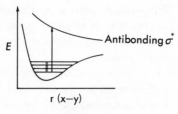

Figure 10-1

brown. Absorption of electromagnetic energy occurs readily in the visible region, and visible absorption is generally sufficient to cause molecular dissociation. Chlorine forms the strongest of the halogen-halogen bonds, and only 58 kcal are required to dissociate 1 mole of chlorine to chlorine atoms. With the other halogens, even less energy is sufficient to cause dissociation. The interhalogens, Br-I, Br-Cl, I-Cl, and F-Cl, easily dissociate from absorption of visible radiation.

With the hydrogen halides, the dissociation process is markedly more difficult. The bond between hydrogen and iodine is the weakest among the hydrogen halides, and even its dissociation requires absorption of radiation of less than 4000 Å in wavelength. Hydrogen fluoride, the strongest of the hydrogen halides, requires absorption of 2100 Å radiation.

The strength of the bond between carbon and halogen depends on the alkyl substituent and the number and type of substituent halogen atoms. Generally, the bond strength decreases in the order D for R—X, X = F > X = Cl > X = Br > X = I. As a result, photodecompositions of alkyl iodides are far more facile than similar decompositions of fluorides, bromides, and chlorides. This same general trend is observed for the tri- and tetrahalogenated methanes so that photochemical chain reactions involving decomposition of iodoform and tetraiodomethane as initiators occur, at least in principle, most readily. The unique spectral properties of alkyl iodides accord to them a rather special place among the halogen derivatives of alkanes.[2] Table 10-1 lists some examples of bond dissociation energies for the hydrogen halides, alkyl halides, and halogens.

Calculation, from these bond dissociation energies, of the necessary absorptions for dissociation is often feasible. The halogens show continuous absorption, even well beyond their observed maxima. Therefore in concentrated enough solution, absorption will be observed at almost any wavelength. The fact remains, however, that absorbed radiation must be sufficiently energetic so as to provide the molecule with an energy equal to the bond dissociation energy.

Photochemical studies of hydrogen halides, alkyl halides, and halogens have been most thorough. Many of these studies have been performed in the gas phase; however, some practical application of photolysis reactions involving the halogens and their derivatives have been liquid phase reactions.

Table 10-1[a]

Selected Bond Dissociation Energies

Bond	D, kcal/mole	Bond	D, kcal/mole
H—OH	120	Cl—Cl	58.0
H—Cl	103.2	Cl—I	50.0
H—Br	87.4	Br—I	42.0
H—I	71.4	Br—Br	46.1
HO—Cl	60.0	I—I	36.1
HO—I	56.0	CH_3—Cl	80.6
HO—Br	56.0	CH_3—Br	67.2
F—F	37.0	CH_3—I	52.6
F—Cl	60.5	t-Bu—I	46.0
$C_6H_5CH_2$—Cl	68.0	$C_6H_5CH_2$—Br	50.5
$C_6H_5CH_2$—I	39.0	C_6H_5—I	57.0
C_6H_5—Cl	85.6	C_6H_5—Br	71.0
CH_2=CH—Cl	104.0		

[a]Data from C. Walling, *Free Radicals in Solution*, Wiley, New York, 1957.
(See J. A. Kerr, *Chem. Rev.*, **66**, 465 (1966) for more recent data.)

Alkyl Halides

In the gas phase, photolysis of the alkyl iodides leads to exclusive and immediate dissociation, eq. (9). There is a great deal of evidence supporting

$$(9) \qquad R—X \xrightarrow{h\nu} R\cdot \ + \ X\cdot$$

the immediate dissociation postulate. First, products can be isolated that indicate the presence of halogen atoms and alkyl free radicals. Second, using flash techniques (Chapter 3), one can observe the absorption spectrum of alkyl free radicals and, in the presence of trapping agents such as oxygen, obtain halooxide radicals.

Free radical reactions involving the halogens, haloalkanes, polyhalo-alkanes, and hydrogen halides have been reviewed by a variety of authors.[1-5] The principal products of the decomposition of methyl iodide in the gas phase are ethane, iodine, methane, diiodomethane, and 1,2-diiodoethane.[6] These products can be accounted for by the chain reaction, eqs. (10–13).

$$(10) \qquad CH_3I \xrightarrow{h\nu} \cdot CH_3^* \ + \ I\cdot$$

$$(11) \qquad \cdot CH_3^* \ + \ CH_3I \longrightarrow CH_4 \ + \ \cdot CH_2I$$

(12) $\qquad$ $2 \cdot CH_2I \longrightarrow ICH_2CH_2I$

$\qquad\qquad\qquad$ $2I \cdot \longrightarrow I_2$

(13) $\qquad$ $2 \cdot CH_3 \longrightarrow C_2H_6$

Step (11) has an appreciable activation energy. Since step (11) is somewhat unfavorable energetically, the reaction of methyl radicals with methyl iodide requires a special methyl radical called a *hot* methyl radical.[7] Hot methyl radicals result if in the absorption process the methyl iodide receives a quantity of energy far greater than the amount necessary for dissociation of the carbon-iodine bond. Oxygen and nitric oxide are well-known free radical scavengers or trapping agents and react vigorously with most ordinary free radicals. Experimental evidence for hot radical intermediates is provided by the observation that the yields of methane and diiodoethane are essentially independent of temperature, and that the addition of small amounts of oxygen or iodine (another radical scavenger) to the reaction fails to change the quantum yield for methane formation.[8-10] A further observation, however, is that pressures of inert gases such as argon or carbon dioxide cause a decrease in the quantum yield of methane produced because of collisional deactivation of the hot methyl radicals. Gas phase decomposition reactions of higher alkyl iodides have been studied on several occasions,[11,12] but they have not received the attention of methyl iodide. Some workers have postulated that *hot* ethyl radicals result from the photolysis of ethyl iodide.[13]

Practically speaking, photochemical chain reactions of alkyl halides are not of great importance except among the polyhaloalkanes. However, photodecomposition is the preferred method of chain reaction initiation for bromotrichloromethane and iodotrifluoromethane. Photochemical addition reactions and hydrogen abstraction reactions with chloroform and carbon tetrachloride have been reported. Photolysis of methylene iodide gives iodine and methylene as the major dissociation products, eq. (14).[14]

(14) $\qquad$ $CH_2I_2 \xrightarrow{h\nu} :CH_2 + I_2$

Recently, DuPont experimenters have trapped carbenoid products from photolysis of methylene iodide in the presence of an olefin.[15]

Dibromodifluoromethane, difluorobromomethane, and trifluorobromomethane as well as others decompose not to give difluorocarbene but instead to give the carbon monohalides, $\cdot \dot{C}F$ or $\cdot \dot{C}Br$.[16,17] No evidence has been found for the hydrocarbon analog of $\cdot \dot{C}F$, $\cdot \dot{C}Cl$, and $\cdot \dot{C}Br$, $\cdot \dot{C}H$. In view of the recent results of Bayes and co-workers (Chapter 5) who found that apparent carbon atoms result from the photolysis of carbon suboxide, such a species is not unlikely.

Polyhaloalkanes

In solution the most important photochemical processes of the poly-halomethanes involve the tri- and tetrahalogenated methanes. Photochemical production of trichloromethyl radicals and bromine atoms from bromotrichloromethane is a well-documented process. The chain process resulting from photochemical decomposition of other polyhalomethanes may involve addition of the polyhalomethyl radical to an unsaturated linkage or hydrogen atom abstraction by the polyhaloalkyl radical from benzylic, allylic, or even unactivated positions. Table 10-2 lists some representative examples of photochemical reactions of polyhalomethanes.

Of these chain reactions of polyhalomethanes, those reactions involving the trichloromethyl radical have been studied extensively. Huyser and co-workers have shown that the abstraction of a hydrogen atom by a trichloromethyl radical proceeds through a transition state resembling (I). Electron-

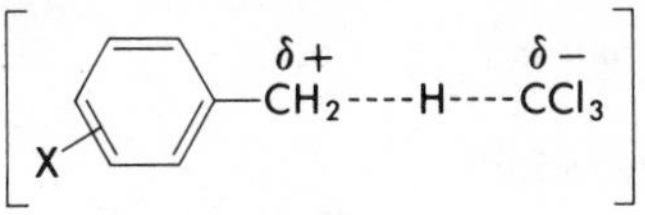

$$\left[\underset{X}{\bigcirc} \overset{\delta+}{-CH_2} ---- H ---- \overset{\delta-}{CCl_3} \right]$$

I

donating substituents on the aryl portion of an aryl hydrocarbon, such as toluene, stabilize the transition state. Quantitative substituent effect correlation is with the Hammett σ^+ substituent constants. Martin and Gleicher

Table 10-2

Addition Reactions of Polyhalomethanes to Olefins

Substrate	Polyhalo-methane	Product
3,3-diethoxy-1-propene[18]	CCl_4	$CCl_3CH_2CHClCH(OEt)_2$
propylene[19]	$CBrCl_3$	$CH_3CHBrCH_2CCl_3$
2-butene[20]	$CBrCl_3$	$CH_3CHBrCH(CCl_3)CH_3$
2-methyl-2-butene[21]	$CBrCl_3$	$CH_3CH(CCl_3)CBr(CH_3)_2$
cyclohexene[21-23]	$CBrCl_3$	1-bromo-2-trichloromethyl-cyclohexane
1-phenyl-1-propene[21]	$CBrCl_3$	$C_6H_5CHBrCH(CCl_3)CH_3$
1-methylstyrene[24]	$CBrCl_3$	$C_6H_5C(CH_3)BrCH_2CCl_3$
3-phenyl-1-propene[21]	$CBrCl_3$	$C_6H_5CH_2CHBrCH_2CCl_3$
1,1-difluoro-1-propene[25]	$CBrCl_3$	$CF_2BrCH(CH_3)CCl_3$
dimethylmaleate[26]	$CBrCl_3$	2-bromo-3-trichloromethyl dimethylmaleate
allyl cyanide[21]	$CBrCl_3$	$CCl_3CH_2CHBrCH_2CN$

Table 10-2 (cont.)

Substrate	Polyhalo-methane	Product
ethylene[27]	CF_3I	$CF_3CH_2CH_2I$
methylacetylene[28,29]	CF_3I	$CF_3CH=CICH_3$
acrylonitrile[30]	CF_3I	CF_3CH_2CHICN
methyl acrylate[31]	CF_3I	3,3,3-trifluoromethyl-2-iodo-methyl acrylate
1,1,1-trifluoro-2-propene[32]	CCl_3I	$CCl_3CH_2CHICF_3$
1,1,1-trifluoromethyl-acetylene[32]	CCl_3I	$CCl_3CH=CICF_3$
ethylene[33]	CBr_4	$CBr_3CH_2CH_2Br$
ethylene[34]	$CF_2=CFI$	$CF_2=CCICH_2CH_2I$
ethylene[33]	$CF_2=CCII$	$CF_2=CCICH_2CH_2I$
ethylene[33]	CF_2ClCH_2I	$CF_2ClCH_2CH_2CH_2I$
2-cyclopropylpropene[36]	$CBrCl_3$	$CCl_3CH_2C(CH_3)=CH-CH_2CH_2Br$
5-methylenebicyclo[2.2.1]-hep-2-ene[37]	$CBrCl_3$	several

Typical Photochemical Substitution Reactions of Polyhaloalkanes

$Y-C_6H_5CH_3$[35]	$CBrCl_3$	$Y-C_6H_5CH_2Br$
$C_6H_5CH_3$[38]	CCl_3CCl_3	$C_6H_5CH_2Cl$

have shown[39,40] that similar substituent effects are important in addition reactions of trichloromethyl radicals to 3-phenyl-1-propenes and 4-phenyl-1-butenes. They propose that complexation between the trichloromethyl radical and the phenyl substituent is important to transition state stabilization, formula (II).

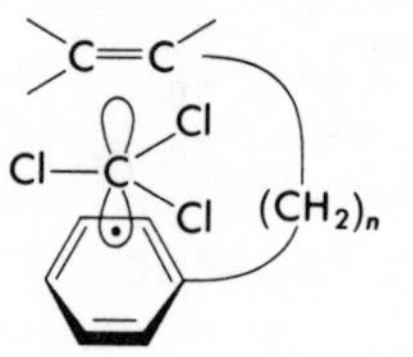

II

Huyser[41] has investigated the tendency of the photo-prepared trichloromethyl radical to abstract hydrogen atoms from the allylic position of olefins and compared this tendency with that of the trichloromethyl group to add to the olefinic double bond. He has found that addition of the trichloromethyl radical is generally the preferred reaction pathway, but with some olefins, such as cyclohexene, hydrogen abstraction may become a competitive process.

Hydrogen Halides

Photochemical reactions involving the hydrogen halides were also recently reviewed.[4] The chain sequence, originally proposed by Kharasch and co-workers,[42] and reviewed thoroughly by Mayo and Walling in the early days of free radical chemistry,[43] involves steps (15–18):

$$(15) \qquad H - X \xrightarrow{h\nu} H\cdot + X\cdot$$

$$(16) \qquad X\cdot + RCH{=}CH_2 \longrightarrow R\dot{C}HCH_2X$$

$$(17) \qquad R\dot{C}HCH_2X + HX \longrightarrow RCH_2CH_2X + X\cdot$$

$$(18) \qquad \text{2 radicals} \longrightarrow \text{nonradical products}$$

Synthetically, the reactions of hydrogen halides with olefins are restricted mainly to hydrogen bromide although Mayo has recently discussed some examples of hydrogen chloride additions.[44]

Hydrogen iodide is proposed to react photochemically according to sequence (19–21).[45,46] Earlier workers have shown the reaction chain length to be short.

$$(19) \qquad HI \xrightarrow{h\nu} H\cdot + I\cdot$$

$$(20) \qquad H\cdot + HI \longrightarrow H_2 + I\cdot$$

$$(21) \qquad 2I\cdot \longrightarrow I_2$$

Hydrogen bromide decomposes differently in the gas phase, but the ultimate reaction products still appear to result from bromine atom intermediates. The addition of bromine atoms produced by the photochemical decomposition of hydrogen bromide to olefins has been shown to be stereospecific and *trans*. Goering and co-workers[47,48] have shown that addition of hydrogen bromide to 1-chloro and 1-bromocyclohexene gives *cis*-1-chloro- or 1-bromo-2-bromocyclohexane, the product of *trans* addition, eq. (22).

$$(22) \qquad \text{[structure]} \xrightarrow[h\nu]{HBr} \text{[structure]}$$

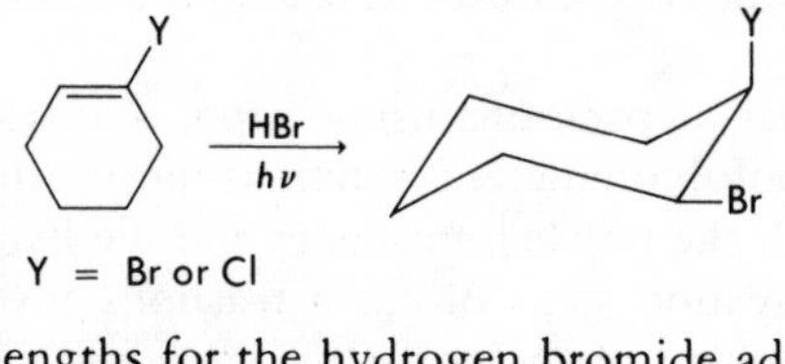

Y = Br or Cl

Chain lengths for the hydrogen bromide addition reactions to olefinic substrates are appreciable.

The possibility of bridged intermediates in bromine atom additions has been suggested by several workers.[49-51]

Thermodynamically, the addition of hydrogen fluoride to olefins is unfavorable. The strength of the hydrogen-fluorine bond (135 kcal/mole) prevents both the normal photochemical decomposition of the bond and the abstraction of hydrogen atoms by carbon radicals from hydrogen fluoride in the propagation of the chain. Addition of hydrogen chloride to olefins is possible.[44,52] However, the chain transfer of hydrogen from hydrogen chloride to carbon is an endothermic process and requires rather stringent experimental conditions. With hydrogen iodide, on the other hand, the addition of the iodine atom to the olefinic double bond is endothermic and frequently highly reversible.

Many halogen atom addition reactions are reversible. Several pieces of evidence point to this reversibility. First, traces of bromine or iodine catalyze the *cis-trans* isomerization of olefins.[53,54] Addition of a halogen atom to the olefin produces an intermediate free radical capable of free rotation about the carbon-carbon bond. Subsequent elimination of the halogen atom produces a mixture of *cis* and *trans* olefins. Second, 1,2-dibromoethylene, when treated with isotopic bromine atoms, yields 1,2-dibromoethylene containing radioactive bromine.[55] Mechanistically this result can only be explained if intermediates possessing carbon-carbon single bonds are important. Addition of a heavy bromine atom followed by elimination of light bromine atom gives a radioactive product.

Reactions of Halogens

Perhaps no single group of reactions has been as important to the development of gas phase photochemical reactions as those reactions involving the halogens and hydrogen halides. Bodenstein and co-workers have reported many studies describing the gas phase photochemical chain decomposition reactions of the molecular halogens.[56-58] For the reactions of chlorine, quantum yields as high as 10^6 have been observed. Kinetically these reactions, like other photochemical reactions, depend on the intensity of the absorbed radiation as well as the concentration of the reactants. Particularly for the chlorohydrocarbons, vapor phase chlorination reactions are often the most practical synthetic methods.

Countless examples of industrial preparations using vapor and solution phase photochlorination and photobromination reactions prove the importance of the technique. As with the polyhalomethanes and the hydrogen halides, the two important propagation steps of chain reactions involving halogen atoms produced by irradiation of molecular halogens are addition and substitution reactions. Examples of compounds prepared commercially and in laboratories by vapor and liquid phase halogenation reactions are too numerous to list. Like the reactions of the hydrogen halides, the relative utility of addition reactions involving the halogens decreases in the order chlorine = bromine > iodine.

In general, the reactivity of the halogen atoms toward either substitution or addition decreases from Cl to I. This reactivity is experimentally evident from a variety of results obtained from substitution at saturated carbon. Since, in a substitution chain reaction, the product-controlling step is a hydrogen abstraction by the halogen atom, it is expected that resonance and inductive contributions to the stability of the radical formed by the hydrogen abstraction process will influence the quantities and nature of the substitution products. In chlorine atom substitution reactions, the product makeup is least influenced by intermediate radical stability, and according to Hammond's postulate,[59] it must be concluded that the transition state for chlorine atom reactions looks only slightly like the intermediate radical. As a matter of fact, chlorine atoms are so reactive that they are often unselective in their attack on carbon-hydrogen bonds, and the nature of the carbon at which the attack occurs is unimportant. Chlorine atoms are so reactive that they give apparent addition rather than substitution products with some aromatic hydrocarbon derivatives.[60]

Halogen atom substitution reactions proceed with great facility for most hydrocarbon systems; however, the products are not only controlled by the resonance stability of the intermediate radical, but are also affected by the solvent and the temperature. Chlorine atoms, whether produced photochemically or by other methods, are extremely reactive free radical intermediates, and as such, they are significantly unselective in their attack on hydrocarbon chains. Thus cyclohexane is more reactive than toluene toward chlorine atom attack, whereas the reverse would be anticipated from the stability of the intermediate radical. This lack of selectivity may be partially controlled by solvent. In an elegant study, Russell has shown that whereas photochlorination of 2,3-dimethylbutane without solvent gives a 3.9:1 ratio of tertiary to primary chloride, in $4M$ benzene a 17:1 preference of tertiary products is observed. With carbon disulfide as solvent, the ratio of tertiary to primary chloride becomes even higher, eq. (23).[61-64] Russell proposes a

(23) Cl_2 + CH$_3$—C—C—CH$_3$ $\xrightarrow{h\nu}$

with CH$_3$ CH$_3$ groups and H H below

CH$_3$—C—C—CH$_3$ + ClCH$_2$—C—C—CH$_3$

with Cl H (3°) and H H (1°)

solvated chlorine atom intermediate. The higher the solvation of the chlorine atom, the more selective is the attack at carbon, eq. (24).

(24) 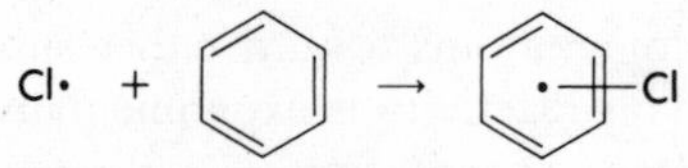   Cl· +   →

The selectivity of chlorine atom attack, although a function of solvent, is not a function of source. Therefore the ratios of tertiary to primary chloride obtained from 2,3-dimethylbutane is similar whether the source of chlorine atoms is photodecomposition of molecular chlorine or photodecomposition of sulfuryl chloride,[64] likewise a source of chlorine atoms, eq. (25).

(25) $SO_2Cl_2 \xrightarrow{h\nu} \cdot SO_2Cl + \cdot Cl$

Photobromination and photoiodination substitution reactions have been studied as well. Since both bromine atoms and iodine atoms are less reactive than their chlorine atom counterparts, attack by these reactants at carbon shows a large preference for the carbon atom giving the most highly stabilized intermediate free radical. In addition, the reaction products from iodination reactions and some bromination reactions suffer from complicating decomposition side reactions.

Hypohalite Decompositions

The hypohalites, mentioned in an earlier chapter, are excellent sources of both halogen atoms and alkoxy radicals. Like the halogens, visible radiation is sufficient to cause homolytic decomposition of both hypochlorites and hypobromites to yield alkoxy radicals and halogen atoms, eq. (26). Chain reactions result, with the alkoxy radical rather than the halogen atom being the chain-carrying species.

(26) $ROX \xrightarrow{h\nu} RO\cdot + \cdot X$

Walling and co-workers have investigated hypohalites extensively and have found that t-butyl hypochlorite and -bromite are effective radical chlorinating and brominating agents. These authors propose a chain sequence to account for the utility of hypohalites, eqs. (27–29).[65-67]

(27) $t\text{-BuOX} \xrightarrow{h\nu} t\text{-BuO}\cdot + \text{X}\cdot$

(28) $t\text{-BuO}\cdot + \text{RH} \longrightarrow t\text{-BuOH} + \text{R}\cdot$

(29) $\text{R}\cdot + t\text{-BuOX} \longrightarrow t\text{-BuO}\cdot + \text{RX}$

t-Butyl hypochlorite is effective as an allylic halogenating agent. It has the unique advantage of producing allylic radicals that are stable to rotation about the olefinic bond. Thus from *cis* or *trans* olefins, one can produce *cis* or *trans* allyl chlorides with retention of stereo-uniformity. Addition products also form, but these products account for but a small portion of the total.

Like chlorine atoms, t-butoxy radicals produced from photodecomposition of t-butyl hypochlorite are somewhat solvated[68,69] so that the ratio of t-butyl alcohol to acetone produced in the presence of a hydrogen donor such as cyclohexane varies with added solvent as well as with temperature, eqs. (30) and (31). Walling has measured the ratio k_a/k_d for photochemically pro-

(30) $. t\text{-}BuO\cdot \ + \ RH \ \xrightarrow{\ k_a\ } \ t\text{-}BuOH \ + \ R\cdot$

(31) $t\text{-}BuO\cdot \ \xrightarrow{\ k_d\ } \ CH_3\overset{\overset{\textstyle O}{\|}}{C}CH_3 \ + \ \cdot CH_3$

duced t-butoxy radicals in a variety of solvents. In addition, he has measured the relative ability of t-butoxy radicals to abstract primary and tertiary hydrogens from 2,3-dimethylbutane. His results indicate that in aromatic solvents, the t-butoxy radical is less reactive.[74] As expected, electron donors favor the reaction of t-butyl hypochlorite with substituted toluenes. Table 10-3 lists some of the observed hypohalite reactions.

In Table 10-4 the relative tendency of photochemically produced alkoxy radicals to abstract hydrogen from cyclohexane rather than decompose via loss of an alkyl radical is given. As expected, when the stability of the allkyl radical to be eliminated increases, more decomposition is observed.

Walling and Padwa[75] have reported intramolecular hydrogen abstraction reactions from the alkoxy radicals produced in the photodecomposition of long chain alkyl hypohalites. Interesting products of the radical rearrangements result. Some examples are given in Table 10-5.

The only prerequisite for intramolecular hydrogen abstraction is that the alkyl chain be three carbons or greater in length. The intramolecular abstraction reaction decreases in importance with increasing temperature.[73-75]

Miscellaneous Halogenating Agents

Sulfuryl chloride, an effective radical chlorinating agent, and the N-haloamides and imides, useful allylic halogenating agents, can also be used photochemically. The behavior of sulfuryl chloride, which was discovered by Kharasch and Brown,[76] has been discussed elsewhere.[1] A reasonable chain mechanism for chlorination of hydrocarbons using sulfuryl chloride is given in eqs. (32–35).

Table 10-3

Decompositions of Hypohalites

Hypohalite	Substrate	Major Product	Reference
t-butyl hypochlorite	toluene	benzyl chloride	65
t-butyl hypochlorite	cyclohexane	cyclohexyl chloride	65
t-butyl hypochlorite	cumene	cumyl chloride	65
t-butyl hypochlorite	2,3-dimethyl-butane	2-chloro-2,3-dimethylbutane	65
t-butyl hypochlorite	2-butene (cis)	1-chloro-2-butene (cis)	67
t-butyl hypochlorite	2-butene (trans)	1-chloro-2-butene (trans)	67
t-butyl hypochlorite	1-butene	1-chloro-2-butene	67
1,1,2-trimethylpropyl-hypochlorite	—	acetone, i-propyl-chloride	72
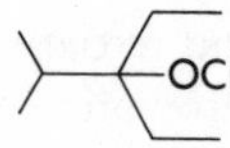 (structure: —OCl)	—	3-pentanone	72
1-i-propyl-1-cyclopentyl hypochlorite	—	1-methyl-7-chloro-3-pentanone	71
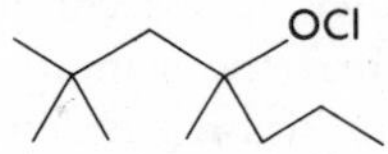 (structure: —OCl)	—	neopentyl chloride, 2-pentanone + others	72
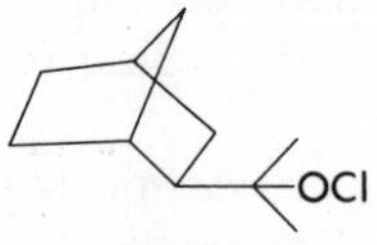 (structure: exo, —OCl)	—	exo-2-chloro-norbornane, acetone	71
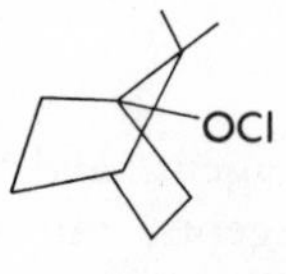 (structure: —OCl)	—	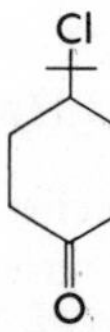 (structure: Cl-cyclohexanone)	71
L-(+)-2-methyl-3-phenyl-2-butyl hypochlorite	—	L-α-phenylethyl chloride	70

Table 10-4

The Relative Rates of Abstraction versus
Decomposition for Selected Hypochlorites[a]

Hypohalite	$Krel = k_a/k_d$[b]
t-butyl hypochlorite	0.021
2-chloro-*t*-butyl hypochlorite	0.121
2-phenyl-*t*-butyl hypochlorite	1.98
2,2-dimethyl-*t*-butyl hypochlorite	76.4
cumyl hypochlorite	0.477
2,2,2-trimethyl-*t*-butyl hypochlorite	>300

[a]Data in this table are taken from C. Walling and A. Padwa, *J. Am. Chem. Soc.*, **85**, 1593 (1963).
[b]$T = 40°$

(32) $\quad\quad SO_2Cl_2 \xrightarrow{h\nu} SO_2Cl\cdot \ + \ Cl\cdot$

(33) $\quad Cl\cdot \ + \ RH \longrightarrow R\cdot \ + \ HCl$

(34) $\quad R\cdot \ + \ SO_2Cl_2 \longrightarrow RCl \ + \ \cdot SO_2Cl$

(35) $\quad\quad SO_2Cl\cdot \longrightarrow SO_2 \ + \ Cl\cdot$

N-haloamides and imides have been discussed considerably in the recent literature.[77-82] Because several substituted N-bromosuccinimides show similar reactivities toward substituted toluenes and other hydrocarbons, Walling, Martin, and Russell have concluded simultaneously that halogenation using N-haloimides occurs via a halogen atom propagation step. This mechanism, originally proposed by Goldfinger and co-workers,[83,84] suggests that the N-haloimides simply act to provide a continual source of molecular halogen, albeit in low concentration. The photochemical decomposition of the haloimide is unimportant to the overall reaction sequence. Instead, photoly-

Table 10-5

Hypohalites Illustrating Intramolecular Hydrogen
Abstraction After Decomposition[a]

Hypohalite	Product
2-methylhexyl hypochlorite	5-chloro-2-methyl-2-hexanol
2-methylheptyl hypochlorite	5-chloro-2-methyl-2-heptanol

[a]Data in this table are taken from C. Walling and A. Padwa, *J. Am. Chem. Soc.*, **85**, 1597 (1963).

sis of the molecular halogen is the important initiation step. The Goldfinger mechanism is further supported by the observation that the succimidyl radical, a necessary intermediate in alternative mechanisms for N-bromosuccinimide bromination, is extremely difficult to prepare by normal schemes.[85] The currently favored mechanism for photochemical halogenations using the N-haloimides is shown in eqs. (36–39).

(36)

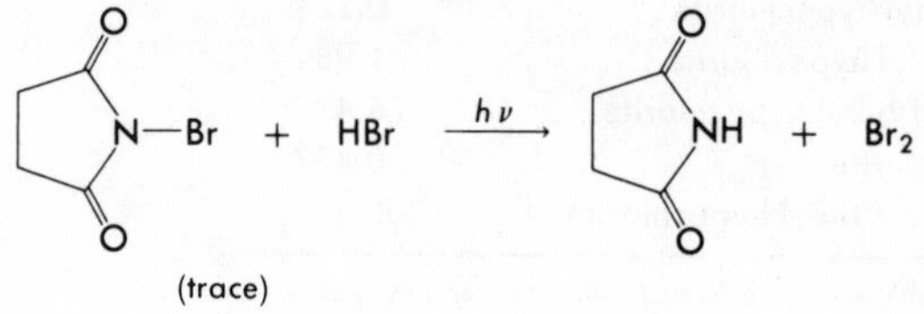

(trace)

(37) $\qquad Br_2 \xrightarrow{h\nu} 2Br\cdot$

(38) $Br\cdot + RCH_2CH=CH_2 \longrightarrow HBr + R\dot{C}HCH_2=CH_2$

(39) $R\dot{C}HCH=CH_2 + Br_2 \longrightarrow RCHCH=CH_2 + Br\cdot$
$\qquad\qquad\qquad\qquad\qquad\qquad\qquad\overset{|}{Br}$

N-chloroimides and amides do undergo photochemical decomposition reactions in which homolytic cleavage of the halogen-nitrogen bond is the rate-determining step.[86] Irradiation of N-chloro-N-acetylamides gives products indicative of homolytic nitrogen-halogen cleavage followed by intramolecular hydrogen abstraction and chlorine atom migration, eqs. (40–41).

(40)

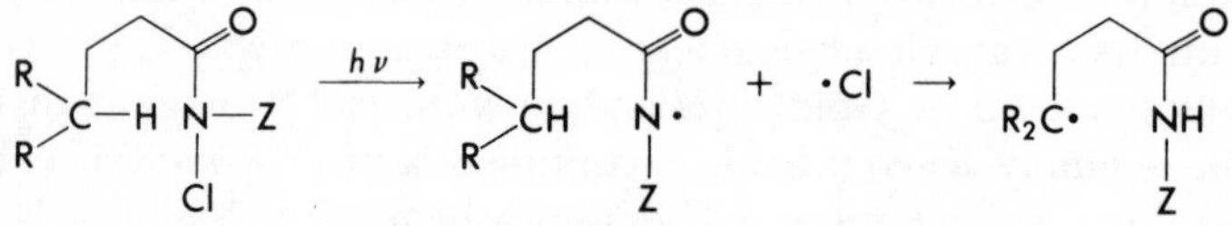

(41)

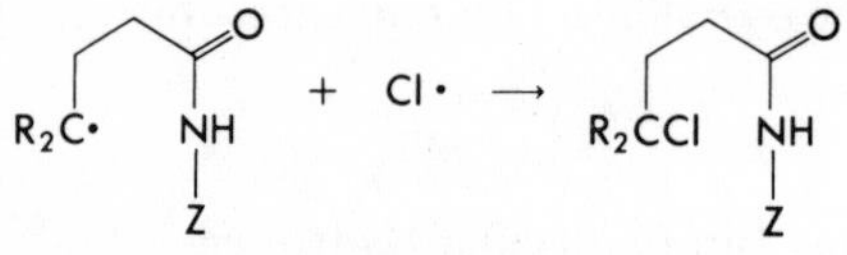

Barton and co-workers have made elegant synthetic application of haloamide decompositions in steroid series.[87]

Radicals on Sulfur

Like the halogens, thiols, disulfides and hydrogen sulfide all are known to cleave photochemically in a homolytic fashion. Harris and Stacy[88] report that the yields obtained from the photochemical additions of simple aliphatic thiols to fluoroolefins are very high. A chain mechanism can be proposed to account for the observed addition reaction, eqs. (42–44). The propagation reaction, eq. (44), occurs readily with thiols so the kinetic chain

$$(42) \qquad\qquad RSH \xrightarrow{\;h\nu\;} RS\cdot + H\cdot$$

$$(43) \qquad RS\cdot + CR_2{=}CR_2 \longrightarrow RSCR_2\dot{C}R_2$$

$$(44) \qquad RSCR_2\dot{C}R_2 + RSH \longrightarrow RSCR_2CHR_2$$

length of the sequence is probably quite long and quantum yields very high. The direction of the addition of thiyl radicals to olefins depends on the stability of the radical produced and to a lesser extent on polar and steric contributions to the transition state for adduct formation. Generally, non-Markownikoff products prevail in the thiol radical additions. Mercapto-acids[89] can be added to olefins in high yields as can dithiols.[90] A chain mechanism like (42–44) is a reasonable reaction pathway. Aromatic thiols and mercaptans also add smoothly to olefins using photochemical means to initiate the reaction sequence. Little is known about the initiation step of thiol additions. A reaction like eq. (45) is not impossible.

(45)

The reaction of hydrogen sulfide with olefins is sometimes useful in synthetic approaches to alkyl mercaptans.[91] Hydrogen sulfide shows a continuous absorption beginning at about 2800 Å. The reaction, like that of aliphatic thiols, occurs with high quantum efficiency, but often suffers from decomposition side reactions of the products.

With thiyl radicals and olefins, addition is the predominant reaction mode. Since both the addition reaction of thiyl radicals to olefins and the chain-propagating hydrogen atom transfer reaction are highly exothermic, abstraction of hydrogen by the thiyl radical is unlikely.

What we have said about mercaptans and hydrogen sulfide applies as well to the thiol acids,[3] thiolphosphoric acids,[3] and disulfides.[3,92] Schaafsma, Bickel, and Kooyman have investigated the photochemical decomposition of dimesityl disulfide in a number of organic solvents of varying viscosity. They find that the rate of photochemical decomposition is viscosity dependent, and they propose that a dynamic equilibrium exists between dissociated but solvent caged sulfide radicals and the undissociated disulfide. As the ease of escape from the solvent cage increases, the rate of photochemical decomposition also increases. Barton and co-workers[93] report that esters of aromatic thiols also undergo photochemical decomposition to yield thiophenolate radicals, eq. (46). They did not observe any decarboxylation

(46) O_2N—⟨NO_2⟩—SOCR → O_2N—⟨NO_2⟩—S· + RĊO·

of the carboxyl radical. German workers have observed that photochemical decomposition of disulfides and diselenides at 77°K gives thiyl and selenyl radicals readily observable by electron spin resonance techniques.[94] Electron donors on the benzene rings of the disulfides lead to more stable sulfide radicals.

Gunning and co-workers have reported extensive studies on photochemical gas phase reactions in which presumably free sulfur atoms are formed. Using carbonyl sulfide as the sulfur atom source, these workers report both the addition of sulfur atoms to olefins and their insertion into carbon-hydrogen bonds.[95,96]

Thioethers decompose photochemically to yield alkyl radicals. Horner and Doerges[97] have isolated methane and ethane among other products from the photolysis of dimethyl sulfide. In addition, Horner and co-workers have reported studies of photochemical decomposition reactions of other organic sulfur compounds. They have investigated the formation of sulfonyl-imine radicals by the photolysis of a sulfonyl azide, eq. (47).[98,99]

(47) $ArSO_2N_3$ $\xrightarrow{h\nu}$ $ArSO_2N$: + N_2
                              $\xrightarrow{RH}$ $ArSO_2{=}NH$

Sulfuryl and sulfonyl halides often yield addition products when photolyzed in the presence of olefins. In every case but the last, the addition reactions involve sulfur radicals formed, among other ways, by photolysis of a sulfur covalent bond.

Oxidation Reactions

Sensitized photochemical oxidation reactions to form both transannular cyclic peroxides and hydroperoxides were discussed in an earlier chapter. Singlet oxygen intermediates, described as $^{\oplus}O{-}O^{\ominus}$ by Kopecky and Reich,[100] were proposed to account for the similarity of the products obtained by photosensitized and wet chemical pathways. Nickon and co-workers, working with steroid systems, suggest that the reaction proceeds via a cyclic abstraction mechanism with rather strict steric requirements when monoolefins are oxidized at the allylic position.[101-104]

In spite of the similarity of the sensitized oxidation process to a radical chain reaction, Schenck and co-workers have shown that the photosensitized process proceeds to give different stereochemical oxidation products when optically active cyclic olefins are oxidized.[105,106]

Polymerization Processes

Photochemical polymerization represents another class of photochemical chain reactions which have been studied extensively because of their great practical importance. Photopolymerizations of many of the common vinyl monomers have been reported and in at least one case, that of styrene, mechanistic interpretations involving a dimeric initiation sequence appear to be applicable. Applying the usual steady state approach to photochemical vinyl polymerization, a three-halves order rate dependence on monomer concentration and one-half order rate dependence on the intensity of the incident radiation determine the polymerization rate.

$$(48) \qquad M \xrightarrow{h\nu} IfM\cdot$$

$$(49) \qquad M\cdot \; + \; M \xrightarrow{k_p} M\cdot$$

$$(50) \qquad 2M\cdot \xrightarrow{k_t} products$$

$$R_p = k_p[M\cdot][M]$$

If we assume steady state radical concentration,

$$If[M] = k_t[M\cdot]^2$$

$$M\cdot = \frac{If[M]}{k_t}$$

Therefore

$$(51) \qquad R_p = k_p \frac{[If]^{1/2}[M]^{3/2}}{k_t^{1/2}}$$

This result is supported by experimental observations.

Expression (51) portrays a general dilemma of kinetic evaluations of free radical chain reactions. In radical polymerizations one can only measure the rate of polymerization as a function of the rate of initiation. As a result, one can only obtain the propagation to termination rate constant ratio $k_p/k_t^{1/2}$. The individual rate constants k_p and k_t cannot normally be evaluated. A way to circumvent this difficulty is provided by photochemistry. Using photochemical techniques, one can provide another independent control of the polymerization rate.   The average lifetime of an individual growing polymer chain can be calculated to be $\tau_s = [M\cdot]_s/2k_t[M\cdot]_s^2$, where τ_s = the average lifetime of the growing polymer chain and $[M\cdot]_s$ the radical concentrations at the steady state.   That is, the average lifetime of each chain equals the concentration of growing polymer chains divided by the rate of their destruction.   The rate of polymerization can be obtained at different average chain lifetimes, and another set of equations become available for the rate constant calculations.

If initiators that decompose photochemically are used to start the chain reaction, one can initiate the reaction simply by beginning illumination. Similarly, cessation of illumination will cause the initiation process and the chain reaction to stop.   Measurement of the decrease in rate of polymerization after the halting of irradiation or the increase in rate of polymerization before the steady state radical concentration is attained provides a measure of the average radical lifetime in the system.   In practice, periods of light and dark are created by placing a rotating shield in the path of the light waves.   A portion of the shield is blocked out with reflecting material, and τ_s is evaluated by altering the speed of the rotating sector.   Absolute values of the rate constant k_p, the rate constant for the propagation step of the reaction, are calculated by this method to be in the neighborhood of 10^3.   For the termination step of the polymerization chain, rate constants in the neighborhood of 10^7 are obtained.[107,108]   Some typical absolute rate constants for vinyl polymerization are given in Table 10-6.

Table 10-6

Absolute Rate Constants for Polymerization Reactions

Monomer	k_p, 30°	$k_t \times 10^{-7}$, 30°
vinyl acetate[108, 109]	1240	3.1
styrene[110]	55	2.5
methyl methacrylate[111]	143	0.61
methyl acrylate[112]	720	0.22

The primary process of unsensitized photochemical polymerization of vinyl monomers involves a π-π^* excitation of the olefin system.   The possibility of bimolecular initiation in which two monomer molecules are involved in the initiation step also exists.   Pryor has suggested that the thermal polymerization of styrene involves a termolecular process in which the first step is a Diels-Alder reaction with the benzene ring being the necessary diene.[113]   The initiation process varies for each individual monomer so that generalizations concerning the primary excitation process are open to question. Much of the work on photochemical polymerization reactions is buried in the patent literature. Boundy and Bayer,[114] in an early treatise on styrene report that certain workers have studied the effect of incident radiation on the polymerization of styrene. They report that the rate is maximum at 2750 Å. Since the π-π^* maximum of styrene is near 2500 Å in hydrocarbon solvents, it can be postulated that this continuous absorption is responsible for the polymerization initiation. Since the rate of polymerization of styrene decreases as the wavelength of incident radiation approaches 2500 Å, the π-π^* maximum, photochemical depolymerization processes are important at shorter wavelengths.

Inhibition of photochemical chain polymerization is an equally important aspect of the problem of polymerization. Additives to the unpolymerized monomer may serve to absorb the activating radiation, or they may serve to stop radical chains by chemical removal of radicals from the system. Addition of certain benzophenone derivatives to the system stabilizes the monomer by the first process. These derivatives include 2-hydroxybenzophenone and its derivatives, mentioned in an earlier chapter, which convert incident radiation into useless energy by the transfer of a hydrogen atom from the hydroxy group to the carbonyl oxygen. Also of some use are hydroxybenzoylfurans and thiophenes as well as certain benzothiazoles, benzoylnaphthalenes, and hydroxyacetophenones. Polymers themselves can be made light fast by incorporating benzoyl and acetyl groups into the polymer chain.

The second type of inhibition is more common. Phenolic and aromatic amine inhibitors have been used for a long time to prevent polymerization of vinyl monomers and to inhibit free radical reactions other than polymerization.[115] The general mechanism for the inhibition process is not well understood although there has been a great deal of experimental investigation. It is proposed that phenols inhibit the polymerization of vinyl monomers by a hydrogen transfer mechanism, whereas aromatic amines inhibit the chain process by an electron transfer process although hydrogen transfer processes are not totally eliminated in the latter case. Less reactive phenoxyl radicals and aromatic amine radicals result from the hydrogen or electron transfer reactions.

Photolysis of Oxygen-Oxygen Bonds

Finally, photochemical as well as thermal decompositions of peroxides and peresters produce chain-initiating free radicals. Chain-induced decompositions also occur. Both acyl and alkyl peroxides undergo photochemical decompositions. Dialkyl peroxides, despite the fact that they do not possess unsaturation, possess continuous absorptions far into the near ultraviolet spectral region so that photodecomposition of these peroxides can be effected with relatively long wavelength irradiation.   Photochemical decompositions of di-t-butyl peroxide in the liquid phase in Pyrex containers (nontransmitting below 3100 Å) indicate that the thermal and the photochemical decompositions lead to similar reaction products.[116] Similar results are obtained with a variety of other dialkyl peroxides.[117-122]   Di-t-butyl peroxide gives acetone, methane, ethane, t-butyl alcohol, and isobutylene oxide as major products of its decomposition, either photochemically or thermally, in the gas phase or in impervious solvent.   McMillan[120-122] has observed that some "hot" methyl radicals result from the photochemical decomposition of dialkyl peroxides in the gas phase.   Addition of radical scavengers such as nitric oxide even in high pressures cannot completely suppress the decomposition of t-butoxy radicals to acetone.   A reasonable explanation for the photochemical decomposition of di-t-butyl peroxide, a typical dialkyl peroxide, involves the mechanism shown in eqs. (52–57).   In solution the decomposition of di-t-butyl peroxide as well as other dialkyl peroxides is influenced by the solvent, and induced decompositions are observed.[123,124]

(52) t-BuOOt-Bu $\xrightarrow{h\nu}$ t-BuO$\cdot$ + t-BuO$\cdot$*

(53) t-BuO$\cdot$* $\longrightarrow$ Me$\cdot$*   + CH_3COCH_3

(54) t-BuO$\cdot$ $\longrightarrow$ Me$\cdot$ + CH_3COCH_3

(55) t-BuO$\cdot$ + t-BuOOt-Bu $\longrightarrow$ t-BuOH   + $\cdot CH_2C(CH_3)_2 OOC(CH_3)_3$

(56)   A$\cdot$ $\longrightarrow$ t-BuO$\cdot$ + $\underset{CH_3}{\overset{CH_3}{\diagdown}} \overset{\overset{\textstyle A\cdot}{|}}{\underset{\diagup}{C}} \overset{CH_2}{\underset{O}{\diagup}}$

(57)   2 radicals $\longrightarrow$ products

Thermal and photochemical homolysis of the peroxide linkage of diacyl peroxides occurs more readily than that of the dialkyl peroxidic bond. Davies reports that the homolytic dissociation of dibenzoyl peroxide requires but 30 kcal/mole.[125] Diacyl peroxides are great favorites as industrial sources of free radicals.   In solution, where most studies of diacyl peroxides have been performed, complete scavenging of all the product free radicals can be obtained.[126]   Even more than the dialkyl peroxides, diacyl peroxides are susceptible to nonfirst-order-induced decompositions in more polar solvents. A typical decomposition chain reaction is that of dibenzoyl peroxide.   The photochemical decomposition of dibenzoyl peroxide in hydrocarbon solvents leads primarily to benzoic acid, benzene, and carbon dioxide.   Varying quantities of biphenyl, phenyl benzoate, and solvent-derived products are also obtained. A probable chain mechanism for the photochemical decomposition of dibenzoyl peroxide is given in eqs. (58–62).

(58) $C_6H_5COOOCOC_6H_5 \xrightarrow{h\nu} 2\, C_6H_5COO \cdot$

(59) $C_6H_5COO \cdot + RH \longrightarrow C_6H_5COOH + R \cdot$

(60) $C_6H_5COO \cdot \longrightarrow C_6H_5 \cdot + CO_2$

(61) $C_6H_5 \cdot + RH \longrightarrow R \cdot + C_6H_6$

(62)   2 radicals $\longrightarrow$ products

Photochemically, the decomposition of diacyl peroxides, unlike that of the dialkyl peroxides, probably results from an n-π^* excitation of the carbonyl group. Since so little excitation energy is necessary for the decomposition, a variety of other absorptions may also contribute to the decomposition process. Recent studies by Walling and co-workers on the direct and photosensitized decompositions of diacyl peroxides suggest that n-π^* triplets lead to oxygen-oxygen bond homolysis.[127]

Peroxy esters, derivatives of hydroperoxides and carboxylic acids, undergo thermal and photochemical peroxide bond homolysis. Thermal decomposition mechanisms have been thoroughly investigated by Bartlett and co-workers, and reviews appear elsewhere.[128] The thermal decomposition of the oxygen-oxygen bond is reported to occur with varying degrees of concerted loss of carbon dioxide from the acyl portion of the molecule[129-131] and in some instances has been reported to be assisted by neighboring groups.[132-134]

References

1. There are many variations of the chain reaction theme. See, for example, C. Walling, *Free Radicals in Solution*, p. 54 ff., New York, Wiley, 1957.
2. See, for example, J. N. Murrell, *The Theory of the Electronic Spectra of Organic Molecules*, p. 296, London, Wiley, 1963.
3. Walling, C., and E. S. Huyser, *Organic Reactions*, Vol. XIII, p. 91, New York, Wiley, 1964.
4. Stacey, F. W., and J. F. Harris, Jr., *Organic Reactions*, Vol. XIII, p. 150, New York, Wiley, 1964.
5. Majer, J. R., and J. R. Simons, *Advances in Photochemistry*, Vol. II, p. 137, New York, Wiley, 1964.
6. West, W., and L. Schlessinger, *J. Am. Chem. Soc.*, **60**, 961 (1938).
7. Schultz, R. D., and H. A. Taylor, *J. Chem. Phys.*, **18**, 194 (1950).
8. Souffie, R. D., R. R. Williams, and W. H. Hamill, *J. Am. Chem. Soc.*, **78**, 917 (1956).
9. Harris, G. M., and J. E. Willard, *J. Am. Chem. Soc.*, **76**, 4678 (1954).
10. Martin, R. B., and W. A. Noyes, Jr., *J. Am. Chem. Soc.*, **75**, 4183 (1953).
11. Herzberg, G., *Proc. Chem. Soc.*, 116 (1959).
12. McMillan, G. R., and W. A. Noyes, Jr., *J. Am. Chem. Soc.*, **80**, 2108 (1958).

13. Schindler, R., and M. H. J. Wijnen, Z. *Physik Chem.* (Frankfort) **34**, 109 (1962).
14. Majer, J. R., and C. R. Patrick, *Nature*, **192**, 866 (1961).
15. Blomstrom, D. C., K. Herbig, and H. E. Simmons, *J. Org. Chem.*, **30**, 959 (1965).
16. Simons, J. P., and A. J. Yarwood, *Trans. Faraday Soc.*, **57**, 2167 (1961).
17. Simons, J. P., and A. J. Yarwood, *Trans. Faraday Soc.*, **59**, 90 (1963).
18. Hall, R. H., and D. I. H. Jacobs, *J. Chem. Soc.*, 2034 (1954).
19. Kharasch, M. S., O. Reinmuth, and W. H. Urry, *J. Am. Chem. Soc.*, **69**, 1105 (1947).
20. Skell, P. S., and R. C. Woodworth, *J. Am. Chem. Soc.*, **77**, 4638 (1955).
21. Kharasch, M. S., and M. Sage, *J. Org. Chem.*, **14**, 537 (1949).
22. Kharasch, M. S., and H. N. Friedlander, *J. Org. Chem.*, **14**, 239 (1949).
23. Heiba, E. I., and L. C. Anderson, *J. Am. Chem. Soc.*, **79**, 4940 (1957).
24. Kharasch, M. S., E. Simon, and W. Nudenberg, *J. Org. Chem.*, **18**, 328 (1953).
25. Henne, A. L., and M. Nager, *J. Am. Chem. Soc.*, **73**, 5527 (1951).
26. M. S. Kharasch, U. S. patent number 2,485,099 [C. A., **44**, 6430 (1950)]. Quoted in C. Walling and E. S. Huyser, *Organic Reactions*, Vol. XII, p. 91, New York, Wiley, 1964.
27. Haszeldine, R. N., *J. Chem. Soc.*, 2856 (1949).
28. Haszeldine, R. N., and K. Leedham, *J. Chem. Soc.*, 1261 (1954).
29. Leedham, K., and R. N. Haszeldine, *J. Chem. Soc.*, 1634 (1954).
30. Haszeldine, R. N., *J. Chem. Soc.*, 3490 (1952).
31. Haszeldine, R. N., and B. R. Steele, *J. Chem. Soc.*, 1199 (1953).
32. Haszeldine, R. N., *J. Chem. Soc.*, 922 (1953).
33. Kharasch, M. S., E. V. Jensen, and W. H. Urry, *J. Am. Chem. Soc.*, **69**, 1100 (1947).
34. Park, J. D., R. J. Seffl, and J. R. Lacker, *J. Am. Chem. Soc.*, **78**, 59 (1956).
35. Huyser, E. S., *J. Am. Chem. Soc.*, **82**, 391 (1960).
36. Huyser, E. S., and J. D. Taliaferro, *J. Org. Chem.*, **28**, 3442 (1963).
37. Huyser, E. S., and G. Echegaray, *J. Org. Chem.*, **27**, 429 (1962).
38. DeMott, D. N., Ph.D. Thesis, University of Kansas, 1963.
39. Martin, M. M., and G. J. Gleicher, *J. Am. Chem. Soc.*, **86**, 233 (1964).
40. Martin, M. M., and G. J. Gleicher, *J. Am. Chem. Soc.*, **86**, 238 (1964).
41. Huyser, E. S., *J. Org. Chem.*, **26**, 3261 (1961).
42. Kharasch, M. S., H. Englemann, and F. R. Mayo, *J. Org. Chem.*, **2**, 288 (1937).
43. Mayo, F. R., and C. Walling, *Chem. Rev.*, **27**, 351 (1940).
44. Mayo, F. R., *J. Am. Chem. Soc.*, **84**, 3964 (1962).
45. See, for example, W. A. Noyes, Jr., and P. A. Leighton, *The Photochemistry of Gases*, New York, Reinhold, 1941.
46. Martin, R. M., and J. E. Willard, *J. Chem. Phys.*, **40**, 2999 (1964).
47. Goering, H. L., P. I. Abell, and B. F. Aycock, *J. Am. Chem. Soc.*, **74**, 3588 (1952).
48. Goering, H. L., and L. L. Sims, *J. Am. Chem. Soc.*, **77**, 3465 (1955).
49. Skell, P. S., and R. G. Allen, *J. Am. Chem. Soc.*, **86**, 1559 (1964).
50. Haag, W. O., and E. I. Heiba, *Tetrahedron Letters*, 3679 (1965).
51. Haag, W. O., and E. I. Heiba, *Tetrahedron Letters*, 3683 (1965).
52. Raley, J. H., F. F. Rust, and W. E. Vaughan, *J. Am. Chem. Soc.*, **70**, 2767 (1948).
53. Wackholtz, F., *Z. phyzik. Chem.*, **125**, 1 (1927).
54. Derbyshire, D. H., and W. A. Waters, *Trans. Faraday Soc.*, **45**, 749 (1949).
55. Steinmetz, H., and R. M. Noyes, *J. Am. Chem. Soc.*, **74**, 4141 (1952).
56. Bodenstein, M., *Sitzber preuss Akad. Wiss.*, 333 (1912).
57. Bodenstein, M., and H. Lütkemeyer, *Z. phyzik., Chem.*, **114**, 208 (1924).
58. Bodenstein, M., and W. Unger, *Z. phyzik., Chem.*, **11B**, 253 (1930).
59. Hammond, G. S., *J. Am. Chem. Soc.*, **77**, 334 (1955).

60. Ecke, G. G., L. R. Buzbee, and A. J. Kolke, *J. Am. Chem. Soc.*, **78**, 79 (1956).
61. Russell, G. A., *J. Am. Chem. Soc.*, **79**, 2977 (1957).
62. Russell, G. A., *J. Am. Chem. Soc.*, **80**, 4987 (1958).
63. Russell, G. A., *J. Am. Chem. Soc.*, **80**, 4997 (1958).
64. Russell, G. A., *J. Am. Chem. Soc.*, **80**, 5002 (1958).
65. Walling, C., and B. B. Jacknow, *J. Am. Chem. Soc.*, **82**, 6108 (1960).
66. Walling, C., and B. B. Jacknow, *J. Am. Chem. Soc.*, **82**, 6113 (1960).
67. Walling, C., and W. Thaler, *J. Am. Chem. Soc.*, **83**, 3877 (1961).
68. Walling, C., and P. J. Wagner, *J. Am. Chem. Soc.*, **85**, 2333 (1963).
69. Walling, C., and P. J. Wagner, *J. Am. Chem. Soc.*, **86**, 3368 (1964).
70. Greene, F. D., *J. Am. Chem. Soc.*, **81**, 2688 (1959).
71. Greene, F. D., M. L. Savitz, H. H. Lau, F. D. Osterholtz, and W. N. Smith, *J. Am. Chem. Soc.*, **83**, 2196 (1961).
72. Greene, F. D., M. L. Savitz, F. D. Osterholtz, H. H. Lau, W. N. Smith, and P. M. Zanet, *J. Org. Chem.*, **28**, 55 (1963).
73. Walling, C., and A. Padwa, *J. Am. Chem. Soc.*, **85**, 1593 (1963).
74. Walling, C., and A. Padwa, *J. Am. Chem. Soc.*, **84**, 2845 (1962).
75. Walling, C., and A. Padwa, *J. Am. Chem. Soc.*, **85**, 1597 (1963).
76. Kharasch, M. S., and H. C. Brown, *J. Am. Chem. Soc.*, **61**, 2142 (1939).
77. Walling, C., A. L. Rieger, and D. D. Tanner, *J. Am. Chem. Soc.*, **85**, 3129 (1963).
78. Walling, C., and A. L. Rieger, *J. Am. Chem. Soc.*, **85**, 3134 (1963).
79. Russell, G. A., and K. M. Desmond, *J. Am. Chem. Soc.*, **85**, 3139 (1963).
80. Pearson, R. E., and J. C. Martin, *J. Am. Chem. Soc.*, **85**, 354 (1963).
81. Pearson, R. E., and J. C. Martin, *J. Am. Chem. Soc.*, **85**, 3142 (1963).
82. Russell, G. A., C. de Boer, and K. M. Desmond, *J. Am. Chem. Soc.*, **85**, 365 (1963).
83. Adam, J., P. A. Gosselain, and P. Goldfinger, *Nature*, **171**, 704 (1953).
84. Adam, J., P. A. Gosselain, and P. Goldfinger, *Bull. soc. chim. Belges*, **65**, 523 (1956).
85. Hedaya, E., R. L. Hinman, and S. Theodoropulos, *J. Am. Chem. Soc.*, **85**, 3052 (1963).
86. Petterson, R. C., and A. Wambsgans, *J. Am. Chem. Soc.*, **86**, 1648 (1964).
87. Barton, D. H. R., A. L. J. Beckwith, and A. Goosen, *J. Chem. Soc.*, 181 (1965).
88. Harris, J. F., Jr., and F. W. Stacey, *J. Am. Chem. Soc.*, **83**, 840 (1961).
89. Buess, C. M., C. N. Yiannios, and W. T. Fitzgerald, *J. Org. Chem.*, **22**, 197 (1957).
90. Marvel, C. S., and R. R. Chambers, *J. Am. Chem. Soc.*, **70**, 993 (1948).
91. Vaughan, W. E., and F. F. Rust, *J. Org. Chem.*, **7**, 472 (1942).
92. Schaafsma, Y., A. F. Bickel, and E. C. Kooyman, *Tetrahedron*, **10**, 76 (1960).
93. Barton, D. H. R., Y. L. Chow, A. Cox, and G. W. Kirby, *Tetrahedron Letters*, 1055 (1962).
94. Schmidt, U., A. Mueller, and K. Markou, *Chem. Ber.*, **97** (2), 405 (1964).
95. See, for example, O. P. Strausz, T. Hikida, and H. E. Gunning, *Can. J. Chem.*, **43**, 717 (1965).
96. Wiebe, H. A., A. R. Knight, O. P. Strausz, and H. E. Gunning, *J. Am. Chem. Soc.*, **87**, 1443 (1965).
97. Horner, L., and J. Doerges, *Tetrahedron Letters*, 757 (1963).
98. Horner, L., and A. Christmann, *Chem. Ber.*, **96**, 388 (1963).
99. Horner, L., A. Christmann, and A. Gross, *Chem. Ber.*, **96**, 399 (1963).
100. Kopecky, K. R., and H. J. Reich, *Can. J. Chem.*, **43**, 2265 (1965).
101. Nickon, A., and J. F. Bagli, *J. Am. Chem. Soc.*, **81**, 6330 (1959).
102. Nickon, A., and W. L. Mendelson, *Can. J. Chem.*, **43**, 1419 (1965).
103. Nickon, A., and W. L. Mendelson, *J. Org. Chem.*, **30**, 2087 (1965).

104. Nickon, A., and W. L. Mendelson, *J. Am. Chem. Soc.*, **87**, 3921 (1965).
105. Gollnick, K., S. Schroeter, G. Ohloff, G. Schade, and G. O. Schenck, *Ann. Chem.*, **687**, 14 (1965).
106. Schenck, G. O., O. A. Neumueller, G. Ohloff, and S. Schroeter, *Ann. Chem.*, **687**, 26 (1965).
107. For a complete discussion of rotating sector methods, see P. J. Flory, *Principles of Polymer Chemistry*, Ithaca, New York, Cornell University Press, 1953.
108. Kwart, H., H. S. Broadbent, and P. D. Bartlett, *J. Am. Chem. Soc.*, **72**, 1060 (1950).
109. Matheson, M. S., E. E. Auer, E. D. Bevilacqua, and E. J. Hart, *J. Am. Chem. Soc.*, **71**, 2610 (1949).
110. Matheson, M. S., E. E. Auer, E. D. Bevilacqua, and E. J. Hart, *J. Am. Chem. Soc.*, **73**, 1700 (1951).
111. Matheson, M. S., E. E. Auer, E. D. Bevilacqua, and E. J. Hart, *J. Am. Chem. Soc.*, **71**, 497 (1949).
112. Matheson, M. S., E. E. Auer, E. D. Bevilacqua, and E. J. Hart, *J. Am. Chem. Soc.*, **73**, 5395 (1951).
113. Pryor, W., Paper given at 149th National Meeting, American Chemical Society, April 6, 1965, Detroit, Michigan.
114. Boundy, R. H., and R. F. Bayer, *Styrene*, p. 256, New York, Reinhold, 1952.
115. Ingold, K. U., *Chem. Rev.*, **61**, 563 (1961).
116. Bredeweg, C. J., Ph.D. Thesis, University of Kansas, 1963.
117. Dorfman, L. M., and Z. W. Salsburg, *J. Am. Chem. Soc.*, **73**, 255 (1951).
118. Volman, D. H., and W. M. Graven, *J. Am. Chem. Soc.*, **75**, 3111 (1953).
119. McMillan, G. R., and M. H. J. Wijnen, *Can. J. Chem.*, **36**, 1227 (1958).
120. McMillan, G. R., *J. Am. Chem. Soc.*, **82**, 2422 (1960).
121. McMillan, G. R., *J. Am. Chem. Soc.*, **83**, 3018 (1961).
122. McMillan, G. R., *J. Am. Chem. Soc.*, **84**, 2514 (1962).
123. Huyser, E. S., and C. J. Bredeweg, *J. Am. Chem. Soc.*, **86**, 2401 (1964).
124. Huyser, E. S., C. J. Bredeweg, and R. M. Van Scoy, *J. Am. Chem. Soc.*, **86**, 4148 (1964).
125. Davies, A. G., *Organic Peroxides*, p. 167, London, Butterworths, 1961.
126. Hammond, G. S., and L. M. Soffer, *J. Am. Chem. Soc.*, **72**, 4711 (1950).
127. Walling, C., and M. J. Gibian, *J. Am. Chem. Soc.*, **87**, 3413 (1965).
128. Bartlett, P. D., in *Peroxide Reaction Mechanisms*, J. O. Edwards (ed.), New York, Wiley, 1962.
129. Blomquist, A. T., and A. F. Ferris, *J. Am. Chem. Soc.*, **73**, 3408 (1951).
130. Bartlett, P. D., and R. R. Hiatt, *J. Am. Chem. Soc.*, **80**, 1398 (1958).
131. Bartlett, P. D., and B. T. Storey, *J. Am. Chem. Soc.*, **80**, 4954 (1958).
132. Bentrude, W. G., and J. C. Martin, *J. Am. Chem. Soc.*, **84**, 1561 (1962).
133. Martin, J. C., and W. G. Bentrude, *Chem. Ind.*, 192 (1959).
134. Martin, J. C., and T. W. Koenig, *J. Am. Chem. Soc.*, **86**, 1771 (1964).

CHAPTER

11

Photochemistry and Nature

There is little doubt that in the future, some of the most significant scientific discoveries will result in biochemistry, the oldest but yet the newest of scientific pursuits. The photochemist must play an important role in the unraveling of some of the more complex, naturally occurring photochemical processes: photosynthesis, vision, skin pigmentation, photochemical growth acceleration, chemiluminescence—the list could go on indefinitely. Of the many important naturally occurring photochemical processes, we shall discuss only three: photosynthesis, chemiluminescence, and the photochemistry of vision.

Photosynthesis

Photosynthesis is the natural reversal of cell metabolism. In its most elementary form, it is the photosensitized conversion of carbon dioxide and water to oxygen and carbohydrates *in vivo*. Every school boy can write eq. (1).

$$(1) \quad 6\,CO_2 \;+\; 6\,H_2O \;\xrightarrow[\text{sensitizer}]{h\nu}\; C_6H_{12}O_6 \;+\; 6\,O_2$$

Stepwise analysis of the photosynthetic cycle shows that carbon dioxide is actually incorporated into fructose type carbohydrates in green plants in the *chloroplast*,[1] the basic structure of which is a flattened, double-membraned structure called a *thylakoid*.[2]   The thylakoid membrane is composed of oblate, spheroidal protein units, called *quantasomes*,[3] which are housed in a lipid matrix.

The total carbon process of photosynthesis may be carried out using quantasomes separated from the plant, providing that the appropriate enzymes and cofactors are also present.   From the work of Nobel laureate Melvin Calvin, the carbon process is described in eqs. (2–11).[4] All of the reactions (2–11) are enzyme assisted.

(2) 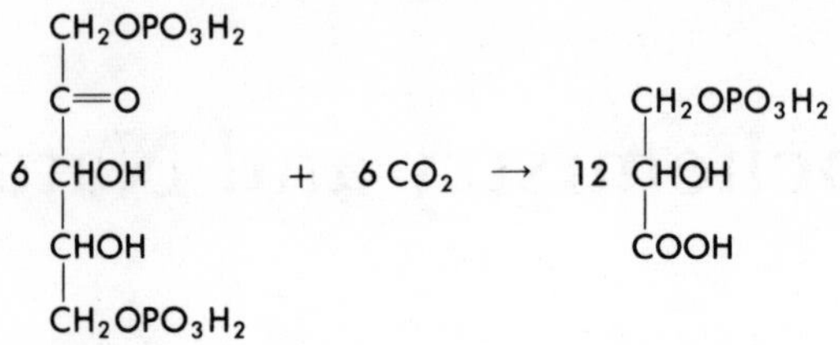
$$6\ \begin{array}{c} CH_2OPO_3H_2 \\ | \\ C=O \\ | \\ CHOH \\ | \\ CHOH \\ | \\ CH_2OPO_3H_2 \end{array} \quad +\ 6\,CO_2 \ \longrightarrow\ 12\ \begin{array}{c} CH_2OPO_3H_2 \\ | \\ CHOH \\ | \\ COOH \end{array}$$

(3)
$$12\ \begin{array}{c} CH_2OPO_3H_2 \\ | \\ CHOH \\ | \\ COOH \end{array} \quad +\ 12\,ATP \ \longrightarrow\ 12\ \begin{array}{c} CH_2OPO_3H_2 \\ | \\ CHOH \\ | \\ CH_2OPO_3H_2 \end{array} \quad +\ 12\,ADP$$

(4)
$$12\ \begin{array}{c} CH_2OPO_3H_2 \\ | \\ CHOH \\ | \\ CH_2OPO_3H_2 \end{array} \quad +\ 12\,NADH \ +\ H^{\oplus} \ \longrightarrow$$

$$12\ \begin{array}{c} CH_2OPO_3H_2 \\ | \\ CHOH \\ | \\ CHO \end{array} \quad +\ NAD^{\oplus} \ +\ 12\,Pi$$

(5)
$$5\ \begin{array}{c} CH_2OPO_3H_2 \\ | \\ CHOH \\ | \\ CHO \end{array} \quad \longrightarrow\ 5\ \begin{array}{c} CH_2OPO_3H_2 \\ | \\ C=O \\ | \\ CHO \end{array}$$

(6)
$$5\ \begin{array}{c} CH_2OPO_3H_2 \\ | \\ CHOH \\ | \\ CHO \end{array} \quad +\ 5\ \begin{array}{c} CH_2OPO_3H_2 \\ | \\ C=O \\ | \\ CH_2OH \end{array} \quad \longrightarrow\ 5\ \begin{array}{c} CH_2OPO_3H_2 \\ | \\ C=O \\ | \\ CHOH \\ | \\ CHOH \\ | \\ CH_2OPO_3H_2 \end{array}$$

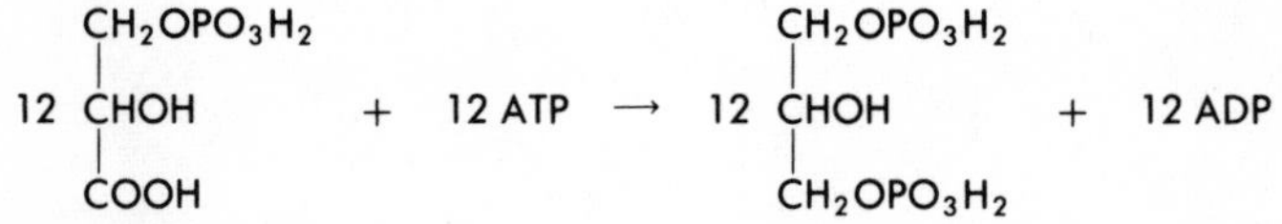

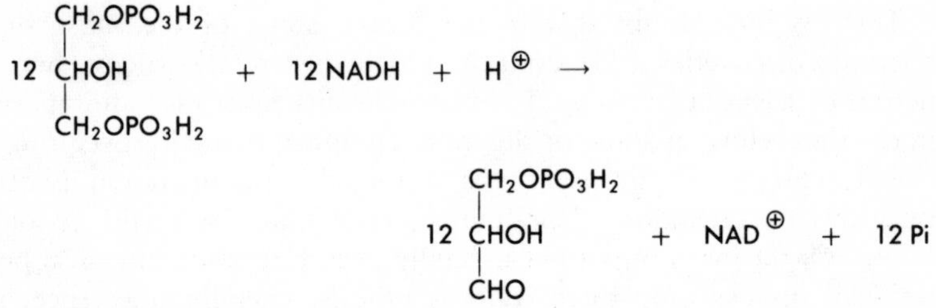

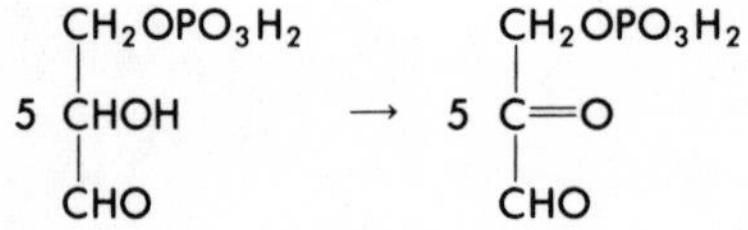

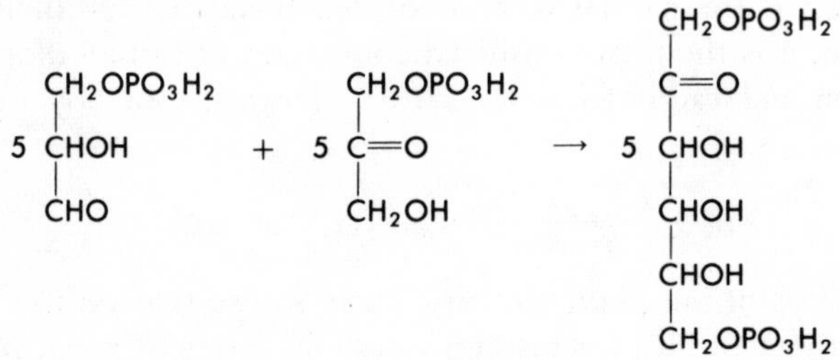

(7)   5
$$
\begin{array}{l}
CH_2OPO_3H_2 \\
| \\
C{=}O \\
| \\
CHOH \\
| \\
CHOH \\
| \\
CHOH \\
| \\
CH_2OPO_3H_2
\end{array}
\quad \longrightarrow \quad 5
\begin{array}{l}
CH_2OPO_3H_2 \\
| \\
C{=}O \\
| \\
CHOH \\
| \\
CHOH \\
| \\
CHOH \\
| \\
CH_2OH
\end{array}
\quad + \quad 5\ Pi
$$

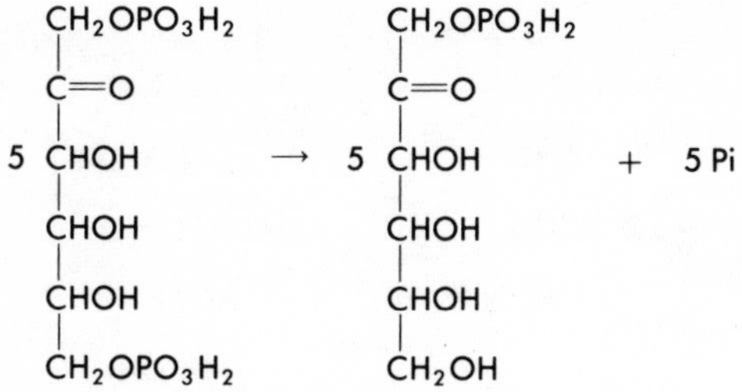

(8)   2
$$
\begin{array}{l}
CH_2OPO_3H_2 \\
| \\
C{=}O \\
| \\
CHOH \\
| \\
CHOH \\
| \\
CHOH \\
| \\
CH_2OH
\end{array}
\quad + \quad 2
\begin{array}{l}
CH_2OPO_3H_2 \\
| \\
CHOH \\
| \\
CHO
\end{array}
\quad \longrightarrow
$$

$$
2
\begin{array}{l}
CH_2OH \\
| \\
C{=}O \\
| \\
HOCH \\
| \\
HCOH \\
| \\
CH_2OPO_3H_2
\end{array}
\quad + \quad 2
\begin{array}{l}
CHO \\
| \\
HCOH \\
| \\
HCOH \\
| \\
CH_2OPO_3H_2
\end{array}
$$

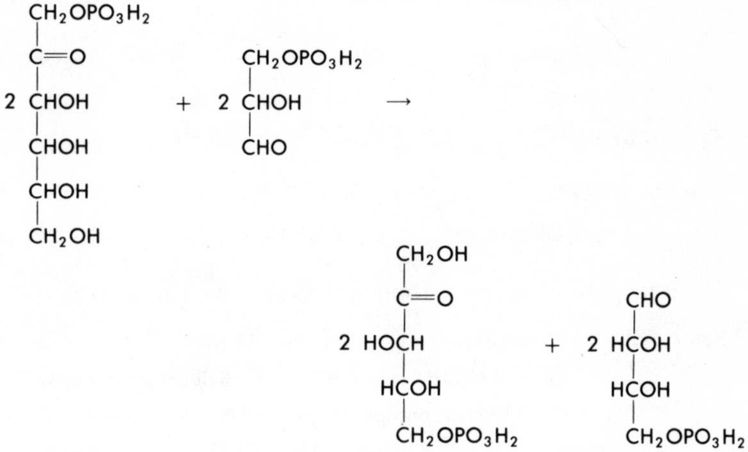

(9)   2
$$
\begin{array}{l}
CH_2OH \\
| \\
C{=}O \\
| \\
HOCH \\
| \\
HCOH \\
| \\
HCOH \\
| \\
CH_2OPO_3H_2
\end{array}
\quad + \quad 2
\begin{array}{l}
CHO \\
| \\
CHOH \\
| \\
CHOH \\
| \\
CH_2OPO_3H_2
\end{array}
\quad \longrightarrow
$$

$$
\begin{array}{l}
CH_2OH \\
| \\
C{=}O \\
| \\
HOCH \\
| \\
HCOH \\
| \\
HCOH \\
| \\
HCOH \\
| \\
CH_2OPO_3H_2
\end{array}
\quad + \quad 2
\begin{array}{l}
CH_2OPO_3H_2 \\
| \\
CHOH \\
| \\
CHO
\end{array}
$$

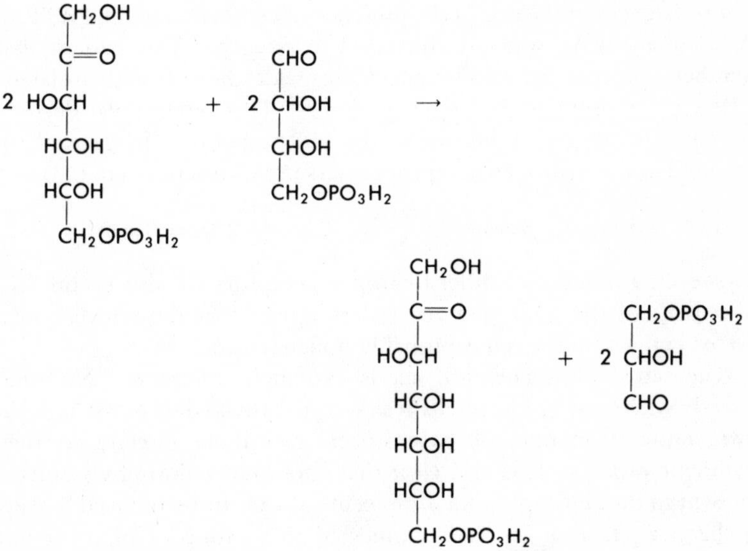

$$
(10) \quad 2 \begin{array}{c} CH_2OH \\ | \\ C=O \\ | \\ HOCH \\ | \\ HCOH \\ | \\ HCOH \\ | \\ HCOH \\ | \\ CH_2OPO_3H_2 \end{array} \quad + \quad 2 \begin{array}{c} CHO \\ | \\ HCOH \\ | \\ CH_2OPO_3H_2 \end{array} \quad \longrightarrow \quad 4 \begin{array}{c} CH_2OH \\ | \\ C=O \\ | \\ HOCH \\ | \\ HCOH \\ | \\ CH_2OPO_3H_2 \end{array}
$$

$$
(11) \quad 6 \begin{array}{c} CH_2OH \\ | \\ C=O \\ | \\ HOCH \\ | \\ HCOH \\ | \\ CH_2OPO_3H_2 \end{array} \quad \longrightarrow \quad 6 \begin{array}{c} CH_2OH \\ | \\ C=O \\ | \\ CHOH \\ | \\ CHOH \\ | \\ CH_2OPO_3H_2 \end{array} \quad \xrightarrow{6 \, ATP} \quad 6 \begin{array}{c} CH_2OPO_3H_2 \\ | \\ C=O \\ | \\ CHOH \\ | \\ CHOH \\ | \\ CH_2OPO_3H_2 \end{array}
$$

The total photosynthetic carbon cycle is described in eq. (12).

$$
(12) \quad 6 \text{ ribulose diphosphate} + 6\,CO_2 + 18\,ATP
$$
$$
+ \quad 12\,NADH \quad + \quad 6\,H^{\oplus} \quad \longrightarrow \quad 6 \text{ ribulose diphosphate}
$$
$$
+ \quad 1 \text{ fructose phosphate} \quad + \quad 17\,Pi \quad + \quad 18\,ADP \quad + \quad 12\,NAD^{\oplus}
$$

Thus, 1 molecule of carbon dioxide is converted to 1 molecule of fructose phosphate within the cell in the presence of cell-manufactured ATP.

Simultaneously, water is converted to oxygen. This part of the photosynthetic process can also be effected outside the cell with isolated chloroplasts and appropriate hydrogen acceptors. This extracellular decomposition of water to oxygen is known as the Hill reaction.[5] In general, quinones are used as the hydrogen acceptor centers in this reaction, eq. (13).

$$
(13) \quad 2\,H_2O \quad + \quad \text{quinone} \quad \xrightarrow[h\nu]{sens.} \quad O_2 \quad + \quad 2 \text{ hydroquinone}
$$

However, a number of other hydrogen acceptors are also useful. The non-specificity of the hydrogen acceptor suggests that the conversion of water to oxygen within the cell is probably nonenzymatic.

The actual photochemical act is extremely complex. No one knows exactly where the chlorophylls reside in the thylakoid, but it is known that two, rather than one, photosensitizers contribute directly to the photosynthetic process. It is also clear that about 600 chlorophyll units must be present in the chloroplast for 1 molecule of CO_2 to be reduced.[6] Apparently, a chemical reaction center is connected to a group of pigment molecules, the sole purpose of which is to transfer electromagnetic energy to the reaction site.

This entire apparatus is self-contained in the quantasome and is referred to as the *photosynthetic unit*. The pigment molecules that function as energy transfer agents are accessory to the fact. That energy transfer is taking place from pigment to pigment is shown by typical energy transfer fluorescence studies in which emission from pigments other than the absorbing pigment is observed.

Eventually, the transferred energy must arrive at some reactive site. According to Franck, this reactive center consists of a fraction of the quantasome chlorophyll that has been modified by its environment in such a way that continued energy transfer cannot take place.[7] Perhaps the entire process is initiated in the photosynthetic unit in an ordinary reduction sequence[8] by hydrogen abstraction at C_{10}.

It is of significance that the quantum yield for certain photosyntheses decreases on the long wavelength side of the chlorophyll absorption. Additional radiation on the short wavelength side of the absorption serves to enhance the quantum yield for the process.[9] Even when separated by fairly long intervals, the two lights still have a large influence on the photosynthetic efficiency. Such an observation suggests that perhaps more than one pigment system is responsible for the photosynthetic process. Maximum efficiency is attained when both systems operate simultaneously or at least nearly so, and the energy absorbed by the two distinctly different pigments is transferred to the reactive center, chlorophyll-a.[10,3] It is surprising that with certain photosynthetic systems, the simultaneous two-system transfer of electromagnetic energy to chlorophyll-a causes chlorophyll-a to fluoresce with a better quantum efficiency than when chlorophyll-a absorbs the radiation itself.[11] Such a result probably is indicative of chlorophyll-a molecules in two or more distinct positions within the photosynthetic unit, one of which is strongly coupled to the extra photosynthetic pigments.

The activities in the photosynthetic unit can be divided into a number of distinct processes, each, it seems, more complex than the step immediately preceding it. These steps are summarized below:

1. Absorption.
2. Energy transfer to the active chlorophyll-a site.
3. Electron-hydrogen transfer processes producing chemically active reaction intermediates.
4. Completion of the carbon and water oxidation cycles.

Step 1 is dual. Absorptions take place in two pigment systems individually, one absorbing in the far red (685 mμ) and the other absorbing at significantly shorter wavelengths. Energy transfer processes are extremely efficient. These apparently occur across a very large number of pigment molecules in a very short period of time. Thus, the photochemical energy arrives at the reactive chlorophyll site almost immediately after absorption, perhaps because the pigment molecules are perfectly oriented within the photosynthetic unit. At the photoreactive site, oxidation reduction, perhaps involving a cytochrome (an iron porphyrin) quinone redox couple, takes place. The oxidized species, perhaps a strong oxidant possessing a metal atom, then reacts with water to yield the observed oxygen. The oxidizing agent is reproduced in the photosynthetic unit in a hydrogen transfer reaction. This second oxidant may be reproduced through the second pigment involved in the photochemical process. It is thought that the second photochemical pigment system produces a reactive site capable of producing an iron (III) cytochrome, a reactive intermediate capable of regenerating the necessary oxidant for the Hill reaction oxidation step.

Somewhere in the reaction process involving this second pigment, a reducing agent capable of reducing one or another of the important cellular pyridine nucleotides (perhaps nicotinamide adenine dinucleotide phosphate, NADP) is produced. A reduced pyridine nucleotide ($NADPH_2$) then participates in carbon dioxide reduction in the Calvin cycle along with the phosphorylating agent adenosine triphosphate (ATP) to produce a mole of ribulose diphosphate, eq. (14).

(14) $\frac{1}{4} CO_2$ +   pyridine nucleotide $\cdot H_2$ $\longrightarrow$

$$\frac{1}{4}(CH_2O)_n + \frac{1}{4} H_2O + \text{pyridine nucleotide}$$

The chlorophyll-a molecule is hydrogenated across the 7 and 8 carbons, and reaction at C_{10} by hydrogen abstraction may be important in the photosynthetic process. It is assumed that a π-π^* excitation either directly or by energy transfer may lead to photosynthesis.

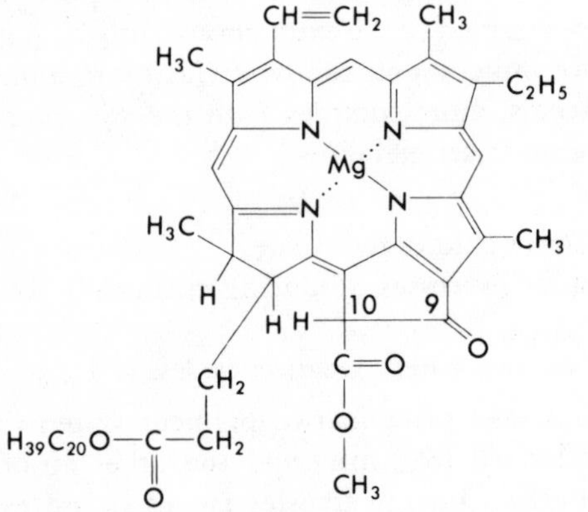

Chlorophyll-a

Natural Chemiluminescence

A number of chemical and biological processes, generally oxidation reactions, produce reaction products in electronically excited states. Degradation of these excited states to the corresponding ground states is accompanied by light emission. Such systems are called *chemiluminescent*. In general, biological oxidations that take place with consequent light emissions are known to occur in some bacteria, in some crustacea, and in the firefly. We shall discuss the firefly primarily, since for it the chemical processes are at least partially understood. First, however, we will discuss simple chemiluminescent systems for which the chemical processes involved and the spectroscopic transitions taking place are reasonably well defined.

One such system is luminol, 5-amino-2,3-dihydro-1,4-phthalazinedione. When luminol is treated with base and an oxidizing agent such as potassium ferricyanide or hydrogen peroxide, light is produced. The products of the reaction, shown in eq. (15), are nitrogen and sodium aminophthalate. Emil

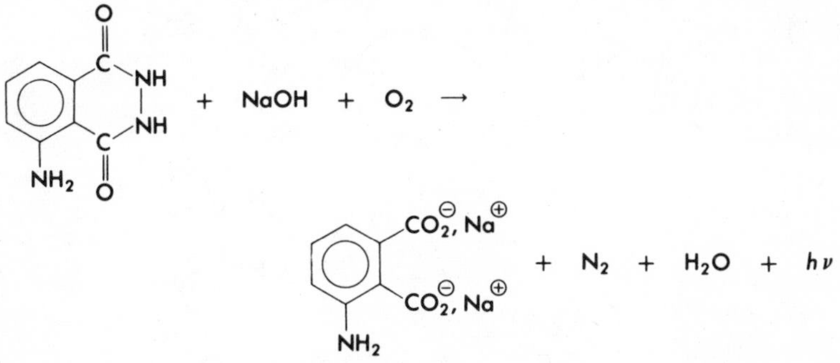

White and co-workers[12] propose that the critical intermediate is the dianion of luminol. The dianion reacts with oxygen to form an azo peroxide, decomposition of which produces the excited state species, eq. (16).

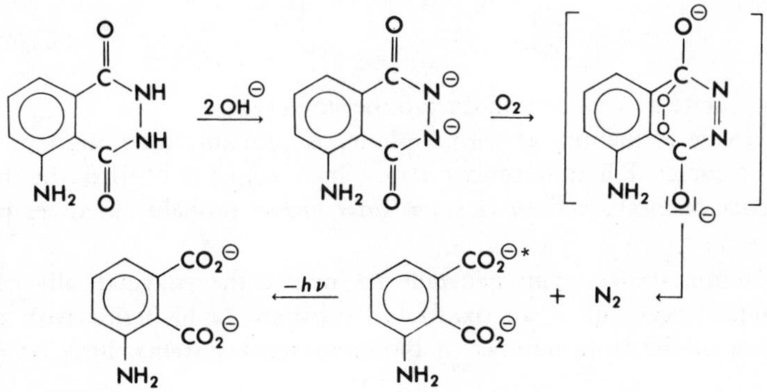

Comparison of diphthalate anion fluorescence with the occurring chemiluminescence verifies that the diphthalate anion is the species responsible for emission.[13] White and Bursey propose that the azo peroxide decomposition yields a vibrationally excited triplet diphthalate species which then crosses to the singlet state from which emission occurs. Synthetic analogs of luminol have also been prepared.[14]

A second laboratory producible chemiluminescent system is lophine. Lophine, 2,4,5-triphenylimidazole, chemiluminesces when treated with strong base in the presence of oxygen also. Substituted imadazoles do likewise, and as is also observed for substituted phthalhydrazides, electron-donating substituents increase the quantum yield of chemiluminescence. With the lophine system, intermediate hydroperoxides are isolable, and these emit light upon treatment with base alone. Furthermore, upon thermal destruction, they are also chemiluminescent. The following mechanism is proposed for lophine chemiluminescence, eq. (17).[15,16]

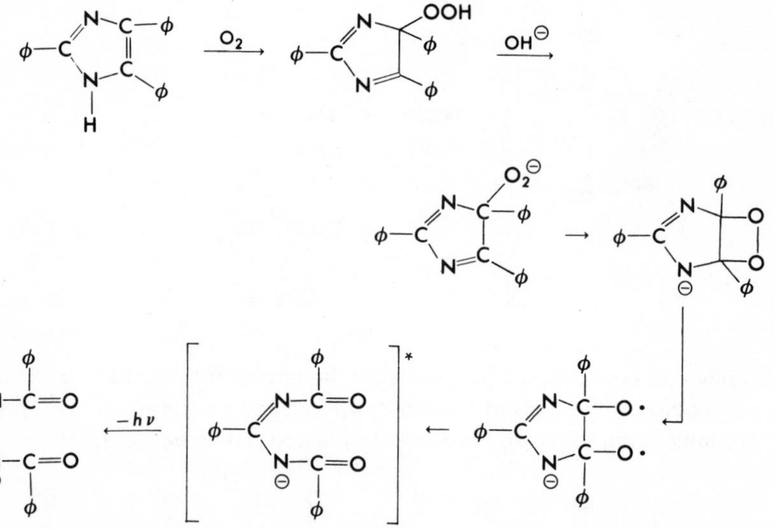

Excited state decomposition is from the singlet state.

Peroxide formation, as with lophine, is probably an important step in certain bacterial luminescences also. It is suggested[16] that the bioluminescence of the bacterium *Achromobacter fischeri* probably involves peroxide formation.

Bioluminescence seems generally to involve the enzymatically catalyzed (luciferase) reaction of an oxidizable substrate (a luciferin) with oxygen. In spite of the large number of bioluminescent systems, little or nothing is known about the chemistry of the luminescence. Firefly luciferin and a number of substituted analogs thereof have been synthesized. The luciferin is known to be

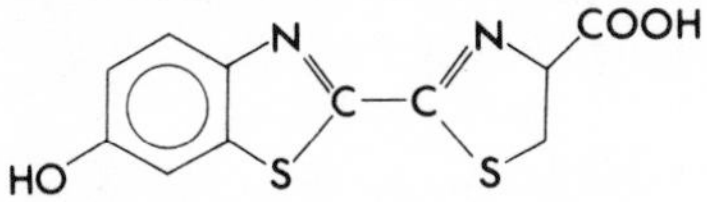

2-(6-hydroxy-2-benzothiazolyl)-Δ^2-thiazoline-4-carboxylic acid.[17,18]

The firefly luminescence requires enzyme luciferase plus Mg^{2+}, adenosine triphosphate, and a source of O_2. The initial reaction leading to light emission requires reaction of the luciferin with the enzyme and ATP to form inorganic phosphate. Enzymatic reaction with molecular oxygen produces the excited species responsible for light emission, the nature of which is yet unknown.

Dehydroluciferin,

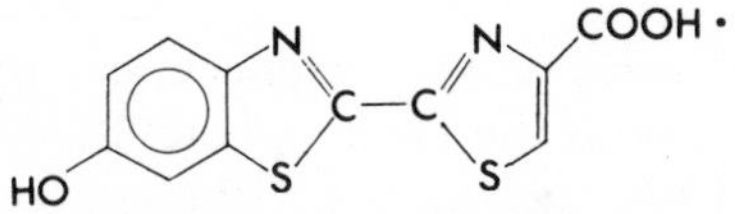

is also isolated from the firefly and may be a product of the biochemical oxidation although such is mere speculation.[19]

Vision

The eye is an unusually sensitive detector capable of detecting wavelengths in the 4000–8000 Å range. The photochemistry within the eye takes place in the retina, a 0.4 mm layer of fantastically sensitive receptor cells located at the rear of the eye proper. In the retina are two distinct cellular units called *rods* and *cones*.* Attached to the retina are a series of neurons which transmit photochemically initiated impulses to the proper receptor centers in the brain.

In function, the rods are responsible for vision in dim light, whereas the cones are generally associated with color response and depth perception. Spectrally, the eye is most sensitive in the 5000 Å region.

Chemically, the photosensitive species responsible for rod vision is a red pigment called *rhodopsin*. Rhodopsin, originally called visual purple, was initially obtained by extraction from frog retina and is a thermolabile protein

---

*Since the eye is capable of detecting light input as low as 10,000 quanta/sec, it can be estimated that the nerve impulse sensitivity of the eye is unusually low per receptor cell per minute—less than 1 photon every 6 minutes.

of approximate molecular weight 40,000 with a broad visual absorption band. Rhodopsin can be photochemically cleaved to a protein fragment called an *opsin*, and a carotenoid species called *retinene*. The entire photo-chemistry of vision is associated with the highly unsaturated carotenoid, retinene, and its *cis-trans* isomerism across C_{11}, eq. (18).

(18)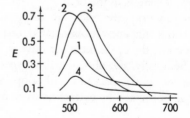

The only action of light in the vision process is to initiate this isomerization of 11-*cis* to all *trans* retinene. All the other reactions take place thermally and in the dark.

Rhodopsin is a chemical combination of 11-*cis* retinene and opsin, the protein. Immediately after isomerism of the chromophore, rhodopsin de-composes (bleaches) to opsin and all *trans* retinene. Through the efforts of Wald and his group[20] intermediates to the bleaching process have been observed at low temperatures. One such intermediate is called *lumirhodopsin*. Yoshizawa and his group[21] have identified still an earlier intermediate called *prelumirhodopsin* at temperatures less than $-140°$. The absorption spectra for the bleaching intermediates is shown in Figure 11-1. Wald suggests that prelumirhodopsin is the all *trans* retinene-opsin combination exactly like the initial 11-*cis* retinene opsin species. Since the conversion of rhodopsin to prelumirhodopsin is almost perfectly reversible, nothing but the *cis-trans* isomerization has transpired.[22]

Upon warming prelumirhodopsin above $-140°$ in the dark, spontaneous conversion to lumirhodopsin occurs. Above $-45°$ lumirhodopsin is con-

1. Rhodopsin at 25°

2. Cooled to−195°

3. Irradiated at 440 mμ to steady state rhodopsin + prelumirhodopsin

4. Warmed to 25° in dark

Cattle Rhodopsin in Glycerol-water Containing   0.1 m Hydroxylamine[22]

Figure 11-1

verted to yet another detectable reaction intermediate called *metarhodopsin*. Both lumirhodopsin and metarhodopsin apparently represent progressive stages in the ring opening of the retinene opsin structure, for in metarhodopsin two new sulfhydryl (SH) groups are evident in the species as is one acid proton binding group. Metarhodopsin then hydrolyzes to opsin and retinene. In Figure 11-2 these **trans**positions are shown diagramatically.

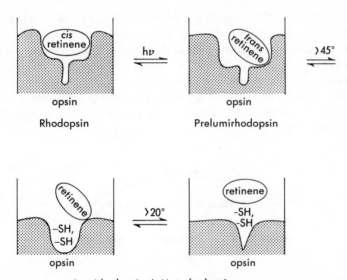

Lumirhodopsin + Metarhodopsin

Figure 11-2

Wald suggests that the exposure of the sulfhydryl groups on the opsin moiety is the critical event in the vision process, and indirectly from these structural groups, the nerve impulse excitation takes place.

It is truly amazing that 1 photon per receptor cell per 6 minutes is sufficient to be detected visually. Clearly, if an electrical process is responsible for visual detection, any current resulting from a single detector cell reception must be amplified many times over. The transport of ionic energy to the nerve centers within the eye by ion carrier processes is probably the most acceptable method for visual excitation currently proposed.

Two additional things must be said about rod vision. First, in the retina of an intact animal, the bleaching process is constantly being reversed, and a steady state exists between the forward and reverse visual process. In the dark, where visual stimulation is at a minimum, the rhodopsin regeneration process proceeds at a maximum rate.   Second, since no process is 100% efficient, the body must be provided with a new source of retinene, and such is the function of vitamin A_1,

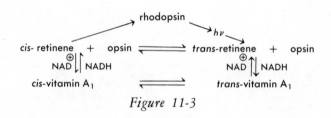

The reformation of retinene from vitamin A_1 requires an oxidation and is enzymatically catalyzed with the participation of diphosphopyridine nucleotide. Furthermore, in the light as rhodopsin is bleached, *trans* retinene is enzymatically reduced to vitamin A_1, which subsequently migrates from the retina to a different position in the eye. In the dark, vitamin A_1 migrates back to the retina where it is reconverted to retinene and subsequently to rhodopsin by an enzymatically catalyzed dark process. The proposed cycle is shown in Figure 11-3.

Figure 11-3

Cone vision is less understood than rod vision. In all probability, several pigments are present in cones. Two known cone pigments, iodopsin and cyanopsin, are retinene combinations of a different opsin known as cone opsin. Iodopsin has an absorption maximum at 555 mμ. The cones, less in number, are significantly less sensitive and serve as finer adjustments in the visual process.

References

1. von Wettstein, D. *Developmental Cytology*, pp. 123–160, New York, Ronald, 1959.
2. Menke, W., *Ann. Rev. Plant. Physiol.*, **13**, 27 (1962).
3. Park, R. B. *The General Physiology of Cell Specialization*, pp. 210–222, New York, McGraw-Hill, 1963.
4. Calvin, M., *Rev. Mod. Phys.*, **31**, 147 (1959).
5. Hill, R., *Proc. Roy. Soc. (London)*, Ser. B, **127**, 192 (1939).
6. Emerson, R., and W. Arnold, *J. Gen. Physiol.*, **15**, 391 (1932).
7. Franck, J., *Proc. Natl. Acad. Sci.*, *U.S.*, **44**, 941 (1958).

8. Krasnovsky, A. A., *Doklady Akad. Nauk. S.S.S.R.,* **60,** 421 (1948).
9. Emerson, R., and C. M. Lewis, *Am. J. Botany,* **30,** 165 (1943).
10. Kok, B., *Biochim. Biophys. Acta,* **21,** 245 (1956).
11. Duysens, L. N. M., *Nature,* **168,** 548 (1951).
12. White, E. H., O. Zafiriou, H. H. Kagi, and J. H. M. Hill, *J. Am. Chem. Soc.,* **86,** 940 (1964).
13. White, E. H., and M. M. Bursey, *J. Am. Chem. Soc.,* **86,** 941 (1964).
14. White, E. H., and M. M. Bursey, *J. Org. Chem.,* **31,** 1912 (1966).
15. Sonnenberg, J., and D. M. White, *J. Am. Chem. Soc.,* **86,** 5685 (1964).
16. White, E. H., and M. J. C. Harding, *J. Am. Chem. Soc.,* **86,** 5686 (1964).
17. White, E. H., F. McCapra, and G. F. Field, *J. Am. Chem. Soc.,* **85,** 337 (1963).
18. White, E. H., H. Wörther, G. F. Field, and W. D. McElroy, *J. Org. Chem.,* **30,** 2344 (1965).
19. White, E. H., H. Wörther, H. H. Seliger, and W. D. McElroy, *J. Am. Chem. Soc.,* **88,** 2015 (1966).
20. Wald, G., J. Durell, and R. C. C. St. George, *Science,* 111, 179 (1950).
21. Yoshizawa, T., and Y. Kito, *Nature,* **182,** 1604ff. (1958).
22. Wald, G., P. K. Brown, and I. R. Gibbons, *J. Opt. Soc. Am.,* **53,** 20 (1963).

General References

Bassham, J. A., and M. Calvin, *The Path of Carbon in Photosynthesis,* Englewood Cliffs, N.J., Prentice-Hall, 1957.

Robinson, G. W., *Ann. Rev. Phys. Chem.,* **15,** 311 (1964).

Spikes, J. D., and B. C. Mayne, *Ann. Rev. Phys. Chem.* **11,** 501 (1960).

Vernon, L. P., and M. Avron, *Ann. Rev. Biochem.,* **34,** 269 (1965).

Wald, G., in *Life and Light,* W. D. McElroy and B. Glass, eds., Baltimore, Johns Hopkins Press, 1961.

Wald, G., P. U. Brown, and I. R. Gibbons, *J. Opt. Soc. Am.* **53,** 20 (1963).

White, A., P. Handler, and E. L. Smith, *Principles of Biochemistry,* New York, McGraw-Hill, 1964.

AUTHOR INDEX

301

Subject Index